To
SAMUEL L. SALTZMAN

THE PHYSIOLOGY OF
THE EYE

by

HUGH DAVSON, D.Sc.(Lond.)

*Scientific Staff, Medical Research Council, Honorary
Research Associate and Fellow of University College,
London*

SECOND EDITION

With 371 illustrations

LITTLE, BROWN AND COMPANY – BOSTON

1963

First Edition	.	.	.	.	1949
Reprinted	.	.	.	.	1950
Second Edition		.	.	.	1963

Printed in Great Britain

PREFACE

It is now rather more than fifteen years since I called at the offices of Messrs. Churchills with a brown paper parcel containing the manuscript of *Physiology of the Eye*, and offered it to them for publication. This was the beginning of an association with the House of Churchill that has become closer as the years have gone by and has resulted in the publication of rather more books than I like to think. Whilst this has been an agreeable if arduous development, it has had an unfortunate consequence for the present book since, at the time it ran out of print, I was heavily engaged and therefore unable to undertake its revision. The task has now been completed and has resulted in about a 50 per cent increase in size, an increase that is the necessary consequence of the tremendous advances made in those aspects of the physiology of the eye that are dealt with in Sections I and II. Thus, it is true to say that in 1948 our knowledge of the vegetative physiology and biochemistry of the eye was rudimentary in the extreme. Now, thanks to the establishment of numerous ophthalmological research organizations—mainly in the U.S.A.—it is safe to say that our knowledge in this branch of ocular science is abreast of our knowledge in comparable fields of physiology and biochemistry. Although, in 1948, the field covered by the title *Mechanism of Vision* rested on a much firmer basis of accurate scientific investigation, the striking improvements in photochemical and electrophysiological techniques that have since taken place have permitted just as rapid progress in elucidating basic problems. Consequently, because I have tried to maintain the same sort of treatment as I had in mind when I wrote the first edition of this book—namely, to present a simple yet thorough exposition of the fundamental principles of ocular physiology—I have had to double the amount of space devoted to these first two sections.

The muscular aspects covered by Section III have been expanded a little to take account of the important advances made possible by the application of modern methods to the analysis of the eye movements, pupillary function, and so on. Sections IV and V rest on the firm theoretical and practical foundation laid by the work of Helmholtz and other classical research workers in the realm of physiological optics, so that they have been tampered with least.

HUGH DAVSON

ACKNOWLEDGEMENTS

In preparing this new edition I have been helped in the way only an author can appreciate by the kindly and skilful assistance of the head librarian of the Thane Library at University College, Mr. C. F. A. Marmoy. Mr. C. A. Evans, Mr. L. J. Shaw and Mr. C. A. Purvis have given invaluable aid in preparing the illustrations, whilst Dr. M. Bradbury was kind enough to read the proofs. To all these kind friends I offer my sincere thanks. In addition, it is a pleasure to acknowledge the secretarial assistance of Miss Mollie Kirk and Miss Edith Souter, and the co-operation of Messrs. Churchills who, in the persons of Mr. J. Rivers and Mr. A. S. Knightley, have made the task of seeing the book through the press so agreeable.

To the authors and publishers from whose works illustrations have been reproduced, I convey my sincere thanks, particularly to Drs. de Robertis, Fine, Gavin, Ishikawa, Jakus, Kleifeld, Pappas, Pirie, Sjöstrand, Smelser, Tousimis and Wanko, for generously providing originals of micrographs.

H. D.

CONTENTS

ANATOMICAL INTRODUCTION

The Three Layers. The globe of the eye consists essentially of three coats enclosing the transparent refractive media. The outermost, protective tunic is made up of the *sclera* and *cornea*—the latter transparent; the middle coat is mainly vascular, consisting of the *choroid, ciliary body*, and *iris*. The innermost layer is the *retina*, containing the essential nervous elements responsible for vision—the *rods* and *cones;* it is continued forward over the ciliary body as the *ciliary epithelium.*

Dioptric Apparatus. The dioptric apparatus (Fig. 1) is made up of the transparent structures—the cornea, occupying the anterior sixth of the surface of

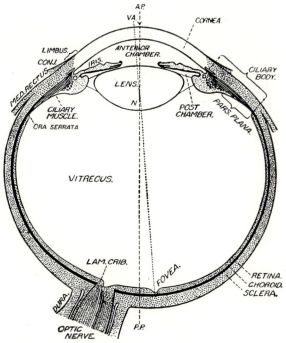

FIG. 1. Horizontal section of the eye. P.P. = Posterior pole; A.P. = Anterior pole; V.A. = Visual axis. (Wolff, *Anatomy of the Eye and Orbit*.)

the globe, and the *lens*, supported by the *zonule* which is itself attached to the ciliary body. The spaces within the eye are filled by a clear fluid, the *aqueous humour*, and a jelly, the *vitreous body*. The aqueous humour is contained in the *anterior* and *posterior chambers*, and the vitreous body in the large space behind the lens and ciliary body. The posterior chamber is the name given to the small space between the lens and iris.

The iris behaves as a diaphragm, modifying the amount of light entering the eye, whilst the ciliary body contains muscle fibres which, on contraction, increase the refractive power of the lens (accommodation). An image of external objects is formed, by means of the dioptric apparatus, on the retina, the more highly specialized portion of which is called the *fovea*.

Visual Pathway. The retina is largely made up of nervous tissue—it is an outgrowth of the central nervous system—and fibres carrying the responses to visual stimuli lead away in the *optic nerve* through a canal in the bony orbit, the *optic foramen* (Fig. 2); the visual impulses are conveyed through the optic nerve and tract to the lateral geniculate body and thence to the cerebral cortex;

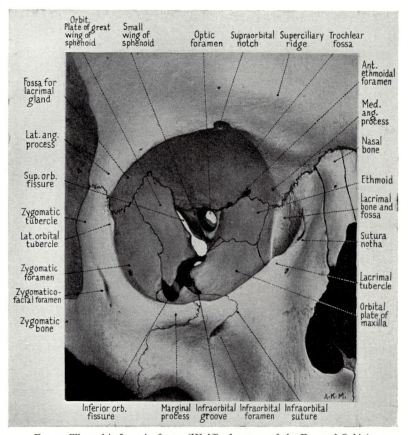

FIG. 2. The orbit from in front. (Wolff, *Anatomy of the Eye and Orbit.*)

on their way, the fibres carrying messages from the medial, or nasal, half of the retina cross over in the *optic chiasma*, so that the lateral geniculate body of the left side, for example, receives fibres from the temporal half of the left retina and the nasal half of the right. The nerve trunks, proximal to the chiasma, are called the *optic tracts*. This decussation may be regarded as a development associated with binocular vision; it will be noted that the responses to a stimulus from any one part of the visual field are carried in the same optic tract (Fig. 3), and the necessary motor response, whereby both eyes are directed to the same point in the field, is probably simplified by this arrangement. It will be noted also that a right-sided event, *i.e.* a visual stimulus arising from a point in the right half of

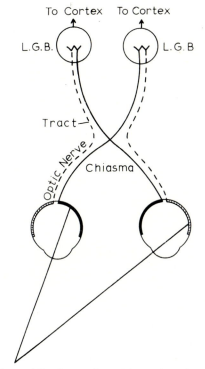

To Cortex   To Cortex

L.G.B.   L.G.B

Tract

Optic Nerve

Chiasma

FIG. 3. The decussation of the optic pathway.

the field, is associated with impulses passing to the left cerebral hemisphere, an arrangement common to all peripheral stimuli.

Vascular Coat

The nutrition of the eye is taken care of largely by the capillaries of the vascular coat; let us examine this structure more closely.

Choroid. The choroid is essentially a layer of vascular tissue next to the retina; it is separated from this nervous tissue by two membranes—the structureless *membrane of Bruch* and the pigment epithelium. The retina comes to an end at the ciliary body, forming the *ora serrata* (Fig. 4), but the vascular coat continues into the ciliary body as one of its layers, the *vessel layer*, which is separated from the eye contents by membranes—the two layers of ciliary epithelium which, viewed embryologically, are the forward continuations of the retina and its pigment epithelium, and the *lamina vitrea*, which is the continuation forward of Bruch's membrane.

Ciliary Body and Iris. The ciliary body in antero-posterior section is triangular in shape (Fig. 5) and has a number of processes (seventy) to which the zonule is attached; viewed from behind, these processes appear as radial ridges to which the name *corona ciliaris* has been given (Fig. 4). The relationship of the iris to the ciliary body is seen in Fig. 5; the blood vessels supplying it belong to the same system as that supplying the ciliary body. Posteriorly, the stroma is

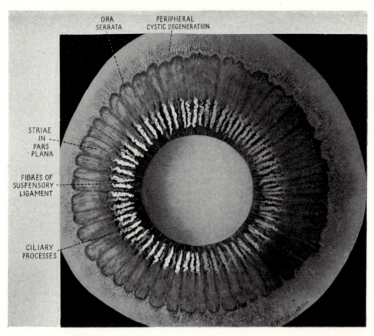

FIG. 4. Posterior view of the ciliary body showing ora serrata and corona ciliaris. (Wolff, *Anatomy of the Eye and Orbit*.)

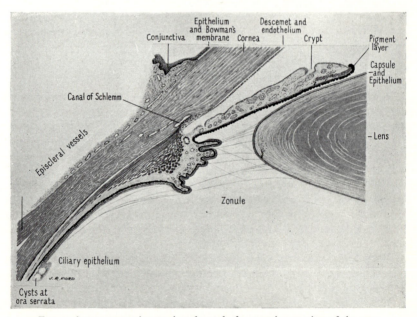

FIG. 5. Antero-posterior section through the anterior portion of the eye. (Wolff, *Anatomy of the Eye and Orbit*.)

separated from the aqueous humour by the *posterior epithelium*, a double, heavily pigmented layer which may be viewed as a prolongation of the ciliary epithelial layers.

Nutrition. The vessels of the vascular coat nourish the internal structures of the eye; so far as the lens is concerned, this process must take place by diffusion of dissolved material from the capillaries through the aqueous humour and vitreous body. The inner (nearest the vitreous) nervous elements of the retina, however, are provided for by a functionally separate vascular system derived from the *central artery of the retina*; this artery, a branch of the *ophthalmic*, enters the globe with the optic nerve and it is its ramifications, together with the *retinal veins*, that give the fundus of the eye its characteristic appearance. The choroid, ciliary body, and iris are supplied by a separate system of arteries, also derived from the ophthalmic—the *ciliary system of arteries*.

The anterior portion of the sclera is covered by a mucous membrane, the *conjunctiva*, which is continued forward on to the inner surfaces of the lids, thus creating the *conjunctival sac*. The remainder of the sclera is enveloped by *Tenon's capsule*.

Muscle. Movements of the eye are executed by the contractions of the six extra-ocular muscles; the space between the globe and orbit being filled with the orbital fat, the movements of the eye are essentially rotations about a fixed point in space.

Nerve Supply. The essentials of the nerve supply to the eyeball are indicated in Fig. 6; sensory impulses (excluding, of course, the visual ones) are conveyed

FIG. 6. Nervous supply to the eye-ball.

through the *long* and *short ciliary nerves*. The long ciliary nerves are composed mainly of the axons of nerve cells in the *Gasserian ganglion*—the ganglion of the trigeminal (N. V); they convey impulses from the iris, ciliary body, and cornea. The short ciliary nerves also contain axons of the trigeminal; they pass through a ganglion in the orbit, the *ciliary ganglion*, into the *naso-ciliary nerve;* the fibres carry impulses from all parts of the eyeball, but chiefly from the cornea.

Motor fibres to the ciliary muscle and the constrictor of the pupil travel by way of the lower division of N. III as the motor root of the ciliary ganglion; post-ganglionic fibres to the muscles are contained in the short ciliary nerves which enter the globe. The extra-ocular muscles are supplied by N. III, IV and VI.

Sympathetic fibres from the superior cervical ganglion enter the orbit as the sympathetic root of the ciliary ganglion and run in the short ciliary nerves to supply the vessels of the globe and the dilator fibres of the pupil. Other sympathetic fibres avoid the ciliary ganglion, passing through the Gasserian ganglion and entering the globe in the long ciliary nerves.

SECTION I

The Vegetative Physiology and Biochemistry of the Eye

AQUEOUS HUMOUR AND THE INTRAOCULAR PRESSURE

THE aqueous humour is a transparent colourless fluid contained in the anterior and posterior chambers of the eye (Fig. 1, p. 1). By inserting a hypodermic needle through the cornea, the fluid may be more or less completely withdrawn, in which case it consists of the mixed fluids from the two chambers. As Seidel first showed, the posterior fluid may be withdrawn separately by inserting a needle through the sclera just behind the corneoscleral junction; because of the valve-like action of the iris, resting on the lens, the anterior fluid is restrained from passing backwards into the posterior chamber, so that subsequently another needle may be inserted into the anterior chamber and this anterior fluid may be withdrawn. In the cat Seidel found that the volume was some 14 per cent of the volume of the anterior fluid, whilst in the rabbit it is about 20 per cent, according to Copeland & Kinsey. The fluids from the two chambers are of very similar composition, so that we may consider the composition of the mixed fluid when discussing the relationships between aqueous humour and blood. Thanks largely to the studies of Kinsey, however, it is now known that there are characteristic differences between the two fluids, differences that reflect their histories, the posterior fluid having been formed first and therefore exposed to diffusional exchanges with the blood in the iris for a shorter time than the anterior fluid.

ANATOMICAL RELATIONSHIPS

The nature of the aqueous humour is of fundamental interest for several reasons. There is reason to believe that it is formed continuously in the posterior chamber by the ciliary body, and that it passes through the pupil into the anterior chamber, whence it is drained away into the venous system in the angle of the anterior chamber by way of Schlemm's canal. As a circulating fluid, therefore, it must be a medium whereby the lens and cornea receive their nutrient materials. Furthermore, because it is being continuously formed, the *intraocular pressure* is largely determined by the rate of formation, the ease with which it is drained away, and by the forces behind the process of formation. To understand the nature of the fluid we must consider its chemical composition and variations of this under experimental conditions, whilst to appreciate the drainage process we must examine the detailed micro-anatomy of the structures that are concerned in this process. Since, moreover, the aqueous humour cannot be considered in isolation from the vitreous body, the posterior portion of the eyeball is also of some interest.

The Vascular Coat

The choroid, ciliary body and iris may be regarded as a vascular coat—the *uvea*—sandwiched between the protective outer coat—cornea and sclera—and the inner neuroepithelial coat—the retina and its continuation forwards as the ciliary epithelium (Fig. 7). This vascular coat is made up of the ramifications of the ciliary system of arteries that penetrate the globe independently of the optic nerve.

FIG. 7. Illustrating the uvea or vascular coat (black) sandwiched between the sclera on the outside and the retina, ciliary epithelium, etc., on the inside.

Ciliary Arteries. The posterior ciliary arteries arise as trunks from the ophthalmic artery (Fig. 8), dividing into some ten to twenty branches which pierce the globe around the optic nerve. Two of them, the long posterior ciliary arteries, run forward through the choroid to the ciliary body where they anastomose with the anterior ciliary arteries to form what has been incorrectly called the *major circle of the iris*; incorrectly, because the circle is actually in the ciliary body. From this circle, arteries run forward to supply the ciliary processes and iris, and backwards—as recurrent ciliary arteries—to contribute to the choroidal circulation.

FIG. 8. Physiological plan of the circulation in man. O.A., ophthalmic artery; M.B., muscular branch; A.C.A., anterior ciliary artery; C.A.I., Circulosus arteriosus iridis major; L.P.C., long posterior ciliary artery; S.P.C., short posterior ciliary artery; P.C.A., posterior ciliary arteries; C.A.R., central artery of the retina; R.A., retinal artery; V.V., vortex vein; I.O.V., inferior orbital vein; A.B., anastomosing branch; C.S., cavernous sinus. (Duke-Elder, *Brit. J. Ophthal.*)

By the *choroid* we mean the vascular layer between the retina and sclera; it is made up of the ramifications of the recurrent ciliary arteries, just mentioned, and of the short posterior ciliary arteries, which enter the globe around the posterior pole. The arteries break up to form a well-defined capillary layer—the *choriocapillaris*—next to the retina, but separated from this by a transparent glassy membrane—the *membrane of Bruch* or *lamina vitrea*. This capillary layer is certainly responsible for nutrition of the outer layers of the retina—pigment epithelium, rods and cones, and bipolar cells—and may also contribute to that of the innermost layer.

Venous System. The venous return is by way of two systems; the anterior ciliary veins accompany the anterior ciliary arteries, whilst the vortex veins run independently of the arterial circulation; these last are four in number, and they drain all the blood from the choroid, the iris and the ciliary processes, whilst the anterior ciliary veins drain the blood from the ciliary muscle and the superficial plexuses, which we shall describe later. According to a recent study by Bill, only 1 per cent of the venous return is by way of the anterior ciliary veins.

Retinal Circulation. As indicated earlier, the innermost part of the retina is supplied directly, in man, by the ramifications of the central retinal artery, a branch of the ophthalmic that penetrates the meningeal sheaths of the optic

FIG. 9. Schematic section of optic nerve and eyeball showing course and branches of the central retinal artery. (Singh & Dass, *Brit. J. Ophthal.*)

nerve in its intraorbital course and breaks up into a series of branches on the inner layer of the retina, branches that give the fundus its characteristic appearance in the ophthalmoscope. As Fig. 9 indicates, the central artery gives off branches that supply the optic nerve*; moreover, the posterior ciliary arteries may send off branches in the region of the optic disk, forming a circle—*circle of Zinn or Haller*—which may form anastomoses with the branches of the central artery of the retina. To the extent that these anastomoses occur, the uveal and retinal vascular systems are not completely independent. Venous return from the retinal circulation is by way of the central retinal vein which, for a part of its course, runs in the subarachnoid space of the optic nerve and is thereby subjected to the intracranial pressure. For this reason, an elevated intracranial pressure may be manifest as an engorgement of the retinal veins.

So much for the general lay-out of the vascular circulation of the eye; as we

* Some authors, for example François & Neetens, speak of a *central artery of the optic nerve*, derived either as a branch of the central retinal artery or entering separately as a branch of the ophthalmic artery. Wolff describes them as *arteriæ collaterales centralis retinæ*. The literature relating to this and other points is well summarized in the careful studies of Singh & Dass (1960).

have seen, the uveal circulation supplies the ciliary body and iris, the two vascular structures that come into close relationship with the aqueous humour. It is important now that we examine these structures in some detail.

Ciliary Body

In sagittal section this is a triangular body (Fig. 5, p. 4), whilst looked at from behind it appears as a ring, some 6 mm wide in man. Where it joins the retina—the *ora serrata*—it appears smooth to the naked eye, but farther forward

FIG. 10. Oblique section of the ciliary body.
(Wolff, *Anatomy of the Eye and Orbit.*)

the inner surface is ridged, owing to the presence of some seventy to eighty *ciliary processes*, and acquires the name of *corona ciliaris* (Fig. 4, p. 4). As the oblique section illustrated in Fig. 10 shows, the ciliary processes are villus-like projections of the main body, jutting into the posterior chamber. According to Baurmann, the total area of these processes, in man, is some 6 cm² and we may look upon this expansion as subserving the secretory activity of this part of the ciliary body, since there is good reason to believe that it is here that the aqueous humour is formed. The vessel-layer of the ciliary body is similar to the choroid; it extends into each ciliary process, so that this is probably the most heavily vascularized part of the eye. Each process contains a mass of capillaries so arranged that each comes into close relationship, at some point in its course, with the surface of the epithelium. As stated above, blood from the ciliary processes is carried away by the vortex veins.

Ciliary Epithelium. The innermost coat, insulating the ciliary body from the aqueous humour and vitreous body, is the *ciliary epithelium*, a double layer of cells, the inner layer of which, *i.e.* the layer next to the aqueous humour or vitreous body, is non-pigmented, whilst the outer layer is heavily pigmented. These cells, which are considered to be responsible for the secretion of the aqueous humour, have been examined with the electron-microscope by Pease and, more recently, by Holmberg and Pappas & Smelser. The striking feature of their structure is the way in which the adjacent cells interdigitate with each other, finger-like protrusions of one cell being enveloped by invaginations of the other (Figs. 11 and 12, Pl. I). Moreover, on the surface facing the aqueous humour there are similar infoldings of the cell membrane. The function of these infoldings is not clear, but they seem to be a characteristic feature of cells that are concerned in transport of fluid; for example, the epithelial covering of the kidney distal tubule, the epithelium of the choroid plexuses, and so on. Likewise, the significance of the lateral interdigitations is not clear; it may well be the means whereby the cells are held together, and it is also seen in the innermost layer of corneal epithelial cells, according to Pedler.

The Iris

This is the most anterior part of the vascular coat; in a meridional section it is seen to consist of two main layers or *laminæ*, separated by a less dense zone, the *cleft of Fuchs*. The posterior lamina contains the muscles of the iris, being covered posteriorly by two layers of densely pigmented cells, the innermost being the posterior epithelium of the iris which is continuous with the inner layer of the ciliary epithelium. The blood vessels, derived from the major circle of the iris (p. 9), run in the loose connective tissue of the laminæ. Both arteries and veins run radially; venous return is by way of the vortex veins.

On its anterior surface the iris is in contact with the aqueous humour, so that it is of some interest to determine exactly how the fluid is separated from the tissue. It is customary to speak of an *anterior endothelium*, continuous with the corneal endothelium anteriorly and the posterior iris epithelium posteriorly, covering the anterior surface of the iris and thus insulating the aqueous humour from the underlying spongy tissue. The weight of recent evidence, however, bears against this so that it would seem that, in man at any rate, the aqueous humour has direct access to the stromal tissue. As we shall see, however, this does not mean that there is any significant bulk drainage of aqueous humour back into the blood in the iris.

The Drainage Route

We have said that the aqueous humour is most probably secreted continuously by the cells of the ciliary epithelium; to make room for the new fluid there must obviously be a continuous escape, or drainage, and this occurs by way of the *canal of Schlemm*. This is a circular canal in the corneo-sclera of the limbus (Fig. 5, p. 4) which comes into relation with the aqueous humour on the one

PLATE I

Fig. 11. Electron micrograph of a section of portions of two adjacent ciliary epithelial cells of the rabbit showing complex interdigitations (B) of their boundaries. Zonular fibres (Z) can be seen in close approximation to the surface of these cells. ER, endoplasmic reticulum; M, mitochondrion. Osmium fixation. × 19,000. (Pappas & Smelser, *Amer. J. Ophthal.*)

[To face p. 12.

FIG. 12. Electron micrograph of adjacent cells of human ciliary epithelium. N, nucleus; m, mitochondrion; v, vesicles; D, desmosomes; ILM, internal limiting membrane; PC, posterior chamber. × 17,000. (Courtesy Ishikawa.)

FIG. 13. Illustrating the canal of Schlemm and its relation to the plexuses of the anterior segment of the eye. C, conjunctival plexus; T, Tenon's capsule plexus; Pl.e, episcleral plexus; PLi, intrascleral plexus; Mc, ciliary muscle; VMc, vein of ciliary muscle; Ac.a, anterior ciliary artery; v.ca, anterior ciliary vein; Pr C, ciliary process; *C*, cornea; c, collector; L, limbus. (Maggiore, *Ann. Ottalm.*)

FIG. 14. Section of the angle of the anterior chamber.
(Wolff, *Anatomy of the Eye and Orbit*).

hand and the *intrascleral venous plexus* on the other, as illustrated by Figs. 13 and 14.

Plexuses of the Anterior Segment. The intrascleral plexus is largely made up of the ramifications of branches of the anterior ciliary veins, but, as Maggiore showed, there is also an arterial contribution, branches of the anterior ciliary arteries passing directly to the plexus and breaking up into fine vessels that come into direct continuity with the finer vessels of the plexus. It connects with the canal of Schlemm by some twenty fine vessels—*collectors*—which thus transport aqueous humour into the venous system. The blood from the plexus is drained away by large trunks into the *episcleral plexus;* from here large veins, also draining the more superficial plexuses—conjunctival and subconjunctival—carry the blood to the insertions of the rectus muscles in the sclera and accompany the muscular veins.

Canal of Schlemm and Trabecular Meshwork. The canal of Schlemm is usually represented as a ring lying in the corneo-sclera, which on cross-section (as in the meridional section of Fig. 14) appears as a circle or ellipse; its structure

FIG. 15. Schematic illustration of lamellæ of scleral meshwork.
(Ashton, Brini & Smith, *Brit. J. Ophthal.*)

is, in fact, more complex, since it divides into several channels which, however, later reunite; hence the appearance of a cross-section varies with the position of the section. The canal is essentially an endothelium-lined vessel, similar to a delicate vein; on the outside it rests on the scleral tissue whilst on the inside, nearest the aqueous humour, it is covered by a meshwork of endothelium-covered trabeculæ—the *trabecular meshwork* or *pectinate ligament*. Aqueous humour, to enter the canal, must percolate between the trabeculæ and finally cross the endothelial wall. On meridional section the meshwork appears as a series of meridionally orientated fibres (Fig. 14), but on tangential section it is seen to consist of a series of flat lamellæ, piled one on top of the other, the fluid-filled spaces between these lamellæ being connected by holes, as illustrated schematically in Fig. 15. The meshwork has been divided into three parts with characteristically different ultrastructures; the innermost portion (1 of Fig. 16) is the *uveal meshwork*; the trabeculæ making up the lamellæ here are finer than those of the outer or *corneoscleral meshwork*, whilst the meshes are larger. Each lamella of the uveal meshwork is attached anteriorly to the corneal tissue at the end of Descemet's membrane, constituting *Schwalbe's ring*,* and posteriorly to the meridional fibres of the ciliary muscle. A pull of these fibres may well operate to open up the meshes of this trabecular structure, thereby favouring passage of

FIG. 16. Schematic drawing of the chamber angle in primates, showing the three distinct parts of the trabecular meshwork. 1, uveal meshwork; 2, trabeculum corneosclerale; 3, inner wall, or pore area. (Rohen, *Structure of the Eye.*)

fluid. The third portion, revealed by the electron-microscope, immediately adjacent to the canal, is called the *pore area* or *pore tissue* and is made up of endothelial cells with an intervening ground substance.

THE DRAINAGE PROCESS

Experimental Study. In 1921 Seidel established beyond reasonable doubt that the aqueous humour was continually formed and drained away. He inserted a needle, connected to a reservoir containing a solution of a dye, into the anterior chamber of a rabbit (Fig. 17). By lowering the reservoir below the intraocular pressure a little aqueous humour was drawn into the needle and then, when the reservoir was raised, this fluid, mixed with dye, was returned to the anterior chamber. Soon the dye mixed with the rest of the fluid. Seidel observed that the dye stained the blood vessels in the surface of the globe—episcleral vessels—indicating that aqueous humour was being carried into the venous system. This passage out would only occur, however, if the pressure in the eye, determined by the height of the reservoir, was at or above 15 mm Hg; when the pressure was reduced below this it was presumed that drainage of aqueous humour ceased.

* *Iris processes* are made up of an occasional lamina of the uveal meshwork that crosses posteriorly to attach to the root of the iris.

Since the pressure within the eye is normally above 15 mm Hg, we may conclude that fluid is being continuously lost to the blood; moreover, the loss presumably depends on the existence of a pressure-gradient between the aqueous humour and the venous system. Since the episcleral vessels are derived from the anterior ciliary system, we may conclude that the dye was not being absorbed from the iris, the venous return from which is by way of the vortex veins which were uncoloured in these experiments. More recent studies, in which isotope-labelled material is introduced into the aqueous humour and the venous blood collected

Fig. 17. Illustrating Seidel's experiment.

from both ciliary and vortex veins, have confirmed that at least 99 per cent of drainage is by the anterior route (Bill).

Aqueous Veins. Confirmation of Seidel's view was provided in a striking manner by Ascher in 1942; when examining the superficial vessels of the globe with the slit-lamp microscope, he observed what appeared to be empty veins but they turned out to be full of aqueous humour, and he called them *aqueous veins*. Usually one of these veins could be followed till it joined a blood vessel, in which event the contents of the two vessels, aqueous humour and blood, did not mix immediately but often ran in parallel streams forming a *laminated* aqueous vein, as illustrated schematically in Fig. 18. If the blood-vein beyond the junction was compressed, one of two things happened; either the blood drove the aqueous humour out of its channel or the aqueous humour drove the blood out. The latter situation was described as the *positive glass-rod phenomenon*, whilst the former, with the blood driving aqueous humour out, was called the *negative*

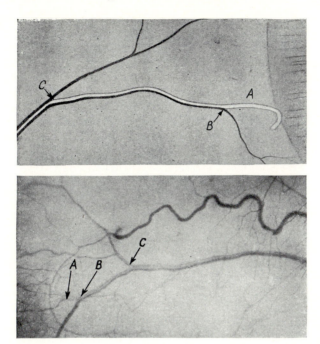

Fig. 18. Typical aqueous veins. *Above:* Sketch made by Ascher (*Amer. J. Ophthal.*) in his original description. *Below:* Untouched photo taken by Thomassen and Perkins. The aqueous vein emerges from the deeper tissue and is visible at *A*. At *B* it joins a blood-vein so that the latter has two strata. At *C* the stratified vessel joins another vein to give three laminæ.

glass-rod phenomenon. These superficial vessels, full of aqueous humour, are probably derived from the deeper vessels of the intrascleral plexus, the pressure-relationships in the collectors from Schlemm's canal being such as to favour displacement of blood throughout the course of the fluid to the surface of the globe as illustrated by Fig. 19.

Fig. 19. Ascher's view of the origin of an aqueous vein.

Goldmann proved conclusively that these vessels contained aqueous humour by injecting fluorescein intravenously. This substance passes very slowly from blood into aqueous humour so that one would not expect any vessel containing aqueous humour to fluoresce immediately after the injection, whilst vessels full of blood or plasma should do so; in fact only the blood vessels did fluoresce. Later, Ashton identified an aqueous vein in a human eye that was about to be enucleated; a wire was tied round the vein and, after enucleation, the canal of Schlemm was injected with Neoprene. After digesting the tissue away a cast of the canal and its connecting vessels remained, and examination showed that the aqueous vein did, indeed, take origin from the canal of Schlemm. Since these fundamental studies, numerous papers elaborating on the function of the aqueous veins under normal and pathological conditions have been described (see, for example, Ascher, 1961).

PHYSIOLOGY OF THE VASCULAR SYSTEM

The vascular circulation of the eye has attracted a great deal of interest because of its close relationship to the formation and drainage of aqueous humour. Space will not permit a detailed description of this aspect of ocular physiology, and we must be content with a few salient points.

Pulses. With the ophthalmoscope an arterial pulse may be observed in the retinal vessels; if the intraocular pressure is increased by compressing the globe the pulse may be exaggerated, since the collapse of the artery during diastole becomes greater; if the pressure is raised sufficiently the pulse will cease, at which point the pressure in the eye is equal to the systolic pressure in the artery from which the retinal artery is derived, namely, the ophthalmic artery. The retinal veins also show a pulse; it is best seen where the large veins lie on the optic disk; it appears as a sudden emptying of this portion of the vein, progressing from the central end towards the periphery followed by a pronounced dilatation, beginning at the periphery and passing centrally. The pulse is not simply a reflexion of events taking place in the right auricle, and is closely related to ventricular systole. The rise in intraocular pressure associated with systole will tend to compress the veins; and a collapse of the latter will take place where the pressure is least, *i.e.* most centrally. The subsequent refilling of the vein will occur in diastole, or late in systole, and will proceed in the reverse direction. The exact time-relationships of the pulse were established cinematographically by Serr.

Pressures. These were studied experimentally by Seidel and later by Duke-Elder; according to the latter author the following values (mm Hg) are associated with an intraocular pressure of 20 mm Hg:

Ophthalmic artery .	99·5	Retinal vein . .	22
Retinal arteries .	75·5	Intrascleral vein .	21·5
		Episcleral vein .	13

Of most importance are the values in the anterior ciliary or episcleral veins; these are probably not independent of the intraocular pressure, however; thus in human subjects Weigelin & Löhlein found the following empirical relationship: $P_{ev} = 0.48 \times P_{oo} + 3.1$, where P_{ev} is the episcleral venous pressure and P_{oo} the intraocular pressure. In animals, too, Macri found a linear relationship between the two.

THE INTRAOCULAR PRESSURE

On the basis of Seidel's studies, we may expect the flow of aqueous humour to be determined by the difference of pressure between the fluid within the eye—

With the aid of this relationship some of the factors determining the intraocular pressure may be easily appreciated. Thus an increase in resistance to flow will increase the intraocular pressure, provided that the rate of formation of fluid does not decrease in proportion. The factors determining the rate of production of fluid are not completely understood, but it seems safe to assume that this is independent of intraocular pressure over a fairly wide range, so that we shall not be far wrong if we conclude that intraocular pressure varies inversely with resistance to flow. Alterations in episcleral venous pressure, P_{ev}, may likewise be expected to be reflected in predictable alterations in intraocular pressure.

Tonographic Measurement of Resistance. The essential principle on which this measurement is based is to place a weight on the cornea; this raises the intraocular pressure and causes an increased flow of aqueous humour out of the eye. Because of this increased flow, the intraocular pressure falls eventually back to its original value, and the rate of return enables the computation of the resistance to flow. Thus:

$$F_o = \frac{P_{oc} - P_{ev}}{R}(t_2 - t_1)$$

F_o being the normal rate of flow, without the weight on the eye, during the period $t_2 - t_1$.

With the weight on the eye we have:

$$F_t = \frac{\dfrac{P_{t_2} - P_{t_1}}{2} - P_{ev}}{R}(t_2 - t_1)$$

Where the average intraocular pressure during the period $t_2 - t_1$ with the weight on the eye is taken as: $\dfrac{P_{t_2} - P_{t_1}}{2}$.

The extra flow,

$$F_t - F_o = \left\{ \frac{\dfrac{P_{t_2} - P_{t_1}}{2} - P_{ev}}{R} - \frac{P_{oc} - P_{ev}}{R} \right\}(t_2 - t_1)$$

$$= \left\{ \frac{P_{t_2} - P_{t_1}}{2} - P_{oc} \right\} \frac{t_2 - t_1}{R}$$

or $\Delta F = \dfrac{t_2 - t_1}{R}.\Delta P$

or $\Delta F = (t_2 - t_1).C.\Delta P$

where C is the reciprocal of R and may be called the *facility of outflow*.

Experimentally the weight is applied to the eye in the form of an electronic tonometer so that it serves also to measure the intraocular pressure when appropriately calibrated. Since, moreover, the calibration of the tonometer had already given the change in volume of the eye associated with changes in P_t, ΔF was also known. Hence by measuring the change in P_t, ΔF was found and these two quantities could be inserted into the equation to give C, the facility of outflow.

The average value found by Grant, who first described the technique, was 0·24 mm³.min⁻¹.mm Hg⁻¹, *i.e.* the flow when the difference of pressure was 1 mm Hg was 0·24 mm³ per minute. Measurements on excised human eyes gave comparable results; in this case fluid was passed into the eye from a reservoir and the rate of movement measured at different pressures.

Location of Resistance. The facility of outflow probably depends mainly on the frictional resistance imposed by the trabecular meshwork; thus Bárány & Scotchbrook have shown that addition of hyaluronidase to the anterior chamber increased the rate of flow of saline through the excised eye, presumably by virtue of breaking down the hyaluronic acid ground substance that is thought to fill the holes in the meshwork. Again, Grant, by curettage of the meshwork, was able to reduce the resistance by a factor of as much as 75 per cent. Under pathological conditions, furthermore, there is reason to believe that the high intraocular pressure in the so-called open-angle glaucoma is due to degenerative changes in the meshwork.*

Venous Pressure. In so far as the aqueous humour must drain into the episcleral venous system, either by way of the intrascleral plexus or more directly along the aqueous veins, the intraocular pressure will vary directly with the venous pressure in accordance with the simple equation given above. Certainly in man there is a good correlation between intraocular pressure and P_{ev}, whilst in cats Macri showed the same thing when he varied the intraocular pressure experimentally. Acute changes of venous pressure will influence the intraocular pressure in a two-fold manner. First, by affecting drainage as just indicated, and second, by a direct transmission of the changed venous pressure across the easily distensible walls of the intraocular veins. The expansion of the veins will be eventually compensated by a loss of aqueous humour from the eye, so that the rise due to this cause may be more or less completely compensated, but the effect on drainage should last as long as P_{ev} is elevated. Experimentally the effects of changed venous pressure may be demonstrated by administering amyl nitrite; the peripheral vasodilatation causes a general increase in venous pressure and leads to a considerable rise in intraocular pressure in spite of a lowered arterial pressure. Again, ligation of the vortex and anterior ciliary veins causes large rises in intraocular pressure, as we should expect. Finally, destruction of the aqueous veins, by restricting the outlets of aqueous humour, may cause quite considerable rises in intraocular pressure in rabbits, according to Huggert.

Arterial Pressure. The arterial pressure can influence the intraocular pressure through its tendency to expand the intraocular arteries; since these are not easily distensible, however, relatively large changes in arterial pressure will be required to produce measurable changes in intraocular pressure. That the arterial pressure does affect the intraocular pressure in this way is manifest in the

---

* Theobald (1960) has summarized the alterations in the meshwork that have been described in open-angle glaucoma; these include replacement of the trabeculæ with amorphous material, degeneration of collagenous tissue with proliferation of endothelium of Schlemm's canal, deposition of pigment granules, and so on. The question as to whether there are actual pores in the wall of Schlemm's canal has not yet been decided in spite of numerous investigations with the electron-microscope (see, for example, Rohen, 1961; Garron & Feeney, 1959; Flocks, 1956; Speakman, 1960). Argemone oil has been accused of causing the glaucoma associated with epidemic dropsy, the toxic principle being sanguinarine and the point of attack being the trabecular meshwork; recent studies, however, have shown that neither the oil nor sanguinarine has an effect on the intraocular pressure (Dobbie & Langham, 1961).

pulse shown in records of the intraocular pressure; the amplitude of this pulse is small, about 1 mm Hg, and coincides with cardiac systole. Thus a change of about 20 mm Hg, which is the pulse-pressure in an intraocular artery according to Duke-Elder, causes a change of only 1 mm Hg in the intraocular pressure.

In the rabbit, ligation of one common carotid artery lowers the intracranial arterial pressure on the side of the ligation, whilst the pressure on the other side rises above normal; hence we may study the effects of lowered arterial pressure on one eye, using the other as a control. Wessely in 1908 found a small lowering of the intraocular pressure on the ligated side and Bárány found that after twenty-four hours the pressure had returned to normal. The immediate effect of the ligation is undoubtedly the result of the fall in arterial pressure which leads to a reduced volume of blood in the eye. As Fig. 24 shows, there is a tendency to compensate for this since alternate clamping and unclamping of the artery

Fig. 24. Intraocular pressure of the rabbit. At points marked *C* the left common carotid artery was clamped, and at points marked *R* it was released. (Davson & Matchett, *J. Physiol.*)

leads to an overshoot on release of the clamp, suggesting that there has been some vasodilatation which would partly compensate for the reduced flow caused by the fall in pressure. The compensation is not complete, however, since Linnér found a 19 per cent decrease in the rate at which blood escaped from a cut vortex vein on the side of the ligature.

Rate of Flow of Aqueous Humour. Other things being equal, we may expect changes in rate of secretion of fluid to produce changes in intraocular pressure in the same sense, but the effects are not likely to be large. Thus, if the intraocular pressure, P_{oc}, is 16 mm Hg, and the episcleral venous pressure, P_{ev}, is 12 mm Hg, the pressure drop, $P_{oc} - P_{ev}$, is 4 mm Hg. If the rate of flow is doubled the pressure-drop must be doubled too, in which case it becomes 8 mm Hg, and if P_{ev} remains the same this means that the intraocular pressure, P_{oc}, rises from 16 to 20 mm Hg. Thus doubling the rate of secretion causes only a 25 per cent increase in intraocular pressure. In practice it is not easy to vary the rate of secretion; as we shall see, the carbonic anhydrase inhibitor, Diamox, reduces the rate and this is accompanied by a fall in intraocular pressure; the same is true of digitalis compounds, according to Simon, Bonting & Hawkins.

By injecting saline continuously into the anterior chamber we may experimentally increase the flow of fluid through the eye and test the applicability of the simple equation relating flow-rate to pressure-drop; Langham found that the equation did not hold, the rise in pressure for a given increase in flow being smaller than predicted, and his results suggested some homeostatic mechanism that decreased the resistance to flow as the intraocular pressure rose. Section of the cervical sympathetic, or ligation of the common carotid, caused the relationship between flow and pressure to become linear, *i.e.* to follow the simple equation:

$$\text{Flow} \times \text{Resistance} = \text{Pressure Drop}$$

and this suggested that the adaptation was largely vascular. More recently, however, Sears has failed to confirm this work, the relationship between pressure-drop and flow-rate being linear. Nevertheless, there seems little doubt that there are possibilities of compensating for increased flow of fluid; thus Davson & Spaziani were able to double the flow of fluid through the cat's eye without necessarily increasing the intraocular pressure.

Effects of Nervous Activity

Sympathetic System. Stimulation of the peripheral end of the cut cervical sympathetic trunk in the rabbit causes a constriction of the uveal vessels associated with a marked fall in the intraocular pressure. Section of the sympathetic, or extirpation of the superior cervical ganglion has, in general, remarkably little immediate effect on the normal intraocular pressure (Greaves & Perkins; Langham & Taylor), although occasionally quite large rises, lasting for thirty minutes, can be observed (Davson & Matchett). Twenty-four hours after ganglionectomy the intraocular pressure is definitely lower than normal, and a study of the dynamics of flow of aqueous humour suggested that this was due to a diminished outflow resistance, since P_{ev} was said to be unaffected by the procedure. As to how a nervous mechanism may influence so mechanical a factor as the resistance to flow of aqueous humour we are not yet clear. If most of the resistance is located in the trabecular meshwork, then it is possible that a changed pull of the ciliary muscle on its insertion into the trabeculæ might open up the meshes and permit a more ready percolation of fluid, as suggested long ago by Fortin. There is no evidence, in the case of superior cervical ganglionectomy, however, to suggest that the extirpation of the ganglion removes any tonic action of the sympathetic on the ciliary muscle.

Parasympathetic. Recently Armaly has obtained a definite lowering of the intraocular pressure on stimulating the parasympathetic root of the ciliary ganglion (Fig. 6, p. 5) by placing electrodes in the orbit. An initial rapid fall was probably caused by a reduction in ciliary blood volume, whereas a more prolonged action could have been due to the opening up of the meshwork resulting from contraction of the ciliary muscle. At any rate, tonography (p. 38) suggested a decreased resistance to outflow.

Trigeminal. Perkins has shown that stimulation of the trigeminal nerve (N. V), especially if brought about mechanically, causes a marked rise in intraocular pressure accompanied by a dilatation of the intraocular blood vessels and a breakdown of the blood-aqueous barrier (p. 37). The effect on intraocular pressure is probably entirely due to the vascular engorgement and is reminiscent of the large rises obtained by irritative lesions.

Facial Nerve. Gloster has shown that stimulation of N. VII causes a rise in intraocular pressure; it is not merely due to a contraction of the extraocular muscles since gallamine did not abolish the effect.

Afferent Impulses. If there is a "centre" controlling the intraocular pressure, we may expect to find evidence of a sensory system capable of keeping the centre informed of the state of the intraocular pressure at any moment. Studies from the laboratories of Vrábec and v. Sallmann have shown that the trabecular meshwork is richly provided with fine nerve fibres, some of which may be sensory, whilst action potentials in the ciliary nerves, in response to alterations in the intraocular pressure have also been described. Nevertheless, as Perkins has shown in a recent study, the evidence for sensory fibres specifically respond-ing to alterations in intraocular pressure, is still not completely satisfactory.

Hypothalamic Centre. Attempts to locate a centre controlling the intraocular pressure have been made by v. Sallmann & Loewenstein and Gloster & Greaves, by inserting stereotactically controlled stimulating electrodes into different parts of the brain. The parts of the brain from which effects on intraocular pressure could be obtained were in the hypothalamus, but since this region contains many centres controlling the autonomic system generally, it is important to distinguish primary effects on the intraocular pressure from the secondary consequences of stimulating these autonomic centres. Thus many stimulated points gave rise to rises or falls in intraocular pressure that were obviously associated with corres-ponding rises or falls of arterial pressure. Nevertheless, other points could be found where a rise or fall of intraocular pressure independent of general vascular changes resulted from stimulation. The falls in intraocular pressure were prob-ably mediated by the sympathetic, since they could be prevented by section of the sympathetic trunk. It is possible, then, that there is a co-ordinating centre in the hypothalamus capable of influencing the intraocular pressure, and subject to afferent impulses carried in the long ciliary nerves. The evidence for this is not completely convincing, however, and we must bear in mind the possibility that there is no central control, local homeostatic mechanisms being adequate to keep the intraocular pressure within a narrow range.

Effects of Drugs

In general, the influence of drugs on the intraocular pressure is not striking, with the exception of those that induce powerful inflammatory reactions in the anterior uvea. Thus nitrogen mustard applied to the cornea causes a congestion of the small vessels of the conjunctiva, iris and ciliary body; the result is a pheno-menal rise in intraocular pressure (Fig. 25). This is associated with the appearance of protein in the aqueous humour, *i.e.* with a breakdown of the blood-aqueous barrier (p. 37). Smaller, but significant increases in intraocular pressure can be produced by the anticholinesterase DFP, whilst smaller effects still are caused by eserine and pilocarpine. Here the action is probably mediated by the para-sympathetic, which presumably has a vasodilator action on the small blood vessels of the uvea. The rises in intraocular pressure obviously belong to the same class as the responses to contusion of the eyeball, irritation of the conjunc-tiva, scratching the iris, and so on. It is interesting that the drug, *polyphloretin,*

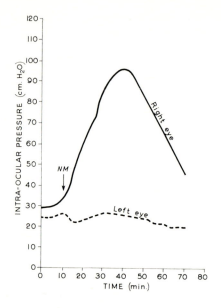

Fig. 25. The effect of instillation of nitrogen mustard (*NM*) into the right eye of the rabbit on its intraocular pressure. (Davson & Matchett, *J. Physiol.*)

Fig. 26. Late effect of pilocarpine on an aqueous vein. (*a*) Immediately after instillation of 2 per cent pilocarpine the aqueous vein contained more blood than before. (*b*) Twenty minutes after instillation the aqueous vein was entirely clear, whilst in the recipient vessel the stream of blood was narrowed. (*c*) Thirty minutes after instillation still more clear fluid and less blood were present in the recipient vessel. The original distribution was restored 150 minutes after instillation. (Ascher, *The Aqueous Veins*.)

known to reduce serous exudates, is able to counteract the action of nitrogen mustard (Cole).

Atropine and Eserine. In the normal human eye the effects of atropine and eserine are often negligible; in eyes disposed to glaucoma, or actually suffering from it, atropine may cause a rapid rise in intraocular pressure, whilst eserine or pilocarpine are employed in maintaining the intraocular pressure within normal levels in glaucomatous subjects. The actions of these drugs, under these conditions, are not completely understood and opinion rather favours an anatomical explanation. Thus the dilatation of the pupil caused by atropine may well be associated with a partial obstruction of access to the canal of Schlemm by the iris root, whilst the contraction of the ciliary muscle caused by pilocarpine or eserine might open up the meshes of the trabecular meshwork; this view is supported by a recent histological study of Flocks & Zweng, who found the meshwork looser in appearance in eyes treated with these drugs. Studies of the effects of these miotic drugs on aqueous veins certainly indicate a more rapid flow of aqueous humour; thus Fig. 26 shows the response in a glaucomatous eye; at first the aqueous vein became dark red, but five minutes later both the aqueous vein and the recipient blood vessel into which it emptied became clear. It could well be that the primary effect of pilocarpine or eserine is vascular, dilating the blood vessels; if this dilatation led to a reduced episcleral venous pressure it would favour drainage, although the increased volume of blood in the eye might cause a temporary rise in intraocular pressure. Certainly the observations on aqueous veins are consistent with this point of view.

Adrenaline. Adrenaline probably acts by virtue of its constricting action on the small blood vessels; after a subconjunctival injection there may be quite a considerable fall in intraocular pressure. According to Weekers, Prijot & Gustin and Becker & Ley, there is no change in resistance to flow; and it has been argued that the cause of the fall in intraocular pressure is to be sought in a reduced rate of secretion of aqueous humour, presumably because the blood supply to the ciliary body is reduced by the constriction of the blood vessels. It seems very likely, however, that the episcleral venous pressure will be reduced by the arteriolar constriction, so that at least a part of the fall in pressure is due to this factor. Observations on the aqueous veins certainly suggest that adrenaline increases flow of aqueous humour, since recipient blood vessels that had formerly been filled with blood filled up with aqueous humour after instillation of the drug.

Diamox. There is a great deal of evidence suggesting that Diamox (acetazoleamide) inhibits the process of secretion of aqueous humour and in so doing produces a striking fall in intraocular pressure. We have seen that in order to produce a fall in intraocular pressure by reducing the flow of aqueous humour this reduction must be very high, and it is not surprising that it has been estimated that production of fluid is reduced by as much as 66 per cent after administration of the drug (Becker & Constant, 1955). On the other hand, it may be that concomitantly with the primary attack on the secretory process there is some form of adaptation of the vascular system to promote drainage; thus, according to Macri & Brown, there is a constriction of the ciliary arteries that leads to a lowered venous pressure and this, of course, would lower intraocular pressure. Certainly not all the evidence indicates such a large fall in rate of secretion as that deduced from the fall in intraocular pressure.

CHEMICAL COMPOSITION OF THE AQUEOUS HUMOUR

Protein

The most obvious chemical difference between aqueous humour and blood plasma is to be found in the protein contents of the two fluids; in the plasma it is of the order of 6–7 g per 100 ml, whereas in the aqueous humour it is only 5–15 mg per 100 ml in man and some 50 mg per 100 ml in the rabbit. By concentrating the aqueous humour and then causing the proteins to move in an electrical field—*electrophoresis*—the individual proteins may be separated and identified. Such studies have shown that, although the absolute concentrations are so low, all the plasma proteins are present in the aqueous humour, so that it is reasonable to assume that they are derived from the plasma rather than synthesized during the secretory process.

Non-Colloidal Constituents

As Table 1 shows, the crystalloidal composition of the aqueous humour is similar in its broad outlines to that of plasma, but there are some striking differences; thus the concentrations of ascorbate (vitamin C), pyruvate and lactate are much higher than in plasma, whilst those of urea and glucose are much less.

TABLE I

Chemical Composition of Aqueous Humour and Blood Plasma of the Rabbit
(after Davson, 1962)

	Aqueous Humour	Plasma
Na . . .	143·5	151·5
K . . .	5·25	5·5
Ca . . .	1·7	2·6
Mg . . .	0·78	1·0
Cl . . .	109·5	108
HCO$_3$ . .	33·6	27·4
Lactate . .	7·4	4·3
Pyruvate . .	0·66	0·22
Ascorbate . .	0·96	0·02
Urea . . .	7·0	9·1
Reducing value (as glucose) . .	6·9	8·3

Concentrations are expressed as millimoles per kilogramme of water.

Gibbs-Donnan Equilibrium. The similarities between the two fluids led some earlier investigators to assume that the aqueous humour was derived from the blood plasma by a process of filtration from the capillaries of the ciliary body and iris; *i.e.* it was assumed that the aqueous humour was similar in origin and composition to the extracellular fluid of tissues such as skeletal muscle. If this were true, however, the ionic distributions would have to accord with the requirements of the Gibbs-Donnan equilibrium, according to which the concentrations of positive ions, *e.g.* Na$^+$ and K$^+$, would be greater in the plasma than in the aqueous humour, the ratio: $[Na]_{Aq}/[Na]_{Pl}$ being less than unity, whilst the reverse would hold with negative ions such as Cl$^-$ and HCO$_3^-$. Moreover, the actual values of the ratios: *Concn. in Aqueous Humour/Concn. in Plasma* would have to conform to those found experimentally when plasma was dialysed against its own ultrafiltrate. In fact, however, as Table 2 shows, the ratios show considerable deviations from what is demanded of a plasma filtrate, and the deviations are not attributable to experimental errors. Thus with a plasma filtrate the ratio: $[Na]_{Aq}/[Na]_{Pl}$ should be 0·945 whilst it is in fact 0·96, indicating that there is an excess of 1·5 per cent of sodium in the aqueous humour. More striking is the

TABLE 2

Values of the Two Distribution Ratios; Concn. in Aqueous/Concn. in Plasma *and* Concn. in Dialysate/Concn. in Plasma. (*Davson,* Physiology of the Ocular and Cerebrospinal Fluids)

	Concn. in Aqueous / Concn. in Plasma	Concn. in Dialysate / Concn. in Plasma
Na . . .	0·96	0·945
K . . .	0·955	0·96
Mg . . .	0·78	0·80
Ca . . .	0·58	0·65
Cl . . .	1·015	1·04
HCO$_3$ . .	1·26	1·04
Urea . . .	0·87	1·00

discrepancy of the bicarbonate ratio, which in the rabbit is 1·26 compared with a value of 1·04 demanded by the Gibbs-Donnan equilibrium.

Aqueous as a Secretion. Studies along these lines have left the modern investigator in no doubt that the fluid could not have been formed by such a simple process as filtration; in consequence the aqueous humour is called a *secretion.* What is implied by this is, essentially, that in order that it should be formed from the blood plasma, something more than a mechanical filtration process that "skims" off the proteins is necessary; the cells of the ciliary epithelium must perform work—what is called *osmotic work*—in order to produce a fluid like the aqueous humour, which is not only different from plasma but also from a filtrate of plasma or dialysate. How this happens is still a closed book; presumably the first step is the production of a plasma filtrate in the stroma of the ciliary processes; this is prevented from passing into the posterior chamber by the tightly packed cells of the ciliary epithelium. We may assume that next these cells abstract from this fluid the various ions and molecules that are ultimately secreted, and together with water they drive them into the posterior chamber. In making the selection, certain ions and molecules may be transferred across the cells to give higher concentrations in the secretion than in the original plasma filtrate, *e.g.* bicarbonate and ascorbate, whilst others are transferred at lower concentrations, *e.g.* calcium, urea, and so on.

Alterations of the Primary Secretion. Once formed, the composition of the fluid may well be modified by metabolic and other events taking place during its sojourn in the posterior and anterior chambers; thus the concentration of glucose could be low because the lens and cornea actually utilize it, whilst the relatively high concentrations of lactate and pyruvate could be the consequence of glycolytic activity by these structures. That this is probably true is shown by comparing the vitreous body with the aqueous humour; the vitreous body, being exposed to both lens and retina, might be expected to have an even lower concentration of glucose than that in the aqueous humour, and higher concentrations of lactate and pyruvate. In fact this is true. Moreover, if lactate and pyruvate are produced in this way, being stronger acids than carbonic acid, they will have decomposed some of the bicarbonate entering in the original secretion, so that the original concentration of bicarbonate must have been higher (and the chloride concentration lower) than that actually found, and recent studies of Kinsey & Reddy have shown that this is indeed true.

Species Variations. The high concentration of bicarbonate in the aqueous humour shown in Table 1 is not a general characteristic common to all species; thus in horse, man, cat, rabbit and guinea pig the ratios: *Concn. in Aqueous Humour/Concn. in Plasma* are 0·82, 0·93, 1·27, 1·28 and 1·35 respectively. Hence in the horse and man the concentrations of bicarbonate are *less* than what would be expected of a filtrate of plasma. Study of the chloride composition shows an inverse relationship, as we might expect, the aqueous humours with high bicarbonates having low chlorides, and *vice versa*. It would seem that the secretion of a fluid with a high concentration of bicarbonate is concerned with the buffering needs of the eye, the bicarbonate being required to neutralize the large amounts of lactic and pyruvic acids formed by lens, retina and cornea. In animals like the rabbit and guinea pig the lens occupies a large proportion of the intra-ocular contents and so the buffering requirements are high; by contrast, in the horse and man the lens occupies a much smaller percentage of the contents (Davson & Luck). Wide species fluctuations in the concentration of ascorbate in the aqueous humour are also found; thus in the horse, man, rabbit, dog, cat and rat the concentrations are about 25, 20, 25, 5, 1 and 0 mg per 100 ml respectively, although the concentrations in the plasma are all of the same order, namely about 1 mg per 100 ml. Unfortunately the significance of ascorbate in the eye is not yet understood, so that the reason why the cat, dog and rat can manage with such low concentrations, whilst the rabbit and other species require high concentrations, is not understood. The suggestion that the lens actually synthesizes ascorbate and pours it into the aqueous humour has been disproved, at any rate as a significant source of the vitamin.

THE BLOOD-AQUEOUS BARRIER

Our knowledge of the relationships between aqueous humour and plasma has been furthered by a study of the exchange of materials between the two fluids, studies of what has come to be known as the *blood-aqueous barrier*. If various substances are injected into the blood so as to establish and maintain a constant concentration in the plasma, then the rates at which the concentrations in the aqueous humour approach that of the plasma are usually very much less than occurs in such tissues of the body as skeletal muscle, liver, etc. It is because of this that we have come to speak of the "blood-aqueous barrier", meaning that substances encounter difficulty in passing from the one fluid to the other.

Experimental Studies

Fig. 27 illustrates the penetration of some substances into the anterior chamber of the rabbit. In general, the substances fall into three categories. First there are the very large molecules like the plasma proteins, dextrans and inulin which penetrate so slowly as to give the impression of an absolute barrier, although studies with isotopically labelled proteins leave us in no doubt that there is some, but very slow, penetration. Because the aqueous humour is constantly being drained away the concentration of these large molecules in the aqueous humour never rises very high and we may speak of a *steady-state* in which the ratio of concentrations is exceedingly low. This of course accounts for the low concentrations of plasma proteins in the aqueous humour. The second category of substance has a much smaller molecule, or may be an ion; the molecule is water-soluble, like urea, creatinine, *p*-aminohippurate, sucrose and so on. Penetration is considerably faster, usually, than that of the proteins. The third group are the lipid-soluble molecules which penetrate very rapidly; these include ethyl alcohol, various substituted thioureas, many sulphonamides. In general, the rate of penetration increases with increasing lipid-solubility, as measured by the oil-water partition coefficient. Water, although not strongly lipid-soluble, belongs to the category of rapidly penetrating substances. Again, the sugars such as glucose and galactose are insoluble in lipid solvents but they also penetrate the barrier rapidly.

FIG. 27. Penetration of some non-electrolytes (*left*) and ions (*right*) into the aqueous humour of the rabbit. The concentration of the given substance in the plasma (C_{Pl}) was maintained constant, and the concentration in the aqueous humour (C_{Aq}) was determined at different times. (Davson, *Physiology of the Ocular and Cerebrospinal Fluids.*)

Mechanism of the Barrier

We may imagine that the cells of the ciliary epithelium continually secrete a fluid, which we may call the *primary aqueous humour,* that is emptied into the posterior chamber and carried through the pupil into the anterior chamber to be finally drained away out of the eye. If a foreign substance, or the isotope of a normally occurring constituent of the aqueous humour, *e.g.* ^{24}Na, is injected into the blood it presumably equilibrates rapidly with the extracellular fluid in the ciliary processes, and thus gains ready access to the cells of the ciliary epithelium. If the substance penetrates these cells easily, then we may expect it to appear in the secretion produced by them relatively rapidly. The primary aqueous humour will therefore contain the substance in high concentration. This circumstance will favour penetration into the aqueous humour as a whole. On mixing with the fluid already present in the posterior chamber, the primary fluid will be diluted, so that it will take time for the aqueous humour as a whole to reach the concentration in the plasma, in the same way that if we were to add a coloured solution to a tank of water, removing fluid from the tank as fast as the coloured fluid was added, in time the concentration of dye in the tank would come up to that in the coloured solution, but the process would take time and be determined by the rate of flow.

Diffusion from Iris. While in the posterior and anterior chambers, however, the aqueous humour is subjected to diffusional exchanges with the blood in the iris, as illustrated in Fig. 28, so that if these exchanges are significant the rate at which the foreign substance comes into equilibrium with the aqueous humour is increased. There is no doubt that lipid-solubility is an important factor in determining the rapidity of these diffusional exchanges.

FIG. 28. Illustrating the diffusional exchanges between aqueous humour in posterior and anterior chambers on the one hand, and the blood plasma in the iris, on the other.

LARGE MOLECULES

On the basis of this scheme, we may interpret the blood-aqueous barrier phenomena qualitatively. Thus large lipid-insoluble molecules such as the plasma proteins will probably be held back partially by the capillaries in the ciliary processes, so that only small amounts will be available to the epithelial cells; penetration into these cells, moreover, will be greatly restricted so that the primary secretion may contain only minimal amounts. During the fluid's sojourn in the posterior and anterior chambers some may diffuse from the iris, but these amounts will be small because of the obstructions that the large molecules will meet in the form of the epithelial covering of the posterior surface of the iris. Because of the sluggishness of all these processes, the concentration in the aqueous humour will never build up to that pertaining in the plasma; in fact, as indicated above, the concentration-ratio never rises above about 1/200 for the plasma proteins.

IONS AND LIPID-SOLUBLE MOLECULES

With substances such as ^{24}Na, the evidence suggests that the primary secretion contains this ion in the same concentration as in the plasma, whilst the contributions of diffusion from the iris are also significant. The over-all rate of penetration into the aqueous humour is thus considerably greater than that of the proteins. With ethyl alcohol penetration is altogether more rapid because of the lipid-solubility of the molecules; this permits of very rapid exchanges across the iris.

Blood-Vitreous Barrier. Early studies on the kinetics of the blood-aqueous barrier tended to ignore the influence of the vitreous body on the penetration of material into the aqueous humour. In general, the vitreous body comes into equilibrium with the blood much more slowly than the aqueous humour and we may speak of a *blood-vitreous barrier*. The vitreous body probably receives material from the choroidal and retinal circulations, but because, with many substances, equilibrium with plasma takes a long time to be achieved, it follows that the vitreous body must also receive material from the aqueous humour in the posterior chamber, the concentration tending to be higher in this fluid. The blood-vitreous barrier is thus complex, and may be illustrated by Fig. 29. A

FIG. 29. The blood-vitreous barrier.

study of the penetration of, say, ^{24}Na into the aqueous humour must take account of the circumstance that quite a considerable fraction of the ^{24}Na passing from plasma to posterior chamber diffuses back into the vitreous body, instead of being carried into the anterior chamber. The extent to which this occurs depends largely on the relative rates at which the vitreous body and aqueous humour come into equilibrium with the plasma. With lipid-soluble substances like ethyl alcohol or ethyl thiourea the discrepancy is small, and the loss of material from the posterior chamber is not serious.* With ^{24}Na and various other ions the losses are very significant.

FIG. 30. The penetration of isotopically labelled sodium into the posterior (broken line) and anterior chambers (full line) of the rabbit. (After Kinsey & Palm, *Arch. Ophthal.*)

* With lipid-soluble substances, however, the penetration of material into the lens becomes a serious factor; in an animal like the rabbit, where the volume of the lens is about twice that of the aqueous humour, this can be a very serious factor.

Mathematical Analysis. In consequence, the mathematical analysis of the process of equilibration becomes highly complex; moreover, the experimental study demands that we measure penetration into both anterior and posterior chambers separately, as well as into the vitreous body and sometimes the lens. It is not feasible to enter into the details of the mathematical analysis, which has been so elegantly carried out by Kinsey & Palm and Friedenwald & Becker. Fig. 30 shows the experimental basis for one such analysis, namely the penetration of ^{24}Na into posterior and anterior chambers. As we should expect, the posterior chamber tends to come into equilibrium more rapidly than the anterior chamber; the interesting feature is the crossing over of the curves, so that at the later stages the anterior chamber is ahead; this is because the posterior chamber is losing material to the vitreous body. A similar situation is found with chloride, studied with the isotope ^{36}Cl. The value of the mathematical analysis of the process of penetration is that it enables one to compute the probable character of the aqueous humour as it is primarily secreted (Kinsey & Reddy, 1959).

Posterior and Anterior Chambers

In describing the chemistry of the aqueous humour we considered simply the fluid obtained by inserting a needle into the anterior chamber and withdrawing all the fluid; the aqueous humour so studied was a mixture of posterior and anterior fluids. When the fluids are withdrawn separately and analysed, their comparative chemistry reveals, in some measure, their different histories. Thus the bicarbonate concentration in the posterior fluid is higher than that in the anterior fluid, in the rabbit, and this is because the freshly secreted fluid has a much higher concentration than in the plasma; while in the posterior chamber, some diffuses back to the vitreous body and some is decomposed by lactic and

TABLE 3

Relative Compositions of Plasma, Aqueous Humours and Vitreous Body in the Rabbit.
(Reddy & Kinsey, 1960)

	Na	Cl	Total CO$_2$	Ascorbate	Lactate	Glucose
Plasma . .	143	109	20·6	0·04	10·3	5·7
Anterior Aqueous	138	101	30·2	1·11	9·3	5·4
Posterior Aqueous	136	96·5	37·5	1·38	9·9	5·6
Vitreous . .	134	105	26·0	0·46	12·0	3·0

Concentrations are expressed in millimoles per kilogramme of water.

pyruvic acids; in the anterior chamber more is decomposed by the acids formed by lens and cornea, and some diffuses back into the blood in the iris. In a similar way we can account for the circumstance that the ascorbate concentration is higher in the posterior fluid; here, the diffusion from the anterior chamber into the blood in the iris is the determining factor. With chloride the concentration is less in the posterior fluid; this is because the freshly secreted fluid has a relatively low concentration of this ion; while in the anterior chamber chloride diffuses from the blood into the anterior fluid. Some recent analyses, including the vitreous body, are shown in Table 3.

Water and Osmotic Exchanges

The aqueous humour and blood plasma are approximately isosmolar, with the possibility that the aqueous humour is slightly hyperosmolar. Thus exchanges of water, apart from those concerned in the formation of the fluid, are normally negligible. When the osmolarity of the blood is altered experimentally, for example by intravenous injection of a hypertonic salt solution, then there is a rapid adjustment of the osmolarity of the aqueous humour, indicating that the barrier to water is relatively slight by comparison with the barrier to salts; and this is confirmed by direct studies with labelled water. The loss of water resulting from the hypertonic injection brings about a fall in the intraocular pressure, and the effectiveness of various solutes in reducing the intraocular pressure is presumably related to the ease with which they may cross the blood-aqueous and blood-vitreous barriers. Thus, if the solute penetrates rapidly into the fluids a difference of osmotic pressure cannot be maintained for any length of time and so the loss of water will be small. For this reason sucrose or sorbitol is effective. The special effectiveness of urea, which may be used clinically to reduce intraocular pressure temporarily, is due to a relatively slow rate of penetration of the barriers, but also to the circumstance that it is not rapidly excreted by the kidneys, so that a high level may be maintained in the plasma for some time; finally, its molecular weight is low, so that from an osmotic point of view a 10 per cent solution of urea is as effective as a 60 per cent sucrose solution.*

Breakdown of the Blood-Aqueous Barrier

Under certain pathological or experimental conditions, the blood-aqueous barrier breaks down, so that substances such as proteins, that are normally almost completely excluded from penetration, now appear in the aqueous humour in measurable amounts. Thus, on treatment of the eye with nitrogen mustard, there is a large increase in the protein content of the aqueous humour, and this is easily revealed in the slit-lamp microscope as a pronounced Tyndall beam. It can be shown, too, that the rates of penetration of smaller molecules, such as sucrose or *p*-aminohippurate, are increased greatly. Presumably the general vascular engorgement causes an increased escape of proteins from the capillaries of the ciliary body and iris, and these find their way into the posterior chamber, or more directly into the anterior chamber from the iris. As to how these large molecules pass through the ciliary epithelium is not by any means clear; cysts have been described in the epithelial cells that apparently burst, emptying their contents into the posterior chamber; or it may be that the proteins pass along the tortuous intercellular paths observed in the electron-microscope.

Fluorescein Test. The dye, fluorescein, normally penetrates the blood-aqueous barrier very slowly, but to a measurable extent because, in the intact eye, it may be detected by the fluorescence it causes in the slit-lamp beam. When the blood-aqueous barrier is broken down, the rate of appearance of fluorescein increases, and the change in rate, measured by some simple fluorimetric device such as that devised by Amsler & Huber or Langham & Wybar, is used as a measure of the breakdown. Clinically this has been found useful in the diagnosis

---

* A recent comparison of the effectiveness of sucrose and urea is that of Galin, Aizawa & McLean (1960). In a man a dose of 1 g per kilogramme of body-weight is effective, the fall in intraocular pressure reaching its maximum in forty-five minutes.

of uveitis, an inflammatory condition associated with breakdown of the barrier.*

Paracentesis. When aqueous humour is withdrawn from the eye in appreciable quantities, the fluid is re-formed rapidly but it is now no longer normal, the concentration of proteins being raised. The fluid is described as *plasmoid*; the breakdown of the barrier is probably caused by vascular engorgement, resulting from the sudden fall in intraocular pressure, since it can be prevented by stimulation of the sympathetic trunk or by application of adrenaline to the eye, according to Wessely. The re-formed fluid seems to be derived both from the ciliary body, presumably by the bursting of Greeff cysts, and also from the iris. The importance of the iris was shown by Scheie, Moore & Adler who observed that, in the completely iridectomized eye of the cat, the fluid, re-formed after paracentesis, contained only about a half as much protein as the re-formed fluid in the other, normal, eye.

RATE OF FLOW OF AQUEOUS HUMOUR

The measurement of the rate of production (or drainage) of aqueous humour is of great interest for the study of the physiology and pathology of the eye, but unfortunately the measurement is not easy. Thus, simply placing a needle in the eye and collecting the fluid dropping out would cause a breakdown of the barrier, and the rate of production of the plasmoid aqueous humour would not be a measure of the normal rate of production. In consequence, essentially indirect methods, largely based on studies of the kinetics of penetration and escape of substances into and out of the eye, have been employed. Space will not allow of a description of the methods. In general, the principle on which most are based is the introduction of some material into the aqueous humour and to measure its rate of disappearance from the anterior chamber. The substance is chosen such that the rate of escape by simple diffusion into the blood stream, across the iris, is negligible by comparison with the escape in the bulk-flow of fluid through Schlemm's canal. Estimates based on this principle agree on a value of some one to one-and-a-half per cent of the total volume per minute. Thus, in the cat, with a volume of about 1 ml, this would correspond to ten to fifteen microlitres per minute, whilst in the rabbit, with a volume of about 0·35 ml, the absolute flow-rate would be less, namely 3·5 to 5·2 microlitres per minute.

Tonography. If the resistance to outflow, or its reciprocal, the facility of outflow, has been determined by tonography, then Grant showed that the actual rate of flow, F, may be deduced from the relationship:

$$F \times R = P_{oc} - P_{ev}$$

provided the intraocular pressure, P_{oc}, and the episcleral venous pressure, P_{ev}, are known. Thus, with a resistance of 4 mm Hg.mm^{-3}.min and values of 16 and 12 mm Hg for P_{oc} and P_{ev} respectively, the flow-rate would be 1 mm^3 per

* A few minutes after an intravenous injection of fluorescein, a line of green fluorescence may be seen along the vertical meridian of the cornea. This is called the *Ehrlich line*, and it results from the thermal currents in the anterior chamber. The rate of appearance of the Ehrlich line was used as a rough measure of rate of flow of aqueous humour, on the assumption that the fluorescein passed first into the posterior chamber. More recently the "fluorescein appearance time", determined with the slit-lamp microscope, has been recommended as a measure of rate of flow of aqueous humour but the method has been criticized by Berggren (1959).

minute (one microlitre per minute). Unfortunately, the value depends so much on the figure chosen for P_{ev} that, as a scientific estimate of rate of production of fluid, it is of little use; clinically, however, it has led to some useful information.*

THE SECRETORY PROCESS

The Ciliary Epithelium. We may conclude this account of the physiology of the aqueous humour by a few remarks on the nature of the secretory process in the ciliary epithelium. In the electron-microscope the epithelial cells nearest the aqueous humour are said to exhibit vesicles within their cytoplasm, and it is thought that the secretion might be elaborated within these, and emptied into the posterior chamber. Certain drugs that interfere with the metabolism of the ciliary epithelium have an unmistakable effect on the production of the aqueous humour; of these the carbonic anhydrase inhibitor, Diamox, has already been mentioned. After treating an animal with Diamox the number of vesicles in the cells is greatly increased, as though the interference with metabolism had in some way reduced the emptying process (Pappas & Smelser).

Diamox. The decrease in intraocular pressure caused by administration of Diamox has attracted a great deal of interest because of its great clinical value; from the scientific aspect, too, the discovery was of fundamental interest since it suggested that at one stage in the production of aqueous humour the conversion of carbon dioxide to bicarbonate-ion is an important step. In animals like the rabbit and guinea pig, which produce an aqueous humour with a high concentration of bicarbonate, Diamox certainly causes a reduction in the concentration of this ion. In those species where the aqueous humour has a relatively low concentration of bicarbonate, Diamox seems to attack the chloride concentration, reducing this. It seems, therefore, that the drug interferes with what we may call an anion-secreting mechanism. It is presumably because of the interference with this that the fluid can no longer be formed at its normal rate.

Cardiac Glycosides. With many secretory processes an important element is the active transport of sodium by the secretory cells; by this is meant that the cells cause the sodium ion to move against gradients of electrochemical potential; in doing this, energy must be supplied, and the cells have to have certain "carriers" that specifically attach themselves to the sodium and enable it to pass preferentially in one direction. The cardiac glycosides, digitalis, ouabain, etc., interfere with this process by competing with sodium for its place on the "carriers", and it is interesting that they are able to reduce the rate of formation of aqueous humour (Simon, Bonting & Hawkins) after intravenous injection into cats.

Dinitrophenol. A less specific way of interfering with the formation of aqueous humour is to inhibit the metabolism that produces the energy for the process; in doing this, of course, one tends to kill the animal because one inhibits other vital activities. For this reason local application is necessary. With the eye, this can be achieved by injection of a poison, dinitrophenol (DNP), into the internal carotid artery or a branch of this. Cole showed that the transport of sodium into the aqueous humour was reduced by this drug.

Ciliary Body Potentials. It is currently assumed that an important element

* Recently Saeteren (1960) has reviewed the limitations of the tonographic method of measuring aqueous flow.

in the secretion of aqueous humour is the transport of sodium across the cells of
the ciliary epithelium and that this is brought about by a process known as *active
transport* instead of simple diffusion; this active process requires energy. The
active transport of sodium is a feature common to many secretory systems, for
example the frog's skin which transports this ion from the outside watery
medium to the inside of the skin. A common feature of the process, although not
essential, is the production of a difference of potential across the secretory
epithelium, the side to which the sodium is transferred becoming positive in
relation to the other side. If electrodes are placed in the aqueous humour and in
the jugular vein a potential is indeed observed, the aqueous humour being some
10 mV positive in relation to the blood (Lehmann & Meesmann; Cole, 1961)
whilst if the ciliary body is stripped away from the eye and maintained in an
artificial medium, a difference of potential may also be observed. By studying
the effects of poisons, and of artificial variations of the potential by means of an
applied electromotive force, Cole has made it extremely probable that the potential is in some way a measure, or at least a sign, of the active transport of sodium.
It must be appreciated, however, that the chemical studies of the aqueous
humour described earlier have made it very likely that *anions*, either chloride or
bicarbonate or both, are transferred against gradients of electrochemical potential, *i.e.* are actively transported, so that the observed potential is doubtless the
sign of both processes, namely transport of positive and negative ions. This may
be why the potential is so small, by comparison with the 50 or more millivolts
observed with the frog skin where only positive ions seem to be actively transported; presumably the potential created by the transport of positive ions by
the ciliary epithelium is largely balanced by an opposite potential associated
with transport of negative ions.*

Hypothermia. We may mention the effects of hypothermia on the production
of aqueous humour; here we are reducing the rate of metabolism and therefore,
presumably, reducing the amount of energy available for the production of
aqueous humour. In fact, there is a considerable fall in intraocular pressure which
is probably due, in part at any rate, to a reduced rate of production of fluid
(Pollack, Becker & Constant); and it is interesting that the cells of the ciliary
epithelium show the same accumulation of cytoplasmic vesicles as was seen after
Diamox (Holmberg & Becker). According to Davson & Spaziani, the reduced
rate of secretion could well be due, not so much to the lowered body-temperature,
as such, but to the decrease in the blood supply to the ciliary body that must
accompany the great reduction in arterial pressure that takes place in hypothermia.

Absorption by Ciliary Body. It is common to think of the ciliary processes
as organs for the production of secretion, in the sense of transporting material
from blood to posterior chamber. It is therefore of considerable interest to
discover that the ciliary processes are capable of actively removing certain
substances from the aqueous humour into the blood. Thus Forbes & Becker
showed that, if diodrast was injected into the vitreous body, it disappeared from
this into the blood but did not appear in the aqueous humour, being apparently

---

* The potentials within the epithelial cells have been measured by Berggren (1960); the
unpigmented cells have a "resting potential" of − 30 mV in relation to the aqueous
humour, whilst the pigmented cells have one of 60 mV. Similar results were obtained by
Miller & Constant (1960).

actively removed by the ciliary epithelium; studies on the isolated ciliary body confirmed that the epithelium was indeed able to accumulate diodrast and also iodide. Essentially similar results had been found by Pappenheimer with the choroid plexuses of the ventricles, and it would seem that these secretory epithelia share with the epithelium of the kidney tubule this power of selecting certain substances—iodide, p-aminohippurate, diodrast—and transporting them against a concentration gradient.

GENERAL REFERENCES

ASCHER, K. W. (1961). *The Aqueous Veins*. Springfield: Charles C. Thomas.

DAVSON, H. (1956). *Physiology of the Ocular and Cerebrospinal Fluids*. London: Churchill.

DAVSON, H. (1962). The intra-ocular fluids. The intra-ocular pressure. In *The Eye*, Ed. Davson, pp. 67–146; 147–196. London: Academic Press.

DEPNER, H. O. (1958). L'état actuel de la tonographie. *Doc. Ophthal.*, **12**, 106–184.

DUKE-ELDER, W. S. (1932). *Textbook of Ophthalmology*, Vol. I. London: Kimpton.

FRANÇOIS, J., & NEETENS, A. (1962). Comparative anatomy of the vascular supply of the eye in vertebrates. In *The Eye*, Ed. Davson, pp. 369–416. London: Academic Press.

LANGHAM, M. E. (1958). Aqueous humour and control of intra-ocular pressure. *Physiol. Rev.*, **38**, 215–242.

PAPPAS, G. D., & SMELSER, G. K. (1961). The fine structure of the ciliary epithelium in relation to aqueous humour secretion. In *The Structure of the Eye*, Ed. Smelser, pp. 453–467. New York: Academic Press.

ROHEN, J. (1961). Morphology and pathology of the trabecular meshwork. In *The Structure of the Eye*, Ed. Smelser, pp. 335–341. New York: Academic Press.

THEOBALD, G. D. (1960). The limbal area. *Amer. J. Ophthal.*, **50**, 543–557.

WOLFF, E. (1961). *Anatomy of the Eye and Orbit*. London: H. K. Lewis. (Revised R. J. Last.)

SPECIAL REFERENCES

AMSLER, M., & HUBER, A. (1946). Methodik und erste klinische Ergebnisse einer Funktionsprufung der Blut-Kammerwasser-Schranke. *Ophthalmologica, Basel*, **111**, 155–176.

ARMALY, M. F. (1959). Studies on intraocular effect of orbital parasympathetic. *Arch. Ophthal., N.Y.*, **62**, 117–124.

ARMALY, M. F. (1960). Schiøtz tonometer calibration and applanation tonometry. *Arch. Ophthal., N.Y.*, **64**, 426–432.

ASCHER, K. W. (1942). Aqueous veins. Preliminary note. *Amer. J. Ophthal.*, **25**, 31–38.

ASHTON, N. (1951). Anatomical study of Schlemm's canal and aqueous veins by means of Neoprene casts. *Brit. J. Ophthal.*, **35**, 291–303.

ASHTON, N., BRINI, A., & SMITH, R. (1956). Anatomical studies of the trabecular meshwork of the normal human eye. *Brit. J. Ophthal.*, **40**, 257–282.

BÁRÁNY, E. H., & SCOTCHBROOK, S. (1954). Influence of testicular hyaluronidase on the resistance to flow through the angle of the anterior chamber. *Acta physiol. scand.*, **30**, 240–248.

BECKER, B., & CONSTANT, M. A. (1955). The effect of the carbonic anhydrase inhibitor acetazolamide on aqueous flow. *Arch. Ophthal., N.Y.*, **54**, 321–329.

BECKER, B., & LEY, A. P. (1958). Epinephrine and acetazolamide in the therapy of the chronic glaucomas. *Amer. J. Ophthal.*, **45**, 639–643.

BERGGREN, L. (1959). Further observations on the appearance of fluorescein in the rabbit eye after intravenous injection. *Acta ophthal. Kbh.*, **37**, 215–218.

BERGGREN, L. (1960). Intracellular potential measurements from the ciliary processes of the rabbit eye *in vivo* and *in vitro*. *Acta physiol. scand.*, **48**, 461–470.

BILL, A. (1962). The drainage of blood from the uvea and the elimination of aqueous humour in rabbits. *Exp. Eye Res.*, **1**, 200–205.

COLE, D. F. (1960). Rate of entrance of sodium into the aqueous humour of the rabbit. *Brit. J. Ophthal.*, 1960, **44**, 225–245.

COLE, D. F. (1961). Electrochemical changes associated with the formation of the aqueous humour. *Brit. J. Ophthal.*, **45**, 202–217.

COLE, D. F. (1961). Prevention of experimental ocular hypertension with polyphloretin phosphate. *Brit. J. Ophthal.*, **45**, 482–489.

COLE, D. F. (1961). Electrical potential across the ciliary body observed *in vitro. Brit. J. Ophthal.*, **45**, 641–653.

COPELAND, R. L., & KINSEY, V. E. (1950). Determination of the volume of the posterior chamber of the rabbit. *Arch. Ophthal., N.Y.*, **44**, 515–516.

DAVSON, H., & LUCK, C. P. (1956). A comparative study of the total carbon dioxide in the ocular fluids, cerebrospinal fluid, and plasma of some mammalian species. *J. Physiol.*, **132**, 454–464.

DAVSON, H., & MATCHETT, P. A. (1951). The control of the intraocular pressure in the rabbit. *J. Physiol.*, **113**, 387–397.

DAVSON, H., & SPAZIANI, E. (1960). The fate of substances injected into the anterior chamber of the eye. *J. Physiol.*, **151**, 202–215.

DAVSON, H., & SPAZIANI, E. (1961). The effect of hypothermia on intraocular dynamics. *Exp. Eye Res.*, **1**, 182–192.

DOBBIE, G. C., & LANGHAM, M. E. (1961). Reaction of animal eyes to sanguinarine and argemone oil. *Brit. J. Ophthal.*, **45**, 81–95.

DRANCE, S. M. (1960). The coefficient of scleral rigidity in normal and glaucomatous eyes. *Arch. Ophthal., N.Y.*, **63**, 668–674.

FORBES, M., & BECKER, B. (1960). In vivo transport of iodopyracet (diodrast). *Amer. J. Ophthal.*, **50**, Pt. 2, 862–867.

FLOCKS, M. (1956). The anatomy of the trabecular meshwork as seen in tangential section. *Arch. Ophthal., N.Y.*, **56**, 708–718.

FLOCKS, M., & ZWENG, H. C. (1957). Studies on the mode of action of pilocarpine on aqueous outflow. *Amer. J. Ophthal.*, **44**, Pt. 2, 380–388.

FRIEDENWALD, J. S. (1957). Tonometer calibration. An attempt to remove discrepancies found in the 1954 calibration scale for Schiøtz tonometers. *Trans. Amer. Acad. Ophthal. Otolaryngol.*, **61**, 108–123.

FRIEDENWALD, J. S., & BECKER, B. (1956). Aqueous humour dynamics. Theoretical considerations. *Amer. J. Ophthal.*, **41**, 383–398.

GALIN, M. A., AIZAWA, F., & McLEAN, J. M. (1960). A comparison of intraocular pressure reduction following urea and sucrose administration. *Arch. Ophthal., N.Y.*, **63**, 281–282.

GARRON, L. K., & FEENEY, M. L. (1959). Study of the trabeculæ by light and electron microscopy. *Arch. Ophthal., N.Y.*, **62**, 966–976.

GLOSTER, J. (1961). Influence of facial nerve on intraocular pressure. *Brit. J. Ophthal.*, **45**, 259–278.

GLOSTER, J., & GREAVES, D. P. (1957). Effect of diencephalic stimulation upon intraocular pressure. *Brit. J. Ophthal.*, **41**, 513–532.

GOLDMANN, H. (1946). Weitere Mitteilung uber den Abfluss des Kammerwassers beim Menschen. *Ophthalmologica, Basel*, **112**, 344–349.

GOLDMANN, H. (1955). Un nouveau tonomètre à aplanation. *Bull. Soc. franc. Ophtal.*, **67**, 474.

GRANT, W. M. (1950). Tonographic method for measuring the facility and rate of aqueous outflow in human eyes. *Arch. Ophthal., N.Y.*, **44**, 204–214.

GRANT, W. M. (1958). Further studies on facility of flow through trabecular meshwork. *Arch. Ophthal., N.Y.*, **60**, 523–533.

GREAVES, D. P., & PERKINS, E. S. (1952). Influence of the sympathetic nervous system on the intraocular pressure and vascular circulation of the eye. *Brit. J. Ophthal.*, **36**, 258–264.

HOLMBERG, A. (1955). Studies on the ultrastructure of the non-pigmented epithelium in the ciliary body. *Acta ophthal. Kbh.*, **33**, 377–381.

HOLMBERG, A., & BECKER, B. (1960). The effect of hypothermia on aqueous humour dynamics. *Amer. J. Ophthal.*, **49**, Pt. 2, 1134–1140.

HÖRVEN, I. (1961). Tonometry in newborn infants. *Acta ophthal. Kbh.*, **39**, 911–918.

HUGGERT, A. (1958). Experimentally induced increase in intraocular pressure in the rabbit eye. *Acta ophthal. Kbh.*, **36**, 750–760.

KINSEY, V. E., & PALM, E. (1955). Posterior and anterior chamber aqueous humour formation. *Arch. Ophthal., N.Y.*, **53**, 330–344.

KINSEY, V. E., & REDDY, D. V. N. (1959). An estimate of the ionic composition of the fluid secreted into the posterior chamber, inferred from a study of aqueous humour dynamics. *Doc. Ophthal.*, **13**, 7–40.

KUPFER, C. (1961). Studies on intraocular pressure. I. *Arch. Ophthal., N.Y.*, **65**, 565–570.

LANGHAM, M. E. (1959). Influence of the intraocular pressure on the formation of the aqueous humour and the outflow resistance in the living eye. *Brit. J. Ophthal.*, **43**, 705–732.

LANGHAM, M. E. (1960). Steady-state pressure relationships in the living and dead cat. *Amer. J. Ophthal.*, **50**, Pt. 2, 950–958.

LANGHAM, M. E., & TAYLOR, C. B. (1960). The influence of pre- and post-ganglionic section of the cervical sympathetic on the intraocular pressure of rabbits and cats. *J. Physiol.*, **152**, 437–446.

LANGHAM, M. E., & TAYLOR, C. B. (1960). The influence of superior cervical ganglion-ectomy on the intraocular pressure. *J. Physiol.*, **152**, 447–458.

LANGHAM, M. E., & WYBAR, K. C. (1953). A fluorophotometer for the study of intraocular dynamics in the living animal. *J. Physiol.*, **120**, 5P.

LEHMANN, G., & MEESMANN, A. (1924). Über das Bestehen eines Donnangleichgewichtes zwischen Blut und Kammerwasser bzw. Liquor cerebrospinalis. *Pflüg. Arch.*, **205**, 210–232.

LEYDHECKER, W., AKIYAMA, K., & NEUMANN, H. G. (1958). Der intraokulare Druck gesunder menschlicher Augen. *Klin. Mbl. Augenheilk.*, **133**, 662–670.

MCBAIN, E. H. (1960). Tonometer calibration. III. *Arch. Ophthal., N.Y.*, **63**, 936–942.

MACRI, F. C. (1961). Interdependence of venous and eye pressure. *Arch. Ophthal., N.Y.*, **65**, 442–449.

MACRI, F. J., WANKO, T., & GRIMES, P. A. (1958). The elastic properties of the human eye. *Arch. Ophthal., N.Y.*, **60**, 1021–1026.

MACRI, F. J., & BROWN, J. G. (1961). The constrictive action of acetazolamide on the iris arteries of the cat. *Arch. Ophthal., N.Y.*, **66**, 570–577.

MAGGIORE, L. (1917). Struttura, comportamento e significato del canale di Schlemm nell'occhio umano, in condizioni normali e patologische. *Ann. Ottalm.*, **40**, 317–462.

MILLER, J. E., & CONSTANT, M. A. (1960). The measurement of rabbit ciliary epithelial potentials *in vitro*. *Amer. J. Ophthal.*, **50**, Pt. 2, 855–862.

MOSES, R. A., & BECKER, B. (1958). Clinical tonography: the scleral rigidity correction. *Amer. J. Ophthal.*, **45**, 196–208.

PEASE, D. C. (1956). Infolded basal plasma membranes found in epithelia noted for their water transport. *J. biophys. biochem. Cytol.*, **2**, Suppl., 203–208.

PEDLER, C. (1962). The fine structure of the corneal epithelium. *Exp. Eye Res.*, **1**, 286–289.

PERKINS, E. S. (1957). Influence of the fifth cranial nerve on the intraocular pressure in the rabbit eye. *Brit. J. Ophthal.*, **41**, 257–300.

PERKINS, E. S. (1961). Sensory mechanisms and intraocular pressure. *Exp. Eye Res.*, **1**, 160–167.

PERKINS, E. S., & GLOSTER, J. (1957). Distensibility of the eye. *Brit. J. Ophthal.*, **41**, 93–102; 475–486.

POLLACK, I. P., BECKER, B., & CONSTANT, M. A. (1960). The effect of hypothermia on aqueous humour dynamics. *Amer. J. Ophthal.*, **49**, Pt. 2, 1126–1132.

REDDY, D. V. N., & KINSEY, V. E. (1960). Composition of the vitreous humour in relation to that of the plasma and aqueous humour. *Arch. Ophthal., N.Y.*, **63**, 715–720.

SAETEREN, T. (1960). The tonographic method of measuring aqueous flow. *Acta Ophthal. Kbh.*, **38**, 511–523.

SCHEIE, H. G., MOORE, E., & ADLER, F. H. (1943). Physiology of the aqueous in completely iridectomised eyes. *Arch. Ophthal., N.Y.*, **30**, 70–74.

SEARS, M. L. (1960). Miosis and intraocular pressure changes during manometry. *Arch. Ophthal., N.Y.*, **63**, 707–714.

SEARS, M. L. (1960). Outflow resistance of the rabbit eye: technique and effects of ace-tazolamide. *Arch. Ophthal., N.Y.*, **64**, 823–838.

SEIDEL, E. (1918). Experimentelle Untersuchungen über die Quelle und den Verlauf der intraokularen Saftströmung. *v. Graefes Arch. Ophthal.*, **95**, 1–72.

SEIDEL, E. (1921). Uber den Abfluss des Kammerwassers aus der vorderen Augenkammer. *v. Graefes Arch. Ophthal.*, **104**, 357–402.

SERR, H. (1937). Zur Analyse der spontanen Pulserscheinungen in den Netzhautgefässen. *v. Graefes Arch. Ophthal.*, **137**, 487–505.

SIMON, K. A., BONTING, S. L., & HAWKINS, N. M. (1962). Studies on sodium-potassium-activated adenosine triphosphatase. II. Formation of aqueous humour. *Exp. Eye Res.*, **1**, 253–261.

SINGH, S., & DASS, R. (1960). The central artery of the retina. *Brit. J. Ophthal.*, **44**, 193–212; 280–299.

SPEAKMAN, J. S. (1960). Drainage channels in the trabecular wall of Schlemm's canal. *Brit. J. Ophthal.*, **44**, 513–523.

v. SALLMANN, L., FUORTES, M. G. F., MACRI, F. J., & GRIMES, P. (1958). Study of afferent electric impulses induced by intraocular pressure changes. *Amer. J. Ophthal.*, **45**, Pt. 2, 211–220.

v. SALLMANN, L., & LOEWENSTEIN, O. (1955). Responses of intraocular pressure, blood pressure and cutaneous vessels to electrical stimulation of the diencephalon. *Amer. J. Ophthal.*, **39**, Pt. 2, 11–29.

VRÁBEC, F. (1954). L'innervation du système trabéculaire de l'angle irien. *Ophthalmologica, Basel*, **128**, 359–364.

WEEKERS, R., PRIJOT, E., & GUSTIN, J. (1954). Mode de l'action de l'adrénaline dans le glaucome chronique. *Ophthalmologica, Basel*, **128**, 213–217.

WEIGELIN, E., & LÖHLEIN, H. (1952). Blutdruckmessungen an den episkleral Gefässen des Auges bei kreislaufgesund Personen. *v. Graefes Arch. Ophthal.*, **153**, 202–213.

THE VITREOUS BODY

THIS is a transparent jelly occupying, in man and most vertebrates, by far the largest part of the globe. As Fig. 1, p. 1, shows, it is bounded by the retina, ciliary body and the posterior capsule of the lens. If the sclera is cut through round the equator, the posterior half with the attached retina comes away from the vitreous body, leaving this suspended from its firm attachments to the ciliary body and pars plana of the retina. To isolate it completely from these attachments careful cutting and scraping are necessary.

CHEMISTRY

When discussing the dynamic relationships between aqueous humour and the vitreous body it was considered sufficient to treat the latter as an essentially aqueous medium; and this is justified by the observation that over 99 per cent of the material in this body is water and dissolved salts. The special features of the inorganic composition have been considered earlier, and here we are concerned with the composition in so far as it bears on the structure and stability of the vitreous body as a gel. If the vitreous body is held in a pair of forceps, or placed on a filter, it drips and after a time only a small skin of viscid material remains; this residue was called by Mörner the *residual protein*, and was considered to constitute the gel-forming material in essentially the same way that fibrin constitutes the gel-forming material of a plasma clot. The liquid dripping away, or passing through the filter, contains the dissolved crystalloids together with a mucopolysaccharide, *hyaluronic acid*, that imparts to the solution a high viscosity by virtue of its high molecular weight and highly asymmetrical molecules. In addition there is a small percentage (0·05%) of soluble proteins, some of which seem to be peculiar to the vitreous whilst others are identical with plasma proteins (Laurent, Laurent & Howe).

Residual Protein or Vitrosin

Purified residual protein may be dissolved in alkali and subsequently precipitated by acid; when the precipitated material is examined in the electron-microscope it appears fibrillar and very similar to collagen;[*] chemically, moreover, it is very like collagen having the typically high proportions of glycine and hydroxyproline but, like the collagen of Descemet's membrane and the lens capsule, containing a polysaccharide which appears to be firmly attached to the protein molecule (McEwan & Suran); finally the bulk of the vitreous body may be

---

[*] The appearance of collagen fibrils in the electron-microscope varies with the source and mode of preparation; the characteristic feature is a cross-striation with a period of 640 Å. In general, if any cross-striation has been described on the fibrils of vitreous body, its periodicity is smaller (120 Å by Schwarz, 1961; 220 Å by Fine & Tousimis, 1961). According to Gross, Maltoltsy & Cohen, the wide-angle X-ray diffraction pattern of vitrosin is characteristic of collagen, whilst the glycine/hydroxyproline ratio is rather less. It seems safest to regard vitrosin as a collagen-like material differing from that typically found in connective tissue proper in a number of minor respects.

liquefied by the enzyme collagenase. Tentatively, therefore, we may suppose that the structure of the vitreous gel is maintained by a framework of branching vitrosin fibrils, in the meshes of which the watery solution of crystalloids, hyaluronic acid and soluble proteins is imprisoned. The concentration of residual protein is so small (0·01%) that the fibrils must be very fine, and the meshwork relatively coarse, if such a small amount of material is to form a coherent jelly.

STRUCTURE

This picture, which may be deduced on purely physicochemical principles, is partly sustained by modern electron-microscopical studies, although there are still many points of uncertainty. The fibrillar basis is certainly well established by the examination of thin sections of frozen vitreous; this is illustrated by Fig. 31, Pl. II, from a recent paper by Fine & Tousimis which confirms earlier studies, particularly those of Schwarz, in this respect. As predicted, the fibrils are very thin being some 200 to 250 Å in diameter, and of indefinite length.* By treating the preparations with hyaluronidase, which breaks up the hyaluronic acid, the fibrils became more distinct, indicating that this material was normally in close association with the collagenous fibrils. Between the fibrils there was a large amount of granular material with diameters of 100 to 4000 Å; presumably this represented the hyaluronic acid and soluble proteins (Schwarz, 1956).

Local Variations in Structure

The picture just presented, of a fibrous framework holding the fluid components of the vitreous in its meshes, would suggest that the vitreous body was essentially homogeneous throughout its bulk; a considerable amount of evidence indicates, however, the existence of differentiation to give microscopically visible structures; these are most probably superimposed on the fundamental basis described above. To appreciate the significance of the differentiation we must review the embryonic history of the vitreous body.

Embryonic History. In the early stages, the optic cup is mainly occupied by the lens vesicle (p. 59); as the cup grows, the space formed is filled by a system of fibrillar material presumably secreted by the cells of the embryonic retina. Later, with the penetration of the hyaloid artery, more fibrillar material, apparently derived from the cells of the wall of the artery and other vessels, contributes to filling the space. The combined mass is known as *primary vitreous*. The *secondary vitreous* develops later as a secretory product of cells of the retina (probably Müller's cells) and it is associated with the increasing size of the vitreous cavity and the involution of the hyaloid system. The main hyaloid artery remains for some time but eventually disappears, and its place is left as a tube of primary vitreous surrounded by secondary vitreous; this tube is called *Cloquet's canal*, but is not a liquid-filled canal but simply a portion of differentiated gel. The *tertiary* vitreous is the name given to the grossly fibrillar material secreted by the inner walls of the optic cup in the region that will later become the ciliary body; this material eventually becomes the zonule of Zinn or suspensory ligament of the lens.

Phase-Contrast Microscopy. When examined in the ordinary light-microscope the vitreous body is said to be optically empty; in the phase-contrast

---

* Schwarz (1961) gives an even smaller value, namely 40–100 Å with an average of 67 Å, whilst Grignolo (1952) described three types with diameters ranging from 150 to 800 Å.

PLATE II

FIG. 31. Shadowcast section of posterior vitreous structure, approximately 0·5 mm anterior to surface of the equatorial retina of the human eye. The orientation of the filaments in the plane of the section suggests a tangential cut through a lamella. The filaments are uniform in width and show a distinct periodicity. × 12,000. The enlarged inset (× 38,000) demonstrates periodicity on filaments. (Fine & Tousimis, *Arch. Ophthal.*)

FIG. 32. Hyaline membrane of ox vitreous body. Phase-contrast. (Courtesy Antoinette Pirie.)

[To face p. 46.

FIG. 34. Shadowcast section of adult human zonule and adjacent vitreous body framework. The widths of the filaments of both zonular and adjacent framework are similar; also the periodicities of the filaments (220 Å). × 13,000. (Fine & Tousimis, *Arch. Ophthal.*)

FIG. 36. Transverse section through the stroma of a human cornea showing several lamellæ (the fibres in stained sections), in each of which the collagen fibrils are orientated parallel with each other and perpendicular to those in adjacent layers. Osmium fixation. × 10,230. (Jakus, in *The Structure of the Eye*, Academic Press.)

microscope, however, Bembridge Crawford & Pirie described three characteristic differentiations; in the anterior portion definite fibres of relatively large diameter were found, whilst in the bulk of the body there were much finer, but still optically resolvable, fibres. Chemically the large fibres seemed to be different from the fine fibres; thus the enzyme collagenase left these large fibres intact whilst it dissolved the fine fibres; again, the enzyme trypsin or chymotrypsin dissolved the large fibres but not the others. Finally, on the surface, there appeared to be a hyaline membrane (Fig. 32, Pl. II). Since phase-contrast microscopy is carried out on perfectly normal fresh tissue it is difficult to rule out these structures as artefacts; nevertheless the electron-microscopical observations, indicating a fibril of the order of 100–200 Å by contrast with these optically visible fibres of the order of 1–2 μ, *i.e.* 10,000–20,000 Å, indicate that the fundamental basis of structure is probably the fine fibril, whilst the larger fibres must be regarded as essentially localized densifications of this primary structure. This is especially true of the zonular fibres proper; electron-microscopical observations of the vitreous in this region indicate large fibres made up of closely aggregated fine filaments, whilst the neighbouring vitreous shows only the fine filaments loosely scattered.

Limiting Membrane. Again, in the electron-microscope there is little evidence for a structured limiting hyaline membrane belonging to the vitreous body; according to Tousimis & Fine the *internal limiting membrane* of the retina belongs to this tissue and cannot be regarded as a limiting membrane of the vitreous; when the vitreous is removed the membrane remains adherent to the cells of the retina and must be regarded as a basement membrane for these cells; as seen in the electron-microscope it is an acellular structure some 1000–2000 Å thick, and is attached to the vitreous by filaments made up of the normal vitreous fibrils.

Cortical Zone. We must regard the hyaline layer, then, as a region in which the fibrils are more densely arranged, so as to give a sufficient difference of refractive index to create the appearance of a membrane in phase-contrast microscopy. This so-called *cortical zone* has been studied by Balazs who has emphasized the presence of numerous stellate cells buried in it; presumably these cells secrete the hyaluronic acid of the vitreous; at any rate they are very granular; however, the possibility that they are phagocytic cannot be ignored, since they certainly engulf particulate matter injected into the vitreous body. It may be that the denser aggregation of fibrils on the surface cortical zone acts as some sort of barrier to the penetration of bacteria, viruses, and proteins, since v. Sallmann showed that hæmoglobin, injected into the excised vitreous body floating in saline, seemed to be held up at the surface.

Chemical Differences. There is chemical evidence for some differentiation of the vitreous body; for example Bembridge *et al.* found that the proportions of vitrosin varied, being highest in the anterior portion where also the electron-microscopists had differentiated the highest density of fibrils. Again Balazs found a very high concentration of hyaluronic acid and vitrosin in the cortical layer, corresponding with its more compact character; finally the concentrations of acid glycoproteins and water-soluble proteins vary with the region analysed.*

* During development there are marked changes in composition; for example the concentration of hyaluronic acid steadily increases. Where different species are compared some very large differences are found; for example the vitreous of the bush-baby (*Galago*) is quite fluid (Luck, 1958) consisting of hyaluronic acid with very little collagen; by contrast the vitreous bodies of the frog and hen are very solid and have very little hyaluronic acid and large amounts of collagen (Balazs, *et al.*, 1959a, b).

Probable Structure

To conclude, then, on the probable structure of the vitreous body we may accept the suggestion of Balazs, illustrated by Fig. 33, where fine filaments of vitrosin form a framework which is filled by heavily hydrated and coiled molecules of hyaluronic acid; in different regions the fineness of the network will vary, leading in the extreme case to the aggregation of filaments to coarse fibres visible in the phase-contrast microscope, for example the coarse fibres described by Bembridge *et al.* or, still more extremely, the fibres of the zonule. Pathologically, localized liquefaction could result from a shrinkage of vitrosin filaments to leave a pool of liquid surrounded by relatively gross fibres (Fig. 33, *right*).

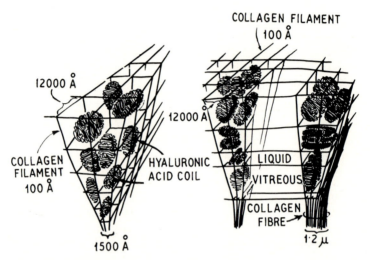

FIG. 33. Schematic picture of the fine structure of the vitreous gel showing network reinforced with hyaluronic acid molecules. *Left:* Random distribution of the structural elements. *Right:* Formation of liquid pool and partial collapse of the network. (Balazs, In *Structure of the Eye.*)

Slit-Lamp Appearance. When viewed *in situ* with the slit-lamp microscope, the vitreous body appears to have a "framework or scaffolding, hanging curtain-like in undulating folds, and moving with each movement of the eye". This is due to the scattering of light by the submicroscopic fibrils of vitrosin which are presumably packed in layers of different density to give alternations of light and dark bands. The impression given is one of folds in an anterior limiting membrane so that Vogt called it the *membrana hyaloidea plicata*. However, as indicated, in the electron-microscope there is no evidence for the presence of a true membrane, only a condensation of the fibrillar structure characteristic of the whole body.

THE ZONULE

Macroscopic Appearance. The zonule, or suspensory ligament of the lens, may be regarded as an extreme instance of differentiation of the vitreous body, its fibrous parts being composed presumably of the same material as that making up the large fibres of the vitreous body described by Bembridge *et al.*, since they are both dissolved by the enzyme trypsin;* the difference between the two is essentially that the zonular fibres have found attachment to the lens capsule whilst the coarse fibres of the vitreous attach to the ciliary body. In the fresh specimen the zonule appears as a thick band-shaped structure attached internally to the equatorial region of the lens capsule; the anterior surface runs straight from the lens to the anterior region of the ciliary processes (Fig. 5, p. 4). The surfaces of the zonule show a marked striation running in a general sense from the lens to the ciliary body; these striations probably represent fibres of highly condensed residual protein; between them is a perfectly homogeneous transparent gel which gives the surface a membrane-like appearance. The space between the anterior and posterior surfaces is criss-crossed by strands of fibrous material, the spaces so formed being once again filled by transparent homogeneous jelly.

Electron-Microscopy. In the electron-microscope the zonular fibres appear as dense aggregations of the fine fibrils that constitute the framework of the surrounding vitreous (Fig. 34, Pl. II). Preparations of the ciliary epithelium made by Pappas & Smelser show that the fibres may be regarded as extensions of the basement membrane of the epithelial cells, which is itself fibrillar in nature. Thus the basement membrane invests the surface of the ciliary body with its processes very closely, so that the attachment of the zonular fibres to the ciliary body may be said to be similar to the "attachment of a tight-fitting glove on one's hand", the mere close approximation of the two membranes—epithelial cell membrane and basement membrane—on an irregular contour, giving a very efficient attachment. No fibrils of the zonule entered the epithelial cells.

GENERAL REFERENCES

BALAZS, E. A. (1961). Molecular morphology of the vitreous body. In *The Structure of the Eye*. Ed. Smelser. New York: Academic Press. pp. 293–310.

GRIGNOLO, A. (1954). Studi sulla struttura submicroscopica dei tessuti oculari. *Boll. d'Oculist.*, **33,** 1–144.

PIRIE, A. (1962). The vitreous body. In *The Eye*. Ed. Davson. London: Academic Press. pp. 197–210.

SCHWARZ, W. (1961). Electron microscopic observations on the human vitreous body. In *The Structure of the Eye*. Ed. Smelser. New York: Academic Press. pp. 283–291.

SPECIAL REFERENCES

BALAZS, E. A., LAURENT, T. C., & LAURENT, U. B. G. (1959a). Studies on the structure of the vitreous body. VI. *J. biol. Chem.*, **234,** 422–430.

BALAZS, E. A., LAURENT, T. C., LAURENT, U. B. G., DE ROCHE, M. H., & DUNNEY, D. M. (1959b). Studies on the structure of the vitreous body. VIII. *Arch. Biochem. Biophys.*, **81,** 464–479.

BEMBRIDGE, B. A., CRAWFORD, C. N. C., & PIRIE, A. (1952). Phase-contrast microscopy of the animal vitreous body. *Brit. J. Ophthal.*, **36,** 131–142.

FINE, B. S., & TOUSIMIS, A. J. (1961). The structure of the vitreous body and the suspensory ligaments of the lens. *Arch. Ophthal., Chicago*, **65,** 95–110.

GROSS, J. (1956). The behaviour of collagen units as a model in morphogenesis. *J. biophys. biochem. Cytol.*, **2,** Suppl., 261–274.

GROSS, J., MATOLTSY, A. G., & COHEN, C. (1955). Vitrosin: a member of the collagen class. *J. biophys. biochem. Cytol.*, **1,** 215–220.

* This finding is the basis of the use of trypsin to liquefy the zonule introduced into cataract surgery by Barraquer.

LAURENT, U. B. G., LAURENT, T. C., & HOWE, A. F. (1962). Chromatography of soluble proteins from the bovine vitreous body on DEAE-cellulose. *Exp. Eye Res.*, **1**, 276–285.

LUCK, C. P. (1958). The vitreous body of *Galago crassicaudatus agisymbanus*. *Nature*, **181**, 719.

McEWEN, W. K., & SURAN, A. A. (1960). Further studies on vitreous residual protein. *Amer. J. Ophthal.*, **50**, 228–231.

MATOLTSY, A. G. (1952). A study of the structural protein of the vitreous body, vitrosin. *J. gen. Physol.*, **36**, 29–37.

MATOLTSY, A. G., GROSS, J., & GRIGNOLO, A. (1951). A study of the fibrous components of the vitreous body in the electron microscope. *Proc. Soc. exp. Biol. Med.*, **76**, 857–860.

PAPPAS, G. D., & SMELSER, G. K. (1958). Studies of the ciliary epithelium and the zonule. I. *Amer. J. Ophthal.*, **46**, Pt. 2, 299–318.

SCHWARZ, W. (1956). Elektronenmikroskopische Untersuchungen an Glaskörperschnitten. *Anat. Anz.*, **102**, 434–442.

SZIRMAI, J. A., & BALAZS, E. A. (1958). Studies on the structure of the vitreous body. III. Cells in the cortical layer. *Arch. Ophthal., Chicago*, **59**, 34–48.

v. SALLMANN, L. (1949). Experimental studies on the vitreous. I. *Arch. Ophthal., Chicago*, **42**, 583–595.

PART 3

THE CORNEA

STRUCTURE

THE cornea is illustrated by the meridional section in Fig. 35; the great bulk (up to 90 per cent of its thickness) is made up of the *stroma* which is bounded externally by Bowman's membrane and the epithelium, and internally by Descemet's membrane and the endothelium. The total thickness in man is just over 0·5 mm in the central region; towards the periphery it becomes some 50 per cent thicker.

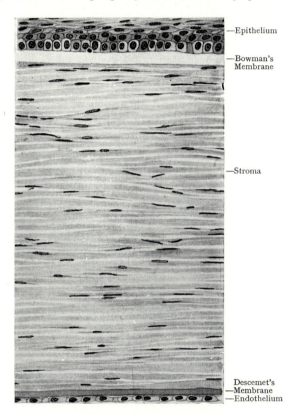

—Epithelium

—Bowman's Membrane

—Stroma

Descemet's —Membrane
—Endothelium

FIG. 35. Meridional section through the human cornea.
(Wolff, *Anatomy of the Eye and Orbit.*)

Epithelium

This may be regarded as the forward continuation of the conjunctiva; it is a squamous epithelium consisting of some five or six layers of cells with a total thickness of 50–100 μ. The cells at the base are columnar, but as they are squeezed forwards by new cells they become flatter so that three layers are recognized:

basal, wing-shaped, and *squamous cells*. The more superficial cells do not show keratinization, as with skin, the process of shedding being accompanied by the breaking up of the cell into fragments (Teng). Replacement of cells occurs by mitotic division of the basal layer, the average life of a cell being some 4–8 days (according to Hanna & O'Brien). Intercellular junctions (*desmosomes, terminal bars* or *nodes of Bizzorere*) are frequent.* Amongst the cells a special, possibly secretory type, has been described by Teng; it may be that they secrete the basement membrane upon which the epithelium rests; this latter is a layer some 100–300 Å thick resolved into an anterior apparently lipid layer and a reticular fibre meshwork in contact with Bowman's membrane.

Regeneration. When the epithelium is stripped off from the underlying Bowman's membrane there is a rapid regeneration, so that within twenty-four hours the surface may be completely covered by a new layer of regenerated epithelial cells derived from multiplication of the conjunctival cells at the periphery. This *single* layer subsequently develops to give, within several weeks, a complete epithelium 4–6 cells thick. Smaller lesions are repaired by migration of neighbouring epithelial cells from all layers, the migrated cells increasing their areas by flattening, and extending pseudopodia.

Stroma and Bowman's Membrane

The Lamellæ and Fibrils. In meridional section the stroma appears as a set of lamellæ, running parallel with the surface, and superimposed on each other like the leaves of a book; between the lamellæ lie the *corneal corpuscles*, flattened in the plane of the lamellæ; they are equivalent to fibrocytes of other connective tissue. The lamellæ are made up of microscopically visible *fibres*, which run parallel to form sheets; in successive lamellæ the fibres make a large angle with each other. In lower animals the lamellæ extend over the whole surface of the cornea and the fibres in adjacent laminæ are at right-angles to each other; in mammals and man the lamellæ are said to be made up of bands some 90–260 μ wide; there is apparently no interweaving of these bands, however, so that essentially the structure consists of layers of fibres arranged parallel with themselves in any given lamella.

The lamellæ in man are some 1·5 to 2·5 μ thick, so that there are at least 200 lamellæ in the human cornea. The fibrous basis of the lamellæ is made up of collagen which constitutes some 80 per cent of the solid matter of the cornea; by submitting the cornea to ultrasonic vibrations in order to break down its structure into its elementary components, Schwarz (1953) observed typical collagen fibrils of 250 to 330 Å diameter, and having the characteristic 640 Å periodicity (p. 45); the fibrils isolated in this way were covered by a dense layer of cement substance which was presumably the mucopolysaccharide. The fibrils were remarkably homogeneous in regard to diameter, in marked contrast to those of the sclera where the diameter varied from 280 Å to 2800 Å, and where the amount of ground substance was very much less. As we shall see, this uniformity in diameter is important for the transparency of the cornea by contrast with the opacity of the sclera. More recently Jakus (1961) has made thin sections of the cornea and examined these in the electron-microscope; these have revealed a

---

* Opinions differ as to whether the desmosomes really represent an intercellular bridge; they could be just two areas of specialized cell membrane, separated by a very fine (100 Å) space.

remarkably uniform arrangement of fibrils, running parallel with each other and at right-angles with those in adjacent layers (Fig. 36, Pl. II). The stromal cells in the human cornea appeared to lie within, rather than between, the laminæ.

Bowman's Membrane. Immediately next to the epithelium, the classical histologists described a layer with no resolvable structure, some 8–14 μ thick in man—*Bowman's membrane** (Fig. 35). In the electron-microscope it became evident that Bowman's membrane is only a less ordered region of the stroma; thus, according to Jakus, and Kayes & Holmberg, the stroma immediately beneath the basement membrane of the epithelium consists of collagen fibrils closely but randomly packed into a felt-like layer which is not sharply differentiated from the remainder of the stroma beneath it. It should therefore be described as *Bowman's layer* rather than Bowman's membrane.

Descemet's Membrane

This is some 5–10 μ thick in man and is revealed as a characteristic differentiation of the stroma in the electron-microscope, although in man the organization is not so precise as in the ox cornea. The collagen is different, having an axial period of 1170 Å in place of the usual banding at intervals of 640 Å, and the carbohydrate is also different but similar chemically to that in the lens capsule (Dohlman & Balazs). Descemet's membrane is secreted by the endothelium.

Endothelium

This is a layer of flattened cells, some 5 μ high and 20 μ wide. Division of endothelial cells only occurs during growth and this is mitotic, in spite of claims to the contrary (v. Sallmann, Caravaggio & Grimes). During growth, multiplication of cells does not keep pace with the increase in area, so the cells become progressively flatter. By contrast with the epithelium, then, the endothelial cells are normally a non-renewable population. After damage, there is considerable mitotic division, and neighbouring cells flatten and spread into the damaged area; Descemet's membrane is repaired after damage by the slow secretion of new material.

CHEMISTRY

The cornea contains some 22 per cent of solid matter, and is thus quite obviously built on a more rigid plan than the vitreous body; this solid matter is mainly collagen, but in addition there are mucopolysaccharides, other proteins than collagen, and crystalloids of which salts make up the bulk. The mucopolysaccharides have been examined in some detail, chiefly by Meyer; they consist of three fractions, namely *keratan sulphate*, *chondroitin sulphate*, and *chondroitin*.

Mucopolysaccharides

This is the name commonly given to a group of polysaccharides containing an amino sugar and widely distributed throughout the animal body where they may act as lubricants in the joints and saliva, as the anticoagulant called heparin, as blood-group substances on the surface of red cells, as ground substance of con-

---

* In many lower mammals, such as the rabbit and mouse, Bowman's membrane is absent, so that only the basement membrane, which is common to all species, separates the epithelium from the stroma proper.

nective tissue, as cement between cells, and so on. Strictly speaking the term mucopolysaccharide should be applied, however, only to the combination between this type of polysaccharide and a protein, the reaction of the complex being predominantly polysaccharidic, whilst the term *mucoprotein* is applied to a complex between protein and carbohydrate where the behaviour is predominantly protein in character.* Perhaps the best known of the polysaccharides is *hyaluronic acid*, already described in relation to the vitreous body; it consists of large asymmetrical molecules (weight of the order of a million or more) made up by the polymerization of N-acetylglucosamine and glucuronic acid, linked together as follows:

Hyaluronic Acid

Hyaluronic acid is specifically broken down by the enzyme, *hyaluronidase*, isolated from streptococci and pneumococci. Chondroitin sulphate was first found in the cornea but also occurs in cartilage; it is built up by the polymerization of N-acetylgalactosamine, glucuronic acid and sulphate, as below:

Chondroitin Sulphate

Chondroitin is the desulphated chondroitin sulphate, whilst the latter has been found in three different forms, called chondroitin sulphate A, B and C, the differences being not so much due to differences in the sugar moieties as in the nature of the linkages.

Histochemically these polysaccharides are identified by their so-called *metachromatic staining* with toluidine blue, whereby the stain acquires a different colour than it had in free solution. The *periodic acid-Schiff test* (P.A.S.) is also characteristic for the chondroitins although there is some doubt as to whether hyaluronic acid reacts positively.

The polysaccharides react easily with proteins to form complexes, but it is by no means certain as to what extent they are bound thus in the tissues. So far as the cornea is concerned, at least a part of the polysaccharide is bound to non-collagenous protein so that extremely vigorous treatment is necessary to extract it (Woodin, 1954)

HYDRATION AND TRANSPARENCY

Swelling

If an excised eye is kept at, say, 4°C in the refrigerator for twenty-four hours or more the cornea will be seen to have lost some of its transparency, becoming

* The term *glycosaminoglycan* is recommended for a polysaccharide containing a hexosamine; more specifically, *glucosaminoglycan* is a polysaccharide containing glucosamine; *galactosaminoglycan*, one containing galactosamine, and so on.

"smoky" in appearance; associated with this optical change there is found an increase in thickness due to absorption of aqueous humour. Thus, with an ox eye, there is an increase of water-content from 77·3 to 82 per cent. Expressed in this way the increase in water-content is not impressive, but expressed as the amount of water per gramme of solid matter the increase is from 3·4 g.H_2O/g. solids to 4·55 g./g., *i.e.* an increase of 33 per cent. The increase in water is associated with an increase in the salt content and corresponds to an uptake of aqueous humour rather than the selective absorption of water (Davson, 1949). If an excised cornea is placed in saline the same increase in water-content, with absorption of salt, is observed; if the epithelium is removed the uptake is just the same, if somewhat more rapid, so that it is clear that we are dealing with an increased hydration of the stroma, which is behaving similarly to many of the inanimate gels studied by the colloid chemists; like these gels the cornea shows a swelling pressure, which may be measured by exerting a contrary pressure to prevent uptake of fluid; it amounts to 75–85 g/cm² in the normal cornea; as the cornea takes up water, the pressure it can exert decreases, whilst it increases as water is withdrawn.

Effect of Temperature. This uptake of fluid by the dead cornea, and its associated loss of transparency, was considered by Cogan & Kinsey to result from the removal of the normal osmotic pressures of tears and aqueous humour that were supposed, in the living eye, to remove water continuously from the cornea as fast as it entered. In the first edition of this book the present author showed the theoretical inadequacy of this theory and subsequent experimental studies have confirmed this criticism. Thus, to quote a crucial experiment, on the basis of the Cogan-Kinsey theory the swelling of the dead cornea should be much more rapid and extensive if the eye were kept at body-temperature than in the refrigerator, yet if the two eyes of a rabbit are excised and the one is kept at 4°C and the other in a moist chamber at the normal temperature of the aqueous humour, namely 31°C, it is found that the eye kept in the warm is almost completely normal, with good transparency, and water-content only slightly different from the average normal figure. Clearly, by cooling the eye we are robbing the corneal tissue of its power of excluding fluid, and this is presumably due to reducing the metabolism of the eye. In other words, the cornea is probably using metabolic energy to resist the intrusion of fluid from the aqueous humour. To understand the factors concerned, let us turn now to the fluid and salt relationships between cornea, on the one hand, and aqueous humour and tears on the other.

Stroma-Aqueous Humour-Tears. The general picture of the relationships between the corneal stroma and the aqueous humour and tears is illustrated schematically in Fig. 37. The stroma, being a mixture of collagen and its associated mucopolysaccharides, may be treated as a gel, and largely by virtue of the polysaccharide this gel has a tendency to take up water.* It is separated from the two fluids from which this water is obtainable by membranes, the epithelium and endothelium. These membranes are permeable to salts and water (Maurice, 1951) so that the swelling tendency of the gel must be resisted by some

---

* It seems well proved that it is the mucopolysaccharide that is responsible for the hydration tendency; thus the fibrils of a swollen cornea are no larger than normal when examined in the electron-microscope (François, Rabaey & Vandermeersche, 1954); again, extraction of the mucopolysaccharides from the cornea reduces its tendency to take up water (Leyns, Heringa & Weidinger, 1940).

active process on the part of either the endothelium or epithelium or both. Removal of the epithelium or endothelium in the intact eye causes a rapid uptake of fluid (Maurice & Giardini). As Fig. 37 indicates, at the limbus the stroma may take up fluid and salts from the pericorneal capillary plexus, since there is no reason to believe that there would not be a filtration from these capillaries as in other parts of the body.

Reversal of Swelling. If the cornea of the excised eye is allowed to swell by keeping it for some time at 4°C, the process may be reversed by transferring the eye now to a moist chamber at 31°C (Davson, 1955) so that either the epithelium or endothelium has actively removed the salts and water that entered at the low temperature; according to Harris & Nordquist this reversal is still possible when

FIG. 37. Illustrating the tendency for the stroma of the cornea to hydrate by virtue of the inward movement of water and salts from aqueous humour, tears and limbal capillaries.

the epithelium has been removed, so that it would appear that it is the endothelium that is able to remove water and salts actively; in the normal eye this active process of removal presumably just balances the influx of fluid from the limbus and tears.

Active Process. As to the nature of the active process, it was early assumed that this could be achieved by the active transport of sodium from stroma to aqueous humour across the endothelial membrane, or from stroma to tears across the epithelium. The salt so transferred would carry with it its osmotic equivalent of water. Such an active transport, if it occurred, should be detectable by modern isotopic methods in which the fluxes of ^{24}Na are measured together with the potential across the cornea. This potential was found by Potts & Modrell, and Donn, Maurice & Mills to be of the order of 10–40 mV, the outside of the eye being negative to the inside; the epithelium was responsible. This is just the opposite of what would be expected were the epithelium actively transporting sodium *from* the stroma, and measurement of the fluxes of this ion showed that it was being actively transported *into* the stroma, from the tears, thus increasing the tendency for this to hydrate. There was no evidence for an active transport of sodium out of the endothelium, however, so that the tendency at present is to suppose an active transport of water (Harris & Nordquist) or a process of *pinocytosis*, whereby fluid is engulfed into vesicles within the endothelial cells and emptied out of these cells into the aqueous humour. Certainly recent studies with the electron-microscope by Donn *et al.* indicate an extraordinary number of vesicles in the endothelial cells capable of engulfing particulate matter when this was presented to them in a suspension.

Metabolic Inhibition. Whatever the mechanism for maintaining normal corneal thickness, metabolic energy is necessary for it, so it is not surprising that when the excised eye is maintained in an atmosphere free of oxygen the hydration increases enormously (Schwartz, Danes & Leinfelder); similarly, metabolic poisons increase thickness. It is for this reason, too, that contact lenses cause fogging of vision; the reduced access of oxygen to the cornea causes failure of the thickness-controlling mechanism with its associated cloudiness of the cornea (Smelser & Ozanics).

Transparency of the Cornea

Scattering of Light. By transparency we mean rather more than the ability of a material to transmit light, we are concerned with the manner in which it is transmitted; thus dark glasses may reduce the transmission to 10 per cent of the incident intensity yet the optical image remains perfect; on the other hand an opal screen may reduce the intensity much less, but because of the *scattering* of the light no image is possible. Thus diffraction, or scattering, of light is the important factor for transparency; and in this respect the cornea is very highly transparent, less than 1 per cent of the light being scattered. The question arises as to how this transparency is attained in an inhomogeneous medium consisting of fibres embedded in a matrix of different refractive index; and furthermore, why the transparency should be affected by increases in hydration of the cornea and changes in intraocular pressure, as when haloes are seen during an acute attack of glaucoma.

Lattice Theory. The problem has been examined in detail with considerable acumen by Maurice (1957) who has shown, from an analysis of the birefringence* of the cornea, that the size of the fibrils, and the difference of refractive index between them and the ground-substance in which they are embedded, are such as to lead one to expect a highly opaque structure, due to scattering of incident light. He has shown, nevertheless, that this scattering may be avoided if the fibres are of relatively uniform diameter and are arranged in parallel rows; in this event the diffracted rays passing forwards tend to cancel each other out by destructive interference, leaving the normal undiffracted rays unaffected. In this way the opacity of the sclera is also explained, since there is no doubt from Schwarz' study that the prime distinction between the two tissues is the irregularity in arrangement and diameter of the scleral fibres. The cloudiness that follows increased hydration could be due to the weakening of the forces that normally keep the fibres arranged in a fixed lattice work; these forces probably depend on a mutual repulsion of the fibres, due to the presence of charges consequent on the ionization of polar groups; increased hydration, by shielding these charges with water molecules, reduces their effectiveness and leads to an irregular arrangement. Again, an increased pressure will presumably do the same thing. It will be recalled that the cornea differs from the opaque sclera in having a high concentration of mucopolysaccharide which seems to act as an embedding medium for the collagen fibrils; hence it is likely that the ordered arrangement of these fibrils depends on this embedding medium.

* The ordered arrangement of the collagen fibrils makes the velocity of light in one plane different from that in one at right-angles; this leads to double refraction or birefringence. From the magnitude and character of this birefringence important information regarding the orientation of the fibrils in the cornea may be obtained (Stanworth & Naylor, 1953; Maurice, 1957).

PERMEABILITY OF THE CORNEA

In a homogeneous medium a dissolved substance will pass from a region of high to one of low concentration by the process of diffusion. When the diffusion from one region to another is restricted by the presence of a membrane, the process is described as one of "permeability", and the degree of restraint imposed on the migration of the solute molecules is measured inversely by the *permeability constant* of the membrane. In general, the ease with which a substance can penetrate cell membranes depends on its lipid-solubility; thus ethyl alcohol, which is highly lipid-soluble, penetrates cell membranes easily, whereas glycerol penetrates with difficulty. The membranes separating the stroma from its surrounding media are formed by layers of closely packed cells; lipid-soluble substances may be expected to pass easily into the cornea because they may pass easily into and out of the cells of these membranes; lipid-insoluble substances, including ions, may be expected to penetrate with difficulty; moreover, the endothelium, with its single layer of cells, might be expected to be the more permeable membrane. When considering this type of membrane, furthermore, we may envisage the possibility of diffusion *between* the cells, rather than through them; this is a route that will be of significance for the lipid-insoluble substances which have difficulty in passing by the trans-cellular route. In general, the qualitative studies of Swan & White, and Cogan & Hirsch, confirm these general principles. Where the substance is an organic base or acid, such as atropine or salicyclic acid, the degree of dissociation is an important factor since the undissociated molecule penetrates more rapidly than the ion; hence the permeability of the cornea to these substances is influenced by pH. The permeability to ions was examined quantitatively by Maurice, who showed that the endothelium was some 100 times more permeable to sodium than the epithelium; the evidence suggested that ions utilized the intercellular route across the membranes. The penetration of water is very rapid through both membranes (Cogan & Kinsey), a feature shared by most cellular membranes.

METABOLISM OF THE CORNEA

Oxygen Consumption. The cornea consumes oxygen, which is derived from the tear fluid and the aqueous humour; when the eyes are closed and access to atmospheric oxygen is removed, diffusion from the conjunctival vessels of the lids is adequate to maintain the supply (Langham).

Pentose Phosphate Shunt. The respiratory quotient is unity, indicating a predominantly carbohydrate metabolism, and recent studies, notably those of Kinoshita, Masurat & Helfant, have shown that carbohydrate is broken down by two pathways. First, the usual process of *glycolysis*, leading to pyruvic acid which is then either reduced to lactic acid or oxidized by way of the citric acid cycle to CO_2 and H_2O. The alternative pathway is by way of the so-called *pentose phosphate shunt*; by this series of reactions, glucose-6-phosphate is converted to glyceraldehyde 3-phosphate (triose phosphate), a pentose phosphate being formed as an intermediary product. The glyceraldehyde 3-phosphate does not accumulate, but is metabolized via pyruvate to CO_2 and H_2O, or it may be converted to hexose phosphate. Ultimately, then, the carbohydrate is completely oxidized to CO_2 and H_2O by this shunt. This pathway, which accounts for some 65–70 per cent of the carbohydrate utilization by the cornea, is considered to be a more primitive mode of metabolism, being common in lower organisms and plant cells; in higher organisms its value may well consist in the production of pentose, a constituent of nucleic acids, etc.

Epithelium. As one might expect, the metabolic activity of the epithelium is responsible for most of the metabolism of the cornea: thus the Q_{O_2} of epithelium and endothelium is of the order of 5–6 compared with about 0·1 in the stroma. According to Herrmann & Hickman, there is a subtle metabolic relationship between the epithelium and the stroma; thus the epithelium is said not to produce any lactic acid, whereas the stromal cells do, the epithelium actually oxidizing the lactic acid produced by these. The stromal cells, on the other hand, require from the epithelium a phosphate-acceptor to permit the conversion of triose phosphate to lactic acid.

Lactate. Whatever the truth of the matter, there is no doubt that a considerable amount of lactic acid is normally formed by the cornea, the concentration being some 110 mg/100 gH_2O compared with 66 mg for the aqueous humour; and this increases under anærobic conditions; some of this diffuses into the aqueous humour and contributes to the high concentration relative to that in the blood.

Supply of Materials

Glucose. The supply to the cornea of materials required for metabolism, notably glucose, is theoretically possible by three routes; namely diffusion from the limbus, where there is a capillary network; diffusion from tears across the

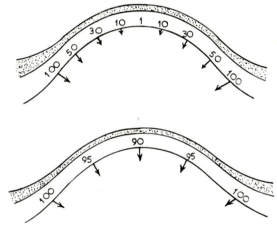

Fig. 38. Illustrating the effects of diffusion from cornea into aqueous humour on the transport of material from limbus to corneal centre. *Above:* Diffusion into aqueous humour is rapid, so that at the corneal centre the effective concentration is low. *Below:* Diffusion out is slow, so that a relatively high concentration can be built up at the corneal centre.

epithelium, and diffusion from aqueous humour. Maurice (1962) has examined the relative significance of these pathways and has shown that, because there is no significant flow of fluid through the stroma from limbus to central region, the transport by simple diffusion will be very inefficient. This is because while the material diffuses slowly from limbus to central region, it will be exposed to concentration gradients from stroma to aqueous humour and tears (Fig. 38). Thus, with a small molecule or ion, if the concentration at the limbus is put equal to 100, the concentration at 6 mm from the limbus will be only 1 when a steady-state has been reached. On the other hand, where diffusion out into the aqueous humour and tears is restricted, as with plasma proteins, then a significant supply from the limbus is practicable, and would account for their presence in the cornea, as well as that of numerous enzymes. The supply of glucose, then, must be from aqueous humour and tears; however, the significance of the tears as a supply is probably negligible since, according to Giardini & Roberts, the concentration in this fluid is very small.

Oxygen Supply. As indicated earlier, the oxygen supply for the epithelium is derived from the atmosphere; it would seem that normally the cornea is not respiring, *i.e.* using oxygen, at its maximum rate since replacing the atmosphere with pure oxygen decreases the concentration of lactic acid in the cornea (Langham). Calculations suggest that the endothelium may obtain all the oxygen it requires from the aqueous humour.

Corneal Vascularization. Under conditions of metabolic stress, for example after injury, when the tissue may be invaded by leucocytes and fibrocytes, the nutritive supply and metabolic reserves may become inadequate, with the result that vessels sprout from the limbal plexus and grow into the stroma—*corneal vascularization*. It is likely that the effects of vitamin deficiency fall into the same category of metabolic stress; thus riboflavine deficiency is associated with corneal vascularization, whilst deficiencies of essential amino-acids, such as tryptophan, lysine and methionine, will also produce the condition. As to what the stimulus for ingrowth of vessels is, we are still ignorant; Campbell & Michaelson found that, if the injury to the cornea occurred too far from the periphery, *i.e.* at the pole of the cornea, vascularization failed to take place, presumably because some chemical stimulant had to diffuse to the periphery and activate the blood vessels.*

Energy Reserves

Analysis of the cornea shows that the epithelium contains glycogen, the actual amount being approximately that found, weight for weight, in skeletal muscle. In the excised cornea this energy reserve is slowly expended, some 50 per cent disappearing in twenty hours at 32°C; it is understandable, therefore, why the cornea of the excised eye may retain a normal hydration and transparency. In the absence of oxygen, however, there is a much more rapid disappearance and this presumably accounts for the rapid development of haziness in corneas whose oxygen supply has been interfered with by wearing contact lenses.

NERVOUS SUPPLY

The innervation of the cornea is probably entirely sensory, mediated by the ophthalmic division of the trigeminal by way of the ciliary nerves. According to Zander & Weddell the fibres travel towards the limbus mainly in the perichoroidal space, and enter the substance of the cornea from three levels, scleral, episcleral and conjunctival. Most of the bundles entering the cornea are arranged radially and give rise, by subdivision, to a plexus in the stroma from which fibres supply the different regions. So great is the branching of any nerve fibre during its course in the cornea that a single axon may innervate an area equivalent to a quadrant. The endings are free, similar to those of pain fibres in other parts of the body; those reaching the epithelium are extremely fine, and send loops between the cells to

---

* The significance of vitamin C in the eye is not clear; the cornea shares in the high concentration observed in the aqueous humour. The vitamin is believed to be concerned with collagen deposition in wound repair, and some recent experiments of Sabatine *et al.* (1961) suggest that it may be concerned with collagen synthesis within the eye.

within one cell-layer of the surface; similarly in the endothelium, the terminations are very fine.

Modalities of Sensation. Since v. Frey's time it has been categorically stated that the cornea is sensitive only to pain, in the sense that all forms of stimulus in man arouse only this sensation. According to Lele & Weddell (1956), however, the sensation of touch, as distinct from that of pain, may be evoked by gentle application of a nylon thread; again, a copper cylinder, maintained at 1·5°C above or below the corneal temperature, evoked a sensation of warmth or cold. By recording from the ciliary nerves of the cat, Lele & Weddell (1959) found action potentials in the myelinated fibres in response to both thermal and mechanical stimuli, and it appeared that the same fibres responded to both types of stimulus. Thus, apparently in contradiction to Müller's Law of Specific Nerve Energies, the sensory fibres of the cornea were able to mediate both thermal and touch sense. According to Kenshalo, however, the sensations evoked by thermal stimulation of the human cornea are not those of warmth and cold but are of different types of "irritation"; thus the nerve endings are *sensitive* to thermal change as well as mechanical, but the sensations evoked with the different stimuli are essentially of the same modality.

Regeneration of Fibres. When the cornea is cut through, as in making a section for cataract extraction, there is a loss of sensibility of the affected region, followed by a return associated with the growth of new fibres from the cut bundles proximal to the scar; there is no sprouting of adjacent uninjured neurones, however, since Rexed & Rexed repeatedly renewed a cut in the periphery and found no recovery of sensibility in the area supplied by the cut fibres.*

RESPONSE OF THE CORNEA TO INJURY

Stromal Repair. The repair processes taking place in endothelium and epithelium have already been described; damage to the substantia propria is associated with the migration of new cells into the damaged area, either by chemotaxis from the limbal capillaries or, if the damage is severe, by the ingrowth of vessels into the stroma—the so-called corneal vascularization. The cells secrete new collagen fibres, but because the orientation of fibres is not so accurate as in normal tissue some degree of light-scattering remains in the scar. When the repair processes are over the wandering cells that moved in settle down to become corneal corpuscles (Maumenee & Kornbluth).

Corneal Graft. The cornea is peculiar in that it is possible to transplant a portion from one individual to another of the same species, *i.e.* to carry out a *homograft*. This may be the result of the low antigenic powers of the collagen of the cornea, or of the absence of a vascular supply through which the antigen-antibody response has to be mediated. An important element in the "take" of the graft seems to be the sealing into place of the donor tissue by the migration of the host's corneal corpuscles to the cut edge of the trephine hole, and the extension of processes into the donor tissue (Hoffman & Messier).

GENERAL REFERENCES

BINDER, R. F., & BINDER, H. F. (1957). Regenerative processes in the endothelium of the cornea. *Arch. Ophthal., N.Y.*, **57,** 11–13.

DAVSON, H. (1955). Anatomy and physiology of the cornea. In *Corneal Grafts.* Ed. Rycroft. London: Butterworth. pp. 11–35.

* The existence or otherwise of a vegetative—autonomic—innervation of the cornea is still a matter of dispute; the latest paper on the subject is that of Lassmann (1961) who disagrees with Wolter's (1956) claim that there were both sympathetic and parasympathetic fibres to the cornea. Mitosis in epithelial cells seems to be affected by the sympathetic system (Mishima, 1957).

GRIGNOLO, A. (1954). Studi sulla struttura submicroscopica dei tessuti oculari. *Boll. d'Oculist.*, **33**, 1–144.

HEYDENREICH, A. (1958). *Die Hornhautregeneration.* Halle: Marhold.

JAKUS, M. (1961). The fine structure of the human cornea. In *Structure of the Eye.* Ed. Smelser. New York: Academic Press. pp. 343–366.

KENT, P. W., & WHITEHOUSE, M. W. (1955). *Biochemistry of the Amino Sugars. N.Y.:* Academic Press.

MAURICE, D. M. (1962). The cornea and sclera. In *The Eye.* Ed. Davson. Vol. I, pp. 289–368. London: Academic Press.

PIRIE, A., & VAN HEYNINGEN, R. (1956). *Biochemistry of the Eye.* Oxford: Blackwell.

STACEY, M., & BARKER, S. A. (1962). *Carbohydrates of Living Tissues.* London: Van Nostrand.

THOMAS, C. I. (1955). *The Cornea.* Springfield: Thomas.

SPECIAL REFERENCES

CAMPBELL, F. W., & MICHAELSON, I. C. (1949). Blood-vessel formation in the cornea. *Brit. J. Ophthal.*, **33**, 248–255.

COGAN, D. G., & HIRSCH, E. D. (1944). The cornea. VII. Permeability to weak electrolytes. *Arch. Ophthal., N.Y.*, **32**, 276–282.

COGAN, D. G., & KINSEY, V. E. (1942). Transfer of water and sodium chloride by osmosis and diffusion through the excised cornea. *Arch. Ophthal., N.Y.*, **27**, 466–476.

COGAN, D. G., & KINSEY, V. E. (1942). The cornea. V. Physiologic aspects. *Arch. Ophthal., N.Y.*, **28**, 661–669.

DAVSON, H. (1949). Some considerations on the salt content of fresh and old ox corneæ. *Brit. J. Ophthal.*, **33**, 175–182.

DAVSON, H. (1955). The hydration of the cornea. *Biochem. J.*, **59**, 24–28.

DOHLMAN, C. H., & BALAZS, E. A. (1955). Chemical studies on Descemet's membrane of the bovine cornea. *Arch. Biochem. Biophys.*, **57**, 445–457.

DONN, A., KAYE, G. I., MALLETT, N. M., & PAPPAS, G. D. (1961). Pinocytosis in the rabbit corneal endothelium. *Arch. Ophthal., N.Y.*, **66**, 835–846.

DONN, A., MAURICE, D. M., & MILLS, N. L. (1959). The active transport of sodium across the epithelium. *Arch. Ophthal., N.Y.*, **62**, 748–757.

FRANÇOIS, J., RABAEY, M., & VANDERMEERSCHE, G. (1954). Étude de la cornée et de la sclérotique. *Ophthalmologica, Basel*, **127**, 74–85.

GIARDINI, A., & ROBERTS, J. R. E. (1950). Concentration of glucose and total chloride in tears. *Brit. J. Ophthal.*, **34**, 737–743.

HANNA, C., & O'BRIEN, J. E. (1960). Cell production and migration in the epithelial layer of the cornea. *Arch. Ophthal., N.Y.*, **64**, 536–539.

HARRIS, J. E., & NORDQUIST, L. T. (1955). The hydration of the cornea. I. Transport of water from the cornea. *Amer. J. Ophthal.*, **40**, 100–110.

HERRMANN, H., & HICKMAN, F. H. (1948). *Bull. Johns. Hopk. Hosp.*, **82**, 182, 225, 260.

HOFFMANN, R. S., & MESSIER, P. E. (1949). *Arch. Ophthal., N.Y.*, **42**, 140, 148.

JAKUS, M. (1946). The fine structure of Descemet's membrane. *J. biophys. biochem. Cytol.*, **2**, Suppl., 243–252.

KAYES, J., & HOLMBERG, Å. (1960). The fine structure of Bowman's layer and the basement membrane of the corneal epithelium. *Amer. J. Ophthal.*, **50**, 1013–1021.

KENSHALO, D. R. (1960). Comparison of thermal sensitivity of the forehead, lip, conjunctiva and cornea. *J. app. Physiol.*, **15**, 987–991.

KINOSHITA, J. H., MASURAT, T., & HELFANT, M. (1955). Pathways of glucose metabolism in corneal epithelium. *Science*, **122**, 72–73.

LANGHAM, M. E. (1952). Utilization of oxygen by the component layers of the living cornea. *J. Physiol.*, **117**, 461–470.

LASSMANN, G. (1961). Die Innervation der Hornhaut. *v. Graefes Arch. Ophthal.*, **162**, 565–609.

LAURENT, T. C., & ANSETH, A. (1961). Studies on corneal polysaccharides. II. Characterization. *Exp. Eye Res.*, **1**, 99–105.

LELE, P. P., & WEDDELL, G. (1956). The relationship between neurohistology and corneal sensitivity. *Brain*, **79**, 119–154.

LELE, P. P., & WEDDELL, G. (1959). Sensory nerves of the cornea and cutaneous sensibility. *Exp. Neurol.*, **1**, 334–359.

LEYNS, W. F., HERINGA, C., & WEIDINGER, A. (1940). Water binding capacity of the cornea. *Acta brev. Neerland. Physiol.*, **10**, 25–26.

MAUMENEE, A. E., & KORNBLUTH, W. (1949). Regeneration of the corneal stromal cell. *Amer. J. Ophthal.*, **32**, 1051–1064.

MAURICE, D. M. (1951). The permeability to sodium ions of the living rabbit's cornea. *J. Physiol.*, **122**, 367–391.

MAURICE, D. M. (1957). The structure and transparency of the cornea. *J. Physiol.*, **136**, 263–286.

MAURICE, D. M., & GIARDINI, A. A. (1951). Swelling of the cornea in vivo after destruction of its limiting layers. *Brit. J. Ophthal.*, **35**, 791–797.

MISHIMA, A. (1957). The effects of denervation and the stimulation of the sympathetic and trigeminal nerve on the mitotic rate of the corneal epithelium of the rabbit. *Jap. J. Ophthal.*, **1**, 65–73.

POTTS, A. M., & MODRELL, R. W. (1957). The transcorneal potential. *Amer. J. Ophthal.*, **44**, 284–290.

REXED, B., & REXED, V. (1951). Degeneration and regeneration of corneal nerves. *Brit. J. Ophthal.*, **35**, 38–49.

SABATINE, P. L., ROSEN, H., GEEVER, E. F., & LEVENSON, S. M. (1961). Scurvy, ascorbic acid concentration, and collagen formation in the guinea pig. *Arch. Ophthal., N.Y.*, **65**, 32–37.

SCHWARTZ, B., DANES, B., & LEINFELDER, P. J. (1954). The role of metabolism in the hydration of the isolated lens and cornea. *Amer. J. Ophthal.*, **38**, Pt. 2, 182–194.

SCHWARZ, W. (1953). Elektronenmikroskopische Untersuchungen uber den Aufbau der Sklera und der Cornea des Menschen. *Z. Zellforsch.*, **38**, 20–49.

SMELSER, G. K., & OZANICS, V. (1953). Structural changes in corneas of guinea pigs after wearing contact lenses. *Arch. Ophthal., N.Y.*, **49**, 335–340.

STANWORTH, A., & NAYLOR, E. S. (1953). Polarized light studies of the cornea. *J. exp. Biol.*, **30**, 164–169.

SWAN, K. C., & WHITE, N. G. (1942). Corneal permeability. *Amer. J. Ophthal.*, **25**, 1043–1058.

TENG, G. C. (1961). The fine structure of the corneal epithelium and basement membrane of the rabbit. *Amer. J. Ophthal.*, **51**, 278–297.

V. SALLMANN, L., CARAVAGGIO, L. L., & GRIMES, P. (1961). Studies on the corneal endothelium of the rabbit. *Amer. J. Ophthal.*, **51**, Pt. 2, 955–969.

WOLTER, J. R. (1956). Uber den Aufbau der Nervenbundel in der Hornhaut des Kaninchenauges. *Klin. Mbl. Augenheilk.*, **129**, 20–26.

WOODIN, A. M. (1954). The properties of a complex of the mucopolysaccharide and proteins of cornea. *Biochem. J.*, **58**, 50–57.

ZANDER, E., & WEDDELL, G. (1951). Observations on the innervation of the cornea. *J. Anat. Lond.*, **85**, 68–99.

PART 4

THE LENS

DEVELOPMENT AND STRUCTURE

THE lens is a transparent biconvex body (Fig. 39); the apices of its anterior and posterior surfaces are called the *anterior* and *posterior poles* respectively; the line passing through the lens and joining the poles is the *axis*, whilst lines on the surface passing from one pole to the other are called *meridians*. The *equator* is a circle on the surface at right-angles to the axis (Fig. 39). Structurally, the lens is divided into the *capsule*, an elastic envelope capable of moulding the lens substance during accommodative changes (p. 294), and by which the attachment to the zonule is made; the *epithelium*, extending as a single layer of cells under the anterior portion of the capsule as far as the equator; and the *lens substance*

Posterior pole

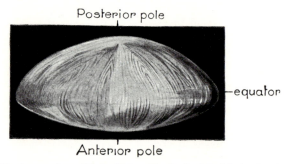

equator

Anterior pole

FIG. 39. The human lens. (Duke-Elder, *Textbook of Ophthalmology*.)

made up of fibres and interstitial cement material. The significance of the intimate structure of the lens substance can only be appreciated with a knowledge of its embryonic and later development.

Embryology

The lens vesicle, on separation from the surface ectoderm, is a sphere whose wall consists of a single layer of epithelium. On their outer aspect the cells of this epithelium secrete a structureless hyaline membrane, the capsule; the cells of the posterior wall and the equatorial region, moreover, undergo marked differentiation and from these the adult lens is formed. The cells of the posterior wall differentiate first, becoming primitive fibres by a process of elongation (Fig. 40); their nuclei ultimately disappear and they remain as an optically clear *embryonic nucleus* in the centre of the mature lens. At the equator, meanwhile, epithelial cells likewise elongate to become fibres; the anterior end of each passes forward towards the anterior pole, insinuating itself under the epithelium, whilst the posterior end passes backwards towards the posterior pole. This process continues, and since each new fibre passes immediately under the epithelium it forces the earlier formed fibres deeper and deeper; successive layers thus encircle the central nucleus of primitive fibres.

FIG. 40. Development of the human lens. (Bellows, *Cataract and Anomalies of the Lens.*)

Fibre Formation

The actual process whereby the developing lens fibres force themselves over less recently formed ones may now be described. The epithelial cells at the equator tend to become arranged in meridional rows (Fig. 41); they assume a pyramidal shape and finally their inner parts elongate and turn obliquely to run under the epithelium of the anterior capsule; the cell is now a young fibre and its inner end, which must now be referred to as its anterior end, grows forward whilst its outer (posterior) end is pushed backwards by a similarly developing cell immediately in front. As the cells grow into the lens substance, the nuclei gradually recede with them, becoming arranged in a wide bend which curves round anteriorly as the process of elongation proceeds; this configuration is termed the *nuclear zone*.

Sutures. A recently formed lens fibre thus has its centre approximately at the equator, whilst the two limbs pass forward and backward towards the anterior and posterior poles respectively to meet the limbs of another cell developing from an "antipodeal" position. If the system were completely symmetrical, the meeting point would be the same for all cells, as illustrated schematically in Fig. 42, A. In fact, no such complete symmetry exists and the fibres meet each other in quite complicated figures which are called *sutures;* the simplest is probably the line-suture of the dogfish (Fig. 42, B) and other lower vertebrates, whilst the human embryonic and adult nuclei have Y- and four-pointed stars respectively (Fig. 42, C and D).

The Lens Fibres. The superficial lens fibres are long, prismatic, ribbon-like cells some 8–10 mm long, 8–12μ broad, and 2μ thick. An equatorial section of the lens cuts these fibres transversely, since they run in a generally antero-

FIG. 41. Meridional section of adult human lens, illustrating the formation of meridional rows and the elongation of the epithelial cells. Zl, zonular lamella; K, lens capsule; E, lens epithelium; EG, level of epithelial border. (Salzmann, *Anatomie u. Histologie d. menschliche Augapfels*.)

posterior direction; the appearance of such a section is shown in Fig. 43, Pl. III, the orderly development of layer after layer of fibres from the cells of the meridional rows leading to a lamellar appearance, the so-called *radial lamellæ.*

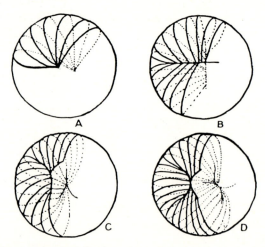

FIG. 42. Diagram showing the formation of lens sutures. A, simple arrangement with no sutures; B, linear sutures only; C, the Y-sutures of the human embryonic nucleus; D, four-pointed star of human adult nucleus. (Mann, *Development of the Human Eye.*)

PLATE III

Fig. 43. Phase-contrast micrograph of equatorial section of guinea-pig lens. Hæmatoxylin-eosin. × 3,300. (Hueck & Kleifeld, *v. Graefes Arch. Ophthal.*)

Fig. 44. *Left :* Optical section of normal human crystalline lens as seen in the slit-lamp microscope. *Right:* Schematic representation of the bands of discontinuity of normal lens as seen in optical section. 1, anterior capsule; 2, anterior disjunctive band; 3, anterior band of adult nucleus; 4, anterior external band of fœtal nucleus; 5, anterior internal band of fœtal nucleus, and so on. (Grignolo, *Boll. d'Oculist.*)

[To face p. 66.

A meridional section, on the other hand, cuts the fibres longitudinally, giving the so-called "onion-scale" appearance (Fig. 41).

Cortex and Nucleus. Since the oldest fibres become more sclerosed and less translucent than the more recently formed ones, the lens is not optically homogeneous; it may be broadly differentiated into a central core—the *nucleus*—and a softer *cortex*. With the slit-lamp the nucleus can be further differentiated into zones, which correspond with the periods at which their fibres were laid down, as in Fig. 44, Pl. III. The lens grows throughout life, increasing from an average weight of 130 mg at 0–9 years to 255 mg at 80–89. The relative thickness of the cortex increases continuously until in old age it represents a third of the total. As a result of this growth, the curvature of the outer zone progressively decreases, *i.e.* the lens becomes flatter; the decrease in dioptric power that would otherwise ensue is prevented by the simultaneous increase in the refractive index of the nucleus. When the increase in refractive index fails to keep pace with the flattening of the surface, the eye becomes hypermetropic; in early cataract the nucleus becomes excessively sclerosed so that the eye becomes myopic.

Electron-Microscopy

The electron-microscope has added a few interesting facts, in particular Wanko & Gavin have described the relations between a given lens fibre and its neighbours. In many regions the cells seem to be regularly separated by a thin extracellular space, which in the dried specimen amounts to some 60 Å; in other regions, notably the equator and suture zones, there is considerable interdigitation of the surfaces. In the equator this is a lateral development to form apparent desmosomes (p. 52), but in the suture zone there is interdigitation between the tips of the fibres from opposite zones (Fig. 45), an interdigitation that may be responsible for the cohesion in this region, but sufficiently labile to permit the adjustments that must occur

Fig. 45. Lens fibres in the suture area. The diagram illustrates how the cortical fibres converge from opposite sectors at the lens suture, where they interlace and at the same time interdigitate with one another and also with fibres located in the same lens sector. (Wanko & Gavin, in *Structure of the Eye*.)

during accommodation (p. 294). The light-microscopists described the capsule as a "structureless membrane"; in the electron-microscope, however, it appears as a regularly lamellated structure, with a cement substance between the layers. It resembles Descemet's membrane and like this its basis is a collagen that shows characteristic differences from the "ordinary collagen" of connective tissue both electron-microscopically and chemically. This difference in ultrastructure is probably related to the special needs of this elastic envelope which it shares with Descemet's membrane; these needs are presumably an extra resistance to internal slip of the fibres under stretch. Its strong positive periodic acid-Schiff reaction is due to the presence of a polysaccharide which is difficult to separate from the collagen (Pirie). The capsule is obviously divided into two layers, the zonular fibres being attached to the outer one, which is therefore called the *zonular lamella*.

THE LENS AS A FUNCTIONAL UNIT

Regional Variations

The essentials of the chemical composition of the lens are shown in Table 4. Because of its history, however, we may expect to find differences in composition according to (*a*) the total age of the lens and (*b*), in a given lens, according to the region selected. Thus the average water-content of the calf lens, containing a high percentage of young fibres, was found by Amoore, Bartley & van Heyningen to be 2·1 g./g. grammes of H_2O per gramme of dry weight (g./g.), comparing with 1·8 g./g. for ox lens. Again, by carefully peeling off concentric zones and analysing them, Amoore *et al.* found the following values from without inwards: 3·67, 2·86, 2·32, 1·79, 1·51 and 1·28 g./g. respectively; thus the water-content of the innermost zone is less than half that of the outermost zone including the capsule.

TABLE 4

Chemical composition of the lens

	Young	Old
Water (%) . . .	69	64
Protein (%) . . .	30	35
Sodium (meq/kg H_2O) .	19	21
Chloride (meq/kg H_2O) .	27	30
Ascorbic acid (mg/100 g)	35	36
Glutathione (mg/100 g) .	2·2	1·5

Sodium and Potassium

The lens is essentially a cellular tissue, so that we may expect a high concentration of potassium and a low concentration of sodium; this is generally true since the figures given by Amoore *et al.*, for example, indicate a value of approximately 20 m-molar for the concentration of sodium in the tissue-water and 120 m-molar for potassium. If this sodium is largely extracellular, whilst the potassium is largely intracellular, we may compute an extracellular space for the lens of about 13 per cent. Direct measurements, however, indicate that this is probably smaller, namely 6–7 per cent (Langham & Davson) so that some of the sodium is intracellular. In tissues such as nerve and muscle, where we also have a mass of cells with high internal potassium and high external sodium, these gradients of concentration are maintained by active processes, in the sense that a part of the metabolic energy of the cells is directed towards "pumping out" any excess of sodium that penetrates into the cells, and towards pumping back any potassium that escapes from the cells. It may well be that the situation in the lens is similar, but it is complicated by the enclosure of the packed cells anteriorly by the lens epithelium and completely by the capsule. The situation may be represented schematically, to a first approximation, by Fig. 46, where a single fibre represents the total; it is surrounded by extracellular fluid of about the same composition as the vitreous and aqueous humour, these latter fluids being presumably in some sort of dynamic equilibrium since there is no doubt that the capsule is freely permeable to small crystalloids (Friedenwald).

The importance of metabolism for the maintenance of the normal sodium, potassium and chloride relationships has been demonstrated by several studies; thus Langham & Davson found that within a few hours *post mortem* the chloride concentration in the lens began to rise, indicating, presumably, an absorption of aqueous humour; again, Harris & Gehrsitz found that cooling the lens *in vitro*,

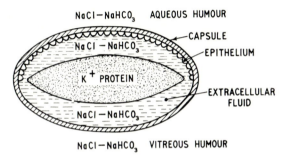

FIG. 46. Illustrating the salt and water relationships of the lens fibres, extra-cellular space, aqueous humour and vitreous body. For simplicity the lens fibres are represented as a single one containing predominantly potassium and protein. The actual volume of the extracellular fluid may be very small indeed, since the fibres are very tightly packed.

thereby inhibiting its metabolism, caused the potassium concentration to fall and that of sodium to rise, processes that could be reversed by re-warming. Presumably, under these conditions, the lens fibres lost their power to pump out sodium and pump in potassium; associated with these ionic shifts there was an increase in water-content which was also reversed on re-warming (Harris, Gehrsitz & Nordquist).

Function of the Epithelium and Capsule

Damage to the capsule of the lens will cause cataract; it also causes the lens *in vitro* to lose potassium and gain sodium in the same way as cooling or the poisoning of metabolism. These facts suggest that the capsule is in some way able to influence the salt content of the lens as a whole, yet it is not easy to reconcile this with the generally high permeability of this structure revealed by the fact that quite large proteins are able to pass through it (François & Rabaey). A membrane with pores sufficiently large to permit the passage of both serum albumin and globulin can hardly exert any restraint on the movements of small ions; moreover, it is a dead structure, being a secretory product of the epithelium, and thus can hardly be expected to carry out active processes involving metabolic energy.* It is possible, however, that the epithelium, which is certainly very active metabolically, does control the salt and water contents of the extracellular phase of the lens, continually

* According to Dische and Ehrlich (1955), however, the capsule can cause the break-down of glucose in the presence of ATP; this may be due, of course, to adherent lens fibres.

pumping out the excess water and salts that may diffuse in from the vitreous body because of the colloid osmotic pressure of the mucoid in this extracellular space. Damage to the capsule might then damage the epithelium; and it would also, perhaps, reduce the cohesion of the lens substance so that there would be more space for fluid to accumulate extracellularly.

Lens Potential. Some recent studies on the potential difference between inside and outside of the lens have complicated the issue even further. Brindley inserted a glass microelectrode into the lens, *in situ*, and as soon as the electrode penetrated the capsule it became negative in relation to another electrode in the vitreous. The potential was 63–68 mV and could be reduced by increasing the concentration of potassium in the vitreous. By carefully dissecting it free of its attachments, the same potential could be measured when the lens was free in a saline solution. It is possible that the potential was an injury potential, due to damage of lens fibres immediately below the capsule, but against this view is the observation of Sperelakis & Potts that the individual lens fibres, when impaled by a microelectrode, gave potentials of only 23 mV, whilst the capsule itself had a characteristic potential across it of 26 mV. Clearly, more work on this *transcapsular potential* is necessary; it could be that the outermost layer of lens fibres formed a coherent layer under the capsule thereby acting as a permeability barrier to the lens *in situ* and perhaps influencing the potential across it.

Transparency and Cataract

In general, then, we may say that the lens is to be regarded as a composite system built up of (*a*) fibre-cells with their own individual membranes separating their contents from (*b*) the interstitial fluid or cement substance which is itself separated by the lens capsule and epithelium from (*c*) the surrounding aqueous and vitreous humours. The transparency of this system must presumably depend on the avoidance of large transitions of refractive index between cells and surrounding cement substance. Moreover, within a given cell, the proteins, which are in a very high concentration, must be dispersed so as to give a non-opalescent solution. Vacuolation—both intracellular and extracellular according to v. Sallmann—and local precipitation of protein are probably features of the loss of transparency that is described as *cataract*. Changes in transparency are certainly associated with changes in salt and water contents (Leinfelder & Schwartz), and the relationship here may be causal. As we shall see, metabolic disturbance invariably leads to cataract; metabolism is necessary for maintaining the normal water and ionic relationships so that we have here an obvious mechanism of cataract formation through metabolic upset; nevertheless metabolic disturbance may lead to quite gross histological alterations, including the death and break-up of lens fibres; and these must be associated with changes in the transmission of light by the lens as a whole.

THE PROTEINS

Table 4 shows that protein is the dominant material present in the solid part of the lens; it was classically separated by Mörner into several fractions, as follows, where the percentages are those given by the more recent study of Krause:

Protein	Per cent
Insoluble albuminoid	12·5
α-Crystallin	31·7
β-Crystallin	53·4
γ-Crystallin or albumin	1·5
Mucoprotein	0·8
Nucleoprotein	0·07

the "insoluble albuminoid" being the residue after extraction of the crystallins etc.

The Crystallins. With the development of electrophoretic techniques (p. 30), particularly in the hands of François & Rabaey, it has been shown that, whereas the α-crystallin does probably represent a single protein, the β-crystallin is made up of several components moving at characteristic speeds during electrophoresis. α-Crystallin is recognized by its greatest speed and the absence of a nitroprusside reaction whilst the β-crystallins give a strong positive reaction indicating the presence of SH-groups in their molecules. According to François & Rabaey, there are at least ten if not thirteen components amongst the soluble proteins whilst Wood & Burgess found only five components, four of them β-crystallins with the positive nitroprusside reaction; they consider that the β-crystallins are so similar chemically that they might well be artefacts formed by the breaking of SH-linkages from some primary protein. They also consider that *in vivo* there might be a similar sort of cleavage taking place as the lens gets older; certainly the proportion of β-crystallins decreases with age and also during cataract.

Albuminoid. There is a very close reciprocal relationship between the insoluble albuminoid and α-crystallin content of lenses; thus in cataractous conditions the insoluble albuminoid fraction increases whilst the α-crystallin fraction decreases; similarly, in a given lens, the proportion of α-crystallin decreases on passing from cortex to nucleus whilst the proportion of insoluble albuminoid increases. It is fairly safe to conclude, therefore, that the insoluble albuminoid is formed from α-crystallin. Certainly it was shown by Woods & Burky that the two are immunologically similar (*cf.* Sirchis, Fromageot & Bernhard, 1956).

"Mucoprotein". Too little is known of this fraction to justify any attempt at description here; the material might better be described as *mucopolysaccharide* (p. 53) and may well be similar to the hyaluronic acid and chondroitins found in the cornea, acting as an intercellular cement.

Embryonic Lens Protein. By the use of ordinary paper-electrophoresis, *i.e.* without the later refinements of agar and high voltages, the proteins of the lens fall into three main categories, the fastest, Group I, being α-crystallin, the middle, Group II, obviously composite and containing the β-crystallins, and the slowest, Group III. This last fraction is highest in concentration in the nucleus of the lens, suggesting that it might be of early origin, and the studies of François & Rabaey have shown that this component is, indeed, laid down in the embryo so that after birth, although Groups I and II continue to be synthesized and to increase in absolute amount, this *embryonic protein* remains the same in absolute amount so that its proportion falls.*

Organ Specificity

As long ago as 1903 Uhlenhuth showed that the immunological characteristics of the lens were unusual. Thus if we inject an extract of, say, ox muscle into a rabbit, the rabbit produces antibodies in its serum that will react with this extract if injected again, to produce the so-called *immune reaction;* if the reaction is carried out *in vitro*, there will be a precipitation of the proteins by the antiserum. This reaction is on quite a strictly species basis, so that the rabbit's serum will not react to sheep muscle for example. If an ox antiserum is prepared to ox lens, by injecting a lens extract into a rabbit, it is found that this antiserum reacts to lens

* Fuchs and Kleifeld (1956) also observed that in rabbits and guinea pigs the proportion of the slow-moving fraction—Group III—decreased.

extracts of all other mammalian species, as well as to those of fishes, amphibians and birds (but not to that of the octopus). The lens is said, therefore, to be *organ* —rather than species—specific and we may conclude that the lens proteins that are responsible for this antigenicity are all built on a very similar plan in the lenses of different species. In general, by the technique of immuno-electro-phoresis,* the presence of a number of different antigens in a lens extract was established; thus when a rabbit antiserum was prepared to human lens, this serum was shown to react with some 9 components of the lens proteins, two in the alpha-, four in the beta- and three in the gamma-crystallin groups. In the fish there were only five, and in the squid none. According to Manski, Auerbach & Halbert, the origin of this organ-specificity lies in the retention, by the lens, of its evolutionary history; thus the mammallian lens can produce anti-bird, anti-amphibian, and anti-fish antibodies because it contains proteins common to these classes; the fish lens, on the other hand, cannot produce anti-bird or anti-mammal antibodies.

Phacoanaphylactic Endophthalmitis. Early workers were unable to detect *homologous* lens reactions, *i.e.* they were unable to produce anti-lens antibodies in a rabbit by injecting an extract of rabbit lens, but with the aid of Freund's adjuvants, Halbert *et al.* were able to do this, so the possibility naturally arises that an animal may produce antibodies to its own lens and thus cause, perhaps, a localized preci-pitin reaction in its lens leading to cataract. In fact, however, the production of very high titres of anti-lens antibodies in the rabbit failed to cause cataract, nor yet could congenital cataract be induced in the progeny of females with high anti-lens titres during pregnancy. Furthermore, human cataract patients had no anti-lens antibodies in their serum. Nevertheless, it is possible to induce a localized anaphylactic response in rabbits by producing anti-lens antibodies in the normal way and then to traumatize the lens; the resulting inflammatory reaction in the eye has been called by Burky *phacoanaphylactic endophthalmitis*.

Proteases

An excised lens, maintained under sterile conditions, eventually undergoes autolysis, *i.e.* non-bacterial decomposition. This is due to the activity of certain proteases that are normally suppressed. They have been studied most recently by Devi, who emphasizes their probable importance in destroying denatured proteins in the lens fibres. Since denaturation results in precipitation of the protein from solution, this would result in a loss of transparency; thus a defective protease activity might lead to cataract. Alternatively over-activity, leading to loss of protein, might also have deleterious effects on the economy of the lens.

Fluorescence

It is well known that in ultraviolet light the lens emits a blue fluorescence; the material responsible for this, extracted by Szent-Gyorgyi from an ox lens, appeared to be a protein, whereas that isolated by François, Rabaey & Recoulès from primate lenses was probably a polypeptide.†

METABOLISM

Lens Culture. The metabolism of the lens is most conveniently studied *in vitro*, and since Bakker in 1936 first maintained a lens in an artificial medium for

---

* In the technique of immuno-electrophoresis, the protein sample is electrophoresed in the ordinary way, so that the proteins move in an electric field and separate from each other by virtue of their different velocities. The electrophoresis is carried out in a gel, such as agar, and a channel is cut in this parallel to the direction of the electric field and antiserum is placed in it; the antibodies diffuse laterally from this channel to meet the various fractions of proteins where they precipitate them, to give characteristic "streaks" in different regions. The number of distinct streaks indicates the number of components in the protein sample that can react with the antiserum.

† The yellow pigment that accumulates in the human lens with age, and reduces thereby the sensitivity of the eye to blue light, is probably a *urochrome*, similar to that found as a breakdown product of protein in urine (McEwan, 1959).

several days with normal transparency, there have been frequent studies of the best medium for the purpose and the most suitable index of viability; outstanding in this respect has been the work of Kinsey and, more recently, Schwartz, and their collaborators. In general, the medium must contain a suitable ionic composition similar to that of the aqueous humour, whilst in order to allow for consumption of glucose and production of lactic and other acids, the medium must be changed regularly. As criterion of normal viability the best is probably the mitotic activity of the epithelium, the cells of which, it will be recalled, are continually dividing to produce new fibres (Kinsey *et al.*). Besides imitating the aqueous humour with regard to ionic make up, a variety of amino acids and vitamins, together with inositol, lactate and glutathione, were added. By using a constant flow of this solution Schwartz kept a lens transparent for some 40 hours, but at the end of this time it was not completely normal, having a higher lactic acid content, for example, than when it began.

Pentose Phosphate Shunt. The tension of O_2 in the aqueous humour is only about 45 mm Hg according to Heald & Langham (1956), so that it is not surprising that most of the consumption of glucose is anaerobic, the Qo_2 being 0·1. As in the cornea Kinoshita & Wachtl (1958) have shown that the pentose phosphate shunt contributes significantly to the oxidative breakdown pathway in addition to the ordinary glycolytic pathway. In addition, van Heyningen (1959) has shown that the lens contains sorbitol and fructose, together with enzymes capable of converting glucose to fructose by way of sorbitol. Thus the metabolic events in the lens may be summarized by the scheme:

$$\text{Glucose} \rightarrow \text{Sorbitol} \rightarrow \text{Fructose}$$

$$\text{Glucose 6-Phosphate} \rightleftharpoons \text{Fructose 6-Phosphate}$$
$$\downarrow \qquad\qquad\qquad\qquad \downarrow$$
$$\text{Pentose Phosphate Shunt} \qquad \text{Glycolysis}$$

Cytochromes. Molecular oxygen is used in biological reactions by way of the cytochrome system; this seems to be confined to the epithelium, according to Kinsey & Frohman, so that it may be that respiration, as contrasted with glycolysis, is confined to this cellular layer unless there are other oxygen-carriers.

Glutathione. In this connection it has been suggested that the tripeptide, glutathione, (glutamyl-cysteinyl-glycine) may play this role:

$$2 \text{ GSH} + \tfrac{1}{2}O_2 \rightleftharpoons \text{GSSG} + H_2O$$

Whatever its function, glutathione must be of importance for the lens since its concentration is some 1000 times that in the aqueous humour; studies on the incorporation of radioactive glycine into the lens show that glutathione is continually being synthesized; in all forms of cataract the fall in concentration of glutathione is striking. Although oxidized glutathione can be reduced in the lens by means of glutathione reductase, and thus act as an oxygen carrier, there seems to be no means whereby it can be reconverted to the oxidized form, hence its role as an oxygen carrier still remains speculative. Another tripeptide in the lens, *glutamyl-α-aminobutyryl-glycine*, is called *ophthalmic acid* but its function, too, is obscure.

Ascorbic Acid. Ascorbic acid (vitamin C) is present in the aqueous humour in high concentration in many species, when this occurs it is also concentrated in the lens, but its significance is not clear since in scurvy the lens shows no defect; furthermore, the *in vitro* preparation seems quite stable without it. It has been suggested that ascorbic acid, together with its reversibly oxidized product, dehydroascorbic acid, acts as a link in a series of reactions carrying hydrogen from substrate to molecular oxygen:

$$\text{Substrate} \xrightarrow{\text{H}_2} \beta\text{-crystallin} \xrightarrow{\text{H}_2} \text{Glutathione} \xrightarrow{\text{H}_2} \text{Ascorbic acid} \xrightarrow{\text{H}_2} \text{O}_2$$

All these steps are, however, highly speculative although Schwartz & Leinfelder have shown that the *in vitro* cultured lens, under strongly anaerobic conditions, may utilize the ascorbic acid- dehydroascorbic acid system.

Meso-Inositol. Another metabolite of unknown significance is *meso*-inositol; its concentration in the aqueous humour is high (Nixon), and it is accumulated by the lens; it is probably concerned in lipid metabolism.

ATP. As with other parts of the body, the energy provided by the breakdown of carbohydrate is made available for synthetic and other activities in the form of "high-energy phosphate", namely ATP; the active role of the epithelium in this respect is shown by the high concentration of this substance in this layer (Frohman & Kinsey).

CATARACT

By cataract we mean any opacification of the lens, which may be a highly localized "spot" or a complete loss of transmission throughout the substance; it may occur as a senile change; as a result of trauma, which presumably injures the capsule and the underlying epithelium; as a result of metabolic or nutritional defects; or as a consequence of radiation damage.

Metabolic Defects. The way in which a metabolic defect can lead to a loss of transparency is not clear, but an important factor must unquestionably be the amount and physical condition of the proteins in the lens fibres; the lens continually produces new proteins and the existing ones are in a continuous state of "turnover", in the sense that they are broken down and resynthesized. These processes require energy which they derive from the ATP produced during the metabolic breakdown of glucose, and it is well established that cataract and senile changes in transparency are associated with impaired protein synthesis. This is probably the main link between cataract and metabolism, but other factors might well be altered internal pH causing precipitation of protein within the fibres, and possibly changes in the amount of mucopolysaccharide cement substance between the fibres. Again, there is the death of the lens fibres, producing gaps in the ordered arrangement, or the partial death leading to vacuolation of the cells, or finally an abnormal proliferation of cells again leading to disorder.*

Glutathione Deficiency. Another striking feature of cataract is the low level of glutathione, the concentration in the lens being inversely related to the degree of opacity; this decrease is due to the failure of the cataractous lens to synthesize glutathione, which was demonstrated by Kinsey & Merriam by showing that the taking up of labelled glycine into the cultured lens, and its incorporation into glutathione, were reduced below normal when the lens was cataractous as a result of treating the animal with naphthalene (p. 76).

* The histology of the cataractous lens has been described in some detail by v. Sallmann (1951, 1957).

Experimental Cataract. Experimentally, cataract may be induced in several ways; for example, by feeding certain sugars such as galactose and xylose, or by inducing diabetes with alloxan; by various dietary deficiencies, such as the absence of essential amino acids; by toxic substances such as dinitrophenol or naphthalene, or by ionizing radiations. Space will not allow of a detailed description of these experiments and for an excellent modern summary the reader is referred to van Heyningen (1962).

Sugar Cataracts

The essential factor is the high concentration of the sugar in the aqueous humour, be it glucose as in diabetes, or galactose and xylose in experimental cataract. The mechanism whereby the increased sugar concentration disturbs the metabolic supply of energy probably varies with the sugar; thus galactose and xylose would appear to block the pentose phosphate shunt that represents quite a considerable proportion of the growing lens' energy supply; this shunt apparently provides the coenzyme, TPNH, which is then involved in producing ATP by TPNH cytochrome reductase (Lerman). Thus galactose inhibits the enzyme glucose 6-phosphate dehydrogenase which oxidizes glucose 6-phosphate to 6-phosphogluconate, the first step in the shunt. Associated with this inhibition of the shunt there is found a reduction in the amount of TPNH, and consequently of ATP, in the lens.

Protein Synthesis. The associated failure of protein synthesis, which is presumably the causal factor in loss of transparency, is due to this loss of energy rather than to the failure of the protein synthetic mechanism *per se*. Thus modern research has established the importance of ribonucleic acid (RNA) in the synthesis of protein. The stages in this process may well be as follows:

Amino-acid + ATP + Enzyme → {Amino-acid − AMP − Enzyme complex}
{Amino-acid − AMP − Enzyme Complex} + Soluble RNA →
{Amino-acid − Soluble RNA Complex}
{Amino-acid − Soluble RNA Complex} + Microsome RNA →
{Amino-acid − Microsome RNA Complex}
↓
Protein

The soluble RNA first combines with the amino acids required for protein synthesis and later transfers them to the RNA in the small particles (microsomes or ribosomes) of the cytoplasm. Here the RNA acts as a template, governing the order in which the amino acids are joined together to give a protein. The lens makes use of this mechanism, as revealed by the incorporation of labelled amino acids into the RNA fractions (Devi, Friel & Lerman); in the cataract due to galactose, however, there is no reduction in the RNA of the lens, so that it is the loss of energy that is important. In the aged lens, however, there is indeed some disturbance in the RNA system.*

Radiation Cataract

The lens is subject to damage by ionizing radiations because it is essentially only those cells that undergo division that are susceptible. If the radiation is confined to the central area of the lens, by screening the equatorial region, no cataract develops (Goldmann & Leichti). If only a sector of the lens is exposed, the damage in this region is much less severe than if the whole lens had been exposed, and it would seem that the undamaged region can exert a protective action on the remainder (Pirie & Flanders). As with other forms of radiation damage, injections

---

* Xylose cataract is different from galactose cataract in its tendency to regress in spite of maintenance on the high xylose diet; moreover it can only be induced in young animals. Xylose does indeed block the pentose phosphate shunt, but its point of attack is different; possibly the coenzyme TPNH is used up in reducing xylose to xylitol.

of cysteine and certain other protective substances, *e.g.* cysteamine, reduce the severity of the lesion.

Glassblower's Cataract. Exposure of the eyes to strong infra-red radiation causes cataract and this was shown by Goldmann in 1933 to be due to the high temperature to which the lens was raised by the absorption of heat; absorption of light by the ciliary body and iris, if sufficiently intense, will also raise the temperature of the lens and cause cataract (Langley, Mortimer & McCulloch).

Toxic Cataracts

Naphthalene and tetralol cause cataract when fed to rabbits; the causative factor may be the robbing of the animal of the sulphur required to detoxicate the poison; iodoacetate causes cataract presumably by inhibiting enzymes containing SH-groups; dinitrophenol is another metabolic poison, interfering with oxidative phosphorylation, but since this metabolic process probably does not take place in the lens its action may not be the simple result of metabolic inhibition.

Reversible Cataracts

Finally, we may mention two interesting forms of cataract that are reversible; when an animal is cooled cataracts may appear which disappear on rewarming, and they are apparently due to a reversible precipitation of proteins in the lens fibres (van Heyningen, 1962). The other form of opacity is hardly a true cataract; it follows the administration of morphia-type alkaloids to rodents and seems to be the consequence of a precipitation of the altered drug on the anterior surface of the lens; it develops in a few minutes and disappears within a few hours (Weinstock & Stewart).

The Calcium Content

Great interest has attached to the calcium content of the lens since it is known that interference in the general calcium metabolism of the organism, such as parathyroidectomy, or in rickets, is associated with the development of cataract. Moreover, in aged, sclerotic or cataractous lenses the calcium content increases. It is unlikely, however, that the deposition of insoluble calcium salts is the primary change in any form of cataract; most probably the breakdown of the proteins and possibly of the lipids, as a result of metabolic disturbances, liberates sulphates, phosphates, and carbonates which are precipitated by calcium already present in the lens. Thus Bellows has shown that in galactose cataract the calcium deposition always follows the primary cataractous changes. Finally we may note that an adequate concentration of calcium in the medium surrounding a cultured lens is important if it is to maintain its normal hydration and cation content (Harris & Gehrsitz).

GENERAL REFERENCES

BELLOWS, J. G. (1944). *Cataract and Anomalies of the Lens.* London: Kimpton.
GRIGNOLO, A. (1954). Studi sulla struttura submicroscopica dei tessuti oculari. *Boll. d'Oculist.*, **33**, 513–652.
MANN, I. (1949). *The Development of the Human Eye.* London: B.M.A. (2nd Ed.)
PIRIE, A., & VAN HEYNINGEN, R. (1956). *Biochemistry of the Eye.* Oxford: Blackwell.
VAN HEYNINGEN, R. (1962). The Lens. In *The Eye.* Ed. Davson. Vol. I. pp. 213–287. London: Academic Press.

SPECIAL REFERENCES

AMOORE, J. E., BARTLEY, W., & VAN HEYNINGEN, R. (1959). Distribution of sodium and potassium within cattle lens. *Biochem. J.*, **72,** 126–133.

BURKY, E. L. (1934). Experimental endophthalmitis phacoanaphylactica. *Arch. Ophthal.*, **12,** 536–546.

BRINDLEY, G. S. (1956). Resting potential of the lens. *Brit. J. Ophthal.*, **40,** 385–391.

DEVI, A., FRIEL, R., & LERMAN, S. (1961). The RNA content and the amino acid-RNA incorporating system in the lenses of various species. *Arch. Ophthal., N.Y.*, **65,** 855–858.

DISCHE, Z., & EHRLICH, G. (1955). The breakdown of glucose and its phosphoric esters in the bovine lens capsule. *Amer. J. Ophthal.*, **39,** Pt. 2, 99–105.

FRANÇOIS, J., & RABAEY, M. (1957). The protein composition of the human lens. *Amer. J. Ophthal.*, **44,** Pt. 2, 347–357.

FRANÇOIS, J., & RABAEY, M. (1958). Permeability of the capsule for the lens proteins. *Acta ophthal., Kbh.*, **36,** 837–844.

FRANÇOIS, J., & RABAEY, M. (1959). Agar electrophoresis at high tension of soluble lens proteins. *Arch. Ophthal., N.Y.*, **61,** 351–360.

FRANÇOIS, J., RABAEY, M., & RECOULÈS, N. (1961). A fluorescent substance of low molecular weight in the lens of primates. *Arch. Ophthal., N.Y.*, **65,** 118–126.

FRIEDENWALD, J. S. (1930). Permeability of the lens capsule. *Arch. Ophthal.*, **3,** 182–193.

FROHMAN, C. E., & KINSEY, V. E. (1952). Distribution of various phosphate-containing compounds and its significance with respect to energetics. *Arch. Ophthal., N.Y.*, **48,** 12–18.

FUCHS, R., & KLEIFELD, O. (1956). Uber das Verhalten des wasserlöslichen Linseneiweiss junger und alter Tiere bei papierelektrophoretische Untersuchung. *v. Graefes' Arch. Ophthal.*, **158,** 29–33.

GOLDMANN, H., & LEICHTI, A. (1938). Experimentelle Untersuchungen über die Genese des Röntgenstars. *v. Graefes' Arch. Ophthal.*, **138,** 722–736.

HALBERT, S. P., LOCATCHER-KHORAZO, D., SWICK, L., WITMER, R., SEEGAL, B., & FITZGERALD, P. (1957). Homologous immunological studies of ocular lens. I and II. *J. exp. Med.*, **105,** 439–452; 453–462.

HARRIS, J. E., & GEHRSITZ, L. B. (1951). Significance of changes in potassium and sodium content of the lens. *Amer. J. Ophthal.*, **34,** Pt. 2, 131–138.

HARRIS, J. E., GEHRSITZ, L. B., & NORDQUIST, L. (1953). The in vitro reversal of the lenticular cation shift induced by cold or calcium deficiency. *Amer. J. Ophthal.*, **36,** 39–49.

HEALD, K., & LANGHAM, M. E. (1956). Permeability of the cornea and the blood-aqueous barrier to oxygen. *Brit. J. Ophthal.*, **40,** 750–720.

KINSEY, V. E., & FROHMAN, C. E. (1951). Distribution of cytochrome, total riboflavin, lactate and pyruvate and its metabolic significance. *Arch. Ophthal., N.Y.*, **46,** 536–541.

KINSEY, V. E., & MERRIAM, F. C. (1950). Synthesis of glutathione in the normal and cataractous rabbit lens. *Arch. Ophthal., N.Y.*, **44,** 370–380.

KINSEY, V. E., WACHTL, C., CONSTANT, M. A., & CAMACHO, E. (1955). Mitotic activity in the epithelia of lenses cultured in various media. *Amer. J. Ophthal.*, **40,** Pt. 2, 216–223.

KINOSHITA, J. H., & WACHTL, C. (1958). A study of the C^{14}-glucose metabolism of the rabbit lens. *J. biol. Chem.*, **233,** 5–7.

LANGHAM, M., & DAVSON, H. (1949). Studies on the lens. *Biochem. J.*, **44,** 467–470.

LANGLEY, R. K., MORTIMER, C. B., & McCULLOCH, C. (1960). The experimental production of cataracts by exposure to heat and light. *Arch. Ophthal., N.Y.*, **63,** 473–488.

LEINFELDER, P. J., & SCHWARTZ, B. (1954). Respiration and glycolysis in lens transparency. *Acta XVII Conc. Ophth.*, pp. 984–991.

LERMAN, I. S. (1960). Pathogenetic factors in experimental galactose cataract. *Arch. Ophthal., N.Y.*, **63,** 128–131; 132–135; 136–139.

MANSKI, W., AUERBACH, T. P., & HALBERT, S. P. (1960). The evolutionary significance of lens organ specificity. *Amer. J. Ophthal.*, **50,** Pt. 2, 985–991.

McEWAN, W. K. (1959). The yellow pigment of human lenses. *Amer. J. Ophthal.*, **47,** Pt. 2, 144–146.

NIXON, D. A. (1959). Inositol concentration in the cerebrospinal and ocular fluids and tissues of the foetal and adult sheep. *Nature, Lond.*, **184,** 906–907.

PIRIE, A. (1951). Composition of the lens capsule. *Biochem. J.*, **48**, 368–371.

PIRIE, A., & FLANDERS, H. P. (1957). Effect of X-rays on partially shielded lens of the rabbit. *Arch. Ophthal., N.Y.*, **57**, 849–854.

SCHWARTZ, B. (1960). Initial studies of the use of an open system for the culture of the rabbit lens. *Arch. Ophthal., N.Y.*, **63**, 643–659.

SCHWARTZ, B., & Leinfelder, P. J. (1955). Ascorbic-dehydroascorbic acid as an oxidation-reduction system. I. *Amer. J. Ophthal.*, **40**, Pt. 2, 224–235.

SIRCHIS, J., FROMAGEOT, P., & BERNHARD, H. (1956). Points communes entre l'α-crystalline et la fraction principale F 1 de l'insoluble du crystallin de boeuf. *C. R. Acad. Sci., Paris*, **243**, 2164–2167.

SPERELAKIS, N., & POTTS, A. M. (1959). Additional observations on the bioelectric potentials of the lens. *Amer. J. Ophthal.*, **47**, 395–409.

VAN HEYNINGEN, R. (1959). Formation of polyols by the lens of the rat with "sugar" cataract. *Nature, Lond.*, **184**, 194–195.

V. SALLMANN, L. (1951). Experimental studies on early lens changes after roentgen irradiation. *Arch. Ophthal., N.Y.*, **45**, 149–164.

V. SALLMANN, L. (1957). The lens epithelium in the genesis of cataract. *Amer. J. Ophthal.*, **44**, 159–170.

WANKO, T., & GAVIN, M. A. (1961). Cell surfaces in the crystalline lens. In *The Structure of the Eye*. Ed. Smelser. pp. 221–233. N.Y.: Academic Press.

WEINSTOCK, M., & STEWART, H. C. (1961). Occurrence in rodents of reversible drug-induced opacities of the lens. *Brit. J. Ophthal.*, **45**, 408–414.

WOOD, D. C., & BURGESS, L. (1961). An electrophoretic study of soluble lens proteins from different species. *Amer. J. Ophthal.*, **51**, 305–313.

WOODS, A. C., & BURKY, E. L. (1927). Lens protein and its fractions. *J. Amer. Med. Ass.*, **89**, 102–110.

SECTION II

The Mechanism of Vision

RETINAL STRUCTURE AND ORGANIZATION

In this section we shall be concerned with the peripheral mechanisms in the visual process. When light strikes the retina, physical and chemical changes are induced that lead eventually to a discharge of electrical impulses in the optic nerve fibres. The "messages" in these nerve fibres are a record of the events taking place in the retina; because of the variety of sensations evoked by visual stimuli, these records must be of almost fantastic complexity when even a simple image is formed on the retina. The aim of investigators in this field of eye physiology is to disentangle the skein; their approaches are various but may be classed generally as psychophysical, chemical, and electrophysiological. Remarkable progress has been made, especially in recent years, but there is still a long way to go before anything approaching an exact picture of the retinal processes can be elaborated. The following description is designed more to show the modes of approach to the various problems rather than to present a theoretical picture of the "mechanism of vision".

THE STRUCTURE OF THE RETINA

Sensory Pathways. The retina is a complex nervous structure made up of a number of layers (Fig. 47) whose significance is best understood by recalling that in other parts of the body, for example the skin, the nervous elements involved in the transmission of sensory impulses to the cerebral cortex consist of (*a*) a specialized arrangement of cells called a receptor-organ, *e.g.* a Pacinian corpuscle sensitive to pressure; (*b*) a neurone connecting the receptor to the spinal cord and medulla (neurone I) with its cell body in the posterior root ganglion; (*c*) a connector neurone to the thalamus (neurone II) with its cell body in the nucleus cuneatus or gracilis, and finally (*d*) a neurone to transmit the impulses to the cortex (neurone III) with its cell body in the thalamus.

With the vertebrate eye, not only are the specialized receptor cells, the *rods* and *cones*, in the retina, but also the cell bodies and connecting fibres of neurones I and II so that the nerve fibres leading out of the eye, which constitute the optic nerve, are the axons of neurone II; the majority of the fibres run to the lateral geniculate body where the impulses, initiated in the rods and cones, are relayed to the occipital lobe of the cortex. The analogy between the two systems is demonstrated in Fig. 48.

The Retinal Layers. We may thus expect to differentiate in the retina a layer of receptors (*layer of rods and cones*), a layer of cell bodies of neurone I, the *bipolar cells* (*inner nuclear layer*) and a layer of cell bodies of neurone II, the *ganglion cells* (*ganglion layer*). The rods and cones are highly differentiated cells and their orderly arrangement gives rise to a *bacillary layer*, consisting of their outer segments; an *outer nuclear layer* containing their cell bodies or nuclei; and an *outer plexiform layer* made up of their fibres and synapses with the bipolar cells. Certain other nerve cells are present in the retina, *e.g.* the *horizontal cells*, with their bodies in the inner nuclear layer, which form connections between a

Fig. 47. Cross-section through the adult human retina in the periphery of the central area, showing details of stratification at a moderate magnification. The left-hand figure shows the structures as they appear when stained with a nonselective method (*e.g.* hæmatoxylin and eosin). The right-hand figure reproduces schematically the same view as it would appear from a study with an analytical method such as Golgi's or Ehrlich's, using many sections to get all details. (1) Pigment epithelium; (2) bacillary layer; (2-*a*) outer segments and (2-*b*) inner segments of the thinner rods and the thicker cones; (3) outer limiting membrane; (4) outer nuclear layer; (4-*a*) outer zone of the outer nuclear layer chiefly composed of the cone nuclei; (4-b) inner zone of the outer nuclear layer composed exclusively of the rod nuclei; (5) outer plexiform layer; (5-*a*) outer zone of the outer plexiform layer composed of the inner rod and cone fibres and of the corresponding portions of Müller's "radial fibres" enveloping the first (here only one shown, beginning with the outer limiting membrane incasing the body and the fibre of a cone and continuing through ventral layers down to the inner limiting membrane); (5-*b*) middle zone of the outer plexiform layer composed of the rod spherules and cone pedicles; (5-*c*) inner zone of the outer plexiform layer made up of the expansions of the nerve cells and of Müller's supporting "radial fibres" whose bodies and nuclei reside in the sixth layer; (6) inner nuclear layer with its four zones: 6-*a*, 6-*b*, 6-*c*, and 6-*d;* (7) inner plexiform layer with its five zones: 7-*a*, 7-*b*, 7-*c*, 7-*d*, and 7-*e;* (8) layer of the ganglion cells; (9) layer of the optic nerve fibres; (10) inner limiting membrane, next to the vitreous. (Polyak, *The Retina*.)

given cone and its surrounding rods and cones, and *amacrine cells* whose functions are not clearly understood although it is thought by Polyak that one group, the so-called *centrifugal bipolars*, transmit impulses from the ordinary (centripetal) bipolars, from the ganglion cells, and from the brain, to the photoreceptors.

Fɪɢ. 48. Illustrating the analogy between a typical cutaneous afferent pathway and the visual pathway. Note the cone has not been treated as a neurone.

Besides the nerve cells there are numerous *neuroglial cells, e.g.* those giving rise to the radial fibres of Muller, which act as supporting and insulating structures. The various layers are indicated in Fig. 47, where the histological appearance is compared with a schematic diagram, whilst the general scheme of interneuronal connections, as envisaged by Polyak, is shown in Fig. 49.

The Rods and Cones. Certain aspects of the structure of the retina will be dealt with more fully when we consider the problem of visual acuity; for the moment we need consider in detail only the rods and cones, and their distribution through the retina. These are the receptors for vision, and it is in their outermost, scleral, portions that the light-energy, transmitted by the dioptric apparatus of the eye, is absorbed. As seen in the light-microscope the rod consists of a rod-like photosensitive portion some 2μ thick and 60μ long—the *"rod proper"*—lying nearest the pigment epithelium and, together with the outer ends of the cones, making up the *bacillary layer*, and an inner part, its long fibre terminating in a *"rod spherule"* which makes a synaptic type of connection with the dendrites of bipolar cells. The cones vary greatly in size and shape with their position in the retina (Fig. 50) becoming long and thin in the central portion; they are similar in general shape to the rods but altogether more robust and are divided into a *"cone proper"* and a conducting part; the cone fibre terminates in a *"cone pedicle"* analogous in function to the rod spherule. The various parts of the rods and cones are indicated in Figs. 50 and 51.

Synaptic Relationships. If it is the rod or cone that absorbs the light-energy of the stimulus, it is the bipolar cell that must transmit any effect of this absorption; consequently the relationship between the two types of cell is of the utmost interest. As seen in the electron-microscope a connection between the rod-

FIG. 49. General scheme of the primate retina. (*a, b*) Rods and cones, or the photoreceptors where the nervous impulses are generated by physical "light" (in the scheme only the left group of the photoreceptors is assumed to be stimulated by light); (*c*) horizontal cells by means of which the impulses are transmitted to the surrounding rods and cones; (*d, e, f, h*) centripetal bipolar cells of the mop, brush, flat, and midget varieties, which "transmit" the impulses from the photoreceptors to the ganglion cells, the bipolars serving as "analysers"; (*i*) centrifugal bipolar cell, a variety of the "amacrine cells," which probably receives the impulses from the centripetal bipolars, from the ganglion cells, and also from the brain by way of the centrifugal or efferent fibres (*t*) and transmits them back upon the photoreceptors (*a,b*); (*l*) an "amacrine cell" which possibly intercepts a part of the bipolar impulses and spreads them over the surrounding territory; (*m,n,o,p,s*) ganglion cells which receive impulses from the centripetal bipolars and transmit them to the brain along their axons called "optic nerve fibres." (Polyak, *The Retina.*)

spherule, for example, and the bipolar cell is similar to the synaptic relationship between two neurones, in the sense that the two cells never fuse but retain their separate identities by virtue of their cell membranes. The relationship may be very close, processes from the bipolar cell being completely enclosed by the spherule, but the presence of cell membranes covering both bipolar process and rod spherule (Fig. 52) shows that there has been no real fusion but simply an envelopment of the bipolar process by the rod spherule. The presence of many vesicles in the spherule is strongly reminiscent of the synaptic vesicles of the nervous system that are considered to contain a transmitter substance which, when liberated by the presynaptic neurone, induces a discharge in the postsynaptic neurone. As we shall see (p. 116) it may well be that the absorption of light by the distal segment induces changes in the rod or cone that cause it to liberate its transmitter and activate a bipolar cell.

The Retinal Zones

The retina is divided morphologically into two main zones, the *central area* (containing Regions I–III) and the *extra-areal periphery* (containing Regions IV–VII).

Fig. 50. Human cones. 1, Near ora serrata; 2, at equator; 3, at macula. *a*, Outer segment; *b*, inner segment; *c*, cone fibre; *d*, cell body and nucleus; *e*, cone foot; *f*, ellipsoid; *g*, myoid. (Duke-Elder, *Textbook of Ophthalmology*.)

Fig. 51. Human rod. *a*, Outer segment; *b*, inner segment; *c*, cell fibre; *d*, cell nucleus; *e*, cell foot; *f*, ellipsoid. (Duke-Elder, *Textbook of Ophthalmology*.)

Fovea. Region I, the *central fovea* (Fig. 53), is a small depression, shaped like a shallow bowl with a concave floor, on the vitreal face of the retina, caused by the bending away of layers 5–9 and a thickening of the bacillary and outer nuclear

Fig. 52. Illustrating the synaptic type of relationship between the rod spherule and a process from a bipolar cell. Note how the process is enveloped by the spherule which contains many vesicles. (After De Robertis, *J. biophys. biochem. Cytol.*)

layers. From edge to edge it is some $1,500\mu$ across in man and thus subtends about $5°$ at the nodal point of the eye; the floor of the fovea is about 400μ across. The fovea, described in this way, is generally referred to as the *inner fovea*, the word "inner" being used to denote the aspect from which the depression is regarded;

the *outer fovea*, some 400μ across, represents a depression in the opposite sense, *i.e.*, a cupping of the outer limiting membrane from outwards inwards (Fig. 53), and corresponds roughly in extent to the floor of the inner fovea; it is caused by the lengthening of the cones in the bacillary layer, the cone proper increasing in length more than the remaining portion. The outer fovea is thus the central portion of the inner fovea; here the receptor elements consist entirely of cones which, as we have seen, are longer and thinner than elsewhere in the retina, being some 70μ long and 1·5μ thick at the base and 1μ thick at the tip. The *"rod-free territory"* is actually rather greater in extent than the outer fovea, being some 500–600μ across and containing some 34,000 cones. Beyond this limit rods appear and their proportion to cones increases progressively. The total number of cones in the territory of the inner fovea amounts to 115,000. As we shall see, the most central, rod-free, portion of the retina is concerned with the highest degree of visual acuity since it is here that the obstruction to light caused by the nerve fibres and other layers is reduced to a minimum and the density of receptors is highest; vision mediated by

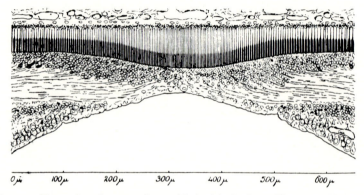

FIG. 53. Illustrating the outer fovea, filled with the long thin cones. Note the thinning of the outer nuclear layer and the practical disappearance of the remaining inner layers in the foveal centre. (Polyak, *The Retina*.)

this portion of the retina is thus spoken of as "foveal vision"; it must be emphasized, however, that the fovea proper embraces both this zone and the walls of the inner fovea where obstructions to the passage of light are not removed, where the cone density is considerably less, and where rods are present, so that it is inaccurate to speak of foveal vision when what is meant is vision mediated by the rod-free area or perhaps even a more restricted central zone (the "central bouquet of cones," for example, some 50–75μ across).

Macula. Mention may be made here of the *yellow spot* or *macula lutea*; this is an ill-defined area of the central retina characterized by the presence of a yellow pigment in the nervous layers; in actuality the region extends over the whole of the central area (Regions I–III) but the intensely pigmented part is limited to the fovea (Region I); the central portion of the fovea (outer fovea) is only slightly pigmented in man, since the pigment is associated with layers beyond number 4 which, as we have seen, are very much reduced or absent here.

Parafovea and Perifovea. Regions II and III are the *parafoveal* and *perifoveal* regions respectively, the outer edge of the former being 1,250μ from the centre of the fovea and that of the latter 2,750μ from the centre, the diameter of the entire central area being thus about 5,000–6,000μ. The cone density is considerably diminished in these regions whilst that of the rods is increased, so that in Region III there are only some 12 cones per 100μ (compared with some 50 per 100μ in the outer fovea) with 2 rods between each pair of cones. The *extra-areal periphery* (Regions IV to VII) is associated with a further decrease in the density of cones and an increase in the proportion of rods. In the whole human retina there are said to be about seven million cones and 75–150 million rods.

GENERAL REFERENCES

POLYAK, S. L. (1941). *The Retina.* Chicago: Univ. Press.
POLYAK, S. L. (1957). *The Vertebrate Visual System.* Chicago: Univ. Press.
ØSTERBERG, G. (1935). Topography of the layer of rods and cones in the human retina. *Acta ophthal. Kbh.*, Suppl. 6.
PIRENNE, M. H. (1948). *Vision and the Eye.* London: Chapman & Hall.

MEASUREMENT OF THE STIMULUS

PHOTOMETRY

Visible Light. Visible light consists of electromagnetic vibrations limited to a certain band of wavelengths—the *visible spectrum*. The limits are given classically as 4000 Å and 7600 Å, wavelengths shorter than 4000 Å being described as ultraviolet, and longer than 7600 Å as infrared. As we shall see, however, the retina is sensitive to wavelengths shorter and longer than these limits. Light is a form of energy and, as such, is amenable to quantitative measurement in absolute units, namely ergs. For physiological purposes, however, that subjective quality of light we call "brightness" or "luminosity" is the one that is of greatest interest, and since this is not uniquely determined by the energy content of the light, but varies widely with the wavelength (p. 132), it has been considered desirable to base measurements of light on a somewhat arbitrary "luminosity basis." Thus, on a luminosity basis, two sources of light are said to be of equal intensity when they produce equal sensations of brightness when viewed by the same observer under identical conditions.

Luminous Intensity. The luminous intensity (I) of a source of light is measured in terms of an arbitrarily chosen standard source of light-energy. Classically, this was a sperm-wax candle made to burn at a certain rate, and it gave rise to the term *candle-power*, a source of light appearing x times as bright as the standard candle having x candlepower. The modern *candela* (abbreviated cd) is fixed in terms of a standard filament lamp. It is such that one square centimetre of the surface of a full radiator at the temperature of solidification of platinum has a luminous intensity of 60 cd in the direction normal to the surface. In effect it has about the same value as the classical candle.

If two sources of light illuminate a screen under identical conditions, to produce identical degrees of illumination, they are said to be of equal intensity. An observer may easily determine whether two identical screens, side by side, are equally illuminated; if they are not equally illuminated (*i.e.* if one appears brighter than the other) he is unable to state exactly how much more intensely illuminated one is than the other, so that in comparing intensities of illumination recourse is had to the photometer, one type of which utilizes as its basis the law that the intensity of illumination of a screen, placed normal to the rays from a point source of light, varies inversely as the square of its distance from the source. Thus, if we have two sources of light, of intensities I_1 and I_2 and at distances r_1 and r_2 from a screen such that they illuminate it equally, we can say:

$$I_1/I_2 = r_2{}^2/r_1{}^2.$$

Hence, if one of the light sources (I_2) is the standard candle, the intensity of the other is given by:

$$I_1 = r_2{}^2/r_1{}^2 \text{ candelas.}$$

Intensity of Illumination. In introducing the measurement of the intensity of a light source, we have mentioned the *degree of illumination*; this is, of course, determined entirely by the amount of light falling on a surface and hence by the intensity of the light source, the distance of this source from the object, and the angle the surface makes with the direction of the incident light. Thus, if we have a screen perpendicular to the direction of the light incident from a point source of intensity I, we may define the *intensity of illumination*, E, by the equation:

$$E = I/r^2, \text{ where } r \text{ is the distance from the source.}$$

When I equals unity, *i.e.* one candela, and *r* equals 1 foot, E is unity and is called 1 *foot-candela*. If *r* is expressed in metres, the unit of illumination is the *metre-candela* or *lux*; expressed in words, it is the illumination of a surface, normal to the incident rays from a source of 1 candela one metre away. The *centimetre-candela* is called a *phot*. If a surface, normal to the incident rays from a source, has an illumination E, its illumination when the surface is inclined at an angle θ to the rays is given by E cos θ.

Luminance. The illumination of the surface does not necessarily define its intensity as a stimulus, since the latter depends on the light entering the eye and so is determined by the light reflected from the surface and the direction of view. If, however, we imagine a white surface that reflects all the light it receives and is, moreover, a "perfect diffuser" in the sense that it appears equally bright from all directions, then the *luminance* of a surface may be defined in terms of its illumination from a standard source. Thus, on the so-called *Lambert system*, a perfectly diffusing surface, normal to the incident light from a source of 1 candela 1 centimetre away, has a luminance of 1 *lambert*. This unit is too large for most purposes and the *millilambert* (mL) represents a thousandth of a lambert; for studies of light thresholds (p. 95) the log micro-microlambert scale is often used. A luminance of 3 log micro-microlamberts means a luminance of $10^3 \times 10^{-12} = 10^{-9}$ lamberts or a millionth of a millilambert; 2 log micro-microlamberts are equivalent to $10^2 \times 10^{-12} = 10^{-10}$ lamberts, and so on. The *equivalent foot-candela*, or *foot-lambert*, is the luminance of a similar screen distant 1 foot from the source.

Surface Intensity. This mode of defining the luminance of a surface in terms of the light incident on it is limited by the ideal nature of a perfectly diffusing surface; a definition that does not involve this would be superior from many points of view. Such a definition is given by describing the luminance in terms of the light emitted by the surface, *i.e.* we can treat the surface as a luminous source, whether it is self-luminous as in the case of a hot body, or whether its luminosity depends on reflected light. Thus if 1 square foot of a surface emits the same amount of light in a given direction as a source of 10 candelas, for instance, we may define the *luminous intensity of the surface* as 10 candelas; the subjective brightness of the surface and hence its intensity as a stimulus will clearly depend on the area from which this light emanates; if it all comes from a small area the brightness will be greater than if it came from a large area. The luminance is thus defined in terms of the candlepower of the surface per unit area, *e.g.* candelas per square foot or candelas per square centimetre. We may then calculate the luminance, in candelas per square foot, of a perfectly diffusing surface illuminated by a source of 1 candela at a distance of 1 foot; this turns out to be $1/\pi$ candelas per square foot, *i.e.* $1/\pi$ *candelas per square foot* = 1 *equivalent foot-candela*. Similarly $1/\pi$ candelas per square centimetre = 1 lambert.

Effectively Point Source. The definition of the luminance of a surface in terms of its candlepower *per unit area* has an obvious physiological basis. By the luminance of a surface we wish to express in a quantitative manner the intensity of the stimulus when its image falls on the retina. An illuminated surface of given area forms an image of a definite area on the retina and the sensation of brightness, or rather the stimulus, depends on the amount of light falling on this area of the retina. If the surface is moved closer to the eye, the amount of light entering the eye is increased in accordance with the inverse square law, but the surface does not appear brighter because the size of the image has increased, also in accordance with an inverse square law, and consequently the actual *illumination* of the retina has not altered. Thus the subjective brightness of an extended source is independent of its distance from the observer. It may be argued that the brightness of a lamp decreases as it is moved away from the eye and eventually becomes so faint that it disappears if it is moved far enough away. This, however, is a consequence of the fact that at a certain distance from the eye the lamp becomes an "effectively point source," *i.e.* its image on the retina is of the same order of size as that of a receptor element; consequently, when it is moved further away still, although its image on the retina becomes smaller, the amount of light per receptor element now begins to fall in accordance with the inverse square law. Thus the definition of luminance in terms of candles per unit area of necessity implies that the surface has a finite area; when this surface becomes effectively a point from the aspect of the size of its image on the retina, its power of stimulating the retina will be determined only by its total luminous intensity, *i.e.* its candlepower, and its distance from the observer. The limiting angle, subtended by an object at the eye, below which it behaves as an effectively point source depends on the particular visual effect being studied and the conditions of observation; for the study of absolute thresholds in the dark it is as big as 30–60 minutes of arc.

Retinal Illumination. We have indicated that the characterization of the luminance of an extended surface by its candlepower per unit area is a sound one physiologically in so far as it indicates the illumination of the retina; the retinal illumination is not, however, completely defined by the candlepower per unit area of the surface being viewed, since the amount of light falling on unit area of the retina depends also on the pupil size; thus from Fig. 54 it is clear that the

FIG. 54. Illustrating the importance of the size of the pupil in defining the stimulus. Above: the pupil is small and only a thin pencil of light from A enters the eye. Below: the pupil is large, permitting a large pencil to enter the eye.

pencils of light that form the image of AB on the retina are larger in the case of the larger pupil. Hence the stimulus required to produce a definite sensation in the eye must be defined in terms of both the luminance, in candles per unit area, and the pupillary area. The unit of retinal illumination suggested by Troland[*] and now given his name is defined by the statement: A troland is that intensity of stimulation that accompanies the use of a pupillary area of one square millimetre and an external stimulus surface luminance of one candela per square metre. It is to be noted that although the troland is referred to as a unit of "retinal illumination," it is not truly so, but is rather an indication of this quantity that is independent of the size of the observer's pupil. To define a stimulus in terms of true retinal illumination we must know the magnification and trans-

[*] This unit of retinal illumination was originally called the *photon*, a term that had already been applied to the quantum of light energy. We may note that, in order to convert the luminance of an extended surface, expressed in millilamberts, to trolands of "retinal illumination", it must be multiplied by $5d^2/2$, where d is the pupillary diameter in mm.

mission of the optical media of the eye. On the basis of a value of 16·7 mm for the distance of the nodal point from the retina, the true retinal illumination is given by:

$$D = 0·36\, \tau_\lambda\, s\, B$$

where B is the luminance of the extended source of light, s is the area of the pupil in cm² and τ_λ is the *transmission factor*, being the ratio of the intensities of light falling on the retina over the light falling on the cornea. This depends on wavelength, varying from 0·1 in the extreme violet where absorption by the yellow pigment of the lens is important, to 0·7 in the deep red; on average with white light it is about 0·5 indicating 50 per cent loss of light (Ludvigh & McCarthy).

When the stimulus in question is due to an effectively point source the pupillary area is of course important, and the stimulus is defined by the candlepower of the source, its distance from the eye and the pupillary area, *i.e.* by the total light flux entering the eye, which is given by the illumination of the pupil multiplied by its area.*

In view of the importance of the adequate definition of the stimuli used in experimental studies of vision, it is worth recapitulating the substance of the last few paragraphs. The luminance of an extended source is defined as its candlepower per unit area; its value as a stimulus is independent of its area and of its distance from the observer. For a given pupillary area it is an indication of the retinal illumination; the troland is a measure of retinal illumination which is independent of the observer's pupillary area; the true retinal illumination may be derived from the troland if the magnification and transmission characteristics of the eye are known. If the stimulus is due to an effectively point source, it is sufficient to characterize it by the total light flux entering the eye.

Light Flux. For the sake of simiplicity, we have so far made our definitions without introducing the concept of *light flux*; this is defined as the amount of visible light energy passing any plane in unit time; its relationship to the luminous intensity of a point source will be clear from the following.

Suppose we have a point source of light of I candlepower; let us imagine the

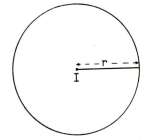

FIG. 55. A source of I candlepower at the centre of a sphere of radius r. $4\pi I$ lumens are emitted per sec. and spread over a surface of $4\pi r^2$; the flux density is I/r^2.

point to be the centre of a sphere of radius r (Fig. 55). The light energy from a point source travels in all directions uniformly through space, and we may think of the sphere being occupied by energy passing through it at a definite rate. The flux, considered thus, is defined in relation to the unit of luminous intensity by

* Stiles and Crawford (p. 206) have shown that pencils of light entering the eye obliquely are less effective as stimuli than those entering the pupil centrally; this effect is not due to aberrations in the optical system but is most likely related to the orientation of the receptors in the retina. A correct definition of the stimulus must therefore take into account the directions of the pencils of light entering the eye.

saying that 4π times the candlepower is the flux emitted by the source, expressed in *lumens*:

$$4\pi \times \text{I (candelas)} = \text{flux (lumens)}$$

(We may note in passing that the lumen, which is an arbitrary unit of power, depending as it does on the candela, may be converted into absolute units by measurement of the energy emitted by the lamp defining the candela. The "mechanical equivalent of light" so obtained is $\dfrac{1}{679\cdot6}$ watts/lumen.

E, the intensity of illumination of the inner surface of the sphere, as defined before is:

$$E = I/r^2$$
$$= 4\pi I/4\pi r^2.$$

Now $4\pi I$ represents the number of lumens of flux falling on the surface of the sphere, and $4\pi r^2$ is the area of its surface. Hence E may be expressed as the ratio of the flux emitted by the source of light over the area on which it falls: flux per unit area, or *flux density*. The units of illumination may therefore be, besides the foot- or metre-candela, a lumen per square foot or a lumen per square metre. Thus:

$$1 \text{ foot-candela } = 1 \text{ lumen/sq ft}$$
$$1 \text{ metre-candela} = 1 \text{ lumen/sq m}$$

In Table 5 the illuminations recommended for different tasks are shown; in Table 6 some luminance levels commonly encountered are presented and in

TABLE 5

Some recommended illuminations

General stores	. .	2–4 foot-candela
Classroom .	. .	5–10 ,,
Billiard table .	. .	20 ,,
Type-setting .	. .	35–50 ,,
Operating table	. .	100 ,,

TABLE 6

Some commonly encountered luminances

Starlit sky . .	.	0·00005 candela/sq ft
Moonlit sky . .	.	0·002 ,, ,,
Full moonlight on snow .		0·007 ,, ,,
Ploughed land at noon in average daylight .	.	130 ,, ,,
Clear sky at noon .	.	1,000 ,, ,,
Sun's disk . .	.	150,000,000 ,, ,,

TABLE 7

Conversion Factors. Illumination. (Value in unit in left-hand column times conversion actor = value in unit at top of column; e.g. 3 foot-candela = 3 × 1·08 × 10 = 32·4 metre-candela)

	Foot-candela	Centimetre-candela	Metre-candela
Foot-candela . . .	1	$1\cdot08 \times 10^{-3}$	$1\cdot08 \times 10$
Cm-candela (Phot) .	$9\cdot29 \times 10^{2}$	1	1×10^{4}
Metre-candela (Lux) .	$9\cdot29 \times 10^{-2}$	10^{-4}	1

Tables 7 and 8 some conversion factors for different units of illumination and luminance.

TABLE 8

Conversion Factors. Luminance. (Value in unit in left-hand column times conversion factor = value in unit at top of column)

	Candela/ft^2	Equiv. Fc.	Candela/cm^2	Millilambert
Candela/ft^2 .	I	3·14	1·08 × 10^{-3}	3·38
Equiv. Fc. .	3·18 × 10^{-1}	I	3·43 × 10^{-4}	1·076
Candela/cm^2	9·3 × 10^2	2·92 × 10^3	I	3·14 × 10^3
Millilambert	2·96 × 10^{-1}	9·29 × 10^{-1}	3·18 × 10^{-4}	I

GENERAL REFERENCE

Walsh, J. W. T. (1953). *Photometry.* London: Constable.

SOME GENERAL ASPECTS OF VISION

Photochemical Reaction. The mechanism by which the energy contained in visible light is transmitted to the nervous tissue of the retina in such a way as to produce that change in its structure which we call a stimulus is a fascinating problem and one that lends itself to physicochemical study. There is a group of chemical reactions that derive a part, or all, of their energy from absorbed light—the *photochemical reactions*;—a biological instance of this type of reaction is the synthesis of carbohydrate by the green leaves of plants, the pigment chlorophyll absorbing light and transmitting the energy to the chemical reactants. It is thus reasonable to inquire whether there is an analogous chemical reaction at the basis of the response of the retina to light, *i.e.* whether or not there are substances in the retina that can absorb visible light and, as a consequence of this absorption of energy, can modify the fundamental structure of the rod or cone to initiate a propagated impulse. One such substance, visual purple, was discovered in the retina as long ago as 1851 by H. Muller, but we owe the early knowledge of its function as an absorber of light to the researches of Kühne, described in his classical monograph of 1878. He was the first to obtain this pigment in solution by extracting the retina and he called it *"Sehpurpur"*, which has been translated as *visual purple*. As we shall see, thanks to the recent studies of Dartnall and Wald, the term visual purple must now be used to describe a class of visual pigments rather than a single entity.

Categories of Vision. Before the detailed study of the photochemical and electrical changes in the retina associated with the visual process is entered into, it would be profitable to discuss some of the more elementary phenomena of vision itself and to indicate the experimental methods available for its study. The visual perception of an object is a complicated physiological process, and attempts have been made to resolve it into simpler categories. Thus, it is common to speak of the *light sense*, defined as the appreciation or awareness of light, as such, and of modifications in its intensity. Secondly, the *colour sense*, which enables us to distinguish between the qualities of two or more lights in terms of their wavelengths, and finally the *form sense* that permits the discrimination of the different parts of a visual image. For the present we shall preserve this simple classification for its convenience, but modern psychophysicists would hesitate to use the term "sense" in relation to the discrimination of form.

THE LIGHT SENSE

The Absolute Threshold. The simplest way to study the light sense is to measure the *threshold* to white light, *i.e.* the minimum light-stimulus necessary to evoke the sensation of light. There are many ways of measuring this, and the general technique will be discussed later. In general, the subject is placed in a completely dark room and the illumination of a test-patch is increased until he is aware of its presence. The patch may be illuminated all the time and its luminance steadily increased, or it may be presented in flashes of varying luminance.

Dark-Adaptation. Early attempts to measure the threshold soon showed that, in order to obtain other than very irregular results, the observer must be allowed to remain in the dark for at least half an hour (*i.e.* he must be *"dark-adapted"*) before any attempt is made to obtain a definite value. If this is not done, it is found that the threshold luminance of the patch is very high if the test is made immediately after the subject has entered the dark room, and that the threshold falls progressively until it reaches a fairly constant value which may be as small as one ten-thousandth of its initial figure. This effect is demonstrated by Fig. 56, in which the illumination of the test patch (in microlux) required to produce the sensation of light in a subject, who had gazed at a bright light for some minutes before entering the dark room, is plotted against time in the dark; the curve is referred to as a *"dark-adaptation curve."*

FIG. 56. Typical dark-adaptation curve. Ordinate: illumination of the test-patch in microlux. Abscissa: duration of dark-adaptation in minutes. (Kohlrausch, in *Handbuch der Normalen und Pathologischen Physiologie.*)

This extraordinary increase in sensitivity of a sense organ on removing it from its normal background of stimuli has not been met in the study of the other senses, and an inference to be drawn from the dark-adaptation curve is that a second mechanism of vision is being brought into play requiring half an hour, or more, to be established at its full level of efficiency. This inference represents the basis of the *Duplicity Theory of Vision*, a theory which assumes that at luminance levels below a certain value (about 0·01 mL) vision is mediated primarily by one mechanism—*scotopic vision*, involving the rods—and above this value by another mechanism—*phototopic vision*, involving the cones; the transition is not abrupt so that there is a range in which the two mechanisms operate together, the *mesopic range*.

Duplicity Theory

Rod Vision. The duplex nature of vision is readily appreciable under conditions of very low illumination. Thus, whereas in daylight, or photopic, vision the subject sees best by direct fixation, so that the image of the object or luminous point he wishes to see falls on the fovea, under night, or scotopic, conditions his best vision is *peripheral*; he must look away from the object he is trying to distinguish so that its image falls on the peripheral retina. Thus, in looking at a dim star one must, as the astronomer Arago said, not look at it; if one fixates it, it disappears. This gives the clue to the anatomical basis of the duplicity theory; the fovea, in its central region specially, contains only cones. Since the fovea is apparently blind at low intensities of illumination, we may conclude that it is the rods that are functional under these conditions. That the rods are indeed responsible for night vision is now well recognized; it was Schultze who put forward this hypothesis on the basis of his comparative studies of animal retinæ; thus he found that the nocturnal owl had a preponderance of rods whilst a diurnal bird, such as the falcon, had a preponderance of cones in its retina.

ACHROMATICITY

Another feature of vision at low luminance is its *achromaticity*, *i.e.* its failure to distinguish colours. Suppose, for example, that the threshold for vision is measured using different wavelengths of light; it is found that these thresholds are different, in the sense that more yellow energy, for instance, is required to give the sensation of light than blue energy, but the "yellow" and "blue" lights are both colourless. Only when the intensities are raised well above threshold do colours appear, *i.e.* when the threshold for stimulation of the *cones* is reached. Thus, on a moonless night colours are not distinguished, whereas in the *mesopic range*, corresponding to around full moonlight, colours may be appreciated but not very distinctly.

LOW VISUAL ACUITY

A very obvious difference between scotopic and photopic vision is the low visual acuity at low luminances; in other words, in spite of the high sensitivity of the eye to light under scotopic conditions, the ability to discriminate detail (*e.g.* to read print) is very low.

Other features of the duplicity theory will be considered later; for the moment we may say that it is now a well established *principle* rather than a theory. In essence it states that at high levels of luminance the relatively insensitive cones are able to operate, whilst the highly sensitive rods are out of action (perhaps through overstimulation). Vision mediated by the cones is coloured and exhibits high powers of discrimination of detail. When the light available is restricted, the insensitive cones no longer operate whilst the rods, after a period of dark-adaptation as shown by Fig. 56, become operative, mediating an achromatic, peripheral, low-acuity type of vision. Over an intermediate range, which may extend up to 1000 times the threshold for cone vision, both rods and cones are operative—the *mesopic range*.

The Differential Threshold or L.B.I.

Instead of using the minimum luminance of a test patch as a means of studying the light sense, we may measure the *differential threshold*—the amount an existing stimulus, which itself produces a sensation of light, must be increased or decreased to produce a change in the sensation.

Measurement. Thus the subject may be presented with a luminous field divided into two, as in Fig. 57a, the luminances of either being varied independently. Beginning with them both equal at I, the right-hand one may be increased

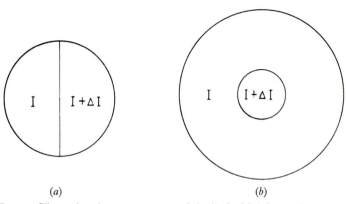

(a)   (b)

FIG. 57. Illustrating the measurement of the liminal brightness increment.

to a value $I + \Delta I$, such that the observer can just detect a difference of subjective brightness. The increment, ΔI, is called the *liminal brightness increment (l.b.i.)* or *differential threshold*. Alternatively, as in Fig. 57b, the subject may look at a large circular field of luminance I, and a smaller concentric field may be thrown on to this with a variable luminance greater than I. With this experimental technique, the measurements need not be confined to those intensities of illumination in which only scotopic vision is operative, but rather the whole range of intensities may be used.

Weber-Fechner Law. The differential threshold, or l.b.i., varies with the initial value of the prevailing luminance, I; for example if I is 100 mL then ΔI

FIG. 58. Intensity discrimination curve. The ratio $\Delta I/I$ is the liminal brightness increment divided by the brightness. If the Weber-Fechner Law held, this ratio would be independent of the value of I. The curve shows that, over a certain range (0·1 to 1,000 mL), this is approximately true. In the scotopic region, however, the ratio increases greatly, *i.e.* the power to discriminate changes in luminance falls off at low levels.

may be in the region of 2 mL; if I is 1000 mL then ΔI is about 20 mL. Over a certain range, however, it may be expressed as a constant fraction of the prevailing luminance, so that the ratio: $\Delta I/I$ is constant. This is the basis of *Weber's Law of Sensation* which applies approximately to all sensory modalities, namely that the difference-limen is proportional to the prevailing stimulus. For example, in the case of the sense of touch or pressure, Weber showed that when two weights resting on the skin differed by about one in thirty they could be discriminated as different weights. Thus if an individual could discriminate between a 30 and a 31 gm weight he could also discriminate between a 3 and a 3·1 gm weight; in other words, the *Weber fraction*, $\Delta S/S$, is constant, where S is the prevailing stimulus and ΔS its liminal difference for perception.

Fechner Fraction. Fechner extended Weber's work to the study of visual discrimination, and the fraction $\Delta I/I$ is frequently called the Fechner-fraction. Fig. 58 represents a more modern study, where the Fechner-fraction, $\Delta I/I$, has been plotted against the intensity level, I. At high intensities, between about 0·1 and 1000 mL, this fraction is fairly constant at about 0·02 to 0·03, indicating that a change of two to three per cent in luminance can be detected; at low luminances the power to discriminate falls off sharply so that at 0·0001 mL two patches must differ by about 50 per cent in luminance if they are to be discriminated.

THE COLOUR SENSE

By means of the colour sense we become aware of those qualitative characteristics of light that depend on its spectral composition. On passing white light through a prism it is resolved spatially into its component wavelengths, and the result is the well-known spectrum; this resolution shows that the sensation of white is evoked by the summated effects of stimuli which, when operating alone, cause entirely different sensations, namely, those of red, orange, yellow, green, etc.

Hue

The spectrum shows a number of characteristic regions of colour: red, orange, yellow, green, blue, indigo and violet; these regions represent large numbers of individual wavelengths; thus the red extends roughly from 7500 to 6500 Å; the yellow from 6300 to 5600 Å; green from 5400 to 5000 Å; blue from 5000 to 4200 Å, and violet from 4200 to 4000 Å. Within these bands of colour there are thus a variety of subtle variations, and a spectral colour or *hue*, has been defined somewhat idealistically as the sensation corresponding to a single wavelength. This is too rigid a definition, both because of the limitations to discrimination of the human eye, and the experimental difficulty in obtaining light confined to a single wavelength.

Thus coloured lights may be obtained by the use of filters, which cut out many wavelengths and selectively transmit others; these filters are never sufficiently selective to confine the transmitted light to a single wavelength and at best they transmit a *narrow band* about a mean position. Hence by a green filter of 5300 Å is meant a filter that transmits mainly green light with a peak of transmission at 5300 Å; transmission at nearby wavelengths is also considerable, however, whilst even at remote wavelengths there may be a little transmission.

Monochromator. A more precise method is by the use of the monochromator, the essential principle of this technique being to select, from a spectrum, just that narrow band of wavelengths that one requires. In practice the band is selected by a movable slit that passes over the spectrum; and its width, in terms of the range of wavelengths, can be reduced by making the slit narrower and narrower. Unfortunately, this decreases the amount of light-energy transmitted, so that once again the experimenter must be content with a band of wavelengths rather than a single one.

Hue-Discrimination. The physiological limit to the differentiation of hues is given by the *hue-discrimination curve*, shown in Fig. 59. The subject is presented with a split field, the two halves of which may be illuminated independently by lights of equal subjective intensity but differing wavelength. Starting with, say, a red of 7000 Å in the left-hand field the wavelength of the light of the right-hand field is shortened till the subject can just discriminate a change in hue, say at 6800 Å; the hue-limen is thus 200 Å. With both fields at 6800 Å, the right-hand field wavelength is again shortened and a new hue-limen obtained. Fig. 59

FIG. 59. Hue-discrimination curve. At any given wavelength, indicated on the abscissa, there is a certain change in wavelength, δλ, that must be made before the change in hue can be discriminated. (Wright, *Researches on Normal and Defective Colour Vision.*)

shows the results for a normal human observer; discrimination is best at about 5000 Å in the blue-green and at 6000 in the yellow, but even here the smallest detectable change in wavelength is about 10 Å.

Saturation. In practice, then, coloured lights are not monochromatic, being generally mixed with more or less white light; the hue is then said to be *impure*, and in the case when the impurity can be accounted for by an admixture of white light, it is said more specifically to be *unsaturated*, the actual colour being called a *tint* of the hue that has been thus diluted. The percentage saturation of a hue is the percentage contributed by the monochromatic light, estimated on a luminosity basis. By mixing white light with a spectral hue, the latter actually changes; thus red becomes pink, orange becomes yellow, yellow becomes green, green becomes yellow, and violet becomes salmon-pink; the yellow-green does, in effect, remain constant and the blue changes very little.

Limits of the Visual Spectrum. The limits are usually given as 4000 Å and 7600 Å, wavelengths shorter than 4000 Å and longer than 7600 Å being characterized as *ultraviolet* and *infrared* respectively. In fact, however, the retina is sensitive to wavelengths well beyond these limits; for example, Wald showed that the insensitivity of the eye to ultraviolet up to 3500 Å is entirely due to absorption by the lens; aphakic subjects are able to see easily with these wavelengths, calling the sensation blue or violet. Again, the failure of early workers to evoke sensation with wavelengths greater than 7600 Å was due entirely to their inability to obtain intense enough sources, the retina being so insensitive to red light. Griffin, Hubbard & Wald were able to evoke sensation with wavelengths as long as 10,000–10,500 Å, and Brindley has found that, when compared on an equi-energy basis (p. 179), the far reds are much more orange than the near reds; for example, a red of 8870 Å could be matched by an orange of 6400 Å.

Just as with white light, we may refer to the luminosity of a given hue and measure it in the same units, and although it may seem somewhat unreal to speak of comparative luminosities of widely different hues, by making use of a suitable colour photometer it is possible to use a scale of luminosity which applies to all the spectral colours in such a way that if all the luminosities of the hues of a spectrum are determined separately, the luminosity of the white light obtained by re-combining the spectrum is equal to the sum of these individual spectral luminosities.

The Flicker Photometer. If it is desired to measure the relative luminosities of two differently coloured sources, the most satisfactory instrument to use is the *flicker photometer*. This is represented diagrammatically in Fig. 60. It consists of a white screen, A, and a Maltese Cross, C, which is placed at such an angle that light from one of the sources (S₂) is reflected down the viewing tube, T. The screen, A, is

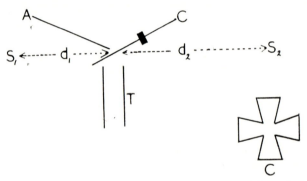

F<small>IG</small>. 60. The flicker-photometer. Light from S₁ is reflected from A down the viewing tube, T. Light from S₂ is reflected from the rotating cross, C. When A and C are equally illuminated flicker ceases. (After Barton.)

likewise placed so that light from the other source (S₁) is reflected down the tube. When the cross is rotated, the eye receives light alternately from S₂ and S₁ by reflection from C and A respectively. If the luminances of the two surfaces are different, a sensation of flicker is experienced which can be made to disappear by adjusting the distances of the two sources from the surfaces which they illuminate. When flicker disappears, the luminances of the two surfaces are equal. If A and C make the same angle with the direction of the incident light, and if their reflection factors are equal, the luminous intensities of S_1 and S_2 will be in the ratio of $d_2{}^2 : d_1{}^2$.

Variation of Hue with Intensity. We have seen that hue and saturation are not absolutely independent, since altering the saturation of a yellow, for example, can actually make it into a green. In a similar way, hue is not independent of luminosity. Thus, as the intensity of a coloured light is increased its subjective hue makes a characteristic shift, and ultimately all wavelengths, if made intense enough, appear the same, evoking a yellowish-white sensation. These shifts are described as the *Bezold-Brücke phenomenon*, after their discoverers. On lowering the intensity there are also characteristic changes which will be discussed later in connection with the Purkinje phenomenon, and ultimately the whole spectrum becomes achromatic, in the sense that at sufficiently low intensity levels all wavelengths appear white and indistinguishable from each other qualitatively. It is therefore important to define the level of luminance at which studies of colour vision are made; the value generally chosen is of the order of 2–3 mL.

Colour Mixtures. If two colours, not too far apart in the spectrum—say a red and a yellow—are mixed, the resulting sensation is that produced by a single spectral hue of intermediate wavelength. The actual position of the resultant hue in the spectrum is determined by the relative luminosities of the two hues that are mixed; if they are equal, the resultant lies midway between; if the red predominates, the resultant lies towards the red end. As the distance apart of the two hues is increased, the resultant hue is found to become progressively unsaturated, *i.e.* it can only be matched with an intermediate spectral hue provided that white light is added to the latter. Eventually a point is reached when the mixture results in white; any two hues that, when combined, give white light are called *complementary colours*. As a result of the classical researches of Young and Helmholtz and more recently those of Wright, the laws of colour mixture have been put on a quantitative basis. In general, it may be stated that any colour sensation, within an average range of intensities, can be produced by a mixture of not more than three *primary spectral wavelengths*, with the reservations that (1) in many cases white light must be added to the comparison colour to obtain a match in saturation as well as in hue. Thus, if it is required to match a given standard colour, say a bluish green, then by varying the intensities of the three primaries it will usually be found that it is impossible to make a perfect match with this standard, the mixture appearing unsaturated by comparison. We must therefore add white to the standard until the two match or, as it is often put, we must subtract white from the mixture to obtain a perfect match in hue and saturation. The three primaries are chosen so that any one cannot be produced by mixing the other two; thus red, green and blue are primaries.*

A given hue may thus be expressed in terms of three coefficients, namely:

$$\text{Colour} = \alpha R + \beta G + \gamma B$$

where the latter determine the relative quantities of these arbitarily chosen primaries. Light is measured on a luminosity basis in most work, so that it would be natural to measure the contributions of the primaries to any given hue in terms of luminosity units, remembering that the luminosity of the hue will be equal to the sum of the separate luminosities of the primaries required to make a match in hue and luminosity. Since the resultant mixture of the primaries will not necessarily correspond in saturation with the given hue to be matched, it is necessary to subtract a certain quantity of white—that is, certain quantities of the three primaries—and this may lead to negative coefficients. There is no

* There are several ways of expressing the "Laws of Colour Mixture". A common one is as follows: given any four lights, it is possible to place three of them in one half of a photometric field and one in the other half, or else two in one half and two in the other, and by adjusting the intensities of three of the four lights to make the two halves of the field indistinguishable to the eye. This appears different from the statement in the text, but is actually the same in so far as it is another statement of the *trivariance* of colour matching, the three variables being the intensities of the three colours that are varied, the fourth remaining constant. The laws governing colour-matching are called *Grassmann's Laws*.

particular theoretical objection to negative coefficients, but they can be avoided by choosing certain hypothetical primaries which do not correspond to any spectral hues. Thus we have seen that a mixture of three spectral primaries gives an unsaturated spectral hue; if the amounts of the primaries which must be subtracted from this unsaturated spectral hue, in order to saturate it, are subtracted from the primaries themselves, we obtain a set of hypothetical primaries which give positive coefficients. Thus Wright used hypothetical primaries, R', G', B', defined by the relationship:

$$R' = 1 \cdot 015 \ R - 0 \cdot 015 \ G$$
$$G' = - \ 0 \cdot 90 \ R + 2 \cdot 00 \ G - 0 \cdot 10 \ B$$
$$B' = - \ 0 \cdot 05 \ G + 1 \cdot 05 \ B$$

where R, G, and B were spectral hues of 6500, 5300, and 4600 Å respectively.

For ease in manipulation, the quantities of the primaries are often expressed in terms of their contributions to colour quality rather than to luminosity; thus the coefficients are defined by the statement that equal quantities of the primaries make white:

White = 0·333 R + 0·333 G + 0·333 B, the units defined in this way being referred to as *trichromatic units*, and since the sum of the coefficients is equal to unity, the equation defining a colour is called a *unit colour equation*. It is a relatively simple matter to transpose from one set of coefficients to another.

The Chromaticity Chart. The unit colour equation is useful because it enables us to express graphically the composition of any hue in terms of the primaries; thus if we construct rectangular co-ordinates so that the ordinates

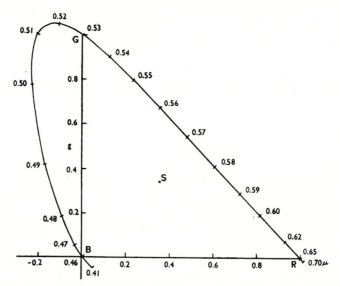

FIG. 61. Chromaticity chart. Units of green are indicated on the vertical line; units of red on the horizontal line. The amount of blue in a given mixture is given by the unit colour equation, R + G + B = 1. The line joining R to G and continuing as a curved loop to B is called the *spectral locus* and shows how the individual spectral hues can be matched by the three primaries. S is standard white. (Wright, *Researches on Normal and Defective Colour Vision.*)

represent green coefficients and the abscissæ red coefficients, then any hue will be given by a point representing its red and green coefficients; since $\alpha + \beta + \gamma = 1$, the blue coefficient will be given by subtracting the red and green coefficients from unity. The locus of spectral hues will be a line (Fig. 61) and white, if defined by the equation above, will be represented by a point whose ordinate and abscissa are 0·333.

THE FORM SENSE

The essential feature exhibited by the form sense is the discrimination between two or more separate stimuli in regard to intensity and spatial extension; we perceive the shape of an object by virtue of our ability to integrate our responses to a large number of separate stimuli of varying intensity arising from different positions on its surface. The appreciation of form is thus a complex perceptual process and the expression "form sense" is very much of a misnomer.

Resolving Power and Visual Acuity

The power of the eye to discriminate on a spatial basis is studied experimentally by measurements of the *resolving power*, the smallest angle subtended at the nodal point of the eye by two points or lines such that they are appreciated

FIG. 62. Snellen letter, grating and Landolt-C. In each case the angle subtended at the eye by the distance, *s*, apparently determines whether the gap will be recognized.

as separate, *i.e.* the so-called *minimum separable*. The visual acuity is defined as the reciprocal of this angle when it is measured in minutes of arc. Thus, under good experimental conditions, resolving powers of the order of 30 seconds of arc, or half a minute, may be measured, corresponding to a visual acuity of $1/0·5 = 2$.

Measurement. The most commonly used test-objects for measuring resolving power are the Landolt-C and the grating (Fig. 62). The Landolt-C can be rotated into eight separate positions which the subject is asked to identify; C's of diminishing size are presented and the errors made in indicating the positions are recorded. Experimentally it is found, as with all psychophysical studies of thresholds, that there is no sharp division between the size of C that can be discriminated and that which cannot; near the "end-point" we will have a range of sizes where the average number of errors in any set of trials increases with decreasing size of C until eventually the answers are purely random. We must therefore somewhat arbitrarily choose an end-point; Lythgoe chose that size of C with which 4·5 out of eight answers were correct, and the actual end-point was computed from the errors obtained with several sizes of C by the application of statistical theory. So far as the resolving power of the eye is concerned, it would appear that the ability to detect the position of the break in the C, which distinguishes it from a complete circle, depends on the size of the break, *s*; in fact, the angle subtended at the eye by this distance, *s*, at the end-point, is indeed the measure of the resolving power of the eye. Thus at a distance of 6 metres, under given conditions, the size of the break, s, was 3·6 mm, at the end-point; this distance subtended 2 minutes at the eye and so the visual acuity was 0·5.

Grating Acuity

If the grating of Fig. 62, consisting of equally spaced black and white lines, is removed sufficiently far from the observer, it appears uniformly grey; at a certain point the lines can be just discriminated and the angle subtended at the eye by the distance s once again is said to indicate the resolving power of the eye. According to Shlaer (1937) the limiting size for resolution subtends some 28 seconds of arc at the eye under optimal conditions, corresponding to an acuity of 2·12.

Snellen Test

The clinical *Snellen test* is essentially a resolution test; it is assumed that the average individual can resolve the details of a letter if they subtend one minute of arc at the eye, and the test letters are constructed so that their details (*e.g.* the gap in a C) subtend this angle, whilst the whole letter subtends five minutes of arc (Fig. 62), when they are at a definite distance from the eye. The chart has several rows of these letters, the sizes in the different rows being graded so that their details subtend one minute at different distances, *e.g.* the smallest letters subtend this angle at 4 metres whilst the largest do so at 60 metres. The subject is placed 6 metres from the chart and the smallest row of letters that can be read correctly is determined. The visual acuity is expressed as the ratio of the distance of the individual from the chart to the distance at which this row of minimum legible letters should be read, asssuming a minimum visual angle of one minute. Thus at 6 metres if the individual can read down to the letters whose details subtend one minute when viewed from a distance of 18 metres his visual acuity is 6/18; if he can read letters so small that they subtend the same angle at only 5 metres, his visual acuity is 6/5, and so on.

Experimental Results. Factors influencing visual acuity will be dealt with in detail later; for the present we need only note that it is markedly influenced by the illumination of the test object, the state of adaptation of the eye, and the pupil size. Under optimal conditions it has a value in the region between 2 and 3 (*i.e.* a minimum separable of about 30–20 seconds of arc) when a grating or Landolt-C is used as test-object.

INDUCTION

The effect of light falling on a given portion of the retina is generally not confined to the retinal elements stimulated; moreover the characteristics of those elements that have been stimulated are altered for an appreciable time, so that their response to a second stimulus is modified. The influence of one part of the retina on another is described as *spatial induction*; by *temporal induction* is meant the effect of a primary stimulus on the response of the retina to a succeeding stimulus.

Spatial Induction

Spatial induction, or *simultaneous contrast*, can be demonstrated by comparing the appearance of a grey square, when seen against a black background, with its appearance when seen against a white background; against the black background the grey appears almost white, whereas it appears quite dark when seen against the white background. The white surround apparently depresses the sensitivity of the whole retina, thereby making the grey appear darker; the net effect of this depression in sensitivity is to accentuate the contrast between the grey and the white surfaces. Where coloured lights are concerned the same principle of a reduction in sensitivity of the retina applies, but now this reduction is confined to certain wavebands, and the subjective result is to enhance the appearance of the complementary colour. Thus, if a white and blue light patch are placed side-by-side, the white patch appears yellow; apparently the blue light falling on one half of the retina has depressed the sensitivity of the whole retina to blue light; the white light falling on the retina is now losing some of its "blueness" because of this loss of blue-sensitivity; removing blue from white leaves a yellow colour, since blue and white are complementaries.

Temporal Induction

In a similar way, if the whole retina is stimulated with white light the sensitivity to a given stimulus following this is reduced, so that the second stimulus appears less bright than it would have done had there been no "conditioning stimulus", as this preliminary, adapting, stimulus is called. This form of induction, which has been called *light-adaptation*, has been studied in detail by Wright in England, and Schouten in Holland.

Binocular Matching. The technique employed was that of binocular matching, based on the principle that the states of adaptation of the two eyes are independent. Thus the observer looks through a binocular eye-piece, each eye seeing the half of a circular patch of light, and these halves have to be matched for equal

FIG. 63. Curve showing the fall in sensitivity of the fovea during exposure to a bright light. The right eye views the bright light whilst the dark-adapted left eye views a patch that must be matched in brightness with the sensation experienced through the right eye. The matching intensity decreases, indicating that the apparent brightness of the light, as seen through the right eye, becomes less and less. (Wright, *Trans. Illum. Eng. Soc.*)

subjective brightness. If, say, the right eye is exposed to a bright light, we may determine the changes in sensitivity of this eye during its exposure to the bright light by matching its half-field with the left half-field, as seen by the dark-adapted eye. This means varying the intensity of the left half-field until the match is made. It is found that the intensity of the left half-field has to be continuously reduced during exposure of the right eye, until it levels off at a constant value which may be about 1/16th of the value at first. This means that the right eye becomes rapidly less sensitive to light from the moment it is exposed to it; this is the phenomenon of light-adaptation and is illustrated by Fig. 63. The phenomenon is, of course reversible, so that if the two eyes are now allowed to match fields of moderate luminance, the left field will, at first, have to be made much weaker than the right because the left eye has remained dark-adapted and has remained the more sensitive; very rapidly, however, this matching field will be made stronger until they finally become equal when both eyes are completely dark-adapted.*

Practical Demonstration. This adaptation is very easy to demonstrate qualitatively; thus if an observer is instructed to stare at a brilliantly illuminated screen for a few minutes with one eye closed, and then this is replaced quickly by one of moderate intensity, he finds, on comparing the subjective brightness of the screen as seen through either eye separately, that the eye that had been kept closed sees the screen as very much brighter. We may note here that the phenomenon of *dark-adaptation*, as revealed by the progressive decrease in the absolute threshold, is a manifestation of temporal induction, in so far as the phenomenon reveals a change in the retina following the cessation of a stimulus, namely of the original bright light to which the observer was exposed before being placed in the dark.

Adaptation to Coloured Lights. The same process of light-adaptation, or successive contrast, is seen with respect to colours; thus with the same binocular matching technique, except that the two fields must be matched for colour rather than subjective brightness, the effects of adapting to a given wavelength of light can be found. The same principle emerges, namely that adaptation of the one eye to, say, green, reduces the sensitivity of this eye to this wavelength, and in order that the other eye may make a match it has to employ much less green than before. Thus two half-fields may be made to match, the right eye viewing a yellow and the left a mixture of red and green, their intensities being adjusted to give the match with the right eye. The right eye is now exposed to an adapting green light for a few minutes and it is found that, on viewing the two fields, the match no longer holds, the right field appearing reddish by comparison with the yellow of the left field. The left field must now be made less green to make the match, and the extent to which the green must be reduced in intensity in this field is a measure of the reduction of sensitivity of the right eye to green.

After-Images. When the eye is exposed to a brief flash of light the subjective sensations last for much longer than the stimulus, and are described as a succession of *after-images*. The phenomena may be classed as inductive, in so far as they reveal changes in the retina or its higher pathways following a primary

* These studies of light-adaptation and their reversal are made with foveal vision and are essentially studies of cone vision, *i.e.* although comparisons are made with a dark-adapted eye, the intensities of the half-fields to be compared are always maintained well above cone-thresholds.

FIG. 64. The successive after-images said to be experienced after viewing a
bright flash. Time-scale in seconds. (Tschermak, in *Handbuch der Normalen
und Pathologischen Physiologie*.)

stimulus; although they have attracted a lot of interest, little of fundamental
value has emerged from their study and it would be a pity to spend much space
on them. As classically described, the responses to a single flash are illustrated
schematically in Fig. 64 where upward movements indicate sensations of brightness (positive after-images) and downward movements sensations of blackness
(negative after-images). If a coloured primary stimulus is used, some of the after-
images are coloured, often with the complementary. The events depicted by Fig.
64 occur rapidly and are exceedingly difficult to resolve, except by such devices
as Bidwell's disc, illustrated by Fig. 65. Here a disc, with a narrow slit in it, is

FIG. 65. Bidwell's ghost. A black disc with
a sector cut out rotates in front of a
brightly illuminated opal screen. The
after-images of the sector are projected
to the left to give the appearance shown.
(Macdougal, *Brit. J. Psychol.*)

rotating in front of a bright opal screen, and the after-images are projected on to
the black disc to give the appearances of *Bidwell's ghost*. A more slowly developing and longer-lasting after-image is that observed after staring for a few minutes
at a bright source and then transferring the gaze to a dimly lit screen. In a little
while a "negative" image of the bright source appears; if the source was coloured
this has the complementary colour, *e.g.* magenta after looking at green; yellow
after looking at blue, and so on.

Intermediate Exposures. The after-effects of exposures intermediate in
duration between the brief flash and the lengthy gaze have been studied under
well controlled conditions by Trezona. Thus, with an exposure of the order of
8 seconds, the after-effects may be classified as follows:

(a) *Persistence of vision*, this being the apparent continuation of the stimulus after it has been cut off, and lasting about 1 sec at rapidly diminishing subjective brightness.

(b) *After-colours*; these may last for seconds or minutes, changing colour frequently. The threshold for these after-colours was very high, of the order of 100,000 trolands of retinal illumination.

(c) *After-blueness*; this was a characteristically different effect from the after-colours mentioned above; it lasts for some seconds and remains the same colour. The threshold was much lower, of the order of 100–1000 trolands and the effect could only be obtained with peripheral vision, suggesting mediation by the rods.

(d) *After-blackness*. This was favoured by long exposures, and consisted of several appearances of the black image of the source.

Liminal Brightness Increment. If a subject was exposed to pairs of bright flashes in the two halves of a test-field, the after-images could be distinguished if the intensities of the flashes differed, the Fechner-fraction, $\Delta I/I$, comparing with that found for direct vision; this was in spite of the fact that with direct vision the two halves of the field could not be distinguished because of the extreme brightness and shortness of the flashes. When the intensities of the flashes became too high, however, there was a fall in discrimination, *i.e.* a rise in the Fechner-fraction, and this was probably due to excessive bleaching of the cones (Brindley, 1959).

Peripheral Origin. This finding, together with the study of the applicability of Bloch's Law (p. 213), strongly suggests that after-images have a peripheral origin, *i.e.* are determined by photochemical events in the receptors. Support for this is given by Craik's experiment, in which the eye was temporarily blinded by exerting pressure on the globe. On exposure of the eye to a bright light nothing was seen, but on restoring the circulation an after-image appeared. The possibility that some of the phases have a central origin must not be ruled out, however; thus Brindley was unable to find any regularity in behaviour of his after-images unless he ignored those appearing within the first 15 seconds; after this time they conformed to rules predictable on photochemical grounds (p. 214).

Value of Contrast

Simultaneous and successive contrast are essentially manifestations of an inductive process that tends to reduce the sensitivity of the retina to an existing stimulus and to enhance its sensitivity to a stimulus of a different kind, *e.g.* the sensitivity to the complementary of the existing, coloured, stimulus. As a result of simultaneous contrast the contours of an image become better defined and, as a result of successive contrast, the confusion that would result from the mixing of successively presented images is reduced.

SPECIAL REFERENCES

BRINDLEY, G. S. (1955). The colour of light of very long wavelength. *J. Physiol.*, **130**, 35–44.

BRINDLEY, G. S. (1959). The discrimination of after-images. *J. Physiol.*, **147**, 194–203.

GRIFFIN, D. R., HUBBARD, R., & WALD, G. (1947). The sensitivity of the human eye to infra-red radiation. *J. opt. Soc. Amer.*, **37**, 546–554.

KOHLRAUSCH, A. (1931). Tagessehen, Dämmersehen, Adaptation. *Handbuch der normalen und pathologischen Physiologie*. Bd. XII/2, pp. 1499–1594. Berlin: Springer.

LYTHGOE, R. J. (1932). The measurement of visual acuity. *M.R.C. Sp. Rep. Ser.*, No. 173.

McDOUGALL, W. (1904). The sensations excited by a single momentary stimulation of the eye. *Brit. J. Psychol.*, **1**, 78–113.

SCHOUTEN, J. F., & ORNSTEIN, L. S. (1939). Measurement on direct and indirect adaptation by means of a binocular method. *J. opt. Soc. Amer.*, **29**, 168–182.

SHLAER, S. (1937). The relation between visual acuity and illumination. *J. gen. Physiol.*, **21**, 165–188.

TREZONA, P. (1960). The after-effects of a white light stimulus. *J. Physiol.*, **150**, 67–78.

TSCHERMAK, A., (1929). Licht- und Farbensinn. *Handbuch der normalen und pathologischen Physiologie*. Bd. XII/1, pp. 295–499. Berlin: Springer.

WRIGHT, W. D. (1939). The response of the eye to light in relation to measurement of subjective brightness and contrast. *Trans. Illum. Eng. Soc.*, **4**, 1–8.

WRIGHT, W. D. (1946). *Researches on Normal and Defective Colour Vision*. London: Kimpton.

ELECTRICAL EFFECTS OF STIMULATION OF THE RETINA

THE SENSORY MESSAGE

WHEN a receptor is stimulated, a succession of electrical changes takes place in its conducting nerve fibre. These changes are measured by placing electrodes on the nerve fibre and connecting them to a device for recording rapidly occurring potential differences, an *oscillograph*. A series of electrical variations, called *action potentials* or "*spikes*" is obtained when the receptor is stimulated. The duration of an individual spike is very short (it is measured in milliseconds) and, as the strength of the stimulus is increased, the *frequency* of the discharge (the number of spikes per second) increases, but the size of the individual spikes remains unaltered ("*all-or-none*" *effect*).

Spike Potentials. Thus the message sent to the central nervous system is in a *code* consisting of a series of spike potentials apparently all with the same magnitude, the frequency being the variable that indicates how strongly the receptor has been stretched. When the nerve fibres from different receptors are compared, *e.g.* touch, temperature, vision, hearing, the action-potentials are very similar in magnitude and time-course; and it has not been possible to correlate any given type of action potential with the type of sensation that it is mediating. In other words, it appears that the elements of the message, like the dots and dashes of the Morse code, are the same for all, whether they indicate a change in temperature or the flash of a light, and we must conclude that it is the places where the messages are carried in the brain—the *central terminations*—that determine the character of the sensation. The intensity of the sensation, as indicated above, is determined by the frequency of the spikes, *i.e.* the number that pass under our recording electrode in unit time.

Recording the Message. The accurate study of the events taking place when a receptor is stimulated demands that the recording electrode should be on or within the receptor or, if this cannot be achieved, on the sensory nerve that makes direct connection with this receptor. Moreover if a recording from a nerve is to be made, the leads should be taken from a single fibre, otherwise the record of events taking place in the many thousands of fibres of a whole nerve would be a very confused and attenuated picture of the events taking place in the single fibres. With the vertebrate eye, these requirements are very difficult to meet, because the receptors—rods and cones—and the first sensory neurones, the bipolar cells, are buried in the depth of the retina; hence if we wish to record from a reasonably accessible nerve, namely the optic nerve, we will be recording from a second-order neurone, namely the ganglion cell. In its passage through the ganglion cell, the original message from the rod or cone and the bipolar cell has been submitted to a process of what the neurophysiologist calls *re-coding*; unnecessary parts of the message being dropped and other parts being accentuated at their expense. Thus, to understand what happens in the receptor cell, it would be a help if we could place our electrode on or within a rod or cone, or failing that, on a bipolar cell, which makes such intimate relationships with the rods and cones. For this reason the invertebrate eye, built on a simpler plan neurologically, was studied by Hartline; and it is to his pioneering studies that we owe so much of our knowledge of sensory mechanisms. Hartline studied the compound eye of the horse-shoe crab *Limulus*, the fibres of its optic nerve being, apparently, processes leading away from the retinula cells on which the light impinges. Thus the study of the electrical changes in these fibres brings us close to the electrical changes occurring directly in response to the impinging of light on a light-sensitive cell.

THE INVERTEBRATE EYE

Ommatidium

Essentially the compound eye of insects and crustaceans is an aggregation of many unit-eyes or *ommatidia*, each of these units having its own dioptric apparatus that concentrates light on to its individual light-sensitive surface, made up of specialized *retinula cells*. The faceted appearance of the compound eye is thus due

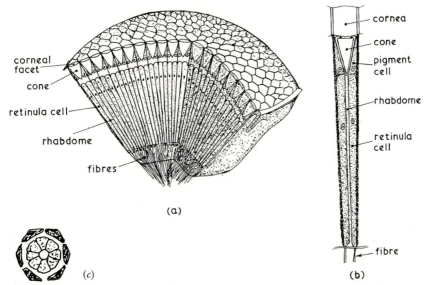

(a)

(c)

(b)

Fig. 66. The faceted eye. (*a*) Cut-away view showing the packing of the individual ommatidia; (*b*) longitudinal section of an ommatidium; (*c*) cross-section of ommatidium.

to the regular arrangement of the transparent surfaces of these unit-eyes (Fig. 66,a). The *ommatidium* is illustrated schematically in Fig. 66,b; light is focused by the *crystalline cone* on to the highly refractile *rhabdom*, which constitutes an aggregation of specialized regions of the *retinula cells*. These retinula cells are wedge-shaped and are symmetrically arranged around the axial canal like the segments of an orange (Fig. 66,c); the rhabdom is made up of the apical portions of these wedge-shaped cells, the separate portions being called *rhabdomeres*. As illustrated in Fig. 67, which shows a cross-section of the *Limulus* (horse-shoe crab) ommatidium, the regions of junction of the retinula cells are characterized by dense staining, so that a cross-section appears like the spokes of a wheel, the axle being the central canal. This canal contains the process of the *excentric cell*; this is apparently a neurone, with its cell body squeezed between the retinula cells at the base of the ommatidium;

its long spear-like process fills the central canal and may be regarded as a dendrite; the central end of the cell consists of a long process that passes out of the ommatidium in the optic nerve.

Excentric Cell. The excentric cell thus constitutes the nerve fibre of the ommatidium, whilst we may regard the retinula cells, with their specialized rhabdomeres, as the cells responsible for absorbing the incident light. Provisionally, then, we may say that the light-stimulus falls on the rhabdom; as a result of chemical changes taking place in this region electrical changes are induced in the excentric cell that culminate in the passage of impulses along the axon-like process of this cell.

Retinula Processes. Actually each retinula cell also has a long proximal process leading out of the ommatidium in the optic nerve; consequently the optic nerve is made up of some 10–20 retinula processes to every one excentric cell process. The significance of these retinula processes is not clear; they do not, apparently, carry action potentials, so that it would appear that the great majority of the "optic nerve fibres" of the compound eye are not nerve fibres at all.

FIG. 67. Cross-section of ommatidium of *Limulus,* showing individual retinula cells with the rhabdomeres represented in white. (After Miller, *Ann. N.Y. Acad. Sci.*)

The electron-microscope has contributed a lot to the understanding of the structure of the rhabdomere; the spokes illustrated in Fig. 67 are apparently made up by innumerable interdigitating villi from the surfaces of contiguous retinula cells; they thus constitute a vast increase in the surface area of the retinula cells and it is here that the photosensitive pigment, responsible for absorbing the energy of the light-stimulus, is apparently concentrated.

Single Fibre Responses

In Fig. 68 are shown Hartline's oscillograms of the amplified potential changes in a single optic nerve fibre of *Limulus* when the eye is exposed to a steady illumination of two separate intensities; that for the upper record is ten times greater than that for the lower. The figure shows that, as with other receptors, the response to a continuous stimulus is intermittent, and that the effect of increasing the intensity of the stimulus is to increase the frequency of the action potentials, but not to modify the magnitude of the individual spikes.

Dark-Adaptation. The phenomenon of dark-adaptation has already been described; in Fig. 69 are shown the electrical discharges of a *Limulus* single fibre in response to light stimuli of the same duration and intensity at intervals of thirty seconds, five, twenty and sixty minutes after a light-adapting exposure of the eye to a bright light. It is quite clear the the frequency of the response increases with the period of dark-adaptation. This suggests that the increase in

FIG. 68. Oscillogram of the amplified potential changes in a single *Limulus* optic nerve fibre due to steady illumination of the eye. Intensity of illumination with upper record ten times greater than for lower record. Full length of each record corresponds to 1 second. (Hartline, *J. Opt. Soc. Amer.*)

FIG. 69. The effect of dark-adaptation on the response of the eye of *Limulus* to a flash of constant intensity. As the eye dark-adapts the frequency and duration of the response increase. (Hartline, *J. Opt. Soc. Amer.*)

sensitivity that occurs during a stay in the dark is a feature of the receptors, *i.e.* the rods and cones of the vertebrate eye, rather than of events in the central nervous system. As we shall see, however, there are many features of adaptation that indicate the intervention of higher nervous activity.

Latency. When the stimulus is a brief flash of light, as in Fig. 70, the discharge occurs entirely after the stimulus is over. The weaker the flash the longer this latency, as Fig. 70 shows; the latency represents the time elapsing between the absorption of light by the rhabdom and the induction of an electrical change in the nearby excentric cell, *i.e.* it is the time required for some photochemical change to take place in the rhabdom. The stronger the flash of light the more rapid will be this photochemical reaction and thus the shorter the latency.

Inhibition. It was considered in the early work on ommatidia that they were entirely independent of each other so far as the discharges in the optic nerve fibres were concerned; recently, however, Hartline, Wagner & Ratliff have shown that adjacent ommatidia may inhibit each other's response. An example

FIG. 70. Responses to flashes of light of decreasing duration as indicated by the size of the break in the upper white line. Note that in the lower records the response occurs entirely after the stimulus; also the long latency in the lowest record. (Hartline, Wagner & MacNichol, *Cold Spr. Harb. Symp. quant. Biol.*)

is shown by Fig. 71. This inhibition must have resulted from an interaction between the responses in the nerve fibres from individual ommatidia, taking place presumably in the plexus of fibres just outside the ommatidia. In the more

FIG. 71. Illustrating inhibition of discharge in one ommatidium by excitation of a neighbouring ommatidium. Ommatidium A, when illuminated alone, gives a frequency of 53 spikes per sec.; ommatidium B gives a frequency of 46 per sec.; when A and B are illuminated together, A has a frequency of 43, and B one of 35 per sec., *i.e.* they have mutually inhibited each other. (Hartline, Wagner and Ratliff, *J. Gen. Physiol.*)

complex eyes of vertebrates we may expect inhibitory effects to be more marked because of the greater possibilities of interaction between individual pathways resulting from the well defined system of interneuronal connections at the level of the bipolar and ganglion cells.

SIGNIFICANCE OF INHIBITION

The importance of inhibition in the sensory pathway may not be immediately evident but will become so when we discuss such phenomena as flicker and visual acuity; for the moment we need only note that it is just as important to prevent a discharge—inhibit—as to initiate one—excite. Thus there is some evidence that a single cone can be excited separately by a spot of light, although we know on optical principles that the image of this spot must cover several cones. In fact several cones are stimulated, in the sense that light falls on them, but only one may actually be excited because the activities of adjacent ones are inhibited by the one that receives the most light, *i.e.* the cone in the centre of the image of the spot of light where the image is most intense. It is through inhibition, then, that unnecessary responses fail to reach the higher levels of the central nervous system. The example shown in Fig. 71 shows inhibition at the lowest level; in the vertebrate retina it may occur at the level of the bipolar cells and ganglion cells and higher still in the geniculate body and cortex.

Mechanism of Activation of the Sensory Neurones

Generator Potential. The electrical events following stimulation have been described as a series of spikes, brief changes in potential taking place across the

FIG. 72. Generator and spike potentials from impaled excentric cell of *Limulus* ommatidium. Duration of illumination indicated by black lines below records. Intensity of illumination decreases from above downwards. Note that the frequency of the spikes increases with the size of the generator potential. (Fuortes, *J. Physiol.*)

nerve fibre's membrane. Those concerned with the way in which light, or some other stimulus, can provoke this electrical change have studied the events leading up to this spike discharge; and in general it appears that the common feature is the establishment in a sensory cell of what is called a *generator potential;* this is a more slowly developing and longer lasting electrical negativity of the cell than the brief spike, and is essentially a "preliminary change" that, if carried far enough, sets off the discharge. The development of this generator potential in the *Limulus* eye was followed by Fuortes, who placed an electrode inside the excentric cell of an ommatidium; when light fell on this ommatidium the energy was presumably taken up by the rhabdom which, as we have seen (p. 112) surrounds the process of the excentric cell. As a result of the chemical changes taking place in the rhabdom, the excentric cell developed a generator potential, becoming negative internally; superimposed on this negativity were the much more rapid and abrupt changes that we call the spikes. This is illustrated by Fig. 72 where the ommatidium has been stimulated with three intensities (100, 2·5 and 0·125 units); the generator potential is indicated by the rise in the baseline and the spikes by the strokes taking off from this; with increasing intensity the generator potential increases, and the spike frequency too.

The most significant feature of this generator potential is, as we have seen, that it is not all-or-none, a weak stimulus producing a smaller potential than a strong one. This permits the process of *summation*; thus two weak stimuli, that themselves only produce small generator potentials, when applied in quick succession may produce a summed generator potential that is sufficiently large to set off a spike discharge.

Chemical Transmitter. According to Fuortes and Rushton, the electrical events can be best described on the assumption that the retinula cells (rhabdom) liberate a substance (transmitter) after absorbing light, and it is this chemical transmitter that activates the sensory neurone, in this case the excentric cell. In the vertebrate eye the light is absorbed by the rods and cones, but it is not certain whether these cells develop generator potentials and spikes themselves, or whether the first significant electrical events take place in the bipolar cells. One hypothesis is that the absorption of light by the rod or cone causes a generator potential to develop in this cell, whilst this generator potential activates a bipolar cell through electrical interaction; in view of the characteristic synaptic relationship between a receptor and its bipolar cell, however, it seems more likely that a chemical transmitter, liberated by the receptor, activates the bipolar cell.

VERTEBRATE OPTIC NERVE FIBRES

It is now time to turn our attention to the messages carried by the single fibres of the optic nerve of the vertebrate eye. These were first studied in the frog by Hartline, who obtained single fibres by cutting down the optic nerve until just one fibre was left; by stimulating different regions of the retina he was able to find a region that, when stimulated, gave spike potentials in the single remaining fibre. Later, potentials from single fibres were recorded in warm-blooded animals by the simple expedient of placing a fine electrode on the surface of the retina in which event, as Rushton showed, the spike potentials were due to the discharges taking place in single giant ganglion cells; alternatively a fine electrode could be inserted into the optic nerve and spikes from individual fibres recorded (Thomson).

Types of Response

Frog Optic Nerve. In general, three types of fibre were found by Hartline in the frog's optic nerve, differing in their responses to a flash of light. In the first place there is a group of fibres (representing on the average some 20 per cent of the total) which behave in essentially the same way as *Limulus* fibres, showing a response which starts almost immediately after the light has been switched on and ceasing when the light has been switched off (Fig. 73, A); these are called ON-fibres; secondly, there is a group (some 50 per cent of the total) which respond with an initial outburst of impulses when the light is switched on and again when the light is switched off (Fig. 73, B); these are called ON-OFF-fibres; during the intermediate period no impulses are recorded. Finally, there is a group of fibres (some 30 per cent of the total) which respond only when the light is switched off (Fig. 73, C); these are called OFF-fibres. The group B, responding to the switching on and off of the light, shows a remarkable sensitivity to changes in the intensity of the stimulus and to the slightest movement of the image on the retina, the greater the change in intensity and the more rapid and extensive the movement of the image, the greater the frequency of the resultant discharge. These OFF-discharges probably represent a release from *inhibition*, the ganglion

Fig. 73. Discharges in a single optic nerve fibre of the vertebrate (frog) eye. Type A: Pure ON-element responding at ON with a discharge maintained during illumination. Type B: ON-OFF-element responding with discharges at ON and OFF but silent during the main period of illumination. Type C: Pure OFF-element responding only at OFF. Signal of the exposure to light blackens out white line above time-marker. Time marked in 0·2 sec. (Hartline, *J. Opt. Soc. Amer.*)

cells giving rise to them presumably being subjected to an inhibitory discharge by bipolar and other retinal neurones (horizontal and amacrine cells?) during the period of exposure to light; when the light was switched off this inhibition ceased and the ganglion cells discharged, the phenomenon being called more generally "inhibitory rebound".

Mammalian Eye. Hartline's work was extended by Granit, and more recently by Kuffler and Barlow, to the mammalian eye where the same pattern of ON-, OFF-, and ON-OFF-responses was revealed, although the phenomena were even more complex. The mammalian retina shows a background of activity in the dark, so that ON- and OFF-effects were manifest as accentuations or diminutions of this normal discharge. In general, ON-elements showed an increased discharge when the light was switched on, and an inhibition of the background discharge when the light was switched off. Similarly, an OFF-element showed an inhibited discharge when the light was switched on but gave a powerful discharge when the light was switched off. The OFF-effect is thus quite definitely a *release from inhibition*.*

* In psychophysical terms the beginning of the ON-discharge may well correspond to the primary sensation of light when the eye is exposed to a flash; the so-called Hering

Receptive Fields

The number of fibres in an optic nerve is of the order of one million, whilst the number of receptors is of the order of 150 million. This means, in neuro-physiological terms, that there is a high degree of *convergence* of the receptors on the ganglion cells, so that a single optic nerve fibre must have connections with many bipolar cells which themselves have connections with many rods and cones. In consequence, the area of retina over which a light-stimulus may evoke a response in a single optic nerve fibre may be quite large; the *receptive field* of a single fibre may be plotted by isolating a single fibre and, with a small spot of light, exploring the retina for those parts that will cause a discharge in this fibre. As Fig. 74 shows, the field increases with the strength of stimulus, so that in order that a light-stimulus falling at some distance from the centre of the field may

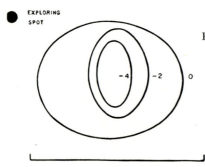

EXPLORING SPOT

FIG. 74. Showing the retinal region with which a single optic nerve fibre makes connections. Each curve encloses the retinal region within which an exploring spot (relative size shown at upper left) produced responses in the fibre at an intensity of illumination whose logarithm is given in the respective curve. Note that the greater the stimulus the greater is the receptive field of the fibre. (Hartline, *J. Opt. Soc. Amer.*)

affect this particular fibre it must be much more intense than one falling on the centre of the field. This shows that some synaptic pathways are more favoured than others.

Summation. As we shall see, this convergence is the anatomical basis for the phenomena of summation; thus a single spot of light falling on the periphery of the receptive field may be too weak to provoke a discharge in the ganglion cell; several spots each too weak to excite will, if presented together in different regions of the field, provoke a discharge. In neurophysiological terms we may say that the ganglion cell requires a certain bombardment by discharges from the bipolar cells, with which it makes synaptic contacts, before it discharges; this bombardment can be provided by a few bipolar cells discharging strongly or by many bipolar cells discharging more weakly. The electrical basis for this summation of effects is essentially the same as that for the summation in the receptors; the ganglion cells develop generator potentials which are this time called *synaptic potentials*; they are not all-or-none, and so can add their effects and ultimately build up to a sufficient height to initiate a spike discharge.

Centre and Periphery. A careful study of the receptive fields in the cat's retina by Barlow, Fitzhugh & Kuffler showed that they were not so simple as had

after-image, that follows rapidly on the primary sensation, would then correspond to the activation of the ON-OFF-elements, whilst the dark-interval following this would re-present activation of the OFF-elements. Finally, the appearance of the Purkinje after-image, rather later, could be due to a secondary activation of the ON-elements described by Grüsser & Rabelo (1958).

been thought, the more peripheral part of the field giving the opposite type of response to that given by the centre. Thus, if at the centre of a receptive field the response was at ON, the response farther away, in the same fibre, was at OFF, and in an intermediate zone it was often mixed to give an ON-OFF-element. In order to characterize an element, therefore, it was necessary to describe it as an *ON-centre* or *OFF-centre* element, meaning thereby that at the centre of its receptive field its response was at ON or OFF respectively. By studying the effects of small spot-stimuli on centre and periphery separately and together, Kuffler demonstrated a mutual inhibition between the two.

So much for the bare facts concerning single-fibre discharges; the contribution of their study to the elucidation of many sensory phenomena will become clearer as we consider these in later parts of this section, and we must now proceed to discuss another electrophysiological phenomenon that has been equally valuable in the interpretation of sensory phenomena, namely the *electroretinogram.*

THE ELECTRORETINOGRAM

The electroretinogram* (ERG) is a record of comparatively slow changes of potential that take place across the retina in a radial direction when light falls

FIG. 75. Typical electroretinogram (ERG). Lowest record, time scale; middle record, stimulus; top record, galvanometer deflection. (Hartline, *Amer. J. Physiol.*)

on it. As classically studied in the intact eye, one electrode is placed on the cornea whilst the other, indifferent, electrode may be placed in the mouth or, in experimental animals, on the optic nerve. Wherever the second, indifferent, electrode is placed, essentially the same cycle of potential changes is recorded on exposure of the eye to light. In Fig. 75 is shown a typical example; the first sign of activity is shown as an *a*-wave corresponding to a decrease in the normal positivity of the corneal electrode; this is conventionally recorded as a down-stroke on the record, and is called a *negative* wave; it lasts less than 0·1 sec. The *a*-wave is followed by a reversal in polarity so that the cornea now becomes strongly positive, and this gives the sharp upward *b*-wave conventionally described as a *positive* wave; the *c*-wave is a much slower rise in corneal positivity and is terminated, when the light is switched off, by the *d*-wave, or off-effect.

* The "retinal currents" now called the ERG were first described by Holmgren in 1865 but were independently discovered by Dewar and McKendrick. Kühne & Steiner (1880, 1881) showed that the same electrical changes could be obtained from the retina removed from the eye, whilst the remaining sclera, choroid and pigment epithelium were unresponsive.

Origin of the ERG

It is well established that the ERG is the record of changes taking place in the retina, and we may ask what is the cause of these fluctuations in potential. Essentially they are changes in the potential difference across the retina since they may be best recorded by a pair of electrodes one on the inner face and the other on the scleral face of the retina. We may recall that a neurone may develop a rapid spike which is reflected in a very brief phase of negativity of an electrode placed exactly at the site of this activity. This change is so rapid, however, that it is unlikely that spike activity on the part of the retinal neurones will have much to do with the ERG.

Slow Potentials. Neurones will also, however, develop a much more slowly occurring change of potential; an example of this is the negativity which has been called the generator potential. In other cases we may record an increase in the normal membrane potential—a hyperpolarization—so that the neurone is said to become *positive*; this change is associated with inhibition of activity. We may assume, therefore, that it is this type of change, rather than spike activity, that is at the basis of the ERG and the questions that present themselves are (*a*) What are the actual changes taking place in the retina? and (*b*) Where are they occurring, *i.e.* in what layer or layers? The answers to these questions are not by any means certain in spite of some ingenious studies by Tomita and Motokawa in Japan, Brindley in England and Brown & Wiesel in America. The obvious approach, and the one followed, is to compare the conventionally recorded ERG with that obtained with a fine electrode placed at known depths in the retina.

Records from a Distance. Thus the conventional ERG electrode on the cornea is recording events at a considerable distance from where they take place,

Fig. 76. The orientated cells, indicated by the rectangles, have become negative in relation to their surroundings and thus become what is known as a *sink* for positive current; the electrode at the top of the figure, at some distance from the sink, thus becomes positive, *i.e.* a *source* of positive current which flows into the sink.

and the actual record must be considerably attenuated so that it is at first thought surprising that it is not completely extinguished. It is only because the cells of the retina are all so well orientated that a record is possible. Thus, we may suppose the situation to be that illustrated by Fig. 76, where the rectangles indicate radially orientated retinal cells; they have become active in the sense that a part of them has become negative in relation to other parts and the rest of the retina. This part would be described as a *sink of current* into which positive current would flow, and it may be shown that a distant electrode, *e.g.* one on the cornea, or closer still, in the vitreous, would record a phase of *positivity.** If the position were reversed, *i.e.* if later this cell, or another, became positive, we should expect to record negativity. If different cells showed opposite effects simultaneously we should expect cancellation of effects, so that the magnitude of the changes recorded at a distance might be much smaller than if the electrode were close to the origins of activity. Thus, on causing our electrode to penetrate into the retina we may expect to find larger potential changes; furthermore, when the electrode comes very close to the cells the record changes polarity; the electrode becomes negative when the cell does, and positive when it becomes positive.

Intra-Retinal Recording. At the site of electrical activity, then, we may expect to find a *reversal of the ERG*, or perhaps, if the events take place in different layers, reversal of some components only. This was indeed found by Tomita

FIG. 77. Representative ERG's at three different electrode depths in the cat's retina. Record A made with active electrode in the vitreous humour; B, from close to the retinal surface of Bruch's membrane; and C, from the choroid close to the choroidal surface of Bruch's membrane. Penetration made in the area centralis. Indifferent electrodes on back of head. (Brown and Wiesel, *J. Physiol.*)

0·8 sec

2·0 mV

and by later workers; an example is shown by Fig. 77 from Brown & Wiesel where record A was taken with the active electrode in the vitreous body; record B deep in the retina, and record C after passing right through the retina across Bruch's membrane† into the choroid. We can see how the record in B has

---

* Space will not permit of a detailed explanation of the effects of recording electrical changes taking place at a distance from the electrode; Brazier (1960) gives a good account.
† Brown & Wiesel (1961) have emphasized the real difference between the local ERG, developed at the site of an intra-retinal electrode, and the diffuse ERG which is best re-

became a positive *a*-wave followed by a negative *b*-wave, and a positive *c*-wave. Thus *a*- and *b*- have been reversed but not *c*- which remains positive in both cases. Brown & Wiesel found that the maximum *b*-wave occurred slightly distal to the inner nuclear layer and thus may have been due to activity in the terminal portions of the receptors (rod spherules or cone pedicles). The *a*-wave was definitely independent of the *b*-wave, as Granit and others had shown, and was localized, on the basis of electrode position for maximal response, at the layer of outer segments. By careful comparison of the ERG's obtained with the conventional and intra-retinal recordings, Brown & Wiesel left no doubt that the conventional negative *a*-wave corresponded to the intra-retinal positive *a*-wave, and the *b*- and *c*-waves also corresponded, quantitative differences being due to the difference in method of recording.*

ORIGIN OF *a*-WAVE

Thus we may associate the *a*-wave with, perhaps, the direct effect of light on the retina since it occurs in the outer segments of the receptors. This view is supported by the circumstance that the latency of the *a*-wave is very short, the interval between the light-stimulus and the beginning of this wave being as little as 3·5 milliseconds; furthermore, Potts, Modrell & Kingsbury showed that, in mice with degeneration of the ganglion and bipolar cells caused by feeding them glutamate, the *a*-wave was normal, although the *b*-wave had disappeared. Again, Dowling found that vitamin-A deficient rats, with their outer segments disintegrated, showed no *a*-wave in their ERG. The *b*-wave was present, and was presumably due to some activity transmitted from receptors since the animals were not completely blind. Finally, Bornschein found that in iodoacetate-poisoned retinæ, where the receptors are specifically attacked, loss of function correlated with failure of the *a*-wave.

Intracellular Records. The *b*-wave depends for its occurrence on propagated electrical activity since it is blocked by local anæsthetics, and so it may be the activity in a new group of cells, perhaps horizontal cells, or perhaps in different regions of the receptors, *e.g.* cone pedicles. Evidence on this point has been provided by studies of the effects of inserting electrodes into individual cells of the retina and recording the electrical changes taking place within them. In this way, as with the excentric cells of the invertebrate eye, we are in less uncertainty as to the events taking place in a given cell than if our electrode is outside the cell, in which case the electrical changes may be the effects of several types. Intracellular recordings from the retina have been described by several groups of workers and we shall have occasion to refer to them again when we discuss the mechanism of colour vision;

corded from the vitreous or cornea. This diffuse ERG, being the summated activity of all the local ERG's, will have an effect on the local ERG, in the sense that distant parts of the retina, acting through the vitreous, will modify the potential at the point where the local ERG is being developed and recorded. Thus an intra-retinal *b*-wave can, under appropriate conditions, be positive—when it represents activity at a distance—or negative—when it represents local activity in the immediate neighbourhood of the recording electrode. The term ERG should thus be used for the conventional record whilst *LERG* (*local electroretinogram*) should refer to the record of true local events uncomplicated by distant effects (which are usually not large).

* Brindley (1956) noticed a profound change in the characteristics of the local record obtained when his electrode had passed to a certain depth in the retina; it was as though the electrode had passed through a membrane of very high resistance; he provisionally identified this *R-membrane* with the external limiting membrane. Subsequent workers (Tomita, Murakami & Hashimoto, 1960; Brown & Wiesel, 1961) have left little doubt that it is Bruch's membrane, separating pigment epithelium from choroid, that is responsible.

for our present purpose the study of Brown & Wiesel (1959) on the cat, designed to correlate with their studies on the cat's local ERG, are most germane. They found that both ganglion cells and bipolar cells gave typical spike discharges in response to illumination, exhibiting characteristics essentially similar to those described above for external recordings of ganglion cells. The responses of these cells are therefore unlikely to be directly related to the ERG where the responses are *slow* changes of potential; some cells, when penetrated, gave only slow and maintained potential changes which were usually an increase in the normal membrane potential, *i.e.* they became hyperpolarized (positive in the conventional terminology). Brown & Wiesel are inclined to identify these cells with the origin of the *b*-wave although the actual polarity of the electrical change is not what one would expect. They consider the *c*-wave to be derived from the pigment epithelium cells and for this there is some evidence; thus Noell (1954) found it abolished in rabbits whose pigment epithelium had been selectively destroyed by iodate poisoning. As Brindley (1960) has pointed out, however, the pigment of this epithelium is melanin so that we should expect the action-spectrum (p. 133) for the *c*-wave to be that of melanin whereas it is that of rhodopsin. Presumably, then, the *c*-wave is a secondary event to electrical changes taking place first in the receptors.[*]

Granit's Analysis

Thus at present the exact correlations between electrical events in the individual cells of the retina and pigment epithelium, and the pooled effect seen in the ERG, is far from perfect and in future discussions we must preserve the more empirical analysis of Granit, who on the basis of many experiments concluded that the electrical changes were the algebraic summation of three potentials. Fig. 78 illustrates Granit's scheme based on experiments in which the various components were isolated by selective blocking with anæsthetics and other agents. According to this, there are three components, designated as PI, PII, and PIII in the order of their disappearance under ether anæsthesia. PI is a slowly developing positive component; with strong stimuli, or after light-adaptation, it tends to disappear; it accounts for the secondary rise in positivity, the *c*-wave. PII is likewise positive but is much more rapid in development and is chiefly responsible for the *b*-wave. PIII is the negative component; it comes on rapidly and is responsible for the initial *a*-wave. The *d*-wave, or "off-effect," is considered to represent an interference phenomenon resulting from the rapid swing of the negative PIII component back to the base-line; if this occurs more rapidly than the fall of the PI and PII components, it will clearly be reflected in a wave of positivity, the *d*-wave.

D.C. Component. According to Brown & Wiesel, however, the off-effect, as seen in the cat's ERG, is due to the cessation of what they call the *d.c. component*; thus as soon as the light is switched on there is an immediate positivity superimposed on the other electrical changes and lasting as long as the light stimulus; when the light is switched off the d.c. component vanishes giving a sudden drop of potential on the record with corneal or vitreal electrode (Fig. 77, A) or rise with the intra-retinal electrode, as in Fig. 77, B).

[*] Noell (1958) has correlated changes in the ERG with development of the retina in the newborn. The appearance of the ERG, on the 8th day, coincides with the appearance of miniature receptors with distinguishable inner and outer segments; since ganglion cell discharges in response to light-stimulation are also obtained at this time, the neural pathway is complete. The ERG appears as an *a*-wave. Subsequent development during the 11–18th days is associated with lengthening of the miniature receptors and the emergence of the *b*-wave; by the 18th day the ERG is adult in appearance, although the *b*-wave is not so high.

FIG. 78. Analysis of the ERG. Above: Dark-adapted frog's eye; P III component and OFF-effect small. Below: Light-adapted frog's eye; P III component and OFF-effect large; P I is missing so that the c-wave is absent. The black line indicates the duration of the stimulus (0·2 sec.). (Granit and Riddell, *J. Physiol.*)

E- and I-Retinæ. The results of numerous experiments by different workers have shown that there is a strong correlation between the magnitude of the negative *a*-wave and the magnitude of the "off-effect"; thus in the light-adapted frog's eye the *a*-wave and "off-effect" are both marked (Fig. 78); in the dark-adapted frog's eye, or the cat's eye, the *a*-wave and "off-effect" are small, in fact the latter is just shown as a slight check in the downward trend of positivity. Granit has divided the retinæ studied into two groups, *E*- and *I-retinæ*, according principally to the predominance of the negative PIII component; thus the retinæ of the cat, rat, and guinea pig are all E-retinæ with small PIII components in their electroretinograms; the pigeon and light-adapted frog retinæ belong to the I-type, with pronounced PIII characteristics. Since those retinæ that give the E-type of response contain predominantly rods, whilst the I-type of response is shown either by retinæ with predominantly cones, as with the pigeon or tortoise, or by retinæ with both types of receptor in which rod function is suppressed (light-adapted frog), it is reasonable to assume that the negative PIII component is mainly associated with cone activity. The available evidence suggests that it is connected with *inhibition* of impulses, as opposed to their initiation.

Excitation. The PII component, on the other hand, is closely associated with the passage of impulses along the optic nerve, *i.e.* with excitation; thus when the PII component is blocked by ether anæsthesia, simultaneous records of the electrical changes in the optic nerve show that the action potentials here are likewise blocked. So strong, indeed, is the correlation that the height of the *b*-wave has been used as an index to the intensity of the optic nerve response. Thus in Fig. 79 we have the ERG analogue of a dark-adaptation curve, obtained by plotting the intensity of the light stimulus necessary to evoke a *b*-wave of fixed height against the time of dark-adaptation of a frog's retina. Dark-adaptation causes the sensitivity of the retina to increase; this is reflected in a decrease in the stimulus necessary to evoke the *b*-wave.

Pre-Excitatory Inhibition. Granit referes to the PIII component as a process of "*pre-excitatory inhibition*"; the correlations between the ERG and sensory phenomena of vision (p. 209) indicate that the first effect of stimulation of the light-adapted retina is one of inhibition; it is as though the slate were being wiped clean in preparation for a new picture. The component is probably associated with those single fibres of the optic nerve that show a discharge at

FIG. 79. The ERG analogue of the dark-adaptation curve. The logarithm of the stimulus necessary to evoke a *b*-wave of fixed magnitude is plotted against time in the dark. As the eye adapts, the stimulus necessary becomes smaller (cf. Fig. 56). (Re-drawn from Riggs.)

"Off" (Fig. 73, C). The comparative rarity of this type of fibre in the mammalian retina is probably due to the fact that mainly E-type retinæ have been studied (cat, rat, guinea pig).

The Human ERG

In man the ERG may be measured with a simple wick-electrode in the inner canthus, or by an electrode maintained in position on the cornea with a contact-lens (Karpe). It was first studied independently by Motokawa & Mita in Japan and Adrian in England. In the light-adapted subject the response to a single bright flash was found by Adrian to be diphasic, as in Fig. 80, a negative *a*-wave

FIG. 80. Human ERG's. A. Response to flash of white light in light-adapted eye. Note initial negative deflection, the *a*-wave. B. Scotopic type of response with no *a*-wave. The lower record of each pair indicates time of stimulation. (Adrian, *J. Physiol.*)

FIG. 81. Human ERG's. Responses to red, orange and blue light stimuli showing transition from photopic to scotopic types of response. (The lower record indicates time of stimulation.) (Adrian, *J. Physiol.*)

being followed by a large positive *b*-wave. Presumably this was mainly a cone response. In the dark-adapted state, with a low-intensity flash, the response was monophasic and much slower—the rod response. With different coloured lights the rod and cone types of response could also be separated, a red flash giving a diphasic cone-response, a blue light a rod-response, and orange-red light a mixed response in which the *b*-wave contained two components, presumably due to the different time-courses of the rod and cone PII components (Fig. 81). Thus, with a mixed retina, and with stimulation such as to excite both rods and cones, we may expect to be able to resolve the *b*-wave into a rod- and cone-component, unless one type of receptor completely dominates the record.

Separation of Components. In fact, recent studies on the human ERG indicate an even greater complexity, perhaps due to the activities of different types of cone as well as of rods. Thus Fig. 82 shows the ON-portion of a single response to a flash of light that was repeated at 1/sec. These conditions, namely intermittent illumination at high intensity, appear to be particularly favourable

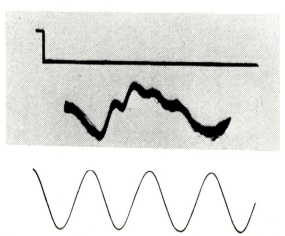

FIG. 82. Initial part of the human ERG when the eye is exposed to a flickering light at a frequency of 1/sec. and an intensity of 250 lux. The curve comprises 10 superimposed records. Uppermost line: light stimulus; Middle: ERG; Bottom: time marking, 50/sec. (Heck & Rendahl, *Acta physiol. scand.*)

for the separation of the different components. As Fig. 82 shows, there are apparently two negative *a*-waves, and four positive peaks, the first resulting from the occurrence of a_2 on the ascending limb of the record. In protanopia, where the red cone mechanism is lacking (p. 193) the third positive peak was missing (Heck & Rendahl). The two negative *a*-waves appear to represent cone and rod activity, according to Armington, Johnson & Riggs. Since the first of these is best elicited with red light whilst the second only after long dark-adaptation, they may be described as "photopic" and "scotopic" components respectively.

GENERAL REFERENCES

ADRIAN, E. D. (1932). *Mechanism of Nervous Action*. Philadelphia.
BRAZIER, M. (1960). *The Electrical Activity of the Nervous System*. 2nd. Ed. London: Pitman.
BRINDLEY, G. S. (1960). *Physiology of the Retina and Visual Pathway*. London: Arnold.
GRANIT, R. (1947). *Sensory Mechanisms of the Retina*. O.U.P. London.
GRANIT, R. (1955). *Receptors and Sensory Perception*. Newhaven: Yale Univ. Press.
HARTLINE, H. (1941–2). The neural mechanisms of vision. Harvey Lectures, Series 37.
RIGGS, L. A. (1958). The human electroretinogram. *Arch. Ophthal.*, **60**, 739–754.

SPECIAL REFERENCES

ADRIAN, E. D. (1945). The electric response of the human eye. *J. Physiol.*, **104**, 84–104.
ARMINGTON, J. C., JOHNSON, E. P., & RIGGS, L. A. (1952). The scotopic A-wave in the electrical response of the human retina. *J. Physiol.*, **118**, 289–298.
BARLOW, H. B., FITZHUGH, R., & KUFFLER, S. W. (1957). Change of organization in the receptive fields of the cat's retina during dark adaptation. *J. Physiol.*, **137**, 338–354.
BORNSCHEIN, H. (1958). Spontan- und Belichtungsaktivität in Einzelfasern der Katze. *Z. Biol.*, **110**, 210–222; 223–231.
BRINDLEY, G. S. (1956). The passive electrical properties of the frog's retina, choroid and sclera for radial fields and currents. *J. Physiol.*, **134**, 339–352.
BROWN, K. T., & WIESEL, T. N. (1958). Intraretinal recording in the unopened cat eye. *Amer. J. Ophthal.*, **46**, Pt. 2, 91–98.
BROWN, K. T., & WIESEL, T. N. (1959). Intraretinal recording with micropipette electrodes in the intact cat eye. *J. Physiol.*, **149**, 537–562.
BROWN, K. T., & WIESEL, T. N. (1961). Analysis of the intraretinal electroretinogram in the intact cat eye. *J. Physiol.*, **158**, 229–256.
BROWN, K. T., & WIESEL, T. N. (1961). Localization of origins of electroretinogram components by intraretinal recording in the intact cat eye. *J. Physiol.*, **158**, 257–280.
DOWLING, J. E. (1960). Night blindness, dark adaptation and the electroretinogram. *Amer. J. Ophthal.*, **50**, 875–889.
FUORTES, M. G. F. (1959). Initiation of impulses in visual cells of *Limulus*. *J. Physiol.*, **148**, 14–28.
GRANIT, R. (1933). The components of the retinal action potential in mammals and their relation to the discharge in the optic nerve. *J. Physiol.*, **77**, 207–240.
GRANIT, R., & RIDDELL, H. A. (1934). The electrical responses of light- and dark-adapted frog's eyes to rhythmic and continuous stimuli. *J. Physiol.*, **81**, 1–28.
GRÜSSER, O. J., & RABELO, C. (1958). Reaktioner retinaler Neurone nach Lichtblitzen. *Pflüg. Arch.*, **265**, 501–525.
HARTLINE, H. K., WAGNER, H. G., & MacNICHOL, E. F. (1952). The peripheral origin of nervous activity in the visual system. *Cold Spr. Harb. Symp. Quant. Biol.*, **17**, 125–141.
HARTLINE, H. K., WAGNER, H. G., & RATLIFF, F. (1956). Inhibition in the eye of *Limulus*. *J. gen. Physiol.*, **39**, 651–673.
HECK, J., & RENDAHL, I. (1957). Components of the human electroretinogram. *Acta physiol. scand.*, **39**, 167–175.

KARPE, G. (1945). The basis of clinical electroretinography. *Acta ophthal. Kbh.*, Suppl. **24**, pp. 118.

KUFFLER, S. W. (1953). Discharge patterns and functional organization of mammalian retina. *J. Neurophysiol.*, **16**, 37–68.

KÜHNE, W., & STEINER, J. (1880). Uber das electromotorische Verhalten der Netzhaut. *Unt. physiol. Inst. Univ., Heidelberg*, **3**, 327–377.

KÜHNE, W., & STEINER, J. (1881). Uber electrische Vorgänge im Sehorgane, *loc. cit.*, **4**, 64–168.

MILLER, W. H. (1957). Morphology of the ommatidia of the compound eye of *Limulus*. *J. biophys. biochem. Cytol.*, **3**, 421–428.

MOTOKAWA, K., YAMOSHITA, E., & OGAWA, T. (1961). Slow potentials and spike activity of retina. *J. Neurophysiol.*, **24**, 101–110.

MOTOKAWA, J., & MITA, T. Uber eine einfachere Untersuchungsmethode und Eigenschaften der Aktionsströme der Netzhaut des Menschen. *Tohoku J. Exp. Med.*, 1942, **42**, 114–133.

NOELL, W. K. (1954). The origin of the electroretinogram. *Amer. J. Ophthal.*, **38**, 78–90.

NOELL, W. K. (1958). Differentiation, metabolic organization and viability of the visual cell. *Arch. Ophthal.*, **60**, 702–733.

POTTS, A. M., MODRELL, R. W., & KINGSBURY, C. (1960). Permanent fractionation of the electroretinogram by sodium glutamate. *Amer. J. Ophthal.*, **50**, 900–907.

RUSHTON, W. A. H. (1949). The structure responsible for action potential spikes in the cat's retina. *Nature*, **164**, 743–744.

RUSHTON, W. A. H. (1959). A theoretical treatment of Fuortes's observations upon eccentric cell activity in *Limulus*. *J. Physiol.*, **148**, 29–38.

THOMSON, L. A. C. (1953). The localization of function in the rabbit retina. *J. Physiol.*, **119**, 191–209.

TOMITA, T. (1950). Relation between the localization of micro-pipette in the retina and the shape of the intraretinal action potential. *Jap. J. Physiol.*, **1**, 110–117.

TOMITA, T., MURAKAMI, M., & HASHIMOTO, Y. (1960). On the R membrane in the frog's eye: Its localization and relation to the retinal action potential. *J. gen. Physiol.*, **43**, Suppl. 81–94.

PART 5

PHOTOCHEMICAL ASPECTS OF VISION

THE VISUAL PROCESS

The receptors that mediate vision at night are the rods which, as mentioned earlier, contain a pigment—*visual purple* or *rhodopsin*—responsible for the absorption of light in the primary photochemical event leading to sensation. According to the photochemist, then, the visual process consists of the absorption of light by a specialized molecule, visual purple or rhodopsin. The absorption of light provides the rhodopsin molecule with a supply of extra energy and it is said, in this state, to be "activated". In this activated state it is highly unstable and so it will change to a new form, *i.e.* the molecule will undergo some form of chemical change by virtue of this absorption of energy. The effects of this change will be to cause an "excited" condition of the rod as a whole and it will be this excited condition that will ultimately lead to the sensation of light.

Photochemical and Thermal Changes

As we shall see, the effects of light-absorption on the rhodopsin molecule are complex because the new molecule formed is not stable but immediately undergoes a succession of changes, which are called *thermal reactions* to distinguish them from the primary *photochemical* change. From an economical point of view we may expect the photochemical and other changes taking place in the retina to be at least partly reversible, otherwise enormous quantities of rhodopsin would have to be synthesized continuously to keep pace with the material destroyed by light.

Regeneration. In fact, the early investigators who observed the bleaching of visual purple in the retina also observed that it would regenerate if the intact retina was allowed to remain in the dark. Subsequent studies on solutions of rhodopsin have indeed shown that, provided the necessary enzymes are present, the photochemical and subsequent chemical changes are, indeed, largely reversible. Tentatively, then, the visual process may be represented schematically as follows:

Rhodopsin ⇌ Activated State ⇌ Bleached Products

As we shall see, the "bleached products" are the results of a highly complex series of changes, so that the rhodopsin molecule alters its "colour", *i.e.* its light-absorbing properties, from the original magenta through orange to yellow and ultimately to white, when it has become vitamin A and a protein, *opsin*. In general, when the retina has been kept away from light for some time—*i.e.* when it has been completely dark-adapted—we may expect to find only rhodopsin in the rods, whilst when the retina is being exposed to light we may expect to find a mixture of rhodopsin with many of its "bleached products", the relative amounts of each product being determined by the intensity of light and the duration of exposure.

ULTRA-STRUCTURE OF THE RECEPTORS

Let us consider the structure of the rod and cone in more detail, as revealed by the electron-microscope. As Fig. 50, p. 85, showed, the rod may be divided into outer and inner segments; since rhodopsin has been shown to be confined to the *outer segment*, the structure of this region is of special interest. Fig. 83, Plate IV, shows that this part consists essentially of a pile of flattened sacs which are probably to be regarded as infoldings of the cell membrane. The structure of the inner segment is quite different (Fig. 84, Plate IV), and it contains large mitochondria tightly packed together to give what the light-microscopists called the *ellipsoid*. This part of the rod is thus presumably concerned with the energy-requiring metabolic events, whilst we may look upon the outer segments as specialized regions for the absorption of light. Thus, there is optical evidence, based on the behaviour of polarized light (Denton) suggesting that the molecules of rhodopsin are spread on to the surfaces of the sacs, the chromophore-groups of the molecule (p. 133) lying in the plane of the discs, *i.e.* at right-angles to the incident light, an arrangement that provides for much more efficient absorption than if the molecules were scattered at random. The outer segment is connected to the inner segment by a cilium (Fig. 84) which suggests that the rod has developed from a primitive ciliated photosensitive cell. In essence, the structure of the cone is not greatly different from that of the rod (Fig. 84).

EXTRACTION AND CHARACTERIZATION OF PHOTOPIGMENT

As mentioned earlier, Kühne observed that visual purple in the intact retina went first yellow and then white when exposed to light; on allowing the eye to remain in the dark the changes were reversed. The problem of the photochemist is to extract from the retina the visual purple, and to elucidate its structural chemistry and the changes it undergoes during exposure to light. Extraction of the pigment is achieved by the use of a "solubilizing agent" such as digitonin or bile salts; these form complexes with the visual purple that permit it to form a homogeneous solution. The amount of pigments obtainable from a single retina is so small that special methods for characterizing them, and the changes they undergo, must be employed; of these the study of absorption spectra has been easily the most profitable.

Density Spectra. A solution of a pigment is coloured because the pigment molecules absorb certain wavelengths more strongly than others, so that white light, after transmission through the solution, has had some of its wavelengths selectively removed. Thus chlorophyll solutions are green because its molecules selectively remove red and blue wavelengths, and hence allow the green and yellow parts of the spectrum to pass through. Visual purple is magenta coloured because its molecules selectively absorb the middle region of the spectrum—blues and greens—allowing a mixture of red and violet lights to pass through with relatively little absorption. The selective absorption of visual purple solutions can be measured by passing a beam of light, whose wavelength can be varied throughout the spectrum at will, through the solution and measuring, with a suitable photocell, the amount of light-energy transmitted. This may be compared with that transmitted through water alone, and the difference gives the light-energy absorbed. The results may be plotted as a density spectrum, as in

PLATE IV

FIG. 83. Electron-micrograph of thin section of outer segment of retinal rod. Osmium fixation. × 90,000. (Courtesy F. S. Sjöstrand.)

[To face p. 130.

Fig. 84. A. Cone showing part of the outer (COS) and inner (CIS) segments and the connecting cilium (*ccc*). Compare the difference in size and shape of this connecting cilium with that of the rod (B). Some filaments of the cilium are indicated (*cf*) and the continuation of the cilium into the outer segment is shown. The outer segment shows a proximal portion in which the structure is less orientated (*ucs*). × 32,000. B. Rod, showing part of the outer (ROS) and inner (RIS) segment and connecting cilium (*rcc*) with two basal bodies (*bb*). × 40,000. *cs*, cone sac; *sm*, surface membrane; *mi*, mitochondria; *rs*, rod sac; *rcc*, rod connecting cilium. (de Robertis & Lasansky, *J. biophys. biochem. Cytol.*)

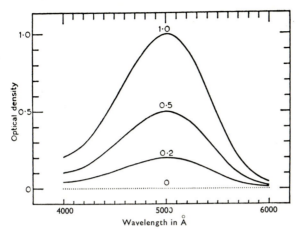

FIG. 85. Density spectra of different concentrations of visual purple. Note that as the concentration is reduced the curve becomes flatter although the wavelength of maximum absorption remains the same. (Dartnall, *The Visual Pigments.*)

Fig. 85, where the optical density of the solution is plotted against wavelength It will be seen that the spectrum has a maximum at about 5000 Å in the blue-green. It is this *wavelength of maximal absorption*, indicated by λ_{max}, that we may use to characterize a given pigment extracted from the retina.

Optical Density. If the absorption of light obeys Beer's Law, it is determined by the length of the path through which the light travels, and the concentration of pigment, in accordance with the equation:

$$\log_e I_{\text{Inc}}/I_{\text{Trans}} = d_\lambda \times c \times x$$

where I_{Inc} and I_{Trans} are the intensities of the incident and transmitted beams respectively, c is the concentration, x the path-length, and d_λ is the *extinction coefficient* for this particular wavelength. This extinction coefficient is the measure of the tendency for the molecules to absorb light of a given wavelength, so that by plotting d_λ against wavelength the *extinction spectrum* so obtained is a measure of the absorption of the different wavelengths. If logarithms to base 10 are used in the above equation, and the concentration is expressed in moles per litre, the *optical density*, D_λ, of a solution is defined as:

$$D_\lambda = \log_{10} I_{\text{Inc}}/I_{\text{Trans}} = \epsilon_\lambda \times c \times x$$

where ϵ_λ is the *molar extinction coefficient*. For a given solution the optical density may be used as the measure of absorption of a given wavelength, and the curve obtained by plotting optical density against wavelength is called a *density spectrum** (Fig. 85). It will be clear from the above equations that the extinction coefficients will be independent of concentration of pigment so that extinction spectra will also be independent of this variable; the optical density, on the other hand, increases with increasing concentration, and the shape of the density spectrum will, indeed, vary according to the concentration of the pigment in the solution being studied. Where the concentration of absorbing material is not directly determined, as in studies on the intact retina, then the shape of the density spectrum gives a clue to the actual concentration present. We may note, finally, that if the density for any

---

* The *absorption spectrum* is given by plotting the percentage of light absorbed against wavelength. Terminology is loose in this respect, however, so that absorption spectrum and density spectrum are terms used interchangeably.

given wavelength is expressed as a percentage of the maximum density (in the case of rhodopsin 5000 Å) then the density spectrum does become independent of concentration, and it may be used to characterize the pigment.

Difference Spectra. It usually happens that visual pigment solutions are contaminated by light-absorbing impurities; if these are unaffected by light, in the sense that they retain their light-absorbing qualities unchanged after exposure, then the true absorption spectrum of the visual pigment may usually be deduced from the *difference spectrum*, given by measuring the absorption spectrum of the solution before and after bleaching with white light; thus, before the bleaching, the absorption will be due to visual pigment plus impurities; after bleaching it will be due to impurities alone if the visual pigment has become colourless. In many cases, of course, the visual pigment does not become colourless, but allowance can usually be made for this residual absorption.

Purity. Retinal extracts may contain mixtures of visual pigments, in which case it becomes important to decide when any extract is homogeneous or not. Dartnall has developed a technique of partial bleaching with selectively chosen wavelengths that permits of an unequivocal demonstration whether or not the preparation contains more than one visual pigment.

DENSITY SPECTRUM AND SCOTOPIC SENSITIVITY

Human Scotopic Sensitivity. The density spectrum of the pigment extracted from the rods of the dark-adapted retina may be used to determine whether this pigment is, indeed, responsible for night vision, since the efficiency of any wavelength in evoking a sensation of light must be closely related to the efficiency with which it is absorbed by the rods. Clearly, if only one per cent of orange light falling on the retina were absorbed, whilst 90 per cent of the blue light were absorbed, we should have to use ninety times as much orange light-energy to evoke the sensation of light. In Fig. 86 two things have been plotted; the smooth curve shows the absorption spectrum of visual purple extracted from a dark-

FIG. 86. Comparison of human retinal scotopic sensitivity at different wave-lengths, as determined by Crawford, with the absorption spectrum of human visual purple. The curve represents the absorption spectrum whilst the plotted points represent human scotopic sensitivity. (Crescitelli & Dartnall, *Nature*.)

adapted human eye, whilst the plotted points are the sensitivities of the dark-adapted human eye to the different wavelengths, the so-called action spectrum of the human eye. As indicated earlier, the dark-adapted eye is achromatic at light intensities in the region of the threshold; the different wavelengths do not evoke the sensation of colour but simply of light, and the experiment consisted of measuring the thresholds for the different wavelengths; the reciprocals of these, measured in quanta, represent the visual efficiencies of the wavelengths. The agreement between the two measurements is striking.*

Sensitivity in Animals. In animals, also, the scotopic sensitivity of the eye can be measured; for example, by determining the intensities of different wavelengths required to evoke a *b*-wave of fixed magnitude in the electroretinogram, or to evoke a discharge of fixed frequency in a single optic nerve fibre. The reciprocals of these values give the sensitivities of the retina at the different wavelengths and, when plotted against wavelength, give, usually, the characteristic "rhodopsin-type" of curve with a maximum in the region of 5000 Å. If the light-adapted retina is employed, on the other hand, there is a characteristic shift in the maximum towards, the longer wavelengths to give a maximum in the yellow-green at 5600 Å. This is the *Purkinje shift* and represents the change in spectral sensitivity of the eye due to passing from rod to cone vision. Under these conditions, of course, the eye appreciates the colours of the stimuli.

THE NATURE OF RHODOPSIN

The rhodopsin isolated from the retina is a chromoprotein with, according to Hubbard, a molecular weight of about 40,000; each molecule has one light-absorbing chromophore group on it. The nature of this chromophore group, responsible for the colour of the molecule and thus of its characteristic absorption, and the nature of its linkage to the protein moiety, are the keys to the photochemistry of vision.

Changes on Exposure to Light

The early workers on visual pigments observed that, after exposure to light, rhodopsin produced a "visual yellow" which was shown by Lythgoe to result from two steps, a substance *transient orange* being first produced which was then converted in the dark to *indicator yellow*, a substance that changed colour with pH. Wald later showed that the final products of bleaching were *retinene*, which was yellow, and *vitamin A* into which retinene was converted if the retina was exposed to light for long enough to prevent the retinene from being converted back to rhodopsin. Vitamin A is an alcohol and it was shown by Morton that retinene was vitamin A aldehyde. Thus retinene must be regarded as the chromophore group of rhodopsin; when attached to the protein moiety—*opsin*—the whole has a magenta colour, due to some interaction between the two molecules. It was originally considered that the action of light was to split off retinene from opsin, but more recent studies from several laboratories have left us with the picture of events illustrated schematically by Fig. 87, based on experiments in

---

* Because we are concerned with the effectivity of the light as it actually reaches the retina we must obviously make allowance for the absorption by the transparent media; thus the lens absorbs blue light preferentially and so reduces its apparent effectivity. Crawford's figures for spectral sensitivity have been corrected for the effects of absorption, scattering, etc.

FIG. 87. Scheme showing the products that may be formed when visual purple is bleached. (Dartnall, *The Visual Pigments*.)

which chemical changes, subsequent to the initial effect of light, could be arrested by cooling the rhodopsin solution to a solid; by controlled warming, the subsequent steps could be identified by the changes in absorption spectrum of the solution. *Lumirhodopsin* is the first product which at − 15°C is converted in the dark to *metarhodopsin*, Lythgoe's transient orange; at room temperature metarhodopsin is rapidly converted to indicator yellow, although half is converted back to a new pigment, *isorhodopsin*, very similar to rhodopsin. Up to this point the chemical linkage between retinene and opsin has remained unbroken, but the acid form of indicator yellow is converted to retinene and opsin, which may then form vitamin A and opsin.

Regeneration of Rhodopsin

In the retina the products of bleaching—retinene and vitamin A—are reconverted to rhodopsin in the dark, and it has been generally considered that this regeneration is the basis for dark-adaptation (p. 145). In isolated systems the regeneration was not nearly so efficient, and the main cause for this turned out to be the necessity for a special isomer of retinene for the combination with opsin (Hubbard & Wald).

Cis (a) FIG. 88. Trans (b)

Retinene Isomers. Retinene and vitamin A contain five double-bonds joining C-atoms, and the presence of these gives the possibility of numerous *cis-trans* isomers, due to the fact that rotation about a double bond is not possible, so that a molecule illustrated by Fig. 88a is different from that illustrated by Fig. 88b.* Of the various possible isomers obtained by rotating the molecule about the different double bonds Wald found two that were capable of condensing with opsin to give photosensitive pigments. One, neo-b retinene or 11-*cis* retinene (Fig. 89), when incubated with opsin gave rhodopsin, whilst the other, isoretinene-a or 9-*cis* retinene (Fig. 89) gave a photosensitive pigment, *iso-rhodopsin*, with λ_{max} of 4870 Å. The reason why reversal of the changes undergone by bleaching is not always possible is because the retinene that splits off from rhodopsin has the *all-trans* form, which is not active for resynthesis; thus retinene in the rhodopsin molecule is in the 11-*cis* of neo-b form, but when split off is in the all-*trans* form. In order to be of further use the all-*trans* must be isomerized, a process that can take place in the retina in the presence of an enzyme, *retinene isomerase*, although mere exposure to light also causes isomerization.

While the retina is being exposed to light, therefore, and for some time after, the rods will contain a mixture of substances which will presumably include isorhodopsin, a stable photosensitive pigment obtained by condensing 9-*cis* retinene with opsin, the 9-*cis* retinene becoming available by the isomerization of all-*trans* retinene liberated from rhodopsin. Recent studies of the so-called flash-photolysis of rhodopsin, in which a solution of rhodopsin is exposed to short very bright flashes of light, confirm that isorhodopsin is, indeed, present (Bridges).

The Primary Change. The fact that only two isomers, both with a similar configuration, will condense with opsin, suggests that there are certain groupings in the opsin molecule into which the retinene must fit (Dartnall, 1957) and this view has been developed by Hubbard & Kropf to account for some of the

---

* By rotating the two parts of a molecule about any of the bonds, single or double, we can clearly form new compounds, but because in the molecule as formed this rotation can occur naturally it will occur so frequently that it will be impossible to separate one isomer from the other and the existing compound can be said to have properties intermediate between the one form and the other. By contrast, once the double-bond has been formed, rotation does not occur about it, so that if some molecules, during the synthesis of the compound, have the halves of the molecule in the *cis*-position, and others in the *trans*-, then the compound behaves, indeed, as a mixture, the two components being separable. To change the configuration, *isomerization*, the double-bond must first be broken down and then reformed.

FIG. 89. Shapes of retinene isomers. The *all-trans* isomer is straight; a *cis*-linkage introduces a bend into the molecule. In addition, the 11-*cis* linkage en-counters steric hindrance and therefore twists the molecule out of the plane in a manner not shown in the diagram. (Hubbard & Kropf, *Ann. N.Y. Acad. Sci.*)

events taking place on exposing rhodopsin to light; their scheme, which is almost certainly too simple (Dartnall, 1962), is illustrated by Fig. 90. According to this, the neo-b-retinene, because of its configuration, fits snugly into a specialized part of the much larger opsin molecule. The absorption of a quantum of light causes the isomerization of the neo-b-retinene, which forces it out of its "nest", although

FIG. 90. Hypothetical scheme showing the effect of light on visual pigments. The 11-*cis* (neo-b) chromophore fits the chromophoric site on opsin. Light isomerizes the chromophore to the *all-trans* configuration, thereby disrupting this fit and yielding the all-trans lumi- and metapigments. Visual excitation is probably triggered in the course of these transformations. (Hubbard & Kropf, *Ann. N.Y. Acad. Sci.*)

its attachment to the protein by chemical bond* is still firm. This is the condition of lumirhodopsin, which is so unstable that it must be kept at $-73°C$; the next stage is a change in the opsin molecule whereby the "nest" opens out to expose certain reactive groupings such as SH-groups. This is thought to correspond to the meta-rhodopsin, or transient orange, stage. Finally the chemical link between retinene and opsin is broken. Since there is no doubt from the work of Morton and his colleagues that meta-rhodopsin does not break down directly, but is first converted to indicator yellow in which the link between retinene and opsin is unbroken, it is clear that Fig. 90 is too simple a view, but it is of value in indicating how, perhaps, visual excitation may occur, namely first of all by the change of shape of the retinene moiety (isomerization), followed by a change in the opsin; according to the diagram, it is the second change that leads to excitation because of its more fundamental character, the mere isomerization of the attached retinene probably being insufficient to exert much influence on the rod as a whole.

COMPARATIVE PHYSIOLOGY OF THE PIGMENTS

Rhodopsin and Porphyropsin

Köttgen & Abelsdorff (1896) observed that the visual purples extracted from mammals, birds and amphibians were different from those extracted from various fresh-water fishes; the former had the usual maximal absorption near 5000 Å whilst the fish pigments had a maximal absorption near 5400, and thus appeared more violet. Wald showed that the retinæ of freshwater fishes gave retinene and vitamin A on bleaching, but it became evident that these were different and have now been called retinene$_2$ and vitamin A$_2$, differing by the presence of a double bond in the beta-ionone ring from what have now been called retinene$_1$ and vitamin A$_1$ of mammals and amphibians. Wald called the pigments obtained from the fish retinæ *porphyropsins* to distinguish them from the rhodopsins of λmax 5000 approx. Subsequent studies showed that marine fish had the rhodopsin type of pigment based on retinene$_1$ whilst euryhaline fishes, spending part of their time in freshwater and part in sea water, gave extracts of intermediate absorption characteristics which were assumed to contain mixtures of rhodopsin and porphyropsin.

Multiplicity of Pigments

Wald's statement that there were only two scotopic types of pigment, rhodopsin and porphyropsin, has been shown, mainly by Dartnall's work, to be incorrect. It is true that all the known pigments are based on only two retinenes, 1 and 2, but presumably because of the widely differing opsins, a very wide range of pigments with characteristic λmax ranging from 5630 Å in the yellow to 4300 Å in the violet has now been demonstrated; in general those with λmax in the long wavelength region—so-called porphyropsins—are based on retinene$_2$, but there is considerable overlap, so that the carp pigment based on retinene$_2$ has a λmax of 5230 Å, whilst the gecko pigment, based on retinene$_1$ has a λmax of 5240 Å. Furthermore, some retinæ gave extracts containing at least two photosensitive pigments of the scotopic type. Even the typical rhodopsin, moreover, differs significantly according to the species of retina from which it is extracted; thus cattle rhodopsin has a λmax of 4990 Å, human 4970 Å, squirrel and frog 5020 Å.

* We owe to the studies of Morton and Collins (see, for example, Collins, 1953) the establishment of the nature of the chemical link; it is of the Schiff-base type between the aldehyde-group of retinene and an amino-group of the protein:

$$C_{19}H_{27}CHO + NH_2.Opsin \longrightarrow C_{19}H_{27}.\overset{\overset{\textstyle H}{\textstyle |}}{C}.N.Opsin$$

Adaptation to Environment. The significance of the wide variations in absorption characteristics of the scotopic visual pigments, found in fish especially, is probably to be sought in the requirements of the animal's habitat. Thus Denton & Warren and Munz independently showed that deep-sea fishes, such as the conger eel, had golden coloured pigments that were apparently adapted for the reception of the predominantly blue light of their habitat, and subsequent study has indeed shown that the λ_{max} of bathypelagic fishes range between 4780 Å and 4900 Å, and are based on retinene$_1$. As Munz has suggested, since some of these deep-sea fish have light-emitting organs, it is probable that their pigments are adapted to correspond with the λ_{max} for *emission* of these organs.[*]

Temporal Variations. There seems no doubt, moreover, that the pigment composition of a retina is not an invariable characteristic; for example, immature (yellow) eels have a mixture of pigments based on retinene$_1$ and retinene$_2$, whereas the adult (silver) eel has only the pigment based on retinene$_1$. Again Dartnall, Landall & Munz found that, in a given population of rudd, the proportions of the two retinal pigments based on retinenes 1 and 2 varied with time of the year, and this was due to the variations in the length of the days; in winter the dominant pigment was that with λ_{max} 5430 based on retinene$_2$, whilst in summer it was that with λ_{max} 5100 based on retinene$_1$. By artificially varying the environmental illumination in an aquarium the proportions of the pigments could be varied.

Retinene and Opsin Variations. In general, we can expect two ways of varying the character of visual pigment; first with a given retinene we may vary the opsin

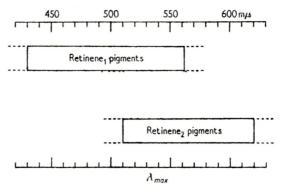

FIG. 91. Illustrating the range of λ_{max} of pigments based on retinene$_1$ and retinene$_2$ respectively. Retinene$_2$ pigments absorb more strongly in the long wavelengths than retinene$_1$ pigments, but there is obviously considerable overlap. (After Dartnall, in *The Eye.*)

part of the molecule; with retinene$_1$ this gives quite a wide range of possibilities permitting pigments that enable the honey-bee, for example, to make full use of ultra-violet light (λ_{max} 4400–4500); the deep-sea fish to have golden retinæ with λ_{max} in the region of 4800 Å; mammals to have pigments with λ_{max} around 5000 and so on up to the chicken's pigment, iodopsin, with λ_{max} on the long-wavelength side in the region of 5600 Å. Another series of pigments may be obtained by varying the opsins attached to retinene$_2$. Fig. 91 shows there is considerable overlap, although retinene$_2$ pigments are clearly those of choice for the longer wave-

* Munz has established some very clear correlations between the spectral quality of the light available in different habitats and the λ_{max} of the predominant visual pigment. Thus in clear oceanic waters the λ_{max} of transmitted light at 200 metres is 4750 Å and this corresponds to that of the absorption maxima of bathypelagic fishes; closer to the surface the λ_{max} for transmission is about 4850–4950 Å corresponding to the λ_{max} of the visual pigments of surface pelagic fishes. With rocky coasts the transmitted light is different from that in the turbid waters near sandy beaches, and there is a corresponding difference in the visual pigments (Munz, 1958).

lengths. If we accept that the pigment or pigments present in the retina are determined by the needs of the species, the question simply resolves itself as to why, in the region of overlap, some pigments are based on retinene$_1$ and some on retinene$_2$; and this presumably depends on non-visual factors such as availability of the vitamin or phylogenetic history. Where abrupt changes in visual conditions occur, such as in the migration of eels or salmon, or in the daylight adaptation of the rudd, a mixture of pigments based on retinene$_1$ and retinene$_2$ permits a relatively rapid transition from the predominance of one type to another, whereas the genetically determined transformations, as, for example, the change taking place when a species emerges capable of living at a great depth, are presumably carried out by a modification of the opsin part of the molecule (Dartnall, 1962).

PHOTOPIC PIGMENTS

Iodopsin. The pigments we have discussed so far are the scotopic ones concerned presumably with the colourless vision of the rods and, where tested, corresponding in their absorption characteristics with the spectral sensitivities of the dark-adapted eyes. What of the cone-pigments?* Wald in 1937 extracted from the chicken retina, containing mostly cones, a pigment with λ_{max} 5620 corresponding to the wavelength of maximal sensitivity to light of high intensity as revealed by the photopic sensitivity curve and the Purkinje shift (Figs. 118, 120, pp. 180 and 181). It is based on retinene$_1$ and undergoes the same cycle of changes undergone by rhodopsin and thus differs from the latter in the opsin part of the molecule; by condensing retinene$_2$ with the chicken opsin Wald, Brown & Smith obtained a new pigment which they called *cyanopsin* with λ_{max} of 6200 Å; this has so far not been extracted from any retina, but it is interesting that the tench and tortoise have maximal photopic sensitivities at 6200 Å.

GENERAL REFERENCES

DARTNALL, H. J. A. (1957). *The Visual Pigments.* London: Methuen.
DARTNALL, H. J. A. (1962). The photobiology of visual processes. In *The Eye.* Ed. Davson. Chapters 17–20. London: Academic Press.
DE ROBERTIS, E., & LASANSKY, A. (1961). Ultrastructure and chemical organization of photoreceptors. In *The Structure of the Eye.* Ed. Smelser. pp. 29–49. New York: Academic Press.
GRANIT, R. (1947). *Sensory Mechanisms of the Retina.* London: O.U.P.
WALD, G. (1956). The biochemistry of visual excitation. In *Enzymes.* New York: Academic Press. pp. 355–367.
WALD, G. (1960). The distribution and evolution of visual systems. In *Comparative Biochemistry.* Vol. I New York: Academic Press.
WALSH, J. W. T. (1953). *Photometry.* 2nd. Ed. London: Constable.
WOLKEN, J. J. (1961). A structural model for a retinal rod. In *The Structure of the Eye.* Ed. Smelser. pp. 173–192. New York: Academic Press.

SPECIAL REFERENCES

BRIDGES, C. D. B. (1961). Studies on the flash photolysis of visual pigments. *Biochem. J.,* **79**, 128–134.
COLLINS, F. D. (1953). Rhodopsin and indicator yellow. *Nature,* **171**, 469–471.
CRAWFORD, B. H. (1949). The scotopic visibility function. *Proc. Phys. Soc. Lond.,* B, **62**, 321–334.

* It is unsound to speak of a cone-pigment as something contrasted with a rod-pigment since the squirrel, with a pure cone retina, has a typical rhodopsin as its photopigment (Dartnall, 1960).

DARTNALL, H. J. A. (1960). Visual pigment from a pure cone retina. *Nature*, **188**, 475–479.

DARTNALL, H. J. A., LANDER, M. R., & MUNZ, F. W. (1961). Periodic changes in the visual pigment of a fish. In *Progress in Photobiology*, pp. 203–213. Amsterdam, Elsevier.

DENTON, E. J. (1954). On the orientation of molecules in the visual rods of *Salamandra maculosa*. *J. Physiol.*, **124**, 17 P.

DENTON, E. J., & WARREN, F. J. (1956). Visual pigments of deep sea fish. *Nature*, **178**, 1059.

DE ROBERTIS, E., & LASANSKY, A. (1958). Submicroscopic organization of retinal cones of the rabbit. *J. biophys. biochem. Cytol.*, **4**, 743–746.

HUBBARD, R. (1954). The molecular weight of rhodopsin and the nature of the rhodopsin-digitonin complex. *J. gen. Physiol.*, **37**, 373–379.

HUBBARD, R., BROWN, P. K., & KROPF, A. (1959). Action of light on visual pigments. *Nature*, **183**, 442–450.

HUBBARD, R., & KROPF, A. (1959). Molecular aspects of visual excitation. *Ann. N.Y. Acad. Sci.*, **81**, 388–398.

HUBBARD, R., & WALD, G. (1952). Cis-trans isomers of vitamin A and retinene in the rhodopsin system. *J. gen. Physiol.*, **36**, 269–315.

KÖTTGEN, E., & ABELSDORFF, G. (1896). Absorption und Zersetzung des Sehpurpurs bei den Wirbeltieren. *Z. Psychol. Physiol. Sinnesorg.*, **12**, 161–184.

LYTHGOE, R. J. (1937). Absorption spectra of visual purple and visual yellow. *J. Physiol.*, **89**, 331–358.

LYTHGOE, R. J., & QUILLIAM, J. P. (1938). The relation of transient orange to visual purple and indicator yellow. *J. Physiol.*, **94**, 399–410.

MUNZ, F. W. (1958). Photosensitive pigments from the retinæ of certain deep-sea fishes. *J. Physiol.* **140**, 220–235.

MUNZ, F. W. (1958). The photosensitive retinal pigments of fishes from relatively turbid coastal waters. *J. gen. Physiol.*, **42**, 445–459.

SJÖSTRAND, F. S. (1953). The ultrastructure of the outer segments of rods and cones of the eye as revealed by electron microscopy. *J. cell. comp. Physiol.*, **42**, 45–70.

WALD, G. (1935). Carotenoids and the visual cycle. *J. gen. Physiol.*, **19**, 351–371.

WALD, G. (1939). The porphyropsin visual system. *J. gen. Physiol.*, **22**, 775–794.

WALD, G., BROWN, P. K., & SMITH, P. H. (1955). Iodopsin. *J. gen. Physiol.*, **38**, 623–681.

WALD, G., DURELL, J., & ST. GEORGE, R. C. C. (1950). The light reaction in the bleaching of rhodopsin. *Science*, **111**, 179–181.

DARK-ADAPTATION AND THE MINIMUM STIMULUS FOR VISION

THE DARK-ADAPTATION CURVE

WE have seen that, in the dark, the sensitivity of the human eye to light increases until a maximum is reached after about 30 minutes; this gives the dark-adaptation curve showing the progressive fall in threshold. We have already concluded that the curve represents the course of recovery of function of the rods. This curve, however, is not smooth, but shows a "kink" so that adaptation consists in an initial rapid phase of recovery of sensitivity, which is finished in about 5–10 minutes, and a slower phase.

Cone and Rod Portions. The first rapid phase has been shown, by many experiments, to represent the increase in sensitivity of the cones in the dark, so

FIG. 92. Dark-adaptation curves with centrally fixated fields subtending larger and larger angles at the eye. With the larger fields peripheral vision comes into play giving the characteristic break in the curve. (Hecht, Haig & Wald, *J. gen. Physiol.*)

that the threshold during the first few minutes in the dark is determined by the cones, the thresholds of the rods still being higher than those of the cones. Numerous lines of evidence support this conclusion. For example, if the area of the light-stimulus used for measuring the threshold is small, and is concentrated on the fovea, the curve of dark-adaptation consists only of the initial part. As the size of the stimulus is increased, so that overlap on to the parafovea, containing rods, occurs, the dark-adaptation curve shows the typical kink with cone and rod portions (Fig. 92). Again, if coloured stimuli are used to test the threshold, during the early portion of the curve the subject appreciates the colour of the threshold stimulus, whilst at the later stages the light is said to be white. Yet again, by varying the state of light-adaptation of the subject before he is placed in the dark, the type of curve may be changed. After a period of weak light-adaptation the cones are nearly at their maximum sensitivity, so that the threshold on going into the dark is very soon determined by the rods; hence the kink comes early or not at all (Fig. 93). If the wavelength of the adapting light is varied, the relative extents to which the thresholds of the rods and cones are raised will be different, so that on placing the subject in the dark after adapting him to red light, for instance, his rods will be relatively active—because red light

FIG. 93. The course of dark-adaptation as measured with violet light following different degrees of light-adaptation. The filled-in symbols indicate that a violet colour was apparent at the threshold, while the empty symbols indicate that the threshold was colourless. (Hecht, Haig & Chase, *J. gen. Physiol.*)

barely influences these—whilst the cones will have a high threshold; the curve for dark-adaptation will therefore have no kink, the rods determining the threshold from the beginning.

Rod Monochromat. Finally, a human subject defective in cone vision, the so-called *rod monochromat*, has a dark-adaptation curve with no kink (Fig. 94). This type of subject is useful since he permits the study of the rod thresholds without interference from the cones; thus, immediately on placing the normal light-adapted subject in the dark his threshold is determined by the cones; in other words the rods are less sensitive than the cones and so we cannot tell what their threshold is. In the rod-monochromat, however, we can measure the rod threshold as soon as he is placed in the dark and this is found to be very high; nevertheless the rods are not incapable of being stimulated, so that in ordinary daylight, although their thresholds are higher than those of the cones, they may be responding to light. However, there seems no doubt from Aguilar & Stiles' study, that the rods become "saturated" at high levels of illumination (2000–

2500 trolands or 100–300 cd/m²) in the sense that they become incapable of responding to changes of illumination (the l.b.i. is infinitely high); the same was shown by Fuortes, Gunkel & Rushton on their rod-monochromat who was virtually blind at high levels of illumination; the rods were responding to light, but not to changes, so that there was no awareness of contrast.

Colour Saturation. An ingenious approach to the problem of assessing the contribution of the rods to sensation at levels of luminance above the cone threshold is that of Mandelbaum & Nelson, who argued that if a subject viewed a patch of violet light at an intensity above cone threshold then it would appear violet, but if the rods were contributing to sensation, too, the appearance would be that of an unsaturated violet because the rods can only contribute a sensation

FIG. 94. Dark-adaptation curves for a normal subject and a rod monochromat. After adaptation to 1600 mL, the normal subject shows a rapid cone adaptation (solid circles) followed by a slow rod adaptation (open circles). The colour-blind shows only a rod curve of the rapid type. (Hecht, Shlaer, Smith & Haig & Peskin, *J. gen. Physiol.*)

of whiteness and not of chromaticity. Thus, the greater the rod activity the less saturated the appearance of the violet. The technique consisted in comparing the appearances of a violet patch as viewed by the two eyes separately in two half-fields side by side; rod function in one eye was abolished by a period of light-adaptation, *i.e.* exposure for some minutes to a bright light; the other eye was maintained in a dark-adapted state. Thus, when both eyes viewed the violet patch the appearance to the light-adapted eye was that of a very saturated violet whilst the appearance to the dark-adapted eye depended on the degree of rod activity; at very low luminances, just above the cone threshold, rod activity was so high that the light was so unsaturated as to be almost indistinguishable from white. At 1000 times cone threshold the violet, as seen by the dark-adapted eye, was still unsaturated, so that in order to make the two half-fields match, the violet light entering the light-adapted eye had to be desaturated with white light by about 50 per cent, and this suggested that rods and cones were active to about the same extent. At 10,000 times cone threshold (about 10 mL) the cones were clearly predominant.

Regeneration of Visual Purple

Light-adaptation is accompanied by the bleaching of visual purple, as shown by experiments involving extraction of pigment from eyes before and after exposure to light. It seems reasonable to suppose, therefore, that the process of dark-adaptation has as its basis the regeneration of rhodopsin in the rods; and the early studies of Tansley and Peskin certainly showed that the time-course of regeneration, as measured by extraction of frog's retinæ after different periods in the dark, corresponded with the time-course of dark-adaptation. By the technique of *reflexion densitometry* the changes in concentration of pigment in the retina have been followed in the intact eye in man and lower animals.*

Fig. 95. o—o, effect of bleaching the dark-adapted retina with lights of intensities 1, 5 and 100 units (1 unit = 20,000 trolands).
●—●, course of regeneration of visual purple. The ordinate indicates the degree of absorption of light in terms of displacement of an optical wedge. (Campbell & Rushton, *J. Physiol.*)

Reflexion Densitometry. The technique is based on the principle of measuring the light reflected from the fundus of the eye; if the retina contains rhodopsin it will absorb blue-green light of 5000 Å in preference to red and violet light, hence the light reflected from the fundus will contain less light of 5000 Å and more of these other wavelengths. The loss of intensity of light, moreover, will give a direct measure of the degree of absorption, and thus of the optical density of the rhodopsin in the retina. Careful analysis of the changes in amount of light after reflexion showed that they were indeed due, in the dark-adapted eye, to the presence of rhodopsin (Campbell & Rushton), the degree of absorption

* Brindley & Willmer (1952) initiated this ingenious technique, and it has been applied by both Rushton (Rushton & Cohen, 1954; Campbell & Rushton, 1955) and Weale (1953, 1962) to human and animal eyes respectively.

of the different wavelengths corresponding approximately with the extinction spectrum of rhodopsin. As Fig. 95 from Rushton shows, exposure to lights of increasing intensity caused decreases in the amount of rhodopsin.

Rates of Regeneration. After complete bleaching the curve of regeneration is slow, the total regeneration requiring 30 minutes, and thus being equivalent to the time for complete dark-adaptation in man, In the cat, where dark-adaptation is considerably slower, the regeneration, measured in a similar way, takes much longer (Weale). Again, in the alligator, which dark-adapts relatively rapidly when the *b*-wave of the ERG is used as a measure of retinal sensitivity, the course of regeneration of pigment is correspondingly rapid (Wald, *et al.*).

Although there is thus a correlation between pigment regeneration and increase in scotopic sensitivity, the quantitative relationship between the two is not the simple linear one that might be predicted on the basis of photochemistry. Thus, exposure of the dark-adapted eye to a flash that only bleached 1 per cent of its rhodopsin caused an increase of tenfold in its threshold. Clearly, absorption of light by rhodopsin has reduced its sensitivity out of all proportion to the amount of bleaching; again, the final 1 per cent of regeneration during the last fifteen minutes of dark-adaptation brings about a disproportionate increase in sensitivity of the eye.

Rhodopsin Concentration and Retinal Sensitivity

Nevertheless, of course, there is a relationship between the amount of rhodopsin in the retina and visual threshold; thus Rushton varied the amount of bleaching by different exposures of humans to light and found that the threshold for rod vision always occurred when 92 per cent of the rhodopsin had regenerated; before this had happened the measured threshold in the dark was always the cone threshold; the remainder of the dark-adaptation curve, *i.e.* beyond the "kink" (Fig. 56, p. 95) corresponded to the regeneration of the remaining 8 per cent. Rushton was led to the belief that the relationship between threshold and rhodopsin concentration would be logarithmic, so that on plotting the log threshold against rhodopsin concentration a straight line should be obtained. Since, with a normal human subject in the dark, the threshold measured is that of the cones during the initial portion of dark-adaptation, it is not possible to find out what the condition of the rods is in the early stages, *i.e.* we cannot measure their threshold by simply exposing the eye to light, because it is higher than that of the cones. Thus we cannot pursue the relationship between rod threshold and rhodopsin concentration below concentrations corresponding to less than 92 per cent of the value in the completely dark-adapted eye.

Logarithmic Relationship. In a study on a rod-monochromat, a subject with defective cones so that the threshold was determined at all states of adaptation apparently by the rods, Rushton showed that the logarithmic relationship applied over a large range of rhodopsin concentration. Independently Dowling, using the time required for the *b*-wave of the ERG to appear after bleaching the rhodopsin in the rat's eye, showed that the logarithm of the threshold was indeed linearly related to the rhodopsin concentration measured chemically by extraction; this is shown in Fig. 96, where the amount of rhodopsin in the retina was varied, either by light-adaptation or by vitamin-A deficiency.*

* Granit, Munsterhjelm & Zewi (1939) were unable to establish any relationship between height of *b*-wave and rhodopsin concentration, but Dowling considers that this is

FIG. 96 (*a*). Dark-adaptation in the rat. As ordinates are plotted the threshold for producing an ERG (left) and the amount of rhodopsin extractable from the retina as a percentage of the dark-adapted value (right). Following light-adaptation the log threshold falls whilst the percentage of rhodopsin rises. ●, Log threshold; ○, rhodopsin.

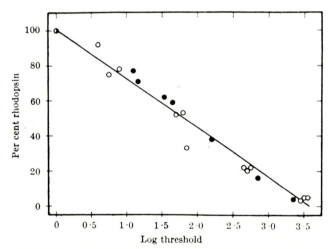

FIG. 96 (*b*). The relation between rhodopsin content of the retina and the visual threshold in animals dark-adapted after exposure to bright light, and in animals night-blind due to vitamin A deficiency. In both cases the log threshold varies linearly with the per cent of rhodopsin in the retina. ●, Night-blindness; ○, dark-adaptation. (Dowling, *Nature*.)

because the *height* of the wave is not the parameter that should be measured. Wald (1954) has suggested an ingenious explanation for the experimental fact, namely that the absorption of a little light has an inordinate effect on threshold in the completely dark-adapted eye. According to this the rhodopsin is compartmented in such a way that the absorption of a quantum of light by any molecule in a compartment prevents all the other molecules from absorbing.

Nervous Events. Although pure photochemical events seem to be mainly responsible for adaptational effects, we cannot rule out nervous influences as well. Thus Arden & Weale found that the rate of adaptation depended on the size of the test-field, the larger the field the greater the rate and they concluded that this was because, during dark-adaptation, the size of the receptive field was actually increasing, *i.e.* the power of the retina to summate was improving. Again, Elenius showed that after strong light-adaptation the rabbit's ERG could require some hours to return to its pre-adaptational state, and he argued that this must have been due to an active inhibition of rod function by the strongly stimulated cones.

THE ABSOLUTE THRESHOLD

Frequency-of-Seeing. In the fully dark-adapted state, the minimum stimulus necessary to evoke the sensation of light is called the absolute threshold. It must be appreciated, however, that this threshold is not a fixed quantity but changes from moment to moment, so that if a subject is presented with a luminous screen

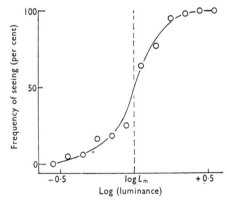

Fig. 97. Typical frequency-of-seeing curve for dark-adapted human observer. (Pirenne, Marriott & O'Doherty, *M.R.C. Sp. Rep.*)

in the dark, we may find a range of luminance over which there will be some probability, but not certainty, of his seeing it. Experimentally, therefore, the screen must be presented frequently at different luminances and the experimenter must plot the "frequency-of-seeing" against the luminance, to give the typical "frequency-of-seeing" curve shown in Fig. 97. From this curve it is a simple matter to compute a threshold on the basis of an arbitrarily chosen frequency, *e.g.* 55 per cent.

Minimum Retinal Illumination. The threshold *stimulus* may be defined in several ways according to the experimental method of measurement. Thus we may express it as the luminance of a large test-screen, exposed for a relatively long time, *e.g.* one second. Since the size of the pupil is important, this must be measured, and the threshold expressed in trolands; furthermore the spectral composition of the light must be defined so that, if necessary, the number of quanta falling on unit area of the retina in unit time may be derived. This definition of the threshold stimulus is thus a statement of the *retinal illumination.*

Experimentally this type of threshold has been found to be of the order of $0.75.10^{-6}$ cd/m² varying between 0.4 and $2.0.10^{-6}$ (Pirenne, Marriott & O'Doherty). This is equivalent to a retinal illumination of $4.4.10^{-5}$ scotopic trolands, and corresponds to the absorption of some 2300 quanta per sec by some 13·4 million rods over which the large test-patch fell. Thus, in each second of time, only one rod in 5800 absorbs a single quantum when the eye is being stimulated at threshold intensity.

Minimum Flux of Energy. If an effectively point source of light is used, the image is concentrated on to a point on the retina so that the concept of retinal illumination loses its application; instead, then, we define the threshold as the *minimum flux* of light-energy necessary for vision, *i.e.* the number of lumens per sec or, better, the number of quanta per sec entering the eye. Experimentally Marriott, Morris & Pirenne obtained a value of 90 to 144 quanta per sec.

Minimum Amount of Energy. Finally, if a very brief flash of light is used as the stimulus (less than 0.1 sec) we may express the threshold as simply the total number of quanta that must enter the eye to produce a sensation. Thus there are three thresholds, the *minimum retinal illumination*, the *minimum light flux* and the *minimum amount of energy*. Of these, it is the last that interests us most since from this we are able to compute just how many quanta of light a single receptor must absorb to be excited.

Minimum Stimulus

This was determined in 1942 by Hecht, Shlaer & Pirenne by the method of presenting short flashes and determining the frequency-of-seeing curves. With a 60 per cent frequency as the end-point for threshold, the amount of energy striking the cornea was 54 to 148 quanta, depending on the observer; after allowing for scattering and absorption by the ocular media the range of useful light-energy was some 5–14 quanta. The image of the flash fell on about 500 rods, so that it was unlikely that one rod received more than a single quantum. This might suggest, therefore, that the minimum stimulus consisted of the simultaneous stimulation of some 11 rods, each absorbing a single quantum, their effects being transmitted to bipolar and ganglion cells by convergence. On this basis, then, the excitation of a single rod at threshold levels is not sufficient for vision, the excitatory effect being insufficient to permit conduction through the various synapses on the visual pathway. Only if several rods are excited will their effects be sufficient to break down these synaptic barriers and permit the passage of the excitation along the visual pathway to higher centres in the brain.

Quantum Fluctuations

The threshold varies from moment to moment and, according to Hecht, Shlaer & Pirenne, this must be due partly, if not wholly, to fluctuations in the number of quanta that a given flash contains when it is repeated. Thus, when we are dealing with very small amounts of light-energy, the actual number of quanta in any given flash will vary. Hence, according to the *uncertainty principle*, when we speak of a flash having an energy, a, we mean that this is the *average energy* the flash would have if it were repeated a large number of times, and the total number of quanta actually measured were divided by the number of flashes. For any given flash, with a mean energy-content of a quanta, we can only speak of the *probability* that it will contain a given number n, or more, quanta; and this probability may be simply calculated. On raising the stimulus-strength, measured by a, over a range of, say, tenfold, the probability that a flash will have a given number of quanta will increase,

FIG. 98. These are probability curves based on quantum theory, showing the chance that a given flash, with average energy shown on the abscissa, will have *n* quanta in it or more. For example, if we employ curve belonging to *n* = 2, the chance of having 2 or more quanta in a flash is about 0·2 (*i.e.* 1 in 5) if the average energy of the flashes is 1 quantum (log 1 = 0). (Hecht, Shlaer & Pirenne, *J. gen. Physiol.*)

and finally become unity. The curve obtained by plotting this probability against the stimulus-strength has a characteristic shape, the steepness depending on the value of *n* as Fig. 98 shows.

Frequency-of-Seeing. Now, if the seeing of a flash depended only on the flash's containing the right number of quanta, say *n*, clearly the frequency-of-seeing will increase as the strength of the stimulus, measured by *a*, increases, because the probability that there will be *n* quanta in a flash increases with increasing value of *a*. Moreover, the shape of the frequency-of-seeing curve should be similar to the shape of the probability curve. As Fig. 99 shows, there is remarkably good agreement between the two, the range of stimulus-strength over which a flash is never seen and always seen being about a factor of tenfold, corresponding with the range over which the probability that a flash has *n* quanta in it varies from 0 to unity. We may note that the slope of the probability curve depends on the number of quanta, *n*, required, becoming steeper the greater the number, so that

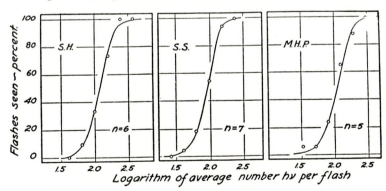

FIG. 99. Frequency-of-seeing curves for three human subjects. The number of times the flash was seen is plotted against the logarithm of the average energy per flash. The curves are theoretical ones, based on the theory of quantum fluctuations in the stimulus, and the fact that the experimental points fall on the curves suggests that the failure to see a given flash was largely due to its not having the required number of quanta in it. (Hecht, Shlaer & Pirenne, *J. gen. Physiol.*)

in order that our frequency-of-seeing curve shall match the probability curve we must choose a suitable value of n, the number of quanta required for vision. Hecht *et al.* found that, with different observers, n varied between 5 and 7, a fact suggesting that the absorption of these numbers of quanta corresponded with the stimulus for threshold vision. Direct measurements of the mean amount of quanta in a threshold stimulus gave values ranging from 6 to 17 quanta actually absorbed; since there is reason to believe that only one in two of absorbed quanta are effective—the *quantum efficiency* of the process is said to be 0·5—this would correspond then to 3 to 8 effective quanta.

Two-Quanta Theories. Since the publication of this study of Hecht *et al.* there have been a number of discussions on the actual minimum number of quanta required to excite vision. There is no doubt that the absorption of one quantum *can* excite a rod, but the phenomena of summation, both temporal and spatial, prove that the excitation of more than one rod is necessary to evoke *sensation*. Thus, it has been found that, within certain limits of area, a given number of quanta in a flash are equally effective if they are concentrated on a small area of retina or spread over a larger one. If only one absorbed quantum was necessary to act as a stimulus, spreading these quanta over a large area should reduce the chance of any one rod absorbing this quantum, so that the threshold should rise. The fact that, within an area subtending some 10 minutes of arc, the stimulus is equally effective, however spread out, means that at threshold more than one rod must be stimulated, their combined effects, transmitted to a bipolar cell, constituting the minimum stimulus for vision. Pirenne inclines to the belief that n is either equal to or greater than 4 although Bouman considers that his own and van der Velden's observations are better fitted by a value of 2.

SPATIAL AND TEMPORAL SUMMATION

The minimum stimulus has been defined in three ways, as we have seen, but the significance of the differences in definition may not be clear unless the importance of spatial and temporal summation is appreciated. It is because of spatial summation that the size of the test-stimulus must usually be stated, and because of temporal summation that the duration of the stimulus acquires significance.

Receptive Fields. Studies on single optic nerve fibres (p. 118) have shown that they have quite extensive "receptive fields" in the sense that a small stimulus applied over a large number of receptor cells can evoke a response in this single fibre. The anatomical basis for this is the convergence of receptors on bipolar cells and the bipolar cells on ganglion cells, so that a single ganglion cell may have synaptic relationships ultimately with many thousands of rods and cones. Because of this convergence, two spots of light falling within the receptive field may be expected to be more effective than a single one of the same light-energy, so that if we are measuring thresholds, the luminance of a single test-patch must be greater than that of two test-patches of the same area falling within the receptive field of a single ganglion cell. Our threshold luminance, expressed in terms of retinal illumination, will be smaller, then, the larger the area. If summation is perfect, moreover, we may expect the following relationship to hold:

$$Intensity \times Area = Constant,$$

the greater the area of the stimulus the smaller the luminous intensity required to excite.

Ricco's Law. This is *Ricco's Law*. Expressed in terms of the actual number of quanta of energy reaching the retina this means that the threshold is independent of the area of the stimulus; thus if we have two stimuli forming images of 1 mm² and 2 mm² on the retina, according to Ricco's Law the luminous intensity of the smaller image will be four times that of the larger one at threshold. The *amounts* of energy falling on the two areas of retina in unit time will be equal, however, since the greater area of the one stimulus exactly compensates for its smaller retinal illumination. The area over which Ricco's Law holds varies with position on the retina, being about 30 minutes of arc in the parafoveal region with eccentricity of 4–7°, and increasing to as much as 2° at an eccentricity of 35° (Hallett, Marriott & Rodger). Over these areas, then, there is complete summation, in the sense that there is no loss of efficiency on spreading the available light-energy over a certain area instead of concentrating it on a much smaller one. When we are determining the minimum amount of energy necessary to excite the sensation of light, then, we must clearly ensure that the area of stimulus is within the limit over which Ricco's Law applies, since beyond this area the summation is ony *partial*, in the sense that the larger stimulus will require more quanta than the smaller one, and will therefore have to have a higher luminous intensity. The existence of this partial summation will be indicated by the fact that the *luminous intensity* of the larger stimulus will be less than that of the smaller one, whilst its partial nature will be indicated by the fact that the *number of quanta* required to excite vision will be greater the greater the area over which they are spread.

Piper's Law. By Piper's Law is meant the statement that over a certain range of areas, where summation is partial, the relationship:

$$\sqrt{Area} \times Intensity = Constant,$$

holds.* In practice partial summation extends over large areas, up to about 24°. Beyond this area there is no further summation, so that increasing the area of the stimulus requires no diminution in its intensity for threshold excitation; beyond this area then, the *luminous intensity* of the test-patch is independent of the area. The *amount of energy* entering the eye, of course, increases as the square of the size of the retinal image so that the threshold, expressed as the number of quanta per sec required to excite, will increase as the area of test-patch increases.†

Probability Summation. Since partial summation extends over large areas of retina, it seems unlikely that convergence can be the sole basis for it, and much more likely that it results from an increased probability that the stimulus will have the necessary number of quanta to stimulate the retina. Thus, we may measure the threshold first with a single patch of light and next with two patches such that their images fall widely apart. If there is any summation at all, the two patches will have a lower luminance than the single one. If we suppose that the two patches are too far apart to permit any convergence of receptors on the same

---

* According to Baumgardt (1959) this relationship follows from probability theory, but there seems little doubt from Barlow's (1958) studies that no simple Law will cover all the phenomena; thus the degree of spatial summation depends on the duration of the stimulus whilst the degree of temporal summation depends on the size of the stimulus. Some of the limitations of studies on area are considered by Hallett *et al.* (1962).

† At the fovea threshold measurements are those for stimulation of the cones and, as we have seen, in the completely dark-adapted condition the thresholds are much higher. This may well be due, not so much to a lower intrinsic sensitivity of the cone as compared with the rod, but to the much smaller degree of convergence exhibited by cones, so that the area over which complete summation is possible is very small. Hence, as ordinarily measured, the threshold will be in the region of partial or no summation. By reducing the size of the test-stimulus to a subtense of 2·7 minutes of arc Arden & Weale (1954) found the threshold intensities to be the same for fovea and parafovea, but their contention that the sensitivities of foveal cones and peripheral rods are equal is probably unsound (Pirenne, 1962, p. 106).

optic nerve fibres, we may nevertheless explain the greater effectiveness of the two patches on a probability basis. Thus, with a single patch the probability of seeing it has a certain value, p, so that the chance that it will not be seen is $(1-p)$. The chance of *not seeing* two patches is $(1 - p)(1 - p)$ which is smaller, so that a lower luminance is necessary for these two patches to have a given "frequency-of-seeing" than for the single one whose probability of not seeing is only $(1 - p)$. We may thus speak of *physiological summation*, when this is due to convergence of retinal elements on optic nerve fibres, and *probability summation*, when the parts of the retina on which the summation occurs may be treated as independent of each other.*

Temporal Summation. By this we mean that a stimulus lasting a short time must be stronger in luminance than a stimulus lasting a long time; thus the stimulus with the longer duration can be considered to be made up of a lot of successively repeated stimuli, and it is these successive stimuli that apparently add their effects. Over a period up to 0·1 sec the Bunsen-Roscoe Law holds:

$$I \times t = Constant,$$

indicating that up to this period the effective stimulus is only the number of quanta entering the eye, and we may say that the summation is *complete*. On a photochemical basis this complete summation is what one might expect, since the limiting factor in the threshold is presumably the absorption of a definite number of quanta, and the chances that this will happen will increase proportionately with the number of quanta entering the eye.

PARTIAL SUMMATION

Beyond a certain time, which has been called the *action time*, the absorption of a second quantum of light will be of no use to help the effects of the absorption of the first, because these effects, *e.g.* production of an electrical change, will subside. We can therefore understand the limited period over which the Bunsen-Roscoe Law applies. Beyond this period, however, we may expect summation on purely probability grounds, since the longer the stimulus the greater the probability it will contain a certain minimal number of quanta, and according to Baumgardt (1959) there should be a square-root relationship between threshold energy and duration of the stimulus; over a certain range the experimental results agree with those predicted on this basis.

GENERAL REFERENCES

PIRENNE, M. H. (1956). Physiological mechanisms of vision and the quantum nature of light. *Biol. Rev.*, **31**, 194–241.
PIRENNE, M. H. (1962). Visual function in man. In *The Eye*. Vol. II. Chaps. 1–11. Ed. Davson. London: Academic Press.
RUSHTON, W. A. H. (1959). Visual pigments in man and animals and their relation to seeing. *Progr. Biophys.*, **9**, 239–283.

* An extreme example of probability summation is given by measuring the frequency of seeing a flash, when two observers are employed, with the frequency of seeing when only a single observer is used; from these we may compute thresholds in the usual way and it is found that the threshold for the "double observer" is less than that for the single one. In a similar way the difference between the binocular and uniocular thresholds of a given subject is accounted for by the increased probability of seeing a flash when using two eyes than one, *i.e.* the two eyes of a subject may be considered as independent from this point of view (Pirenne, 1943).

SPECIAL REFERENCES

AGUILAR, M., & STILES, W. S. (1954). Saturation of the rod mechanism in the retina at high levels of illumination. *Optica Acta*, **1**, 59–65.

ARDEN, G. B., & WEALE, R. A. (1954). Nervous mechanisms and dark-adaptation. *J. Physiol.*, **125**, 417–426.

BARLOW, H. B. (1958). Temporal and spatial summation in human vision at different background intensities. *J. Physiol.*, **141**, 337–350.

BAUMGARDT, E. (1959). Visual spatial and temporal summation. *Nature*, **184**, 1951–1952.

BOUMAN, M. A. (1955). Absolute threshold conditions for visual perception. *J. opt. Soc. Amer.*, **45**, 36–43.

BRINDLEY, G. S., & WILLMER, E. N. (1952). The reflexion of light from the macular and peripheral fundus oculi in man. *J. Physiol.*, **116**, 350–356.

CAMPBELL, F. W., & RUSHTON, W. A. H. (1955). Measurement of the scotopic pigment in the living human eye. *J. Physiol.*, **130**, 131–147.

DOWLING, J. E. (1960). Night blindness, dark adaptation and the electroretinogram. *Amer. J. Ophthal.*, **50**, 875–889.

DOWLING, J. E. (1960). Chemistry of visual adaptation in the rat. *Nature*, **188**, 114–118.

ELENIUS, W. (1958). Recovery in the dark of the rabbit's electroretinogram. *Acta physiol. scand.*, **44**, Suppl. 150.

FUORTES, M. G. F., GUNKEL, R. D., & RUSHTON, W. A. H. (1961). Increment thresholds in a subject deficient in cone vision. *J. Physiol.*, **156**, 179–192.

GRANIT, R., MUNSTERHJELM, A., & ZEWI, M. (1939). The relation between concentration of visual purple and retinal sensitivity to light during dark adaptation. *J. Physiol.*, **96**, 31–44.

HALLETT, P. E., MARRIOTT, F. H. C., & RODGER, F. C. (1962). The relationship of visual threshold to retinal position and area. *J. Physiol.*, **160**, 364–373.

HECHT, S., HAIG, C., & CHASE, A. M. (1937). The influence of light adaptation on subsequent dark adaptation of the eye. *J. gen. Physiol.*, **20**, 831–850.

HECHT, S., HAIG, C., & WALD, G. (1935). The dark adaptation of retinal fields of different size and location. *J. gen. Physiol.*, **19**, 321–337.

HECHT, S., SHLAER, S., & PIRENNE, M. H. (1942). Energy, quanta and vision. *J. gen. Physiol.*, **25**, 819–840.

HECHT, S., SHLAER, S., SMITH, E. L., HAIG, C., & PESKIN, J. C. (1948). The visual functions of the complete colorblind. *J. gen. Physiol.*, **31**, 459–472.

HUBBARD, R., & KROPF, A. (1959). Molecular aspects of visual excitation. *Ann. N.Y. Acad. Sci.*, **81**, 388–398.

MANDELBAUM, J., & NELSON, E. (1960). Rod activity at photopic intensities. *Arch. Ophthal.*, **63**, 402–408.

MARRIOTT, F. H. C., MORRIS, V. B., & PIRENNE, M. H. (1959). The minimum flux of energy detectable by the human eye. *J. Physiol.*, **145**, 369–373.

PIRENNE, M. H. (1943). Binocular and uniocular thresholds of vision. *Nature*, **152**, 698–699.

PIRENNE, M. H., MARRIOTT, F. H. C., & O'DOHERTY, E. F. (1957). Individual differences in night-vision efficiency. *Med. Res. Council Sp. Rep. Ser.*, No. 294.

RUSHTON, W. A. H., & COHEN, R. D. (1954). Visual purple level and the course of dark adaptation. *Nature*, **173**, 301–304.

RUSHTON, W. A. H. (1961). Dark-adaptation and the regeneration of rhodopsin. *J. Physiol.*, **156**, 166–178.

RUSHTON, W. A. H. (1961). Rhodopsin measurement and dark-adaptation in a subject deficient in cone vision. *J. Physiol.*, **156**, 193–205.

WALD, G. (1954). On the mechanism of the visual threshold and visual adaptation. *Science*, **119**, 887–892.

WEALE, R. A. (1953). Photochemical reactions in the living cat's retina. *J. Physiol.*, **122**, 322–331.

WEALE, R. A. (1962). Further studies of photo-chemical reactions in living human eyes. *Vison Res.*, **1**, 354–378.

PART 7

FLICKER

CRITICAL FUSION FREQUENCY

THE sensation of "flicker" is evoked when intermittent light stimuli are presented to the eye; as the frequency of presentation is increased a point is reached—the *critical fusion frequency*—at which the flicker sensation disappears to be replaced by the sensation of continuous stimulation. The study of flicker has turned out to be a valuable method of approach to the fundamental problems of visual phenomena—it is amenable to fairly accurate measurement and it represents a perceptual process intermediate in complexity between intensity discrimination and form perception.

The Talbot-Plateau Law. This generalization states that, when the critical fusion frequency has been reached, the intensity of the resultant sensation, *i.e.* the brightness of the intermittently illuminated, but non-flickering, patch, is the mean of the brightness during a cycle. Thus if the subject's view of an illuminated patch, of luminance 5 mL, is interrupted by rotating an opaque disc in front of it from which a sector has been removed, the resultant sensation will be equal to that given by a continuous stimulus of luminance equal to 5 × Area of Sector/ Total Area of Disc. This law finds a useful application in many experimental studies in which it is desired to cut down the illumination by accurately determined amounts; by varying the size of the sector in the rotating disc, different average intensities of illumination per cycle may be achieved and, so long as the critical fusion frequency is exceeded, these will appear as different steady luminances.

EFFECT OF LUMINANCE ON FUSION FREQUENCY

In general, the greater the luminous intensity of the flickering light, the higher must be its frequency to attain fusion. This is illustrated by Fig. 100 where the critical fusion frequency has been plotted against the logarithm of the retinal illumination in trolands. With foveal observation, the relationship is linear over

FIG. 100. Dependence of critical fusion frequency on the intensity of the stimulus. With foveal fixation (0°), the Ferry-Porter Law holds over a wide range. With eccentric fixation, the curves show discontinuities indicating the activity of the rods. (Hecht, Shlaer & Smith, *Cold Spr. Harb. Symp. Quant. Biol.*)

a wide range, between 0·5 and 10,000 trolands, and this is the basis of the so-called *Ferry-Porter Law* which states that the critical fusion frequency is proportional to the logarithm of the luminance of the flickering patch. At very high luminances the fusion frequency passes through a maximum in the region of 50 to 60 cycles per sec. At very low luminances, in the scotopic range, the fusion frequency is remarkably low, of the order of 5/sec, so that under these conditions the temporal resolution of the fovea is extremely small, a separation of 200 msec between successive stimuli not being discriminated.

Peripheral Vision. With peripheral vision, where use of both rods and cones is possible, there is an obvious discontinuity in the graph, indicating the limited application of the Ferry-Porter Law; by plotting the logarithm of the fusion frequency against the logarithm of the luminance, as in Fig. 101, the break in continuity becomes more obvious and may be seen to occur in the region of a

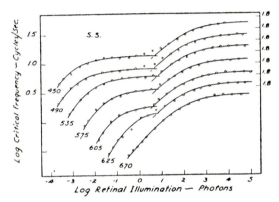

FIG. 101. The log of the fusion frequency has been plotted against the log of the stimulus intensity. With red light, no break occurs in the curve. The ordinates to the left apply to the topmost curve; the others have been moved down in steps of 0·2 log units, and their exact positions are indicated to the right. (Hecht, Shlaer & Smith, *Cold Spr. Harb. Symp. Quant. Biol.*)

retinal illumination of ten trolands (log 10 = unity), and corresponds to the transition from predominantly cone to predominantly rod vision. In Fig. 101 the different curves correspond to the use of different wavelengths of light, and it is seen that no break occurs with a red light of 6700 Å, as one would expect since this wavelength tends to stimulate only cones.

Rod Vision. The low fusion frequencies obtainable with rod vision might suggest that these receptors would not give as high fusion frequencies as the cones at high luminances, if they could be studied in isolation. This view of the rods as less discriminating from the point of view of temporal resolution has been amply confirmed by many experiments. Thus Hecht *et al.* studied a rod-mono-chromat, a subject with apparently non-functional cones. The curve obtained by plotting fusion frequency against log luminance did, indeed, show a break, suggesting the operation of two mechanisms, but it was argued that these corresponded to two types of rod, since the break occurred with red light;* the highest fusion frequency measured was only 21/sec so that the rods do, apparently, have less powers of mediating temporal resolution than the cones.

* The features of vision by the rod monochromat are discussed further on p. 192.

Significance of Ferry-Porter Law. The experimental finding—that to produce fusion the frequency of stimulation must be increased when the intensity of the light stimulus is increased—is, at first thought, surprising. The fact that fusion is possible is clearly dependent on the existence of an "after-effect" resulting from a single stimulus, so that a succeeding stimulus can fall on the retina while it is still responding positively to the first; on purely photochemical grounds one might expect the after-effect to last longer the more powerful the primary stimulus, since a greater quantity of light-sensitive substance would be decomposed; if this were the case, clearly the minimum time elapsing between this stimulus and the next, such that the latter arrives while the eye is still responding strongly to the first stimulus, will be greater with the more powerful stimulus and therefore the critical fusion frequency should be lowered. The response of the eye to illumination, however, is far too complex to be described simply in terms of a primary photochemical reaction—the latter is the first stage only in a process that is elaborated in the nervous structures of the retina and higher visual centres. The study of the ERG has thrown valuable light on the mechanism of flicker and has emphasized the importance of inhibition, besides excitation, in determining this form of resolution.

THE ERG AND THE INTERPRETATION OF FLICKER

The ERG in response to a single flash of light is a characteristic sequence of potential changes considerably outlasting the duration of the flash; a second flash, falling on the eye during these changes, starts off a new series of events, but the extent to which it will modify the existing state of the retinal potential will depend on how soon it follows; and we may envisage a condition, with rapidly repeated stimuli, such that the potential never falls to its baseline and, moreover, if the frequency is high enough, such that the record appears unbroken and smooth. From the point of view of the ERG we may call this the critical

Fig. 102. Flicker as shown by the frog's ERG. The light stimuli are shown at the bottom of each record as white rectangles. Top: Dark-adapted eye with no appreciable flicker. Middle and bottom: Light-adapted eye showing flicker with fusion when the stimuli are sufficiently frequent. (Granit & Riddell, *J. Physiol.*)

fusion frequency but this need not mean, at any rate without further proof, that the subjective sensation is likewise smooth. Fig. 102 from Granit & Riddell illustrates the phenomenon of fusion in the ERG of the light-adapted frog; as the frequency of the intermittent light-stimuli increases, the record becomes smoother, whilst the amplitude of the potential change decreases.

Importance of Inhibition

In the dark-adapted frog's eye, or the rod-dominated retinæ of the cat and guinea pig, the fusion frequency was low, and below fusion successive stimuli seemed merely to result in successive *b*-waves imposed on the declining limbs of the previous *b*-wave. In the light-adapted frog eye, or the *I*-type of retina (pigeon, squirrel, etc.), a much higher fusion frequency was obtained, and an analysis of the ERG at frequencies below fusion indicated that the fluctuations of potential with successive stimuli were now characteristically different, the results of successive stimuli being to impose a negative *a*-wave on the preceding *b*-wave, *i.e.* the succession of events was *a-b-a-b-a* as opposed to *b-b-b-b-b*. If the *a*-wave really is a measure of pre-excitatory inhibition, then the high frequency of flicker is possible with the cone-dominated *I*-retinæ because, before the excitatory effects of each flash, there is a preliminary inhibition of the excited state remaining from the previous flash. Since the size of the *a*-wave, *i.e.* of the inhibitory P III component, increases with increasing stimulus-strength, we have a reasonable explanation of the effects of luminance on fusion frequency.*

Rod-Type ERG. Furthermore, the great difference between rod and cone vision might be explained on the basis that the rods are less susceptible to inhibition than the cones. Thus in the rod-dominated retina of the cat at ordinary stimulus intensities the flicker is determined, according to Granit, by a different process; here the negative, inhibitory, component is relatively unimportant, and the sensation of flicker is dependent on the primary excitation (the *b*-wave in the ERG) dying down sufficiently to allow the next stimulus to evoke a new *b*-wave which will appear as a notch on the descending limb. In the absence of a pronounced P III component, this will necessitate a considerable pause between individual light-stimuli if they are to be appreciated as distinct, *i.e.* the fusion frequency will be low.†

Subjective and ERG-Flicker

Subsequent studies of the flicker-ERG have tended to confirm Granit & Riddell's view, but we must remember that the explanation begs the question as to the justification of considering the *a*-wave as peculiarly inhibitory. Moreover, we cannot be certain that unevenness on the record necessarily means a flicker sensation, nor can we be certain that a smooth record corresponds to subjective fusion. This is well exemplified by the study of the human ERG when the sub-

---

* The falling off in fusion frequency with very high luminances seems to be due to the intensification of the *a*-wave under these conditions, the flicker-ERG consisting solely of *a*-waves (Heck, 1957).

† We may note that in the typical rod-ERG the response to the first flash of a series of intermittent flashes is always very much larger than the succeeding responses; this is apparently not due to the light-adaptation that takes place to some extent during repeated exposure of the retina to flash stimuli; the relative amplitudes of first and successive responses depend critically on the duration of the dark phase between the two, as though the retina had to recover from an inhibitory condition imposed by the first flash (Arden, Granit & Ponte, 1960).

jective sensation can be compared with the electrical record. Subjectively, as we have seen, we may obtain fusion frequencies of the order of 60/sec or more by suitably increasing the luminance of the flickering patch; in the early studies of the human ERG, however, the fusion frequency rose to a maximum at about 25/sec, further increases in luminance causing no increase in fusion frequency. The human ERG, under photopic conditions, was apparently similar to that given by a rod-dominated retina, so that a smooth record did not correlate with subjective sensation. This could be because the ERG is, in general, the pooled response of all the receptors in the retina, and since rods are in such a huge majority in the human retina the ERG-response to flickering stimuli should be a rod-response. The *subjective sensation*, however, might be determined by the cones, in spite of their numerical inferiority, presumably because, under photopic conditions, their pathways to higher centres are more favoured, or because of their greater cortical representation.

Cone Activity. If this were true it ought to be possible, by adequate amplification of the ERG, and by increasing the intensity of the light stimuli, to bring out the cone activity in the ERG when the rod activity was suppressed. How can we suppress the rod activity, however? The flicker-ERG gives us just this

FIG. 103. The critical fusion frequency (FFF) as a function of stimulus-intensity as indicated by the human ERG. Ordinate: flashes/sec.; Abscissa: luminance in lux. Note logarithmic scales. (Dodt & Wadensten, *Acta ophthal. Kbh.*)

opportunity since, as we have seen, the ERG record becomes smooth at a luminance of about 10 lux with a fusion frequency of about 25/sec. Thus the rod-response can no longer follow the stimuli and any irregularity in the record obtained by increasing the luminance must now be due to cone activity. Dodt in 1951 was able to demonstrate just this; he increased the luminance of the flashes to far greater levels than earlier workers had used, and by employing an opal contact lens that enabled large areas of retina to be stimulated he found that, beyond 10 lux, flicker again appeared on the record, and the curve of fusion frequency against luminance corresponded with the subjective sensation. Fusion frequencies as high as 70/sec were obtained as Fig. 103 from Dodt & Wadensten shows. Even in the cat, moreover, Dodt & Walther were able to demonstrate a cone-type of ERG at sufficiently high luminance.

The Cone-ERG. The capacity of the rods to have their contribution to the ERG suppressed by use of an intermittent stimulus has permitted the study of the contribution of cones in some detail, and from thence it has been a simple step to the analysis of cone function in the intact retina. For example, by studying the effectiveness of different wavelengths in producing a cone-ERG under intermittent stimulation, Dodt & Walther found a typical photopic sensitivity curve with maximum in the yellow-green at 5500 Å compared with the scotopic maximum of about 5000 Å determined by measuring sensitivity of the retina in the dark-adapted state. This is the characteristic Purkinje shift (p. 133). Again, the characteristics of a single cycle of potential change, *i.e.* a single ERG, can also be studied by choosing frequencies that are well below fusion of the cone-ERG but of course above those for rod fusion; in general the *a*-wave is well defined and may be resolved into *two*, whilst the *b*-wave has *three*, components, suggesting the activities of different types of cone (Heck). In the completely colour-blind (rod-monochromat) there was no cone-ERG at all.

GANGLION CELL DISCHARGES

We may ask what takes place in the optic nerve during flicker and fusion; the answer was provided by Enroth.* It will be recalled that single cells, or optic nerve fibres, respond to a flash of light in different manners and are described as Pure ON-, Pure OFF- and ON-OFF-elements according as they give a burst of spikes at ON, OFF or both at ON and OFF. In the cat the ON-OFF ganglion cells are in the majority so that these were studied most, but the ON-response of such a cell was essentially the same as a pure ON-response from the point of view of flicker, so that the same general principles of behaviour were valid; the same applied to the OFF-responses.

Fusion

To consider the pure ON-element, the first few flashes usually caused a simple spike discharge with no silent period between; this corresponds with the non-flickering period of the ERG. Soon each flash caused a burst of spikes in step with the stimulus (Fig. 104); as the frequency of flashing increased, the burst became shorter but remained in step. At a certain frequency of flashing fusion occurs, in the sense that now the spike discharges, if they occur at all, bear no relationship with the stimuli. The unit shown in Fig. 104 gave a discharge, corresponding to what would be seen with steady illumination, but others (usually OFF- and ON-OFF-elements) remained completely silent during fusion. Decreasing the flash-rate brought about an immediate flicker in the record. With ON-OFF elements, at low flickering rates the ON- and OFF-discharges behaved independently, each "flickering" with the ON- and OFF-phases of the light cycle. Usually fusion of the one response occurred before that of the other, so that if, for example, the ON-element fused first, the record was the same as that for a flickering OFF-element.

Ferry-Porter Law. The remarkable feature emerging from this study was the relationship between the fusion frequency for a given ganglion cell and the frequency of its spike discharge in response to a single flash; if the spike discharge

---

* The main results were described by Enroth in her thesis (1952); they have been extended by Dodt & Enroth (1954) and Grüsser & Rabelo (1958).

FIG. 104. Response of ON-element to repetitive flash stimuli leading to fusion, in the sense that when the flash-frequency reaches a certain value, marked by the arrow, the response is a discharge that bears no relationship to the frequency of flash-stimulation. Before this phase is reached the spike bursts are synchronous with the light flashes, beginning after a latency indicated by the dotted lines on the records marked 1 and 5. Upward movement of signal indicates onset of flash. (Enroth, *Acta physiol. scand.*)

had a high frequency the fusion frequency was high, and *vice versa*. Since, usually, spike discharge frequency increases with increasing intensity of light, we have an electrophysiological basis for the Ferry-Porter Law relating fusion frequency with light intensity.

Pre-Excitatory Inhibition. The mechanism of fusion is doubtless related to the pre-excitatory inhibition of the succeeding stimulus on the excitatory effect of the preceding one, and we may assume that the actual period between flashes that permits fusion is determined by the latency of this pre-excitatory inhibition and the latency of the excitatory response. Thus, to consider an OFF-element; at the end of the first flash it discharges, after a latency of a few msec. The second flash will inhibit this discharge provided the latency of its inhibitory effect is not too long, and as Fig. 105 shows, it will be when the dark period is equal to the difference between the two latencies. These latencies are variable, so that simple relationships between them and flicker-rate are not to be expected, although in general there is, indeed, a strong correlation between the length of the dark period and the difference of latencies (Grüsser & Rabelo).

Post-Excitatory Inhibition. With ON-elements, the significant factor is probably the post-excitatory inhibition that brings to an end the discharge in response to the onset of the flash. This inhibition is seen when the element is stimulated with a single flash of light; the response is a *primary activation* lasting about 20–70 msec and consisting of a burst of spikes; this is followed by a *discharge pause* of 80–250 msec and then a *secondary activation*. The discharge pause represents post-excitatory inhibition, and fusion will presumably occur when the flashes are so timed that the primary activation of the one flash is due to fall in the discharge pause of the preceding one. According to Grüsser & Rabelo, the latency of onset of the primary activation is the determining factor.

FIG. 105. Diagrammatic representation of OFF-latency and pre-excitatory inhibition latency during flicker of an OFF-element. Flashes are indicated by black rectangles. *A*, the dark interval is too long for the inhibitory effect of the light flash to affect the OFF-response; *B*, the interval is shorter, but the OFF-response has not been completely inhibited; *C*, there is fusion because the dark period is equal to the difference between the OFF-latency and the inhibitory latency. (Enroth, *Acta physiol. scand.*)

EFFECT OF DARK-ADAPTATION

On the basis of Granit's analysis, we may expect the subjective phenomenon of flicker to show marked variations according as the human eye is light- or dark-adapted, *i.e.* according as the cone or rod mechanism predominates. This is, indeed, the case but the effects are complex for reasons that will become evident.

Experimental Study

Let us suppose that a subject is placed in a box and that he looks at a flickering test-patch through a small window; the walls of the box may be illuminated to any desired intensity and thus the subject's state of light- or dark-adaptation may be controlled accurately. The flickering patch may likewise be given any desired luminance, so that we may make two kinds of measurement of the effects of dark-adaptation, *i.e.* we can make the walls of the box darker and darker and keep the luminance of the test-patch at a level such that rods only will be stimulated; alternatively we may make the walls of the box darker and darker as before, thereby increasing the dark-adaptation, but we can keep the luminance of the flickering test-patch at a level above the threshold for cone vision. It is very important to keep in mind this distinction in experimental approach as the effects of dark-adaptation are greatly different in the two cases. A third method, extensively adopted in the earlier work on this subject, consists in placing the subject in a dark room and varying the luminance of the flickering test-patch from the very highest levels to the lowest, threshold, ones; in this case, however, it is very difficult to control the adaptation of the eyes—at the low levels of illumination of the test-patch the eyes will be more or less completely dark-adapted, but at the high levels they will be only partially so, and to different degrees, owing to the effects of the test-patch.

Rod Vision. If the subject is placed in the box and is allowed to view a flickering patch of luminance below the cone threshold, then the effects of dark-adaptation are precisely those we should expect on the basis of the Ferry-Porter Law; as the dark-adaptation proceeds, the test-patch appears brighter and brighter and consequently we may expect the fusion frequency to increase with dark-adaptation—this is the case as Fig. 106 (lower curve) shows; the general level of fusion frequency is low (3 to 12 cycles/sec).

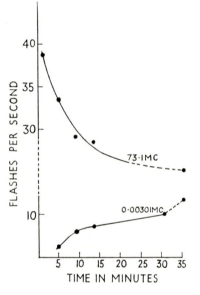

FIG. 106. The effect of dark-adaptation on critical fusion frequency. When the patch is of photopic intensity, dark-adaptation decreases c.f.f. When the patch is of scotopic intensity, dark-adaptation increases c.f.f. (10° eccentric fixation). (After Lythgoe & Tansley, *M.R.C. Sp. Rep.*)

Photopic Vision. If, on the other hand, the flickering patch has a high luminance, so that both rods and cones are stimulated, the effect of dark-adaptation (decreasing the illumination of the walls of the box) is in the opposite sense, the critical fusion frequency falling from a value of nearly 40 cycles/sec in the light-adapted eye to about 25 cycles/sec in the completely dark-adapted condition (Fig. 106, upper curve). The curves shown in Fig. 106 were obtained with 10° eccentric view, *i.e.* both rods and cones were being stimulated by the test patch; if central vision alone is used, the effects of dark-adaptation are said by Granit to be very small, hence the peripheral cones are apparently behaving differently from foveal cones. As we shall see in more detail in the next section, the peripheral cones differ in their organization from the foveal ones, in the sense that many share the same bipolar cell with rods, and it is just possible that these effects of dark-adaptation are due to the increased activity of rods that takes place.

Rod-Cone Interaction. In other words, the rods may well inhibit the cones. A particularly good example of this rod-cone interaction was described by Dodt

& Heck in the cat, using the ERG as the criterion of flicker and fusion. Fig. 107 shows the effects of dark-adaptation on fusion frequency; with a scotopic stimulus, below the cone threshold (1 lux), the fusion frequency increases to a limiting rate of about 30/sec, the highest value for rod vision in the cat. This is the effect we have already seen in man. When a moderately high stimulus-intensity is employed (90 lux), the fusion frequency corresponds at first to that of the rods; during dark-adaptation, however, the cones apparently take over, since the fusion frequency rises above the rod limit. After 15 minutes of dark-adaptation, nevertheless, the fusion frequency falls and eventually becomes equal to that obtained with pure rod stimuli; presumably the rods have taken over again and suppressed cone activity.

Fig. 107. Fusion frequency of cat's ERG. Lower curve shows that with a weak stimulus (1 lux) the fusion frequency increases with dark-adaptation to reach a maximum, characteristic of the rods. Upper curve shows that, with a moderately high intensity of light (90 lux), dark-adaptation causes an increase of fusion frequency, due to cone activity, but after a time the fusion frequency falls to that characteristic of rod vision, presumably because the rods are inhibiting the cones. (Dodt & Heck, *Pflüg. Arch.*)

SIZE OF PATCH AND THE LIGHT-DARK RATIO

Granit-Harper Law. In general, if the size of the flickering patch is increased, its luminance being held constant, the fusion frequency increases; the effects can be large, so that a retinal area of 10 mm^2 may have a fusion frequency of say 60 cycles/sec whilst an area of 0·001 mm^2 of the same luminance may have just about half this. According to the so-called Granit-Harper Law, the fusion frequency is proportional to the logarithm of area. Varying the stimulus area, however, causes alterations not only in the total number of retinal elements stimulated, but in the relative extents to which peripheral and foveal elements enter into the response, and it would only be accidental if any simple relationship were found to hold over the whole retina. As Landis states: "Area as a determinant of fusion frequency is a complicated affair. Not only is the size of the retinal area a determinant, but its position on the retina, its shape, whether it is discrete or composed of several parts, all enter into the areal effect."

Light-Dark Ratio. The effects of varying the light-dark ratio are even more complex and the results described are so frequently contradictory that one hesitates to make any generalization. Some recent results of Lloyd & Landis are illustrated in Fig. 108 where fusion frequency has been plotted against logarithm of luminance, the different symbols representing different light-dark ratios. With very small and very large ratios fusion frequency is lower than with intermediate ratios.*

FIG. 108. Critical fusion frequency (C.F.F.) plotted against logarithm of light intensity (log I) for different light-dark ratios. (Lloyd & Landis, *J. opt. Soc. Amer.*)

SUBJECTIVE ASPECTS

Brücke-Effect. v. Brücke in 1864 observed that the subjective brightness of a flickering patch of light could be higher than that experienced when the patch was presented continuously; the best effect was obtained with a flicker-rate of some 10 cycles/sec. It will be recalled that, according to the Talbot-Plateau Law, the sensation at fusion is the mean of the sensation during the light and dark intervals, hence the subjective brightness of the flickering light is very considerably greater than what would be experienced at the critical fusion frequency, since with a light-dark ratio of 0·5 this would be one half that experienced with steady presentation of the bright patch. According to Bartley the optimum condition for eliciting this Brücke-effect is when the bright phase lasts one third the time of the dark phase. Under these conditions, then, the

* The effects of light-dark ratio have been exhaustively described by Landis (1954). Collins (1956) has made an elaborate analysis of the effects of varying not only the light-dark ratio but also the *wave-form, i.e.* the manner in which the flash comes on and goes off; he has combined these characteristics of the intermittent stimulus into a single parameter, which he calls the *flicker index.*

after-effect of the first stimulus accentuates the effect of the second, a finding that probably explains the observation of Strughold that visual acuity may be improved by use of a flickering light of some 5–6 cycles/sec.

Subjective Flicker-Rate. Another interesting subjective observation, recorded by Bartley, is that the actual flicker sensation, at the instant when flicker is about to disappear, does not correspond at all with the objective flash-rate. Thus at low levels of luminance it is possible to obtain fusion at 4 flashes per sec, nevertheless the flicker sensation at a flash-frequency just below this is that corresponding with a flashing light in the region of 10–20 per sec. Conversely, at a high luminance, such that fusion is attained with 40 flashes per sec, the flicker *sensation*, as it gives place to fusion, has about the same subjective frequency as that observed with an objective rate of 4 flashes per sec, *i.e.* in the region of 10–20 per sec. Thus the final flickering sensation, obtained just before flicker disappears, seems to be independent of the actual flicker-rate.

GENERAL REFERENCES

BARTLEY, S. H. (1941). *Vision: A Study of its Basis.* New York: Nostrand.
GRANIT, R. (1947). *Sensory Mechanisms of the Retina.* London: O.U.P.
LANDIS, C. (1954). Determinants of the critical flicker-fusion threshold. *Physiol. Rev.,* **34**, 259–286.

SPECIAL REFERENCES

ARDEN, G., GRANIT, R., & PONTE, F. (1960). Phase of suppression following each retinal *b*-wave in flicker. *J. Neurophysiol.,* **23**, 305–314.
COLLINS, J. B. (1956). The influence of characteristics of a fluctuating visual stimulus on flicker sensation. *Ophthalmologica, Basel,* **131**, 83–104.
DODT, E. (1951). Cone electroretinography by flicker. *Nature,* **168**, 738.
DODT, E., COPENHAVER, R. M., & GUNKEL, R. D. (1958). Photopischer Dominator und Farbkomponenten im menschlichen Elektroretinogramm. *Pflüg. Arch.,* **267**, 497–507.
DODT, E., & ENROTH, C. (1954). Retinal flicker response in cat. *Acta physiol. scand.,* **30**, 375–390.
DODT, E., & HECK, J. (1954). Einflüsse des Adaptationszustandes auf die Rezeption intermittierender Lichtreize. *Pflüg. Arch.,* **259**, 212–225.
DODT, E., & WADENSTEN, L. (1954). The use of flicker electroretinography in the human eye. *Acta ophthal. Kbh.,* **32**, 165–180.
DODT, E., & WALTHER, J. B. (1958). Der photopischer Dominator im Flimmer-ERG der Katze. *Pflüg. Arch.,* **266**, 175–186.
ENROTH, C. (1952). The mechanism of flicker and fusion studied on single retinal elements in the dark-adapted cat. *Acta physiol. scand.,* **27**, Suppl. 100, p. 67.
GRANIT, R., & RIDDELL, H. A. (1934). The electrical responses of the light- and dark-adapted frog's eyes to rhythmic and continuous stimuli. *J. Physiol.,* **81**, 1–28.
GRÜSSER, O. J., & RABELO, C. (1958). Reaktionen retinaler Neurone nach Lichtblitzen. *Pflüg. Arch.,* **265**, 501–525.
HECHT, S., SHLAER, S., & SMITH, E. L. (1935). Intermittent light stimuli and the duplicity theory of vision. *Cold Spr. Harb. Symp. Quant. Biol.,* **3**, 237–244.
HECHT, S., SHLAER, S., SMITH, E. L., HAIG, C., & PESKIN, J. C. (1948). The visual functions of the complete colorblind. *J. gen. Physiol.,* **31**, 459–472.
HECK, J. (1957). The flicker electroretinogram of the human eye. *Acta physiol. scand.,* **39**, 158–166.
LLOYD, V. V., & LANDIS, C. (1960). Role of light-dark ratio as a determinant of the flicker fusion threshold. *J. opt. Soc. Amer.,* **50**, 332–336.
LYTHGOE, R. J., & TANSLEY, K. (1929). The adaptation of the eye: its relation to the critical frequency of flicker. *Med. Res. Council Sp. Rep. Ser.,* No. 134.

PART 8

VISUAL ACUITY

THE perception of flicker demands the resolution of two stimuli separated in time ; by visual acuity is generally meant the power of the eye to resolve two stimuli separated in space, *i.e.* it is fundamentally related to the spatial relationships between receptor elements as opposed to the temporal characteristics of the response of a single element.

Central and Peripheral Viewing

As with the other aspects of vision that we have so far considered in detail, the resolving power of the human eye differs markedly according as the conditions of viewing favour rod or cone vision. Thus, visual acuity in the dark-

FIG. 109. The variation of visual acuity with eccentricity of vision as measured along the horizontal meridian of the temporal retina. Five intensity levels, varying from 9·0 to 4·6 log micromicrolamberts were employed (9·0 log micromicrolamberts = 10^9 micromicrolamberts = 1 mL). At 25° and 30° all the curves, except for 4·6 log micromicrolamberts, practically run together and are designated by single points. (Mandelbaum & Sloan, *Amer. J. Ophthal.*)

adapted eye with parafoveal vision and scotopic luminous intensities is only a small fraction of that obtained with foveal vision and high luminous intensities. Nevertheless it would be wrong to consider this as a difference in rod and cone functions *per se*, since peripheral vision under photopic conditions gives a low order of visual acuity. This is illustrated by Fig. 109, which shows visual acuity as a function of angle of view, foveal acuity being put equal to unity. Thus at 5° the acuity is only about a quarter of that found with foveal vision, and at 15° only about one seventh.

Cone Density. The fall in visual acuity correlates fairly well with the fall in density of distribution of cones, which become more and more rare as we progress to the periphery of the retina. Density of receptors *per se*, however, is also not the determining factor since the rod density is very high throughout the retina yet visual acuity under scotopic visions is always less than that under photopic conditions as Fig. 109 shows except, perhaps, in the extreme periphery. As we shall see, it is the synaptic organization of the receptors that is the important factor.

PHOTOPIC VISUAL ACUITY

Effects of Luminance of Test-Object and Adaptation

If the luminance of the test-object is such as to stimulate the cone mechanism, Lythgoe has shown that the curve showing the variation of visual acuity with the luminance of the test-object varies according to the experimental conditions ;

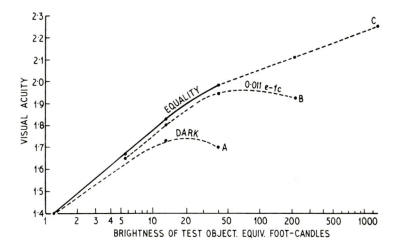

FIG. 110. Illustrating the effects of the brightness of the surround (*i.e.* state of adaptation of the eye) on visual acuity. A, black surround: visual acuity increases with increasing brightness of test-object only up to a certain point. B, surround brightness 0·011 e.f.c. C, surround brightness varied continuously so as to be equal to that of test-object. (Lythgoe, *Med. Res. Council Sp. Rep.* By permission of the Controller of H.M. Stationery Office.)

if the subject is placed in a dark box and is allowed to see the test-object through a small window, he can be considered to be in a state of dark-adaptation even though the luminance of the test-object is high enough to stimulate cone vision. In this case the acuity increases up to a maximum at approximately 10 e.f.c. and then begins to fall (Fig. 110, A) ; if the walls of the box are given a luminance of 0·011 e.f.c., *i.e.* if the subject is only partly dark-adapted, the acuity continues to increase to a maximum at approximately 50 e.f.c. but then falls off (Fig. 110, B). If the luminance of the box is continuously adjusted so that it is equal to that of the test-object, it is found that visual acuity increases progressively with the luminance of the test-object (Curve C). If the luminance of the box is made greater than that of the test-object, generally the acuity is lower than when the luminances are equal. Thus with visual acuity we are confronted again with some form of retinal interaction in so far as the acuity of the central retina is influenced by the general illumination of the eye, *i.e.* by light-adaptation.

Adaptation. We have seen that dark-adaptation increases visual acuity under scotopic conditions ; this effect is doubtless due to the increased sensitivity of the rods ; the curves in Fig. 110 indicate that light-adaptation, under photopic conditions, increases visual acuity, and consequently dark-adaptation decreases it ; since dark-adaptation increases the sensitivity of the cones (although not to the same degree as that of the rods) it is clear that the effect of dark-adaptation on photopic visual acuity is not closely connected with changes in sensitivity of the cones *per se*.

Normal Visual Acuity

We have so far considered variations in the visual acuity, but have said little about its absolute magnitude. It is customary to think of the visual acuity being determined by the "grain" of the retinal mosaic of cones—thus the Snellen letters are constructed on the assumption that the average person can resolve points separated by one minute of arc, and this limit has been considered to be roughly determined by the diameter of a single cone. Thus if we consider two white points on a black field, if these are so close together that their images fall on a pair of adjacent cones it is clear that they would not be appreciated as separate since a single, larger, white point would produce the same effect; only if one unstimulated cone is between the two images should the points appear as discrete. If we take Polyak's figure of $1·5\mu$ for the diameter of the base of a foveal cone, this would permit a resolving power of approximately twenty seconds of arc ; the best figure for visual acuity indicates a resolving power of this order. When, however, visual acuity is measured by the power to detect a break in a contour, *e.g.* with a vernier scale adjustment, or to detect the presence of a single line on a uniform background, a far greater resolving power is found (of the order of four seconds of arc for the contour break and $0·5$ sec for the line), and numerous explanations have been put forward to explain the apparent anomaly.

The "One-to-One" Relationship. If the individual retinal cones are to be considered as the units on the basis of which resolving power is to be determined, as opposed to groups of cones, there must be a so-called "one-to-one" relationship between cones and optic nerve fibres ; in other words, two adjacent cones must be able to convey their impulses along independent paths ; if two cones, close together, were connected to the same bipolar cell, the impulses relayed from this cell would be characteristic of neither cone separately, so that it would be difficult to conceive of a "local sign" being attached to either cone, and consequently resolving power could not be so fine as to permit the differentiation of stimuli separated by one unstimulated cone. For some time this "one-to-one" relationship between retinal cone, bipolar cell, and ganglion cell has been assumed to hold in the fovea, but it is relatively recently that Polyak demonstrated its existence, although not in the simple, clear-cut form originally postulated.

MIDGET CELLS

According to the results of Polyak's studies, the rods and cones make synapses with a variety of different types of bipolars ; many of these connections are of the multiple type, such as with the diffuse "mop" variety which serves as a pathway for the impulses from many rods and cones. There is thus, in these cases, no "one-to-one" relationship between receptors and bipolars. However, Polyak identified a *"midget bipolar"* (Fig. 111, *h*) which shows promise of subserving this special relationship ; this cell has a single dendrite which disperses in the neighbourhood of the cone pedicle into a number of short thick and thin secondary or tertiary branchlets, forming a compact bunch, or bouquet, looking like the half-open flower of a dandelion ; the shape is such as to fit

FIG. 111. Some of the types of receptor-bipolar synapses in the retina. *a*, rod; *b*, cone; *d*, *e*, *f*, bipolars that make several synaptic relationships with receptors; *h*, midget bipolar; *s*, midget ganglion cell; *m*, parasol ganglion cell (used here to typify the type that makes several synaptic relationships with bipolars). (Polyak, *The Retina*.)

exactly the cone pedicle. There is thus a special synaptic relationship between a cone and this type of bipolar, in the sense that a cone makes relations with only a single one. Similarly *"midget ganglion cells"* (Fig. 111, *s*) have been identified which, in practically all cases examined, make an individual synapse with the axon of the midget bipolar, each tiny teledendron of the latter being enveloped by the dendritic tree-top of a single midget ganglion cell, a tree-top which is of approximately the same size as that of the teledendron. However, strictly speaking, there is no absolute "one-to-one" relationship between cones, bipolars, and ganglion cells owing to the fact that cones, even in the central area, make connections with diffuse bipolars besides with a midget ; similarly, the same midget bipolar that makes a "private" synapse with a midget ganglion also makes contact with the diffuse varieties of bipolars. The "one-to-one" relationship thus exists only by virtue of a peculiar synaptical arrangement between a cone and its related midget bipolar and ganglion cells ; although a share of the impulses excited in a cone is directed into collateral channels (diffuse bipolars, horizontal and amacrine cells) the main or specific cone influence seems to remain restricted to this special channel.

SPATIAL SUMMATION

Thus spatial summation of stimuli, such as is observed with rod vision, could only be mediated in the central (cone) area by means of the subsidiary synaptic connections and it is therefore not surprising that very little evidence of this type of summation by the cones has been obtained. Lythgoe suggested that the increased visual acuity obtained by light-adaptation (*vide, e.g.* Fig. 110) is due to an inhibition of these subsidiary nervous paths so that the cones, during light-adaptation, tend to react more and more as single units. Some of the types of receptor-bipolar-ganglion cell links, described by Polyak, are shown in Fig. 111.

Diffraction and Chromatic Aberration. Having established the existence of a "one-to-one" relationship between cone and optic nerve fibre for the central region of the retina, we can postulate a certain local sign attached to any foveal cone, so that we have a basis for the differentiation by the higher centres between the stimulation of two adjacent cones and two separated by one unstimulated cone. In the absence of diffraction and aberration effects, then, a figure of twenty seconds of arc could be taken as the anatomical limit of resolution of two points by the most central portion of the fovea. Diffraction and chromatic aberration, however, must certainly be taken into consideration ; it is all very well to assume that the image of a grating or Landolt-C will be a clear-cut replica of the original, but let us suppose that the white break in the Landolt-C at the limit of resolution produces an image two, three, or four times its "geometrical size"; clearly it will stimulate two, three, or four cones so that it will be impossible to localize the break exactly ; moreover, the black line of the Landolt-C has the same thickness as its break ; if the white points on the inside and outside of the black contour all produce images extending over one or more cones there will be no unstimulated cone on the retina and, on the simple view so far taken, a Landolt-C whose black line subtends only twenty seconds of arc should be invisible.

DIFFRACTION RINGS

As a result of diffraction, a point of light produces an image of finite size on the retina ; the image consists of a central bright spot surrounded by successive dark and bright rings ; with a pupillary diameter of 3 mm and with light of wavelength 5550 Å, the central spot will have a diameter of rather more than $3 \cdot 8\mu$, subtending some 47 seconds of arc at the nodal point of the eye ; that is, there should be a definite overlapping of cone stimulation even when the stimulus arises from a theoretical point source. In general, the light falling in the bright rings concentric with the central bright disc only amounts to 16 per cent of the whole, so that the much greater overlapping due to these rings can probably be ignored.

CHROMATIC ABERRATION

The effects of chromatic aberration are even more serious ; they will be discussed in more detail in a later section (p. 468) ; for the moment we must note that the effect is to make the image of a point source into a large disc covering some four cones.

RETINAL IMAGE

As a result of these combined effects the image of a grating, for example, will not consist of a series of bright and black patches on the retina ; long before the resolution limit of such a grating has been reached, the image will be such that *no cone will be unstimulated* ; this is shown by Fig. 112 from Hartridge where the relative luminances of the different parts of the image of a grating on the retina are plotted ; in the middle of the geometrical shadow of the black

FIG. 112. The distribution of light intensity in the image of an edge (*A*) and a grating (*B*) on the retina as calculated by Hartridge. (Shlaer, *J. Gen. Physiol.*)

lines, the intensity is some 40 per cent of what it would be if there were no black lines at all ; beneath the image of the white bar the intensity is only 60 per cent. In the same figure the distribution of light in the region of the geometrical edge of an extended object is shown ; it is seen that there is no clear-cut shadow, light falling on the retina several cones' width within the geometrical shadow.

Criterion for Resolution. Clearly the classical conception of the basis of visual acuity—which demands that two resolvable points should be such that their images have an unstimulated cone between them—must be abandoned, since it fails to fit the observed facts of visual acuity. If we adopt Hartridge's criterion of the limit of resolution of two points, namely that their images must be sufficiently far apart so that there is a cone between that is *less stimulated than the rest*, we are not only provided with a way round our difficulty, but we can also explain the extremely high order of visual acuity exhibited in the detection of the break in a contour. Thus although a cone, falling under the geometrical image of a black bar, is stimulated, it receives less light than adjoining cones falling under the geometrical images of the white bars, and there is thus a peripheral basis for the resolution of points closer together than might otherwise have been expected.

INDUCTION EFFECTS

According to Hartridge's analysis, the limit to resolution is determined almost exactly by the "grain" of the retinal mosaic of cones, *i.e.* by the diameter of a central retinal cone. It may be mentioned here that local inductive effects, whereby the sensitivity of cones adjacent to the most strongly stimulated one is depressed (pp. 104, 207), assist in the resolution process, *i.e.* the inductive effects *amplify* the differences in response of adjoining cones on which the image of a grating falls.

Detection of Breaks in Contours. The high degree of resolution exhibited in the recognition of breaks in contours, where the limit is of the order of 4 seconds of arc, appears, at first sight, to present greater difficulties. On the classical view, the limit to detection of a break in a contour would be determined by the break being of such a size that the image of the line above the break fell

FIG. 113. The break in the contour is recognized, on the classical view, by the fact that the lower cones in the row are stimulated whilst the upper ones are not.

FIG. 114. Illustrating how the break in the contour is reproduced accurately in the diffraction shadow, which extends to some distance to the right of the geometrical shadow. Above the break the shadow is slightly deeper than below, hence the cones above are slightly less strongly stimulated than those below.

on a row of cones whilst the image of the line below the break fell on another row (Fig. 113) ; the break in the contour would be recognized by the existence of some stimulated and some unstimulated cones in a row. Such a view demands, however, a cone size much too small for the observed resolution.

ABERRATIONS

When diffraction and chromatic aberration are taken into account, the image of the contour extends to a considerable distance beyond the geometrical shadow, but the *break* in the contour is accurately reproduced, even though at a considerable distance (Fig. 114). Let us imagine that the edge of the shadow falls along a row of cones (Fig. 114) ; at the break in the contour the cones below the break receive less illumination than those above it, but it is impossible, of course, that any number of cones in a row could be unstimulated whilst others were stimulated. The basis for the recognition of the break in the contour must be that in the region of the break some cones will be slightly less strongly stimulated than others. Hartridge has calculated that the variation of luminance in the shadow is sufficiently great to permit a significant difference in stimulus-intensity for the cones in the region of the break, even when the latter only subtends an angle of a few seconds at the eye ; *i.e.*, by moving along the retina a distance corresponding to 4 seconds of arc, a sufficient change in illumination is obtained to have an effect on the response of the cones. On this view, the edge of the shadow does not have to fall on any line of cones ; the shadow varies continuously in luminance from left to right ; at any point above the break, the luminance will be always rather less than at any point in the same vertical line below the break ; so long as that difference in luminance is adequate to cause a differential stimulation of cones at the two points, we have the basis for the recognition of the break in the contour. Diffraction and aberration, by causing a progressive decrease in luminance of the image of the line to left and right, thus provide the basis for discrimination which would be impossible with a geometrical image.

Resolution of a Single Line. Hecht & Mintz have shown that a line may be detected against a uniformly bright background when it subtends only 0·5 seconds of arc at the eye ; the image of such a line on the retina consists of nothing more than a slight variation in luminance to left and right of the geo-metrical image ; this is so slight that even along the line corresponding to the geometrical shadow the luminance is only 1 per cent less than that in regions unaffected by the line ; nevertheless this difference of luminance is considered to be adequate to cause a differential cone stimulation that could be interpreted as a localized change in luminance, *i.e.* the increment corresponds to the value of $\Delta I/I$ found for the prevailing level of luminance. On this view, it would appear that the limiting factor in the detection of a line is the liminal brightness increment.

Effect of Luminance of Test-Object. Interpretation

An adequate explanation for the simple phenomenon of the progressive increase in visual acuity that may be attained by increasing the luminance of the test-object has so far baffled all investigators in this field. Hecht considered that increasing the luminance brought into operation more and more cones, and so the effective mosaic became finer and finer and thereby permitted better and better resolution. In the simple form in which it was presented the theory was inadequate, but as modified recently by Pirenne and his colleagues, it may well account for many of the phenomena.

Multiple Unit Hypothesis. Their point of view is best illustrated by a diagram (Fig. 115). We have seen that the requirement for maximal visual acuity is the effective one-to-one relationship between cones and optic nerve fibres. Any deviations from this relationship must reduce resolving power. Thus, as Fig. 115 shows, a perfect three-to-one relationship would give a visual acuity of one third the maximum, since the effective size of the receptor is three times as large. The visual acuity, other things being equal, must therefore depend on the size of the effective retinal units that can be brought into opera-tion, and Pirenne, Marriott & O'Doherty have suggested that it is mainly

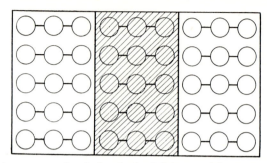

FIG. 115. Illustrating the concept of retinal units in defining resolving power. *Left:* The cones behave in a perfect one-to-one manner, so that the effective retinal mosaic for discriminating a grating is constituted by rows of single cones. *Right:* Because of convergence in the visual pathway, three cones behave as units, hence the grating at limiting resolution must be three times as wide.

because increasing the luminance of the test-object brings into operation smaller units, *i.e.* smaller groups of receptors converging on a single optic nerve fibre, that the basic relationship between visual acuity and luminance pertains.

LIMITING LIGHT-FLUX

Thus the large units are able to summate light-stimuli falling over large areas and therefore their threshold will be lower than that of the smaller units in which summation will be more limited. On this basis we might expect that the flux of light-energy reaching the eye from the white break in the Landolt-C, corresponding to maximal visual acuity, would be the same for the various luminances. Thus under scotopic conditions we might expect it to be equal to the minimum flux necessary for vision, of the order of 150 quanta/sec and according to Pirenne *et al.* this is roughly true. Similarly, with photopic vision, the minimum flux to excite the cones is of the order of $2 \cdot 5 . 10^{-12}$ lumens/sec, and if the fluxes emitted from the breaks of the Landolt-C's are calculated for different luminances these correspond approximately up to visual acuities of about 2. Beyond this, however, the amount of light entering the eye from the break is well above the threshold flux. As Pirenne has indeed pointed out, it is highly unlikely that this can be a complete explanation since threshold measurements are made under vastly different conditions from measurements of visual acuity, where large parts of the retina are stimulated by the surroundings of the Landolt-C.

SCOTOPIC VISUAL ACUITY

The essential features of scotopic visual acuity have already been described, and are illustrated by Fig. 109 (p. 166) ; the generally low order is presumably due to the synaptic organization of the rods such that the functional units are large. A study of the completely colour-blind subject with defective cone vision confirms this limitation of the rods ; however great the luminance employed the visual acuity could not be improved beyond $0 \cdot 17$, *i.e.* a value only about one tenth that found for cone vision in the normal eye. Under mesopic conditions, and with peripheral vision, both rods and cones are active, yet Mandelbaum & Sloan found that usually the rods dominated the picture, presumably because they were operating far above their thresholds by comparison with the cones.

PUPIL-SIZE, WAVELENGTH AND EYE MOVEMENTS

The Effect of Pupil-Size. Decreasing the size of the pupil will decrease the effects of aberrations on the optical image, and thus should improve visual acuity ; on the other hand, when the pupil becomes sufficiently small, diffraction effects become important. Finally, the smaller the pupil the smaller the amount of light that may enter the eye ; under scotopic conditions, at any rate, this must be an important factor. Experimentally it is found that with pupil-sizes below 3 mm the visual acuity is independent of pupil-size because the improvement in the retinal image due to reducing aberrations is compensated by the

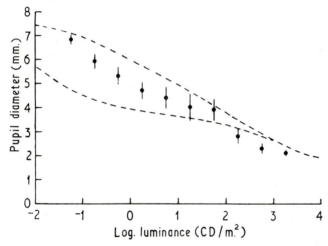

Fig. 116. The broken lines indicate the natural pupil-sizes corresponding with the luminances shown on the abscissa; the points indicate the optimum pupil-sizes appropriate to these luminance levels. (Campbell & Gregory, *Nature*.)

deleterious effects of diffraction. Increasing the pupil-size beyond 3 mm decreases visual acuity at high intensities of illumination, presumably because of the aberrations in the optical image. If a human subject is placed in a room that is darkened steadily the size of the pupil naturally increases, and it was shown by Campbell & Gregory that the size attained was, in fact, optimal for visual acuity at this particular luminance. Thus, by using artificial pupils they determined the optimum sizes for given levels of luminance, and they compared these with the actual values that the pupils took up under the same luminances. The results are shown in Fig. 116 where the plotted points indicate the optimal pupil size for different luminance levels, whilst the broken lines indicate the natural pupil-size under the same conditions.

Influence of Wavelength. In general, the use of different coloured lights has little effect on visual acuity provided their luminance be adequately maintained ; the use of monochromatic, as opposed to white, light should abolish chromatic aberration so the fact that monochromatic light is not preferable indicates that physiological mechanisms, leading to suppression of the coloured fringes, come into play ; in fact Hartridge found that artificially doubling the chromatic aberration of the human eye failed to influence visual acuity. It has been argued that, because colour vision is mediated by at least three types of cone, the use of monochromatic light would impair visual acuity since, with green light, say, only the green-sensitive cones would be operative and so the retinal mosaic would be much grosser, the intervening red-sensitive and blue-sensitive cones being functionless in this respect. Whilst under certain critical conditions it is possible to isolate one cone-mechanism from the rest, *e.g.* a blue-sensitive one, and when this is done to find that the visual acuity is indeed reduced, nevertheless under the ordinary conditions of measuring visual acuity it seems very likely that all types of cone would be operating, and so effects of wavelength would be negligibly small.

The Effect of Eye Movements

Troxler Phenomenon. The question as to whether involuntary movements of the eyes play a role in determining visual acuity has been agitated repeatedly. As we shall see, the eyes are never absolutely still, so that the contours of the retinal image are repeatedly falling on new sets of receptors; and we may expect the OFF-effects to be just as important as the ON-effects, if not more so, in the interpretation of the retinal image by the brain. Troxler noted that when fixation was maintained by an effort, peripheral images tended to disappear, to reappear immediately on moving the eyes ; this is the *Troxler phenomenon*, and suggests that, for peripheral vision at any rate, the eyes must move if the perception of contours is to be maintained.

Stabilized Retinal Image. With foveal fixation it requires a special optical device to demonstrate the same effect ; Ditchburn & Ginsborg and Riggs *et al.*, working independently, showed that with a "stabilized retinal image", such that however the eyes moved the image of a fixated object remained on the same part of the retina, the image would disappear within a few seconds and, if it was that of a fine line, would fail to reappear. The actual involuntary movements made by the eye are small, so that it is presumably the renewal of the stimuli at the contour that determines the retention of the visual percept.

Significance of Eye Movements. To what extent, however, these movements contribute to the acuity of visual perception it is not easy to say. That is : Are the movements merely a device to prevent fading of the image, or do they make a positive contribution? Mandelbaum & Sloan, in the study illustrated by Fig. 109, used flash-exposures of their Landolt-C's lasting 0·2 sec, so that it is very unlikely that eye movements could have contributed appreciably, yet their visual acuities recorded are not unusually low. Furthermore, if visual acuity were better with long exposures than with short this could be attributed rather to the extra time given the subject to make several tries at resolution rather than to the eye movements ; these extra tries would improve resolution on a purely statistical basis.

Off-Effects

According to Pirenne (1958) visual acuity under scotopic conditions is, indeed, improved if the subject is allowed to make quite large movements of the eyes, so that it can be argued that it is the OFF-effects, resulting from these movements, that are significant, rather than the continuous ON-effects from the white break in the C. This view is illustrated by Fig. 117 where the Landolt-C is large enough for resolution at the given level of illumination. The C has been moved and the receptors that have been covered by the movement have indicated this by their OFF-discharges. At the break, however, there has been no OFF-effect, and it is the absence of OFF-effect in the region of the break that determines the perception of its position. If the break were too small, or the illumination too low, then the C would behave as an O, in the sense that the receptors under the break would not be stimulated, and movement

FIG. 117. Illustrating the effects of an eye movement on the retina on which is projected the image of a Landolt-C. The initial position is in black; cones with crosses on them experience an OFF-effect whilst the remainder remain unaffected; it may be that it is the absence of OFF-effect at the break that signals the presence of the break.

of the C would cause OFF-effects to take place over the whole contour. For scotopic vision the movements would have to be large and greater than the involuntary movements whose maximum extent is only of the order of 10 minutes of arc ; with photopic vision, on the supposition that OFF-effects were also of importance, the involuntary movements might well be adequate.

GENERAL REFERENCES

HARTRIDGE, H. (1947). The visual perception of fine detail. *Phil. Trans.*, **232**, 519–671.
HECHT, S. (1937). Rods, cones and the chemical basis of vision. *Physiol. Rev.*, **17**, 239–290.
PIRENNE, M. H. (1962). Visual acuity. In *The Eye*. Vol. 2. Chap. 9. Ed. Davson. London: Academic Press.

SPECIAL REFERENCES

CAMPBELL, F. W., & GREGORY, A. H. (1960). Effect of size of pupil on visual acuity. *Nature*, **187**, 1121–1123.
DITCHBURN, R. W., & GINSBORG, B. L. (1952). Vision with a stabilised retinal image. *Nature*, **170**, 36–37.
HECHT, S., & MINTZ, E. U. (1939). The visibility of single lines at various illuminations and the retinal basis of visual resolution. *J. gen. Physiol.*, **22**, 593–612.
LYTHGOE, R. J. (1932). The measurement of visual acuity. *Med. Res. Council Sp. Rep. Ser.*, No. 173.
MANDELBAUM, J., & SLOAN, L. L. (1947). Peripheral visual acuity. *Amer. J. Ophthal.*, **30**, 581–588.
PIRENNE, M. H. (1957). "Off" mechanisms and human visual acuity. *J. Physiol.*, **137**, 48–49 P.

PIRENNE, M. H. (1958). Some aspects of the sensitivity of the eye. *Ann. N.Y. Acad. Sci.*, **74,** 377–384.

PIRENNE, M. H., MARRIOTT, F. H. C., & O'DOHERTY, E. F. (1957). Individual differences in night-vision efficiency. *Med. Res. Council Sp. Rep. Ser.*, No. 294.

POLYAK, S. L. (1941). *The Retina*. Chicago Univ. Press: Chicago.

POLYAK, S. L. (1957). *The Vertebrate Visual System*. Chicago Univ. Press: Chicago.

RIGGS, L. A., RATLIFF, F., CORNSWEET, J. C., & CORNSWEET, E. F. (1953). The disappearance of steadily fixated visual test objects. *J. opt. Soc. Amer.*, **43,** 495–501.

SHLAER, S. (1937). The relation between visual acuity and illumination. *J. gen. Physiol.*, **21,** 165–188.

PART 9

WAVELENGTH DISCRIMINATION AND THE THEORY OF COLOUR VISION

The problem of colour vision has attracted the interest and excited the speculation not only of physiologists but of physicists, psychologists, anatomists, philosophers, and poets with the inevitable result that the subject abounds with theories whilst sound experimental facts are comparatively rare. It will be quite impossible to review the multiplicity of theories of colour vision ; all that we can hope to do is to indicate the more outstanding facts and the lines along which any explanation will probably be developed if it is to conform to accepted principles of nerve physiology.

THE PURKINJE PHENOMENON

We may introduce this account by studying the alterations in visual characteristics that take place on passing from scotopic to photopic vision.

Scotopic and Photopic Spectral Sensitivity Curves

Scotopic Sensitivity Curve. As we have seen, the scotopic sensitivity curve is obtained by measuring the absolute threshold of the dark-adapted eye for different wavelengths, and plotting the reciprocals of these thresholds, which measure sensitivity, against the wavelength. In a sense, then, this curve represents the relative luminosities of the different wavelengths so that, if we had a spectrum containing equal energies in all the wavelengths, the blue-green at about 5000 Å would appear brightest, and the red and violet darkest. The spectral sensitivity curve is thus sometimes described as the *luminosity curve for an equal-energy spectrum.*

Photopic Sensitivity Curve. The photopic sensitivity curve is the measure of the relative effectiveness of the different wavelengths in exciting the light sense at levels well above threshold ; at these levels the lights excite the sensation of colour as well and, since this is mediated by the cones, it would not be surprising if the curve of spectral sensitivities really indicated the relative sensitivities of the cones to different wavelengths. Thus we may take two patches, A and B, of light of different wavelengths and adjust their intensities until they appear equally bright by the method of flicker-photometry (p. 100). We may then compare B with a new patch of light, C, of another wavelength, and so on through the spectrum. The reciprocals of these amounts of energies will be measures of the sensitivity of the eye to the different wavelengths and they give the curve of Fig. 118. The maximum occurs at 5550 Å in the yellow-green instead of at 5000 in the blue-green for scotopic vision. On comparing the two sensitivity curves, as in Fig. 119, it will be seen that there are characteristic changes in sensitivity of the eye on passing from scotopic to photopic vision, which are given the general name of *Purkinje shift.*

Shift in Sensitivity. Purkinje in 1823 observed that the relative luminosities of hues changed as the luminance was reduced (the *Purkinje shift*), and the nature

Fig. 118. Photopic luminosity curves. The curve in full line is that shown by Jainski whilst that in broken lines is the C.I.E. curve. (Le Grand, *Optique Physiologique*.)

of the change can be predicted from the curves of Fig. 119. Thus let us consider an orange of 6500 Å and a yellow-green of 5500 Å ; under photopic conditions their luminosities are roughly in the ratio of 13 : 100, the yellow-green being some 8 times brighter than the orange ; on referring to the scotopic curve it is seen that the same colours have luminosities in the ratio : 2 : 56, *i.e.* the yellow-green is now some 28 times brighter than the orange. In general, the short wave-

Fig. 119. The scotopic luminosity curve (open circles) compared with the photopic curve (full circles). (After Hecht.)

lengths will become brighter in comparison with the long wavelengths as the luminance level is reduced. It should be noted that the Purkinje phenomenon becomes apparent at levels where colour is still perceived, in the mesopic range where both rods and cones are operative ; the shift in the apparent luminances of coloured lights is thus due to the super-imposition of a rod effect—stimulating only the light sense—on the cone effect. The photopic and scotopic sensitivity

curves are thus curves for cones and rods acting essentially alone ; at intermediate luminances, where both are operative, the sensitivity curve lies between
these limits.

Red Light and Dark-Adaptation. We may note from the luminosity curves
that red light is much less luminous to the dark-adapted than to the light-
adapted eye in comparison with other wavelengths ; in fact it is now generally
considered that the rods are barely sensitive to the extreme red end of the spectrum, so that the dark-adapted eye may be exposed to fairly high luminance
levels of deep red light—bright enough to permit reading with ease and hence
to allow the photopic mechanism to function—without serious loss of dark-
adaptation. This principle was applied extensively during the war ; chart-
rooms were illuminated with red light and night-fighter pilots wore special red
dark-adaptation goggles which permitted them to read in a well-illuminated
room and yet maintain a considerable degree of dark-adaptation.

Iodopsin. Photochemical studies have demonstrated the remarkable correspondence between the absorption spectrum of rhodopsin and the scotopic
sensitivity curve, from which it has been concluded that scotopic vision is
mediated by this single pigment, rhodopsin. May we conclude that the photopic
sensitivity curve corresponds to the presence of a cone-pigment with a maximum
in the yellow-green at about 5500 Å? This question is not easy to answer because
cone vision is obviously more complex than rod vision, changes in wavelength
being accompanied by changes in qualitative sensation that we call colour ;

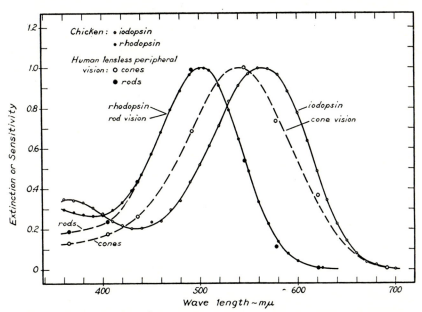

FIG. 120. Absorption spectra of chicken rhodopsin and iodopsin compared
with the spectral sensitivity of human rod and cone vision. The scotopic
(rod) sensitivity agrees with the absorption spectrum of rhodopsin over
most of its course. The photopic (cone) sensitivity curve does not coincide
exactly with the absorption spectrum of iodopsin, being displaced some
20 mμ toward the blue from this absorption spectrum. (Wald, Brown &
Smith, *J. gen. Physiol.*)

and, as we shall see, wavelength discrimination requires the presence of several pigments, contained in separate types of receptor. The chicken retina contains practically only cones and Wald was able to extract from this a pigment, which he called *iodopsin*, with an absorption spectrum not greatly different from the photopic sensitivity curve. This is illustrated by Fig. 120, where both scotopic and photopic sensitivity curves have been drawn, whilst the plotted points represent absorption spectra of rhodopsin and iodopsin respectively. The agreement between rhodopsin absorption and scotopic sensitivity is good, as we have seen before ; the maximum absorption of iodopsin, at 5620 Å, is some 200 Å closer to the red end of the spectrum than the photopic sensitivity maximum measured, in this case, on a subject with a lens-less eye to reduce effects of absorption by the ocular media.

Electrophysiological Aspects

Frog ERG. We may expect the Purkinje effect to be manifest in all mixed retinæ, whilst in pure rod (guinea pig) or pure cone (squirrel) retinæ it should

FIG. 121. The Purkinje phenomenon in the frog's retina. The curves are luminosity curves and it is seen that the wavelength of maximum luminosity changes from 5600 Å to 5000 Å on passing from photopic to scotopic conditions. Double contour of rod graph indicates limits of variability. (Granit & Wrede, *J. Physiol.*)

be absent. The electroretinogram has been a useful tool in the study of this phenomenon ; thus we may use the reciprocals of the relative amounts of light-energy to evoke a *b*-wave of fixed magnitude as the index to sensitivity of the retina to different wavelengths ; if the light- and dark-adapted eyes are compared in the frog, for example, there is the same characteristic shift in sensitivity to longer wavelengths on passing from dark- to light-adaptation (Fig. 121).

Flicker ERG. Even in the cat, whose retina is very much dominated by rods, a shift in spectral sensitivity can be obtained by employing the flicker method of analysis of the ERG. It will be recalled that the rods are unable to follow a light-stimulus flickering at more than about 25 cycles/sec. With a very strong light, flickering at, say, 50 cycles/sec the responses on the record are thus cone responses, and we may measure the effectiveness of the different wavelengths in producing an electrical effect of fixed magnitude. Under these conditions the maximum sensitivity shifts from 5000 Å to 5500 Å (Dodt & Walther). In the pure cone eye of the squirrel there is no Purkinje shift so that only high critical fusion frequencies of flicker are found and the spectral sensitivity shows a maximum in the yellow-green that is barely affected by dark-adaptation (Arden & Tansley).

Single Fibres. Studies with single fibres of the optic nerve, or of large ganglion cells in the retina show essentially the same sort of Purkinje shift but, as we shall see, this change belongs to a certain type of element which Granit has called the *dominator*.

Photochromatic Interval

The threshold stimulus for the different wavelengths gives us the scotopic sensitivity curve which, as we have seen, refers only to the light sense since no colour

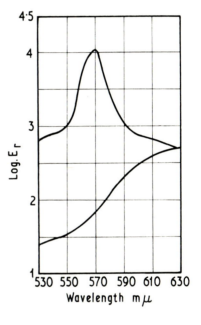

FIG. 122. Illustrating the photochromatic interval. The lower curve indicates the thresholds for the sensation of light (absolute thresholds) whilst the upper curve indicates the thresholds for the sensation of colour. Note that the thresholds coincide in the orange-red. (After Dagher *et al.*, *Visual Problems of Colour.*)

sensation is evoked (except possibly in the deep red). If the threshold stimulus for a given wavelength is increased, at a certain value the sensation of colour is reached (the *specific threshold*). The interval in luminance between the absolute light threshold and the specific threshold is called the *photochromatic interval*. In Fig. 122 some results obtained by Dagher, Cruz & Plaza on a human subject are shown for the interval between 5300 and 6300 Å, *i.e.* over the green-orange-red part of the spectrum. The lower curve represents the absolute thresholds whilst the upper curve represents the specific thresholds. It will be seen that the interval becomes negligibly small at the red end of the spectrum, which means that the threshold for red light corresponds to the threshold for cone vision. At the fovea, too, the photochromatic interval is very small or non-existent.

Cone Thresholds

Dark-Adaptation Curves. As stated above, if the photopic sensitivity curve represents the sensitivities of the cones, then if we can determine the thresholds for cone vision at different wavelengths we may obtain a spectral sensitivity curve which should be similar to that obtained by simple matching techniques. The problem is, of course, to be sure of stimulating only cones when measuring a threshold ; in the completely dark-adapted eye this is impossible, except at the extreme red end of the spectrum, because the rods are the more sensitive. Wald made use of the fact that immediately after light-adaptation the first portion of the dark-adaptation curve (Fig. 56, p. 95) represents cone sensitivity *i.e.*, under these conditions we may actually measure cone thresholds. By using different wavelengths for the light-stimulus he was able to plot a cone sensitivity curve which had a maximum at 5550 Å and was similar in essentials to the C.I.E. curve of Fig. 118.

Fig. 123. Sensitivity curves for foveal and peripheral cones compared with that for rods. Top curve: rods. Bottom curves: cones. The broken line refers to peripheral cones. (After Wald, *Science*.)

Foveal Thresholds. Again, if vision is confined to the fovea by making use of flash stimuli of small extent, the thresholds should be determined by the cones. Under these conditions the subject usually states that he perceived the colour of the stimulus. By comparing results obtained in this way with those obtained by the dark-adaptation technique, we may compare the sensitivities of foveal and peripheral cones. As Fig. 123 shows, the curves are very similar, the foveal cones being less sensitive, except in the red part of the spectrum where they are about the same.

Increment Thresholds. Finally, we may note that measurement of the liminal brightness increment is a measure of the sensitivity of the retina under particular conditions of exposure to light; and according as to whether the rods or cones are the more sensitive under the particular conditions, the one or other type of receptor will determine this increment, or differential threshold as we have called it. By choosing suitable conditions of light-adaptation it is possible to ensure that the cones will be the more sensitive (*e.g.* by adapting with blue light to which the rods are so much more sensitive than the cones) and therefore it is possible to measure their thresholds with different wavelengths of light and obtain spectral sensitivity curves. This technique was developed by Stiles & Crawford and has been exploited widely in the measurement of spectral sensitivity curves. As we shall see, the measurements may be so refined that we may determine not only the thresholds of the cones in general, but thresholds of different types of cone (p. 189).

WAVELENGTH DISCRIMINATION

As emphasized earlier, the difference between the scotopic and photopic sensitivity curves is not just the shift in maximal sensitivity to a different wavelength described as the Purkinje effect ; there is the difference that vision becomes chromatic under photopic conditions, and the subject is able to state not only that light is present but that it belongs to a certain part of the spectrum. Before studying the mechanism of this wavelength discrimination, we may ask why it is that the retina is achromatic under scotopic conditions. The answer is that under scotopic conditions only one type of receptor is operating, the rods, and that these rods are physiologically identical in that they all have the pigment rhodopsin as their photopigment. Such a functionally homogeneous retina cannot act as a wavelength discriminator.

Homogeneous Retina. To make this clear we may consider the responses in the optic nerve fibres of *Limulus* which, we may recall, are derived directly from the photoreceptors. A study of their responses to different wavelengths

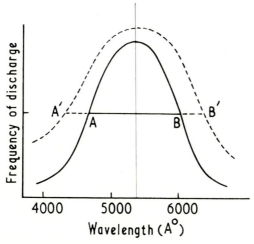

FIG. 124. Theoretical wavelength-response curve for a single receptor of *Limulus* retina. The maximum response will occur at 5200 Å, the absorption maximum of the retinal pigment. With wavelengths of light corresponding to the points A and B, the responses will be identical, so that no discrimination between these two wavelengths is possible.

gives a typical sensitivity curve, with maximal sensitivity at 5200 Å corresponding to the wavelength of maximum absorption of its photopigment. If we were to plot the intensity of response in a single fibre against wavelength we would obtain a curve roughly like Fig. 124. In a sense, then, this receptor, and thus the eye, is showing some wavelength discrimination, in that it is responding with different frequencies of spike discharge to different wavelengths. A little consideration will show, however, that this receptor could not discriminate between changes of wavelength and changes of intensity; and even if we could keep intensity constant its discrimination is limited. Thus, at the points A and B on the curve, the responses are the same but the wavelengths are widely different ; by drawing other lines parallel to the abscissa, cutting the curve in two points, many other pairs of spectral hues could be obtained producing identical responses. Moreover, this curve was obtained by keeping the energy content of the stimulus the same ; new curves would be obtained by varying the energy content, as indicated by dotted lines, so that in fact with a single wavelength we would be able to mimic the responses of all other wavelengths of the spectrum simply by varying the intensity of this single wavelength. Hence a retina containing a single type of receptor is unable to discriminate changes in both wavelength and intensity.

Multiple Receptor Hypothesis. The position becomes different if we have several types of receptor, with different photosensitive pigments ; these would have different response curves and it is not difficult to show that the effects of varying wavelength on the pattern of discharges in the several types might be unique and not matchable by a change in intensity. Thus, for example, with six receptors a green light of wavelength 5300 Å might evoke spike responses in these having say, 15, 34, 65, 20, 4, 2 spikes per sec. A yellow light of 6000 Å might give a different set of responses, say 35, 65, 45, 20, 15, 7 spikes per sec ; and it would be these *patterns* of discharges that would be characteristic of the respective wavelengths for this particular energy level of the stimuli. Increasing the energy would increase the frequencies of discharge, but it could well be that they would be able to maintain a unique pattern that could not be mimicked by other lights however much we varied the intensity. Clearly, the more types of receptor we have, the more certain we will be of having a unique type of response for a given combination of wavelength and intensity. As we shall see, Nature has economized in this respect, since it appears that only three types of receptor suffice for human wavelength discrimination.

THE YOUNG-HELMHOLTZ THEORY

Trivariance of Colour Vision

We have already seen that colour-matching experiments have led to the generalization that we may match any colour by a mixture of three primary spectral wavelengths provided we admit that the match is not perfect so far as saturation is concerned. Thus if we wish to match a given colour X, we may place it in one half of a photometric matching field and in the other half we may project a mixture of red, green and blue lights ; by varying the relative intensities of these we may match our colour from the point of view of chromaticity, but the mixture that we have made will be unsaturated, so we must add some white to X to make the match perfect in respect to both chromaticity and saturation. Thus our mixing equation would take the form:

$$\alpha R + \beta G + \gamma B = X + x \; White$$

or,
$$\alpha R + \beta G + \gamma B - x \; White = X$$

But, since white may be represented by a mixture of red, green and blue, say: $\alpha' R + \beta' G + \gamma' B$, we may subtract these from the left-hand side of the equation, and we are left with an equation that defines our colour, X, in terms of only three variables:

$$(\alpha - \alpha')R + (\beta - \beta')G + (\gamma - \gamma')B = X$$

It is in this sense, then, that we are able to say that colour vision is a *trivariant phenomenon* ; we can, in essence, describe any colour-stimulus in terms of three variables ; normal human colour vision is thus *trichromatic*.

Spectral Mixture Curves. The trichromaticity of colour vision tells us that *any* colour can be matched in terms of three primary stimuli. If we confine

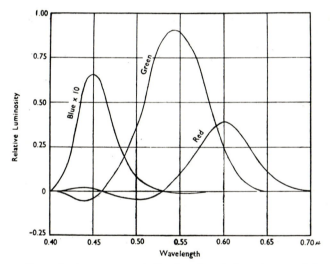

Fig. 125. Spectral mixture curves indicating the relative amounts of the three primaries that are required for matching any spectral wavelength. For example, with a blue of 0·50 μ (5000 Å), the relative contributions are about 0·33 Green, 0·1 (÷ 10) Blue, and 0·05 Red. (Wright, *Researches on Normal and Defective Colour Vision*.)

ourselves to matching the spectral colours we may represent this process by the chromaticity chart of Fig. 61, p. 102; alternatively we may plot the individual contributions of our red, green and blue primaries to the different spectral colours as in Fig. 125. As abscissæ we have the wavelengths of the spectral hues we wish to match, and as ordinates are plotted the amounts of each individual primary required for each match. These *spectral mixture curves* show us at a glance how much of a given primary is required to match a spectral hue ; thus a yellow of 6000 Å requires some 0·25 units of green and some 0·4 units of red with no blue. A blue-green of 5000 Å requires about 0·4 units of green, 0·01 unit of blue* and some "negative red".

Three-Receptor Hypothesis

These curves lead naturally to the hypothesis that any colour sensation may be evoked by stimulating three fundamental receptors to varying extents. Thus we see that a yellow sensation may be created either by passing yellow light of, say, wavelength 6000 Å into the eye, or we may create exactly the same sensation by passing into the eye a mixture of quite different lights, lights that by themselves would have excited the sensations of green and red respectively. Thus the colour mixing phenomena are essentially phenomena of confusion or failure to distinguish ; the light of wavelength 6000 Å is physically different from the lights of 5300 Å and 6500 Å that are used for the match, but the eye cannot distinguish between the light of 6000 Å and the mixture. The phenomena illustrate too the economy of Nature ; if an eye is to discriminate single wavelengths from mixtures then a large number of receptors must be necessary, but it is very questionable whether this discriminatory power would have much biological survival value, and instead the trivariance of colour sensation suggests that Nature "makes do" with a very limited number of receptors.

The Fundamental Mechanisms

The three-receptor hypothesis is the essential basis of the Young-Helmholtz trichromatic theory of colour vision ; in essence it has come to mean today that the retina contains three types of cone that respond differently to the same

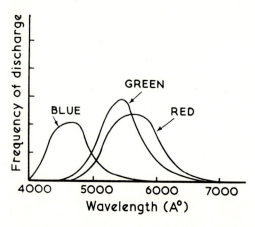

FIG. 126. Theoretical wavelength-response curves for three hypothetical receptors maximally sensitive to red, green and blue respectively.

wavelengths ; thus a "blue" cone would respond most prominently to the short end of the spectrum, and only a little to lights of the middle region and perhaps not at all to very long wavelengths ; a "green cone" would respond preferentially to the middle regions, and so on. Each mechanism, or cone-type, may therefore be regarded as having its own spectral sensitivity curve, and we may look on the spectral mixture curves of Fig. 125 as being related to the spectral sensitivity curves of the separate mechanisms. Thus, to refer to the figure,

* The contribution of blue to any mixture is very small, in terms of luminosity, so that the values have been multiplied by ten in the Figure.

we might say that the yellow light of wavelength 6000 Å had excited the green mechanism by 0·25 units and the red mechanism by 0·4 units and had failed to excite the blue mechanism at all. Thus the match occurred because the yellow light did exactly what the green and red lights would have done if they had fallen simultaneously on the retina. On this basis, then, we could plot three sensitivity curves for the three mechanisms, using as ordinates the frequency of discharge, say, in the nerve fibres leading from these fundamental mechanisms as in Fig. 126.

Spectral Sensitivities. The next problem, of course, is to decide on the true spectral characteristics of these mechanisms ; the colour-mixing phenomena tell us we can use any three primaries, so we can have an infinite number of sets of spectral mixture curves. Which, if any of these, is the correct set? Various methods were used to derive the true fundamental response curves, as they were called.

ADAPTATION

For example, Wright used as his criterion the effects of adaptation. He has shown that if the eye is adapted to white light the sensitivity to all wavelengths is depressed in proportion ; however, if the adapting light is coloured, there is a certain preferential depression of sensitivity to this colour, so that a subject who has been adapted to red, for instance, requires more red to make a match with white than he did before the adaptation. If the adapting light is yellow, both the red and green sensations are depressed, and so on. Thus if there are, indeed, three fundamental sensations, it should be possible to adapt the eye to at least one or two hues such that sensitivity to these alone is depressed, since these alone should be stimulated. Wright found that a blue of 4600 Å and a red of 7600 Å behaved in this way, and he suggested that these were two of the primary sensations ; violet he concluded was definitely not a fundamental sensation since it was considerably modified by adaptation of the eye to red light. The wavelength corresponding to the third sensation, which from its position cannot be stimulated alone, was deduced to have the value of 5300 Å, *i.e.* in the green. On the basis of this reasoning Wright drew a set of spectral sensitivity curves.

COLOUR-BLIND

Other workers studied the so-called colour-blind, and on the assumption that their colour defect was the consequence of one of the mechanisms' being absent (p. 193), they were able to deduce, from the colour-blind person's matching phenomena, the characteristics of the spectral sensitivity curve of the missing mechanism, and thence that of the remainder.

Two-Colour Threshold Technique

Liminal Brightness Increment. Stiles developed an extremely ingenious technique for the identification of separate cone mechanisms in the human eye. The method is based on the measurement of increment thresholds, or liminal brightness increments (l.b.i.). It will be recalled that the l.b.i. for white light is measured by the extra luminance of a test patch, ΔI, necessary for it to be distinguished against its white background of luminance I. By successively increasing the background luminance, I, we get a series of steps, ΔI, and by plotting log ΔI against log I we find that the graph has a characteristic shape. Thus, over the range of scotopic vision it may be represented by Fig. 127; at very low luminance, the increment threshold, ΔI, is approximately constant and equal to the absolute threshold ; at a certain point the graph becomes a straight line of slope unity,* and finally there is a point where the rod mechanism is said to be saturated.

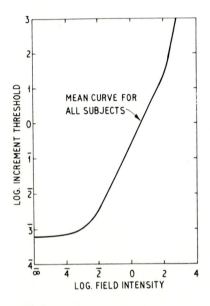

FIG. 127. Showing the variation of the liminal brightness increment (l.b.i. or increment threshold) with field intensity. For details see text. (After Aguilar & Stiles, *Optica Acta.*)

Rod and Cone Mechanisms. This type of graph is only obtained, however, if a single mechanism is operating over the whole range of luminance, *i.e.* if the rods only are active; and the type of curve shown in Fig. 127 could only be obtained by using special techniques to keep the cones from coming into play. In general, then, when the luminance comes up to a certain point the cones become the more sensitive and they now determine the l.b.i. and the graph of log ΔI against I shows a characteristic break, or kink, indicating the taking over of the new "mechanism", in this case the taking over of the threshold by cones in place of rods. This is illustrated by Fig. 128. In this way we have identified, then, the operation of a new mechanism. By varying the wavelength of the background, and of the test-stimulus, we may create conditions that favour one or the other mechanism and so study it over a large range of luminance ; *e.g.* by using a red background and measuring the liminal brightness increment with a blue test-stimulus we may suppress cone activity and study rod activity. In this way, then, we may not only identify the presence of rod and cone mechanisms but we may also measure their spectral sensitivities, using the l.b.i. as a measure of threshold for any given wavelength, care being taken that the background and test-stimulus are such that only one of the two mechanisms is operative.

* It is over this range that the Fechner fraction, $\Delta I/I$, is constant; so that we have the relationship:
$$\log \Delta I = \log I + Constant$$
so that with a logarithmic plot we should have a straight line with slope equal to unity.

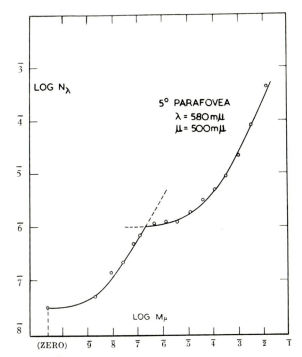

Fig. 128. The curve obtained by plotting the logarithm of the liminal brightness increment (N_λ) against logarithm of the background intensity (M_μ). In this case the background was blue-green and the central patch a yellow of 5800 Å. The left part of the curve represents increment thresholds for rod vision; at the break and beyond, the increment thresholds are determined by the cones. N_λ and M_μ are expressed as erg sec^{-1} (deg. of arc)$^{-2}$. (Stiles, *Proc. Nat. Acad. Sci. Wash.*)

Cone Mechanisms. The same technique can be applied to identify different cone mechanisms, and Stiles found, indeed, that under appropriate conditions of background and test-stimulus the presence of three mechanisms could be established with maximum sensitivities in the red, green and blue. Subsequent studies indicated that the blue mechanism is complex, and can be described as being made up of three, π_1, π_2, and π_3, whilst the green and red mechanisms are called π_4 and π_5 respectively. The discovery of five, as opposed to three, cone mechanisms certainly demands some modification of the Young-Helmholtz trichromatic theory, but since this really is a statement of fact, namely the practical trivariance of colour vision, in the sense that the phenomena of mixing can be explained in terms of only three variables, this suggests that the extra information that is sent to the higher centres by virtue of the three types of blue mechanism is somehow lost.

COLOUR-BLINDNESS

Since the study of the colour-defective human subject (usually described somewhat inaccurately as the colour-blind) has thrown some light on the more general aspects of colour discrimination, it is right that we devote some space to the main experimental findings at this juncture. In general, a colour-defective subject is one whose powers of discrimination between lights of different wave-lengths are more limited than normal ; the extent of this defect may range from complete failure of wavelength discrimination—*monochromatism*—through *dichromatism*, where the discrimination is so limited that we must postulate the absence of one of the three fundamental mechanisms, to the *colour-anomalous*, where the defect is a difference from average behaviour, in the sense that the protanomalous uses more red than the average in matching a yellow with a mixture of red and green.

Rod Monochromatism

The more frequently occurring type of completely colour-blind is one whose cones are apparently pathologically defective ; the subject is therefore called a *rod monochromat*, and we have already seen that his visual functions are largely what one might expect on the basis of the duplicity theory ; thus he shows no Purkinje phenomenon, having a spectral sensitivity curve corresponding only to the scotopic type. Such monochromats occur with a frequency of about one in thirty thousand.

Visual Characteristics. There is by no means complete agreement as to the essential feature, if there is one, of the so-called rod monochromat; being more common than the cone monochromat, the rod monochromat is called "typical", but various studies indicate that all the features of this condition cannot be forced into a single type. Walls & Heath have emphasized the complexities in some of the visual characteristics of the "typical" achromat; thus we have already seen that the plot of critical fusion frequency against luminance shows a break, as in normals, suggesting the operation of two types of receptor, and sometimes the dark-adapta-tion curve also shows a "kink". These findings led v. Koenig and later Hecht to postulate the presence of "photopic rods" in the retina of the monochromat. In general, we may regard "typical" achromatopsia as a retinal dystrophy with the following signs, not all of which need be present in any subject: (*a*) achromatic vision; (*b*) low visual acuity, of the order of 0·1 to 0·3, better at moderate luminance than at high; (*c*) no Purkinje shift; (*d*) avoidance of very bright lights; (*e*) nystagmus; (*f*) some signs of macular dystrophy. The post-mortem study of Larsen showed that cones were indeed present in the retina, with most of them apparently normal.

Three Types. Walls & Heath suggested that some cases could be accounted for on the assumption of the absence of functional cones together with the presence of rods in the fovea, whilst others could be described as containing, in addition to rods, the "blue-type" cones postulated by trichromatic theory, the "red" and "green" cones being non-functional or absent. More recently Blackwell & Blackwell have reported on a study of nine subjects whose psychophysical findings allowed them to be placed in three categories: (*a*) typical rod monochromats with all visual functions determined by rods; (*b*) a group with a scotopic luminosity curve very similar to normal except in the blue where sensitivity was low, possibly due to the presence of the yellow xanthophyll macular pigment (they were using central fixation); this suggested that these achromats possessed rods in the fovea. At photopic luminances the sensitivity curve shifted towards the short-wave end of the spectrum, to give a maximum at about 4400 Å, suggesting the coming into play of "blue cones". The third group were intermediate between (*a*) and (*b*).

Cone Monochromatism

The cone, or atypical, monochromat is extremely rare, occurring with a frequency of only one in a hundred million ; in this condition visual acuity is perfectly normal, but there is no discrimination of coloured lights if their luminosities are made equal. It might be thought that the retina, in this condition, contained only one type of cone, but if this were so we should expect the photopic spectral sensitivity curve to be abnormal. Thus, under photopic conditions the sensitivity of the eye to the different wavelengths must be the average sensitivity of the three or more cone mechanisms in the retina ; removal of two of the mechanisms would leave the retina with only one type, and now the spectral sensitivity curve should coincide with the sensitivity curve of a single mechanism. In fact, Weale found the photopic sensitivity curve of the cone monochromat to lie within the normal range. It may well be, therefore, that the defect is one of central integration ; the peripheral mechanisms for colour discrimination may be present, but not the central mechanisms that interpret the complex patterns of messages in the neurones.

Dichromatism

Colour-Matching. The dichromat is one who can match all colours with suitable mixtures of only two, instead of three, primaries. The colour mixing equation will therefore be of the form:

$$C = aA + \beta B$$

where A and B are the primaries ; instead of a pair of rectangular co-ordinates being required to represent their colour mixing data (p. 102), the latter may be exhibited in the form of a straight line where any point on this line corresponds to a definite mixture of the two primaries. It will be clear, without any mathematical analysis, that the range of colours that a dichromat can appreciate as distinct will be very restricted compared with the range of the normal individual, since it is obviously possible to obtain more variations by mixing three things than two.

Missing Mechanisms. According to the classical interpretation, the *protanope* is missing the fundamental red sensation—he is red-blind ; the *deuteranope* lacks the green sensation and the *tritanope* the blue. If this viewpoint is correct, we may anticipate the appearance of the spectrum to the protanope, for example, from a consideration of the curves in Fig. 125, and imagining that the curve corresponding to the red sensation has been removed. In the region between 7600 and about 6500 Å no colour sensation should be experienced, *i.e.* the protanope's spectrum should be shortened ; between 6500 and about 5000 Å the sensation should be that of green only (although it may be called yellow) ; with the introduction of the blue sensation at about 5000 Å, changes in hue should be appreciated and colour discrimination should be approximately normal.

Hue-Discrimination Curves. Thus the curve, obtained by plotting the difference in wavelength necessary for a dichromat to appreciate a change in hue, as ordinates, against the wavelength, as abscissæ, (the hue discrimination curve) should be much simpler than that of a trichromat; in Fig. 129 are shown typical curves for the protanope and deuteranope (that of the normal trichromat is shown in Fig. 59, p. 99) ; it is seen that the maximum discrimination occurs in the region 4800–5000 Å where the blue mechanism is operative. Discrimination falls away rapidly on both sides of this point as we should expect.

Neutral Point. The dichromat can match all hues (spectral and non-spectral and including white) by appropriate mixtures of two primaries ; since white

FIG. 129. Hue-discrimination curves for deuteranope (left) and protanope (right). The smallest change in wavelength, necessary to produce a change in the sensation of hue, has been plotted against the wavelength. Greatest sensitivity is in the blue-green region. (Wright & Pitt.)

can be formed by a certain mixture of these primaries it follows that there will be a certain point in the spectrum which will appear to the dichromat as white—this point is called the *neutral point* and occurs at 4955 Å with the protanope and at 5000 Å with the deuteranope.

An important characteristic of the dichromat, emphasized by Pitt, is the fact that those colour matches holding good for the normal trichromat are appreciated as colour matches by the dichromat, although the inverse proposition is of course not true. Thus trichromatic white is appreciated as white by the dichromat; this white is made up of the three fundamental primaries, red, green and blue, in certain proportions; the protanope does not see the red in this white and we may thus expect him to match a mixture of green and blue with white; similarly a deuteranope would match a purple (red plus blue) with normal white.

Iso-Colour Chart. We have seen that for the normal trichromat the locus of spectral colours is given by a curved line in the colour chart, where each point represents by its co-ordinates the coefficients in the unit colour equation; by joining the two ends of this curve, to make a closed figure, we get the locus of certain non-spectral hues obtained by mixing blue and red, the purples (Fig. 61). All points within this closed figure represent non-spectral hues appreciated by the trichromat. The locus of spectral colours for the dichromat is a straight line only, and since this cannot enclose space, all colours appreciated by the dichromat are spectral hues. This means that for all those numerous hues lying within the normal trichromatic locus, which are appreciated by the trichromat as different, there will correspond only a few spectral colours in the dichromat's colour range; in other words, to the dichromat, for any given spectral hue there will be a large number of non-spectral hues that are indistinguishable from it.

A determination of the colour-mixing data for dichromats permits the construction of iso-colour charts; in Fig. 130 that for a protanope is given. The normal trichromatic spectral locus is drawn in in the usual manner, and trichromatic white is indicated by a star. The neutral point of the protanope, *i.e.* the point on his spectral locus where the mixture of his two primaries gives white, lies at 4955 Å;

and an iso-colour line can be drawn through this point A, and the star representing trichromatic white, since the latter is appreciated as white by the protanope too. The line cuts the red axis at C, which corresponds to a very reddish purple. All colours represented by this line, ranging from blue to reddish purple, appear to the protanope as identical and white. From the data on the spectral hue discrimination of the protanope (Fig. 129), it is possible to mark off points on the spectral locus corresponding to just discriminable differences in hue, and the directions of the iso-colour lines passing through these points may be calculated from colour-mixing data (it will be remembered that between 5300 and 7600 Å all spectral colours appear the same to the dichromat). The iso-colour lines are drawn in the figure, and they divide the trichromatic colour area into a series of zones; all trichromatic

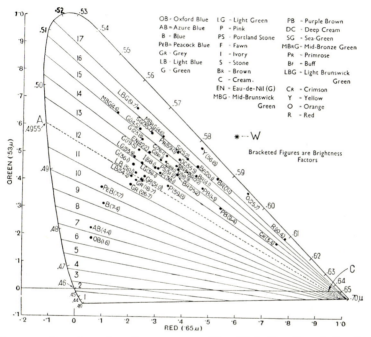

FIG. 130. Iso-colour chart for protanope. (Pitt, *Med. Res. Council Sp. Rep.* By permission of the Controller of H.M. Stationery Office.)

hues represented by points in any one zone are indistinguishable by the dichromat, provided the luminosity is kept constant. For the protanope there are seventeen zones, whilst the deuteranope has some twenty-seven. The iso-colour charts permit one to determine whether any pair of hues can be discriminated by a dichromat, and provide a rational interpretation of the numerous and hitherto uncorrelated facts of dichromatic matching and errors in discrimination.

Luminosity Curves. If dichromatism does, indeed, represent the loss of one of the cone mechanisms we may expect the photopic luminosity curve to be different from normal in dichromatism. The regions of maximum luminosity are, in fact, shifted; that for the protanope lying at about 5400 Å and for the deuteranope at about 5700 Å. Furthermore we should expect the loss of the red mechanism to cause a shortening of the visible spectrum, and in the protanope this is indeed found, the reds at the end of the spectrum appearing grey. Again the loss of one of the "colour mechanisms" presumably corresponds to the dysfunction of one group of cones ; in this case we may expect a loss of absolute luminosity, *i.e.* the thresholds for vision in the dichromat should be generally higher than for the trichromat. With the protanope this is very well established in the red end of the spectrum and, according to Hecht, both protanopes and deuteranopes have a general loss of sensitivity over most of the spectrum, the average rise in threshold of the protanope being 49 per cent and that of the deuteranope 39 per cent. Subsequent studies on a uniocular deuteranope, *i.e.* on a subject with one eye normal and the other deuteranopic, showed that this difference in threshold was quite definite (Graham & Hsia).

Deuteranope. Pitt's analysis of deuteranopia suggested, however, that this could not be simply accounted for by the loss of the green mechanism ; rather the deuteranope behaved as though he had, in place of the red and green mechanisms, a single one corresponding to a weighted mean of the normal red and green mechanisms ; the deuteranope, on this basis, is indeed a dichromat, in the sense that his colour-mixing data can be expressed as a function of only two variables, but he behaves as though his red and green mechanisms were in some way linked so that they cannot act independently.

Tritanope. The tritanope is rare, constituting, according to Wright, only one in 13–65,000 of the population by comparison with one in a hundred males for protanopia and deuteranopia. The tritanope seems to lack the blue mechanism, so that his discrimination is good in the red-green part of the spectrum but bad in the blue-green region ; the neutral point is in the yellow at 5750 Å.

Anomalous Trichromats

Here the subject requires three primaries to match all colours, but uses different proportions from those of the average ; frequently this deviation from the average or "normal" is associated with defective discrimination, but not always according to Pickford. The abnormalities may be roughly classified as *protans*, *deuterans* and *tritans* ; thus a protan is a trichromat who requires more red to match a yellow than does a normal trichromat. The anomalous trichromat differs from the dichromat in that he will not accept matches that the normal makes ; thus the protanope matches a blue-green with white, but he will also accept as white a mixture of this blue-green with red. The protan will match a spectral yellow with an orange, *i.e.* he requires more red for his match than normal, but he will not accept the normal's red-green mixture as a yellow. Anomalous trichromasy is common, amounting to nearly 6 per cent of the male population.

CONE PHOTOPIGMENTS

By the method of reflexion densitometry Campbell & Rushton and Weale were able to demonstrate the presence of rhodopsin in the living eye. By applying the same technique to the fovea, Rushton was able to demonstrate the presence of two cone pigments, which he has called *erythrolabe* and *chlorolabe*. The existence of a cone pigment was first established by exposing the eye to a strong orange light, which might be expected to bleach this pigment in preference to rhodopsin ; by subsequently measuring the absorption of yellow light after reflexion from the fovea, a curve for regeneration of cone pigment was obtained. This regeneration was much faster than that of rhodopsin, being complete in 5–6 minutes.

Erythrolabe and Chlorolabe. A study of the effects of bleaching with different wavelengths indicated the presence of two pigments, and these were isolated by studying a protanope who, according to classical theory, is missing the red mechanism and thus might be expected to have one fewer pigment.

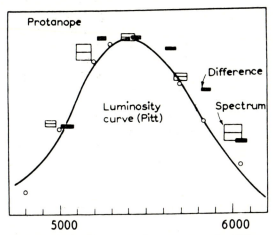

FIG. 131. The black and white rectangles represent the difference spectrum of the foveal pigments in the protanope, and presumably therefore correspond to the absorption spectrum of the green-sensitive pigment, chlorolabe. The curve represents the luminosity curve of the protanope as determined by Pitt, whilst the circles represent the actual luminosity curve of one of the subjects studied by reflexion densitometry. (Rushton, *Progress in Biophysics*.)

The curve of Fig. 131 shows the absorption spectrum of what is apparently a single photopigment in the protanope's fovea, and corresponds remarkably well with the photopic spectral sensitivity curve of the protanope, as determined by Pitt. The protanope's fovea is thus behaving like the dark-adapted periphery,

FIG. 132. Difference spectra of two pigments in the normal fovea. The left curve represents chlorolabe and the other erythrolabe. (Rushton, *Progress in Biophysics*.)

in the sense that its spectral sensitivity curve corresponds to the absorption spectrum of a single pigment, green sensitive, with a maximum at about 5400, and called *chlorolabe* because it absorbs green light preferentially. In the normal eye the absorption could be shown to be compounded of that by two pigments, and the second was given the name of *erythrolabe*, with a computed λ_{max} of about 5900 Å; the absorption spectra of the two pigments are indicated by Fig. 132.

Deuteranope. A study of the deuteranope showed, as Pitt had suspected, that he did not simply lack the green-absorbing pigment, chlorolabe ; in fact his fovea contained both pigments, with rather more erythrolabe and less chlorolabe than normal, so that his deficiency is not at the photochemical level, unless the cones contain mixtures of the pigments instead of the individual ones separately.

Blue-Absorbing Pigments. What of the blue-absorbing pigments, whose presence must be postulated to account for the phenomena of wavelength discrimination, in particular those described by Stiles? So far Rushton has not been able to identify the presence of any blue-absorbing materials in the fovea, but this may well be due to their occurrence in very low concentrations.*

ELECTROPHYSIOLOGY OF WAVELENGTH DISCRIMINATION

It is not, of course, sufficient to demonstrate the presence of "mechanisms" by either subjective or by photochemical methods ; the physiologist will only be satisfied when he can tap the messages whereby these mechanisms transmit their separate information. Thus, if there are red-, green- and blue-sensitive cones, these must respond in specific fashions to light of any given wavelength falling on the retina, and somehow these responses must be transmitted to bipolar cells and ganglion cells and pass along the optic nerves to the lateral geniculate bodies. The messages will, of course, be altered, but it is essential to appreciate that the neurones through which they are carried will be unable to *add* anything ; the wavelength discrimination must have been carried out at the moment of reception of the light-stimulus, and subsequent alterations in the messages can only be described as a *re-coding* of the information, with perhaps the scrapping of some details and alterations of emphasis of the different parts. Thus, to consider the "blue mechanisms," there might be three types of "blue cone", but if their separate messages were all pooled in a single type of bipolar cell, the extra information would be lost. The fact that these mechanisms are shown to exist by psychophysical methods, however, shows that their special messages have indeed survived the re-coding processes so that it is difficult to escape the conclusion that there are several types of cone that are specially sensitive to blue light.

Single Optic Nerve Fibres

Ideally, then, it would be desirable to study the responses of individual rods and cones ; since, however, we are still not certain whether the records obtained

* The Japanese workers, Hanoaka & Fujimoto, have measured the absorption of light by the outer segments of single cones of the carp retina in histological sections. The cones showed the presence of pigments absorbing maximally in the regions of 5000 and 5750 Å, corresponding, perhaps, to the presence of rhodopsin and iodopsin; other bands at 5350 and 6200 Å might have corresponded to the presence of porphyropsin and the synthetic cyanopsin, obtained by combining chicken opsin with retinene$_2$.

with microelectrodes deep in the retina, and thought to be recording events in single cones, really were doing so, we may begin more profitably with a study of the messages as they leave the eye in the optic nerve, or as these originate in the large ganglion cells of the retina. Granit studied single unit responses from the retina of the frog and many other animals.

Dominators and Modulators. With the dark-adapted frog eye, and scotopic stimuli, the responses were the same whatever unit was picked up, the maximal response corresponding to the wavelength of maximal absorption of rhodopsin, about 5000 Å. In the light-adapted frog eye the wavelength-response curves varied with the unit picked up ; they fell into two categories described as *dominators* and *modulators*. The dominators were the most common and gave broad sensitivity curves with a maximum at the wavelength for maximal photopic sensitivity as found by the ERG, namely at about 5550 Å (Fig. 133). The modulators had relatively narrow spectral sensitivity curves confined to one portion

FIG. 133. Wavelength-response curves in single fibres of the frog (continuous line) and snake (interrupted by dots) optic nerve. The greatest response has been put equal to 100. The dominator. (Granit, *Nature*.)

FIG. 134. Wavelength-response curves in single fibres of the optic nerve of the rat (dots), guinea pig (broken lines), frog (line in full) and snake (line interrupted by circles). The modulators. (Granit, *Nature*.)

of the spectrum, so that it was possible to speak of a red-sensitive modulator whose peak of maximal sensitivity occurred at, say, 6000 Å ; a green-sensitive modulator with a peak at 5300 Å, and so on. Fig. 134 illustrates the modulators isolated by this electrophysiological method from various eyes.

The Optic Nerve Message. Thus, so far as the *message* carried by the ganglion cells to the lateral geniculate bodies is concerned, we may say that it is organized apparently on a dual basis ; the dominators indicate, by their frequency of discharge, the intensity of the prevailing light ; under scotopic conditions their sensitivities correspond to the absorption of the scotopic pigment; rhodopsin in the case of the frog and mammals, and porphyropsin in the case of many fresh-water fishes. In the light-adapted mixed retina the dominator has the sensitivity corresponding to the photopic sensitivity curve. The second half of the message conveys information about the spectral composition ; thus the red modulators would respond preferentially to red light falling on the retina, whilst the green and blue modulators would be much less affected, hence the message corresponding to the illumination of the retina with red light at photopic intensity might be a small discharge in the dominator, high discharge in the red modulator and small or negligible discharges in the green and blue modulators.

Opponent-Type Responses. In the goldfish Wagner, MacNichol & Wolbarsht found a rather more complex set of messages. In this species the ON-OFF type of response is most frequent and it was these elements that were studied from the point of view of wavelength discrimination. It at once became apparent that an element that with white light behaved as an ON-OFF element, with monochromatic light would behave either as a pure ON- or a pure OFF-element, depending on the wavelength; this is illustrated by Fig. 135 where it is seen that with wavelengths of 4000 to 5500 Å the element behaves as a pure ON-element, whilst from 6000 to 7500 Å it is behaving as a pure OFF-element. It will be recalled that the essential feature of the OFF-element is really the silent period

FIG. 135. Variation of type of response from a single ganglion cell with change of wavelength of stimulus. Duration of stimulus is indicated by step in the signal trace at the base of each series of records. With the shorter wavelengths (4000–5500 Å) the element behaves as an ON-element, whilst at the longer wavelengths (6000–7500 Å) it behaves as a pure OFF-element. (Wagner, MacNichol & Wolbarsht, *J. gen. Physiol.*)

during the illumination of the retina, which is due to an active inhibition of the retina, the OFF-discharge being a release from this inhibition. The type of response illustrated by Fig. 135 thus demonstrates that the messages carried by a ganglion cell may be inhibitory over the red end of the spectrum and excitatory over the blue-green region. In other units the opposite relationship was found, the blue-green region being inhibitory. Furthermore, when the receptive field of any given unit was studied it was found that its wavelength-dependence altered according as the centre of the field was studied or the periphery ; thus, if the central region was inhibited by red the periphery was excited by this band. As the authors emphasized, the messages tended to be "opponent" in character, so that if red light inhibited, its complementary, green, tended to excite.

Peripheral Responses

Several workers have placed micro-electrodes deep in the retina and have measured slow potentials in response to illumination ; these were thought at first, for example by Svaetichin in the fish* retina, to represent records from the inside of individual cones, but subsequent studies, *e.g.* those of Svaetichin & MacNichol, suggest that they are derived from "a structure between the receptor and the ganglion cells"; thus even at this stage there has been some re-coding of the message.

Slow Graded Potentials. In general, the records obtained from microelectrodes that were apparently inside individual retinal cells, were not spike discharges but what have been called graded potential responses consisting of either an increase of the normal resting potential, a *hyperpolarization*, or a decrease, *depolarization*. The responses were graded in the sense that the change of potential increased with increasing intensity, whereas a spike potential is all-or-none in character. According to the depth of the electrode in the retina the responses were of two main types ; an L-type which responded in the same way with all wavelengths and therefore gave a "luminosity message" (Fig. 136)

FIG. 136. L-type of response of unit in fish retina; the polarity of the electrical change does not alter with varying wavelength of stimulus. (Svaetichin & MacNichol, *Ann. N.Y. Acad. Sci.*)

(*a*)   (*b*)

FIG. 137. (*a*) C-type of unit, of the red-green variety, giving responses of opposite polarity according as the wavelength of the stimulus lies in the red or green regions of the spectrum. (*b*) C-type, of yellow-blue variety. (Svaetichin & MacNichol, *Ann. N.Y. Acad. Sci.*)

and a C-type which gave opposite electrical effects according as the retina was stimulated with red and green or blue and yellow lights (Fig. 137, *a*, *b*). The messages carried by this second type thus indicated the chromatic nature of the stimulus, and the units were called *chromatic*, or C-units, being subdivided into *R-G* (red-green) and *Y-B* (yellow-blue) categories. Thus, as with the studies on fish ganglion cells, the four main bands of the spectrum seem to be

* The fish retina has been studied with microelectrodes because the cones are very large so that intracellular recording becomes practicable; moreover, the colour vision of fishes has been studied very extensively from a behavioural point of view, and there is no doubt that their colour discrimination is good and similar to that of man (see Svaetichin & MacNichol, 1958, for references).

organized into an "opponent colour" arrangement, so that a given element tends to be excited or inhibited by a pair of wavelength regions.

L-Units

The wavelength for maximal response of the L-unit corresponded remarkably well with the fish's wavelength for maximal photopic sensitivity as determined by behavioural methods. This maximum varies with the fish's habitat in a similar way to the variation in the scotopic pigment of bathypelagic fishes described earlier (p.138). With fish inhabiting depths of 30 to 70 metres, where the transmitted light is almost a monochromatic blue, the sensitivity maximum of the L-units was 5000 to 5300 Å. With fish found in the yellowish shallow water of the Caribbean Sea the L-units had sensitivity maxima in the region 5500 to 6000 Å. Furthermore at depths of 30–70 metres a wavelength discrimination mechanism would be of no use since the light would be almost monochromatic, and no C-type units were indeed found in fish taken from these depths ; the fishes were *cone monochromats*.

Localization of Potentials

By ejecting a dye from the tip of the pipette-electrode, it was shown that, when it was recording these slow potentials, it was in the region of the large horizontal cells and large cone synapses that L-type responses were obtained, and in the inner nuclear and plexiform layers near amacrine and bipolar cells that C-type responses were obtained. Thus chromatic responses were certainly secondary to primary changes that had occurred in receptors, whilst the luminosity type of response may possibly have been derived from cones, but by no means certainly.

Responses in the Lateral Geniculate Body

Pure ON-Elements. Let us now consider the messages as they occur higher up in the visual pathway, namely in the cells of the lateral geniculate body. In the monkey, which has good colour discrimination, de Valois recorded from individual geniculate cells. As with the ganglion cells and optic nerve fibres, there were pure ON-elements that responded by increased frequency of discharge on illuminating the retina ; the responses were very sensitive to changes of wavelength so that their wavelength-response curves seemed to be typical modulators ; these modulator type elements were especially numerous in the region to which the foveal ganglion cells projected.

ON- or OFF-Elements. A second type of element, the most common was the ON or OFF, responding with increased discharge at ON or else responding with inhibition during ON and a discharge at OFF. As to whether the cell behaved as an ON- or OFF-element depended on the wavelength of the stimulating light. Thus cells could be found to respond at ON with red stimulation and at OFF with green stimulation, so that if the response, measured by the number of spikes, is plotted against wavelength for equal energy stimuli, we get the two curves of Fig. 138. From this we see that with a green of 5300 Å there is an inhibition of the existing spontaneous discharge followed by a large discharge at OFF ; with a red of 6400 Å there is a discharge at ON whilst at OFF there is some inhibition of spontaneous activity. With other elements the opposing wavelength bands were in the blue and yellow. It is clear that units of this type should be hardly affected by white light since this may be regarded as the combination of two of the complementary opponent stimuli, red-green,

FIG. 138. The responses of a Red-ON, Green-OFF element to different wavelengths of light, the energy-contents of the stimuli being the same. (DeValois, *J. gen. Physiol.*)

blue-yellow, etc. In fact, up to very high intensities, white light produced no response in these elements.

Pure OFF-Elements. Finally pure OFF-elements were of the dominator type with maxima at 5100 and 5500 Å, presumaby corresponding to scotopic and photopic pigments.

The Complex Message. Once again, then, the study of the messages in the optic pathway indicates the importance of inhibition and the OFF-discharge, besides simple excitation, in determining the code in which the nature of the stimulus is transmitted to the brain. Thus when a green light falls on the retina some fibres will carry bursts of discharge at ON whilst others will be inhibited, so that their spontaneous discharge is reduced ; still others will perhaps show no response at all, neither excitation nor inhibition. The message sent to the brain is therefore complex, and it is by virtue of its complexity that it tends to be unique for the given band of wavelengths and flux of energy, so that a red light cannot mimic the responses evoked by a green light. The problem of the neurophysiologist is now to examine how perhaps just three types of receptor, each containing a unique pigment or mixture of pigments, can influence the bipolar cells in such a way that the ganglion cells are caused to discharge in this highly complex pattern.

THE HERING THEORY

Although this theory was considered as antagonistic to the Young-Helmholtz theory, it is now appreciated that in essence it is simply a modification of this, since it accepts the essential trichromasy of human vision and merely puts forward hypotheses as to the manner in which this trichromasy is brought into being.

Opponent Process Theory. As restated by Hurvich & Jameson in their so-called *opponent process theory*, the essence of the theory is the postulation of opposite and mutually exclusive responses, somewhere in the neural pathway, to certain bands of wavelengths and to black and white. The paired stimuli are Red-Green, Yellow-Blue and White-Black, and they are considered to oppose each other since mixtures of the pairs do, indeed, tend to cancel each other out from a chromatic viewpoint, red and green and blue and yellow becoming eventually white, whilst black and white give the neutral grey sensation that one experiences in the dark. Space will not permit of a detailed description of the theory, which has been developed in quantitative form by Hurvich & Jameson ; as indicated above it is really a trichromatic theory in spite of the postulation of four fundamental sensations, red, green, yellow and blue. The concept of opponent processes in the nervous pathways, whereby certain bands of wavelengths cause inhibition of ganglion cells whilst others have excitatory effects, is obviously supported by electrophysiological studies We may assume that some receptors, when excited by light, inhibit bipolar cells and through them ganglion cells by virtue of the liberation of a special type of chemical mediator, similar to the inhibitory action of Renshaw cells on motor neurones. Other receptors might excite by virtue of having a different chemical mediator. If, now, the two types of receptor contained different photopigments, it is easy to see how different wavelengths could exert opposite nervous influences, the one inhibitory the other excitatory.

GENERAL REFERENCES

BRINDLEY, G. S. (1960). *Physiology of the Retina and Visual Pathway.* London: Arnold.

GRANIT, R. (1947). *Sensory Mechanisms of the Retina.* London: O.U.P.

HARTRIDGE, H. (1950). *Recent Advances in the Physiology of Vision.* London: Churchill.

LE GRAND, Y. (1948). *Optique Physiologique.* Vol. 2. Paris: Editions de la "Revue D'Optique".

MARRIOTT, F. H. C. (1962). Colour vision. In *The Eye.* Vol. 2. Ed. Davson. London: Academic Press. Chaps. 12–16.

RUSHTON, W. A. H. (1959). Visual pigments in man and animals and their relation to seeing. *Progr. Biophys.*, **9**, 239–283.

STILES, W. S. (1959). Colour vision: the approach through increment-threshold sensitivity. *Proc. Natl. Acad. Sci. Wash.*, **45**, 100–114.

WILLMER, E. N. (1943). *Retinal Structure and Colour Vision.* Cambridge: C.U.P.

WRIGHT, W. D. (1946). *Researches on Normal and Defective Colour Vision.* London: Kimpton.

SPECIAL REFERENCES

AGUILAR, M., & STILES, W. S. (1954). Saturation of the rod mechanism at high levels of illumination. *Optica Acta*, **1**, 59–65.

ARDEN, G. B., & TANSLEY, K. (1955). The spectral sensitivity of the pure cone retina of the squirrel (*Sciurus carolinensis leucotis*). *J. Physiol.*, **127**, 592–602.

BLACKWELL, H. R., & BLACKWELL, O. M. (1961). Rod and cone mechanisms in typical and atypical congenital achromatopsia. *Vision Res.*, **1**, 62–107.

CAMPBELL, F. W., Rushton, W. A. H. (1955). Measurement of the scotopic pigment in the living human eye. *J. Physiol.* **130**, 131–147.

DAGHER, M., CRUZ, A., & PLAZA, L. (1958). Colour thresholds with monochromatic stimuli in the spectral region 530–630 μ. *In* Visual Problems of Colour. *N.P.L. Symp.*, No. 8., pp. 389–398.

DE VALOIS, R. L. (1960). Colour vision mechanisms in the monkey. *J. gen. Physiol.*, **43**, Suppl. 115–128.

DODT, E., & WALTHER, J. B. (1958). Der photopischer Dominator im Flimmer-ERG der Katze. *Pflüg. Arch.*, **266**, 175–186.

GRAHAM, C. H., & HSIA, Y. (1958). Colour defect and colour theory. *Science*, **127**, 675–682.

GRANIT, R. (1943). A physiological theory of colour perception. *Nature, Lond.*, **151**, 11–14.

HANOAKA, T., & FUJIMOTO, K. (1957). Absorption spectrum of a single cone in carp retina. *Jap. J. Physiol.*, **7**, 276–285.

HECHT, S. (1947). Colourblind vision. I. Luminosity losses in the spectrum from dichromats. *J. gen. Physiol.*, **31**, 141–152.

HURVICH, L. M., & JAMESON, D. (1957). An opponent-process theory of colour vision. *J. Psychol. Rev.*, **64**, 384–404.

MACNICHOL, E. J., & SVAETICHIN, G. (1958). Electric responses from the isolated retinas of fishes. *Amer. J. Ophthal.*, **46**, Pt. 2, 26–46.

PITT, F. H. G. (1935). Characteristics of dichromatic vision. *Med. Res. Council Sp. Rep. Ser.*, No. 200.

SVAETICHIN, G. (1956). Spectral response curves from single cones. *Acta physiol. scand.*, **39**, Suppl. 134, 17–46.

SVAETICHIN, G., & MACNICHOL, E. F. (1958). Retinal mechanisms for chromatic and achromatic vision. *Ann. N. Y. Acad. Sci.*, **74**, 385–404.

WAGNER, H. G., MACNICHOL, E. F., & WOLBARSHT, M. L. (1960). The response properties of single ganglion cells in the goldfish retina. *J. gen. Physiol.*, **43**, Suppl. 45–62.

WALD, G. (1945). Human vision and the spectrum. *Science*, **101**, 653–658.

WALD, G., BROWN, P. K., & SMITH, P. H. (1955). *Iodopsin. J. gen. Physiol.*, **38**, 623–681.

WALLS, G. L., & HEATH, G. G. (1954). Typical total colour blindness reinterpreted. *Acta ophthal. Kbh.*, **32**, 253–297.

WEALE, R. A. (1953). Cone monochromatism. *J. Physiol.*, **121**, 548–569.

WEALE, R. A. (1962). Further studies of photo-chemical reactions in living human eyes. *Vision Res.*, **1**, 354–378.

WRIGHT, W. D. (1952). The characteristics of tritanopia. *J. opt. Soc. Amer.*, **42**, 509–521.

STILES-CRAWFORD EFFECT; ADAPTATION; PHOTOPIC SENSITIVITY CURVES

WE may conclude this account of modern research devoted to the elucidation of the mechanism of vision with a few special aspects of phenomena that have already been discussed in a more elementary fashion.

DIRECTIONAL SENSITIVITY OF THE RETINA

Pupillary Diameter. Stiles & Crawford decided to develop an indirect method of measuring pupillary diameter. They argued that the larger the pupil the greater the amount of light that would enter the eye and hence the greater the apparent brightness of a luminous field ; the amount of light would increase in proportion to the area of the pupil and this in proportion to the square of its diameter. They found that the calculated diameter never increased beyond 5·5 mm although the maximum diameter actually measured was about 8 mm. This discrepancy was shown to be due to the circumstance that, as the pupil became larger, the retina received relatively more rays of light that struck it obliquely ; if these oblique rays were less efficient than those entering through the centre of the pupil, then the discrepancy could be explained. The effects are large, so that if the subjective brightness of a pencil entering at the very periphery of the pupil is compared with one entering centrally, it may be only 15 per cent of this.

Cone Phenomenon. It was shown that the phenomenon was peculiar to the cones, both foveal and peripheral, and this has provided a valuable method for determining whether rods or cones are concerned in a given visual event. Thus Donner & Rushton, studying the responses of a single ganglion cell in the frog, showed that when it behaved as a scotopic dominator its responses were independent of the direction of incidence of the pencil of light; when it behaved as a photopic dominator, after light-adaptation, it showed directional sensitivity ; moreover, in the mesopic range when a hump appears on the sensitivity curve in the blue, this "blue hump" was shown to be insensitive to direction, and thus to be due to activity of rods, probably of a special type called "green rods" (Denton & Wyllie).

Variation with Wavelength. The magnitude of the directional effect varies with wavelength (Stiles, 1937) ; moreover, if monochromatic light is used there is a change in its subjective hue as the angle of incidence of the rays varies ; this is called the Stiles-Crawford effect of the second kind. Brindley showed that colour-matches could be upset by changing from direct to oblique incidence, so that it would seem that the forms of the fundamental response curves of the cone mechanisms responsible for wavelength discrimination change with angle of incidence of the radiation. Since the shape of an absorption spectrum depends on the density of the pigment in solution (p. 131), and since the shape of the sensitivity curve presumably depends on that of the absorption spectrum of the cone-pigment, we can conclude that the effective optical density of pigment in the cone varies with direction of incidence.

Wave-Guide Theory. The most plausible explanation for the phenomenon is that put forward by Wright & Nelson to the effect that light entering directly along the axis of a cone is more likely to be retained by a series of total internal reflexions than light entering obliquely ; this *wave-guide theory* has been developed quantitatively by Enoch.*

ADAPTATION

Rod Adaptation

The main phenomena of adaptation have been already described throughout this Section, and here we shall discuss only some special aspects. By dark-adaptation we mean the recovery of sensitivity of the retina following exposure to light ; so far as rod vision in man is concerned, there is little doubt that this process is largely determined by the regeneration of rhodopsin, although the relationship between retinal sensitivity and concentration of rhodopsin in the retina is not so simple as had been at first thought (p. 145).

Foveal Adaptation

With human foveal, *i.e.* cone, vision, Wright has established the existence of an essentially similar process that takes place far more rapidly however, presumably because cone pigments regenerate more rapidly (p. 145). The reverse process, which we may call foveal light-adaptation, constitutes a decrease in sensitivity of the retina during continued exposure to light ; it was studied by Wright with his binocular matching technique, the change in sensitivity of one eye, during exposure to light, being measured by comparing the subjective sensations in the two eyes. The curve of decrease in sensitivity falls over a period of some 50 sec to reach a plateau with a sensitivity about one sixteenth of the original value (Fig. 63, p. 105).

Alpha-Adaptation. A much more rapid adaptive effect was described by Schouten & Ornstein, who measured the effect of a small glare-source of light, stimulating a peripheral part of the retina, on the brightness-sensation experienced by the fovea. Thus the two eyes would view independently the two halves of an illuminated field, and these would be adjusted in luminosity to give a match. The peripheral glare-source, entering one eye only, would now be switched on, and immediately the match would be disturbed, the half of the field seen by the eye with the glare-source appearing much darker. By raising its luminance till a match was obtained the decrease in sensitivity could be determined. This α-*adaptation*, as Schouten & Ornstein called it, is complete within a fraction of a second and was thought to differ from the β-adaptation of Wright in that its effect extended to the whole retina, even though only a small part was stimulated. Provided exposure to the glare-source was short, recovery of sensitivity was rapid. Thus long before Wright, in his binocular

---

* Enoch has attempted to implicate this wave-guide phenomenon in the mechanism of wavelength discrimination; thus the various wavelengths would be brought to modes in different parts of the cone, and if pigments were distributed unevenly we could envisage different responses in the same cone to the various wavelengths. The fact that the appearance of monochromatic light is practically unchanged when it reaches the retina through the sclera (Brindley & Rushton) rather discounts this theory. It also shows that wavelength discrimination in man is not mediated by colour filters in front of the cones. In birds, however, the coloured oil-droplets seem to fulfil this role (see, for example, Donner).

matching studies, had made his first measurement of retinal sensitivity, this had presumably decreased by a factor of about five because of this rapid α-adaptive process.

Veiling Luminance

Subsequent work, notably that of Fry & Alpern has shown, however, that the phenomenon is not one of retinal interaction but is due to the scattered light from the glare-source. The effect of this scattered light is to behave as a "veiling luminance", decreasing the sensitivity of the whole retina. We may regard the phenomenon as one of very rapid adaptation, but not, as originally thought, of inhibition of the whole retina by a stimulus falling on only a part.

Changes of Sensation. According to Wright, the change in sensitivity of the fovea, following exposure to a bright light may be indicated graphically as in

Fig. 139. Schematic representation of α- and β-adaptation. The eye is exposed to light during the interval AB. The dotted lines represent the virtually instantaneous α-adaptive decrease and increase in sensitivity. (Wright, *Trans. Illum. Eng. Soc.*)

Fig. 139. The dotted line represents the almost instantaneous α-adaptive process. On switching off the light, there is a rapid increase in foveal sensitivity, continued as a slower β-adaptive recovery.

Development of the Visual Sensation

If we take into account the general phenomena of adaptation, we may predict, in a crude way, the course of the visual sensation when the eye is exposed to a bright light. At first, because of the relatively high accumulation of photo-pigments in the cones, the sensation will be intense, but because of the decomposition of these we may presume that the sensation, on this photochemical ground, will fall off, until a steady state is reached with regeneration of pigment keeping pace with decomposition. On these photochemical grounds then we may expect sensation to grow to a peak, decline and level off to a steady state. Because of the rapid α-adaptive process, however, these slower changes will be modified, in the sense that the rise in sensation will be slowed by the reduced sensitivity of the retina, whilst the fall will be more rapid, and to a lower level than would have prevailed if there had been no α-adaptation. The actual response, as measured, is shown in Fig. 140 where it is seen how rapidly the sensation

F<small>IG</small>. 140. Actual sensation curve during the first 200 msec. of stimulation by a bright light. (Wright, from Schouten.)

of brightness declines; in Fig. 141 this curve of sensation is shown to be made up of the algebraic sum of a "primary change" depending on the photochemistry of the receptors, and the inhibitory α-adaptation. In the same figure there is the analogy with the electroretinogram, the α-adaptive process being likened to the inhibitory P III component.

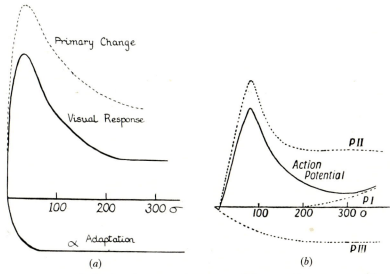

F<small>IG</small>. 141. (a) Indicating the composite nature of the sensation curve resulting from stimulation with a bright light. (b) Illustrating the analogy between α-adaptation and the P III component of the ERG. (Wright & Granit, *Brit. J. Ophthal.*)

Simultaneous Contrast

At the time when the effects of the glare-source described by Schouten & Ornstein were interpreted as being due to an adaptive effect of one part of the retina on the rest, it was natural to assume that this α-adaptation lay at the basis of simultaneous contrast, whereby the apparent brightness of a grey patch is diminished by surrounding it with a white background. However, with the demonstration that the glare-source effect was due to scattered light within the eye, this interpretation becomes suspect. However, the fact of simultaneous contrast remains, in the sense that a patch of light appears much darker if surrounded by a white background than if surrounded by a black one; so it may well be that the stimulation of the surrounding retina does, indeed, reduce the sensitivity of the central retina to light.

Successive and Meta-Contrast

It is thought that the phenomena of successive contrast, or temporal induction, are associated with the slower β-adaptation; here we are dealing with the effects of one stimulus on a succeeding one, both of them falling on the same part of the retina; the phenomena are essentially of an adaptive nature in the sense that the first stimulus depresses the sensitivity of the retina for a succeeding, like, stimulus.

Meta-Contrast. By *meta-contrast* is meant the inductive effect of a primary light stimulus on the sensitivity of the eye to a previously presented light stimulus on an adjoining part of the retina; it is a combination of temporal and spatial induction, or successive and simultaneous contrast. The effect is produced by illuminating the two halves of a circular patch consecutively for a brief duration. If the left half only, for example, is illuminated for 10 msec, it produces a definite sensation of brightness. If, now, both are illuminated for the same period, but the right half some 20–50 msec later, the left half of the field appears much darker than before, and near the centre may be completely extinguished. The left field has thus been inhibited by the succeeding, nearby, stimulus. The right field, moreover, appears darker than when exposed alone— it has been inhibited by the first stimulus (*para-contrast*). The phenomenon may be described as α-adaptation—a nervous inhibitory action of one stimulus on the response to another, but it emphasizes what the conception of α-adaptation fails to do, namely the mutual effects of two stimuli *on each other* ; the second stimulus inhibits the first whilst the first inhibits the second. Baumgardt & Ségal have shown that, by varying the interval between the presentation of the two halves of the illuminated field, a variety of intermediate degrees of meta-contrast may be achieved; moreover, these may be reproduced as after-images, but in the latter process the time relationships are altered so that if, for example, the left half of the field was dark and the right half bright in the primary sensation, the reverse relationship could be found in the after-image.

Adaptation and the Colour Sense

So far we have considered the effects of adaptation on the light and form senses; we know from the phenomena of spatial and temporal induction that the colour sense can be appreciably affected by adaptation, but it is only comparatively recently that serious quantitative measurements of the specific effects of any given wavelength have been made.

Colour Matches. Wright has applied his binocular matching technique to the problem. For example, the right eye was made to view a yellow patch ; the left eye was presented with a patch which could be illuminated by the subject with three primary colours, red, green, and blue, and their proportions and intensities could be varied so that a match, both in hue and intensity, could be made with the yellow viewed by the right eye. The right eye was then exposed to an adapting light for three minutes and both eyes once again viewed their respective test and comparison patches. As a result of the adaptation it was found that the previous match no longer held in respect to either brightness or hue; and the change was measured by adjusting the intensities of the primaries as quickly as possible until a correct match was made. By repeating the matches every thirty seconds the course of recovery from adaptation could be plotted as three separate curves corresponding to the recoveries of the red, green, and blue sensations. In general, it was found that adaptation to any given wavelength had a general and specific effect ; there was a general reduction in sensitivity of the eye to all wavelengths, together with a specific reduction in sensitivity to the adapting wavelength. Consequently, a match that holds for one state of adaptation of the eye does not necessarily hold good for another. Thus with a yellow test-colour, a match was made with equal amounts of red and green before adaptation of the right eye to a white light; after adaptation, a match was made with red and green in the proportions of 38 : 60, *i.e.* far more green was required by the dark-adapted left eye to match the sensation experienced by the light-adapted right eye, a fact which indicates that an adapting white light depresses the sensitivity to red more than to green.

Colour-Mixing Equations. This observation does not, however, indicate that the colour-mixing equations, applicable for one level of luminance, are inapplicable for another; in fact, there is some reason to expect that, in the same eye, matches will hold independently of the condition of this eye, at any rate over a fairly wide range of light-adaptation. Thus if we take a mixture of red and green in one half of a field and match it with a mixture of yellow and white in the other, then the fact that there is a match means that the retina is responding in essentially the same way in the two halves of the field; any change in the retina, caused by adaptation to any wavelength, will influence the receptors receiving both halves of the field in the same way, so that although the subjective sensation will be altered the two halves may be expected to appear the same, and the match will be said to hold in spite of the adaptation of the retina. Thus, presentation of the two halves of the field to the two eyes separately, as in the binocular matching technique, would indicate a failure of the match, but that is because we are comparing two eyes in different states of adaptation. In practice, colour-matches do, indeed, hold under different conditions of adaptation.

Artificial Colour-Defectiveness. Nevertheless, if very high adapting luminances are employed, Wright showed that uniocular colour matches may be upset, and the phenomenon was investigated in some detail by Brindley. On the basis of the trichromatic theory, the maintenance of colour matches in spite of adaptation implies that the forms of the three spectral response curves remain unaltered, since it is essentially because of their characteristics that the laws of colour matching are what they are. Thus, to consider the Red and Green response curves and their contribution to Yellow, the matching of Red + Green to equal yellow is represented by Fig. 142; here the yellow stimulus matches the mixed Red and Green stimuli because it stimulates the Red by 3 units and the Green by 2 units. If we now adapt to red light so that the shape of the Red curve is altered, then now our yellow radiation is stimulating the Red and Green mechanisms in different proportions and the match may no longer hold. By using very extreme conditions of adaptation such as might be expected to bleach the photopigment specifically from one type of cone completely, we might expect to achieve a state of artificial dichromatism, or, if we put two types of receptor out of action, one of monochromatism. In fact, all these disturbances of colour-matching may be produced (Brindley). For example, by adapting to a very bright violet light, an artificial tritanopia may be produced so that all spectral wavelengths may be matched by suitable mixtures of only two primaries, a red and a blue. With a very bright red or blue-green light this artificial tritanopia may be converted into an artificial monochromatism, in which large parts of the spectrum can be matched with a single wavelength; thus a "red monochromatism" was obtained by strong violet and blue-green adaptation, presumably because only the red mechanism was operative. Under these conditions all spectral colours from 5000 Å to 7000 Å could be matched by suitably varying the intensity of a yellow stimulus of 5780 Å. The sensation

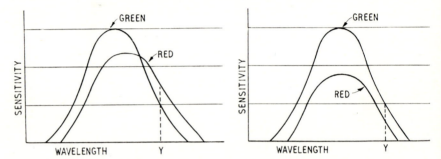

FIG. 142. Showing that, if the forms of the fundamental response curves are altered by an adapting light, colour matching will be upset. *Left:* the yellow stimulus, Y, produces responses in the green and red mechanisms in the ratio of 2 : 3. *Right:* the same yellow stimulus produces responses in the ratio 1 : 2 because selective adaptation has altered the shape of the red mechanism's response curve.

was that of a very unsaturated red or pink. After adaptation with violet and red, a "green monochromatism" was obtained, so that all wavelengths between 4800 Å and 6200–6300 Å could be matched with a yellow, both fields appearing this time as an unsaturated blue-green*. Finally, a "violet monochromatism" was obtained by adaptation to a bright yellow light; over the range of 4000 Å to 5000 Å all wavelengths were matched with violet of 4470 Å, both fields appearing as a very saturated violet. Presumably, then, Brindley was putting the fundamental mechanisms out of action selectively, but of course the remaining mechanisms could hardly be called normal since they would have been subjected to quite considerable bleaching, so that the density of pigment in them would be less than that pertaining with normal trichromatic vision.

Bezold-Brücke Phenomenon. When the intensity of a monochromatic light is increased considerably, there is a change of its subjective hue so that it can be matched with a different monochromatic light of lower intensity; this is the Bezold-Brücke phenomenon. The shifts are illustrated in Fig. 143, where

---

* In a paper published in the *Philosophical Transactions* in 1898, Burch described these "red" and "green" monochromatisms after adapting to strong violet + green or violet + red lights. It should be noted that these states last only for a short time, of the order of 10 seconds.

the lines join wavelengths of the same apparent hue when viewed at ten, and over a thousand, trolands; the arrows indicate the invariant hues, namely a blue of 4760 Å, a blue-green of 5080 Å and a yellow of 5700 Å; thus oranges and reds at high intensities are equivalent to a yellow at moderate intensity, and so on. Peirce in 1877 suggested that these shifts could be explained on the basis of the Young-Helmholtz theory, with the assumption that the three sensitivity curves altered relatively to each other when the intensity-level of stimulation increased. Thus, if an orange at moderate intensity stimulated the red mechanism very strongly and the green mechanism only weakly, then increasing the intensity of the orange might be expected to increase the green's response more strongly than that of the red, and thus to shift the subjective sensation

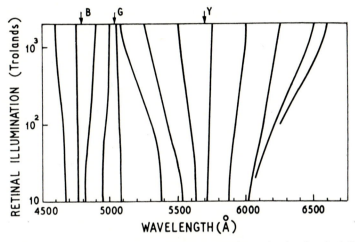

FIG. 143. Wavelengths having the same hue at different levels of retinal illumination. For example, an orange of about 6000 Å shifts towards the red when the retinal illuminance is increased from 10 to 1000 trolands. The arrows indicate the invariant hues. (Walraven, *J. opt. Soc. Amer.*)

towards the green end of the spectrum, *i.e.* to make an orange approach a yellow. On this basis, the invariant hues would correspond to the crossing-over points of the three sensitivity curves. This is true of the invariant yellow at 5070 Å if we accept Pitt's sensitivity curves, but as Walraven has shown, further assumptions are necessary to account for the other two invariant colours. As presented, the theory of Peirce, and its modification by Walraven, are obviously too naive, but the general principle that the relative shapes of the response curves of the cone mechanisms will alter with intensity is in accordance with what would be expected on electrophysiological grounds.

Bloch's Law

If the sensation of brightness is due primarily to the absorption of quanta of light, we may expect that the intensity of this sensation, induced by a flash, other things being equal, will be determined by the product: $I \times t$, a large intensity, I, and short time, t, being equivalent to a smaller intensity and longer time. For threshold studies this relationship has already been described, and is the basis of the so-called Bunsen-Roscoe Law familiar to the photochemist. For flashes above threshold this relationship was found to hold by Bloch in 1885 and is called *Bloch's Law*. According to Brindley (1952) the relationship holds down to flash-durations of extreme brevity, at least as short as $4\cdot1.10^{-7}$ sec when the retinal illumination was $3\cdot10^8$ trolands, and the greatest duration over which it extends is probably of the order of $0\cdot03$ sec (Brindley, 1959).

After-Images. According to Brindley, Bloch's Law applies with some precision to the subjective brightness of after-images, so that if a subject is exposed to two half-fields illuminated independently, the product of $I \times t$ being the same for each half-field but the values of I and t being different, then the after-images are indistinguishable.* This emphasizes that the long-lasting effects of a light stimulus are largely determined by the photochemical changes in the receptors. Especially strong support for this view is the finding that Bloch's Law breaks down at extremely high intensities and short exposures; thus if two flashes are exposed in the top half-field at an interval of 4 msec and the the same two flashes in the bottom half-field at an interval of $0\cdot28$ msec, the total quantities of light are the same but, if the intensities are very high, the after-images of the upper and lower fields are distinguishable. The breakdown is probably related to Hagins' discovery that with a single bright flash-exposure of the rabbit's retina, the amount of rhodopsin bleached, as determined by reflexion densitometry, was never greater than 50 per cent of the total, however intense the stimulus, although a second flash, separated from the first by a few hundredths of a second, would bleach a further 50 per cent. This failure to bleach is due to the production of stable photosensitive products, according to Wulff *et al.* and Bridges.

PHOTOPIC SENSITIVITY CURVES

The curves shown in Fig. 118, p. 180, give the relative sensitivities of the light-adapted eye to different wavelengths, *i.e.* under conditions where the cones apparently determine the sensation. As we have seen, this sensation may well be mediated by three types of cone, so that one might expect to find discontinuities in the curve in regions where one type of cone tends to "take over" from another. In fact, as we have seen, Stiles was able to create conditions where the "taking over" by the separate mechanisms could be demonstrated with some precision, but this required conditions that ensured that he was measuring the threshold for the new mechanism, *i.e.* by light-adaptation with carefully chosen wavelengths the mechanisms with which he was not concerned could be depressed in sensitivity sufficiently to allow the single mechanism to manifest itself. Under the ordinary conditions of measurement of photopic sensitivity, where essentially what we are doing is to match different wavelengths for brightness sensation, thereby finding the relative energies required for equal sensation, we may expect all mechanisms to be operative to some extent, and thus to obtain a smooth curve of spectral sensitivity.

"Humps" on the Curves

By reducing the size of the test-patch, or by using peripheral parts of the retina, however, some evidence for discontinuities, in the form of "humps"

* That is, provided the after-images appearing during the first 15 sec were ignored.

on the sensitivity curves, can be obtained; at these humps the retina is presumably specially sensitive to a selected region of wavelengths. For example, Thomson found evidence for extra sensitivity in three regions of the spectrum, one at 4600 Å, another at 5200 Å and a third between 5800 and 6100 Å. Again, by studying the periphery, Weale found two humps indicating extra sensitivity in the blue at 4600 Å and in the green at 5400 Å. Using a rather different technique, Auerbach & Wald identified what they called a violet receptor with maximum sensitivity at 4350 Å.

Squirrel. Humps on the sensitivity curve are not peculiar to man; thus Fig. 144 shows the mean results for a number of different species of squirrel, animals that are interesting because their retina is a pure cone one. There are two obvious peaks at 5350 and 4900 Å respectively, and here it is interesting

FIG. 144. Mean spectral sensitivity curve for several species of squirrel, determined electroretinographically. Ordinate: percentage sensitivity. Abscissa: wavelength in mμ of stimulating light. Intensity was adjusted so that at each wavelength the same number of quanta/sec fell on to the retina. (Tansley, Copenhaver & Gunkel, *Vision Res.*)

that neither of these coincides with the absorption peaks for the pigments that can be extracted from the squirrel retina, which is actually a rhodopsin with λ_{max} of 5020 Å (Dartnall). By selectively adapting the retina with blue or green light the two humps could be selectively depressed, and this suggests that there are different pigments mediating blue and green sensitivity.

Colour Matching

Not only may the sensitivity curves be "abnormal" under certain conditions but also the phenomena of colour-matching.

Foveal Tritanopia. König, in 1894, discovered that the central fovea is tritanopic, blues and greens, and whites and yellows being confused if the matching fields were kept very small and central fixation was accurately maintained. Later Willmer rediscovered the phenomenon and suggested that the blue receptor—apparently lacking in the central fovea—was the rod, which behaved as a colour receptor under photopic conditions. However, this tritanopia is probably due, as Hartridge showed, to the use of very small fields *per se*, since a similar dichromacy could be observed in the periphery, provided the field was made small enough. This loss of blue sensitivity may be due to a relative rarity of the "blue" cones, so that unless the field is large enough an insufficient number are stimulated to permit their effects to be manifested.

Fovea and Periphery. Frequently, however, an increased sensitivity to blue may be demonstrated under suitable conditions; in general, according to Weale, the visual functions of the different regions of the retina may be summarized as follows:

Retinal Area	Extent from centre nasally	Type of Vision
Foveal centre	50′	Tritanopia
Fovea	2° 30′	Trichromatic
Parafovea	4° 10′	Trichromatic, with enhanced blue sensitivity
Perifovea	9° 10′	Anomalous trichromacy with enhanced blue sensitivity
Inner periphery	14° 10′ to 24° 10′	
Intermediate periphery		
External periphery	77° 35′	Dichromacy with enhanced blue sensitivity

Thus, in the periphery, the sensitivity to blue seems to be *enhanced*.

SPECIAL REFERENCES

AUERBACH, E., & WALD, G. (1954). Identification of a violet receptor in human colour vision. *Science*, **120**, 401–405.

BAUMGARDT, E., & SÉGAL, J. (1946). La localisation du mécanisme inhibiteur dans la perception visuelle. *C. R. Soc. Biol., Paris*, **140**, 431–432.

BRIDGES, C. D. B. (1961). Studies on the flash photolysis of visual pigments. *Biochem. J.*, **79**, 128–134.

BRINDLEY, G. S. (1952). The Bunsen-Roscoe law for the human eye at very short durations. *J. Physiol.*, **118**, 135–139.

BRINDLEY, G. S. (1953). The effects on colour vision of adaptation to very bright lights. *J. Physiol.*, **122**, 332–350.

BRINDLEY, G. S. (1959). The discrimination of after-images. *J. Physiol.*, **147**, 194–203.

BRINDLEY, G. S., & RUSHTON, W. A. H. (1959). The colour of monochromatic light when passed into the human retina from behind. *J. Physiol.*, **147**, 204–208.

BRINDLEY, G. S. (1960). *Physiology of the Retina and Visual Pathway*. London: Arnold.

DARTNALL, H. J. A. (1960). Visual pigment from an all-cone retina. *Nature*, **188**, 475–479.

DENTON, E. J., & WYLLIE, J. H. (1955). Study of the photosensitive pigments in the pink and green rods of the frog. *J. Physiol.*, **127**, 81–89.

DONNER, K. O. (1953). The spectral sensitivity of the pigeon's retinal elements. *J. Physiol.*, **122**, 524–537.

DONNER, K. O., & RUSHTON, W. A. H. (1959). Rod-cone interaction in the frog's retina analysed by the Stiles-Crawford effect and by dark-adaptation. *J. Physiol.*, **149**, 303–317.

ENOCH, J. M. (1960). Waveguide modes: are they present, and what is their possible role in the visual system. *J. opt. Soc. Amer.*, **50**, 1025–1026.

ENOCH, J. M. (1961). Visualization of wave-guide modes in retinal receptors. *Amer. J. Ophthal.*, **51**, Pt. 2, 1107–1118.

FRY, G. A., & ALPERN, M. (1953). The effect of a peripheral glare source upon the apparent brightness of an object. *J. opt. Soc. Amer.*, **43**, 189–195.

HAGINS, W. A. (1955). The quantum efficiency of bleaching of rhodopsin *in situ*. *J. Physiol.*, **129**, 22–23 P.

SCHOUTEN, J. F., & ORNSTEIN, L. S. (1939). Measurements on direct and indirect adaptation by means of a binocular method. *J. opt. Soc. Amer.*, **29**, 168–182.

STILES, W. S. (1937). The luminous efficiency of monochromatic rays entering the eye pupil at different points and a new colour effect. *Proc. Roy. Soc.*, B, **123**, 90–118.

STILES, W. S., & CRAWFORD, B. H. (1933). The luminous efficiency of rays entering the eye pupil at different points. *Proc. Roy. Soc.*, B, **112**, 428–450.

TANSLEY, K., COPENHAVER, R. M., & GUNKEL, R. D. (1961). Spectral sensitivity curves of diurnal squirrels. *Vision Res.*, **1**, 154–165.

THOMSON, L. C. (1951). The spectral sensitivity of the central fovea. *J. Physiol.*, **112**, 114–132.

WALRAVEN, P. L. (1961). On the Bezold-Brücke phenomenon. *J. opt. Soc. Amer.*, **51**, 1113–1116.

WEALE, R. A. (1953). Spectral sensitivity and wavelength discrimination of the peripheral retina. *J. Physiol.*, **119**, 170–190.

WILLMER, E. N. (1946). *Retinal Structure and Colour Vision*. Cambridge: C.U.P.

WRIGHT, W. D. (1939). The response of the eye to light in relation to the measurement of subjective brightness and contrast. *Trans. Illum. Eng. Soc.*, **4**, 1–8.

WRIGHT, W. D. (1946). *Researches on Normal and Defective Colour Vision*. London: Kimpton.

WRIGHT, W. D., & GRANIT, R. (1938). On the correlation of some sensory and physiological phenomena of vision. *Brit. J. Ophthal*. Mon., Suppl. No. 9.

WRIGHT, W. D., & NELSON, J. H. (1936). The relation between the apparent intensity of a beam of light and the angle at which the beam strikes the retina. *Proc. Phys. Soc.*, **48**, 401–405.

WULFF, V. J., ADAMS, R. G., LINSCHITZ, H., & KENNEDY, D. (1958). The behaviour of flash-illuminated rhodopsin in solution. *Arch. Ophthal.*, **60**, 695–701.

SECTION III

The Muscular Mechanisms

THE EXTRAOCULAR MUSCLES AND THEIR ACTIONS

APART from its importance in the treatment of squint, an adequate knowledge of the movements of the eyes, and their neuromuscular control, is of considerable value in understanding the physiological mechanisms concerned with the maintenance of posture; moreover, it would seem that our perceptions of objects, and particularly of their spatial relationships, are determined in part by the laws governing the movements of the eyes.

The Muscles

The Recti. The muscles concerned with the eye movements are six in number: the *medial* and *lateral recti* which determine sideways movements; the *superior* and *inferior recti* causing primarily upward and downward movements, and the *superior* and *inferior obliques* which, when acting alone, primarily cause the eye to twist around its antero-posterior axis.

FIG. 145. Insertions of the rectus muscles. The medial rectus is to the right. (Duke-Elder, *Text-book of Ophthalmology*.)

The insertions of the rectus muscles are indicated in Fig. 145, and since the muscles arise from a common origin at the apex of the orbit, their main actions of elevation, depression, adduction (*i.e.* pulling towards the nose) and abduction, are not difficult to appreciate.

The Obliques. The superior oblique (Fig. 146) likewise arises from the apex of the orbit but after running above the medial rectus almost to the orbital margin, it becomes tendinous as it passes through a cartilaginous pulley, the trochlea, and turning sharply backward, downwards, and laterally over the eye it is inserted into the postero-lateral aspect of the sclera. Since the muscle pulls from above on an attachment behind the equator of the eye, it acts as a depressor.

The inferior oblique (Fig. 147) arises from the anterior part of the orbit, in the antero-medial corner of its floor. It passes laterally and backwards beneath

FIG. 146. Extrinsic muscles of the eye from above. 1, superior rectus; 2, levator palpebræ superioris; 3, medial rectus; 4, lateral rectus; 5, superior oblique; 6, reflected tendon of superior oblique; 7, annulus of Zinn; 8, optic nerve; 9, ophthalmic artery. (Duke-Elder, *Text-book of Ophthalmology.*)

FIG. 147. Extrinsic muscles of the eye. Lateral view. 1, levator palpebræ superioris; 2, superior rectus; 3, lateral rectus; 4, inferior rectus; 5, inferior oblique; 6, superior oblique. (Duke-Elder, *Text-book of Ophthalmology.*)

the inferior rectus and is inserted into the postero-lateral aspect of the globe. Pulling from below on an attachment behind the equator the inferior oblique thus acts as an elevator.

The Muscle Fibres and their Innervation

The human extraocular muscle fibres range in diameter from 10 to 50μ and have been classed as coarse and fine. They run the whole length of the muscle. The coarser fibres tend to form a central core within the muscle, whilst the finer fibres form an outer coat.

Innervation. In discussing the innervation of the extraocular fibres we are entering a confusing field and it is important to try and separate the facts from their interpretations.

Motor Innervation

The large muscle fibres have characteristic myelinated nerve fibres terminating in typical end-plates ; many of these muscle fibres have two end-plates—a feature that is rare in other mammalian muscles where a single fibre usually supplies only a single end-plate on a given muscle fibre (Feindel, Hinshaw & Weddell; Kupfer). Some fibres may run some distance along a muscle fibre giving off twigs and fine endings closely applied to the fibre at intervals; since these may be recognized as branches of typical motor axons terminating in end-plates, we may conclude that these fine terminals are motor in function.

The motor unit, *i.e.* the number of muscle fibres supplied by a single motor axon, is remarkably small being probably of the order of 6, although the difficulty in establishing whether a given fibre is sensory or motor may result in some error in the estimate. This compares with some 100 to 150 for limb muscles (Torre, 1953). Because of its short twitch-time the fusion frequency for an extraocular muscle is very high indeed, of the order of 350 impulses per sec, and this permits a large variation in tension—over a range of tenfold— on passing from a single twitch to a fused tetanus. These two features, namely small size of motor unit and small twitch/tetanus tension ratio, permit a high degree of gradation of the strength of contraction.*

Duke-Elder showed that the extraocular muscles were highly sensitive to acetylcholine on intravenous injection; because of its rapid destruction by cholinesterase, acetylcholine is ineffective in causing contraction of other voluntary muscles, unless given by close arterial injection; its action on the eye muscles is presumably due to the greater sensitivity of these to the drug (Brown & Harvey, 1941).

Sensory Innervation

In 1946 Daniel described spiral nerve endings surrounding fibres of the human extraocular muscle ; he surmised that they were sensory in function, responding perhaps to thickening during contraction. Later Cooper & Daniel identified definite muscle spindles in human muscles, a single rectus containing

* According to Wolter (1952) the motor innervation is fourfold in type: medullated fibre with typical end-plate; the grape-like termination of unmedullated fibres on the fine muscle fibre described by Woollard and Hines; two other non-medullated types with characteristic terminations are considered to be parasympathetic and sympathetic and able to cause contraction of the muscle fibres. On this view the extraocular muscles have some of the characteristics of cardiac fibres along with those of typical skeletal muscles.

as many as 50, a number comparable with those in a lumbrical muscle of the hand; the spindles were concentrated near the origin of the muscle and that was why they had not been discovered earlier. In general the structure of the spindle was similar to that classically described in other muscles; 2–10 fine muscle fibres (intrafusal) are enclosed in a capsule whilst an adjacent nerve trunk sends fibres into the capsule to end on the intrafusal fibres. The innervation is both motor and sensory; thus the gamma efferents—fine motor fibres—by causing the muscle fibres in the capsule to contract are able to increase the sensitivity of the spindle to stretch; whilst the sensory endings encircle the nuclear bag. Besides man, the higher apes and artiodactyls—goat and sheep—possessed well defined spindles in their extraocular muscles. In certain species, notably the cat and monkey, no spindles were found but the richness of the innervation of the muscles certainly suggests the presence of simpler organs, perhaps just spirally wound endings encircling single muscle fibres (Cooper & Fillenz).

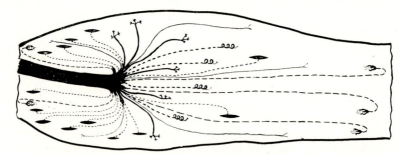

FIG. 148. Much simplified diagram of a human rectus oculi muscle, full length. The origin is on the left and the insertion on the right. The sensorimotor nerve (black trunk) is seen entering the muscle at the junction of the proximal and middle thirds. The muscle spindles are most numerous peripherally and in the proximal third of the muscle. Their nerves (composed of sensory fibres and gamma efferent fibres) are indicated by dotted lines. In the middle third of the muscle are the motor nerve endings whose nerve fibres are shown as solid black lines. Here also, mainly just distal to the band of motor nerve endings, are the simple spiral endings. At both the origin and insertion of the muscle tendon endings are seen (with their afferent nerve fibres shown as broken lines). The lines ending in small Ys represent nerve fibres supplying various of the other endings that are to be seen in eye muscles. (Cooper, Daniel & Whitteridge, *Brain*.)

Subsequent work, notably that of Wolter, suggests that the sensory apparatus in the human extraocular muscles is even more varied ; in all, he has described some six different types of ending, varying in complexity from the spindle to relatively simple terminations, which may be distinguished from motor endings by the circumstance that they end in connective tissue between fibres. A simplified scheme of the innervation of a muscle fibre is shown in Fig. 148.

On purely anatomical grounds, therefore, we may conclude that the muscles are able to send messages to the brain indicating their state of tension at any moment, a sine qua non for the efficient perfomance of any muscular act requiring precision.

Defining the Movements

Axes of Rotation. In describing the actions of the muscles, we are concerned with changes in the direction in which the eye is "pointing" *i.e.* the orientation

of the *fixation axis* (defined as a line joining the point of fixation with the centre
of rotation of the eye; Fig. 149). As a *primary position* or starting point, we
may consider that position in which the eye is looking straight ahead when the
head is erect. If the fixation axis swings horizontally, the eye is said to *adduct*
or *abduct*, according as it swings towards or away from the nose; if the fixation

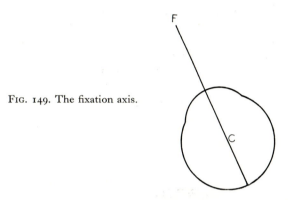

FIG. 149. The fixation axis.

axis swings vertically, the eye is *elevated* or *depressed*. After any purely horizontal
or vertical movement of the fixation axis from the primary position, the eye is
said to have reached a *secondary position*. If the eye executes a movement which
causes both a horizontal and vertical displacement of the fixation axis (*e.g.* if
the eye looks up and to the right) it is said to adopt a *tertiary position*.

Experiment has shown that the movements of the eye in general can be

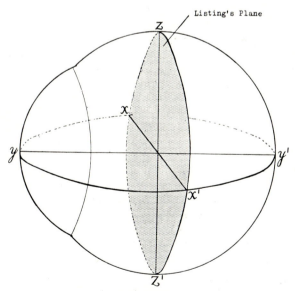

FIG. 150. The primary axes of rotation and Listing's plane. *xx'*, transverse
horizontal giving elevation and depression; *yy'*, antero-posterior giving
rolling or torsion; *zz'*, vertical, giving adduction or abduction.

approximately described as rotations about a fixed point,* the *centre of rotation*, situated some 13·4 mm behind the anterior surface of the cornea. To define a movement it is, of course, not sufficient to indicate the centre of rotation, but an *axis*, passing through the centre, about which the eye turns, must be given; thus adduction or abduction is achieved by rotation about a vertical axis, the *z-axis* (Fig. 150); elevation or depression by rotation about a transverse horizontal axis, the *x-axis*. The fixation axis can be made to point in any direction by rotating the eye first about one axis and then about the other—alternatively the necessary position of the eye can be attained by a single rotation about an axis intermediate between the *x*- and *z*-axes. It is worth noting that when the eye is in the primary position the *x*- and *z*-axes are in a vertical frontal plane— called *Listing's plane* (Fig. 150)—and that *any* direction of the fixation axis can be obtained by rotating the eye about an axis lying in this plane.

Torsion or Rolling. The physiologist is concerned not only with the direction of the fixation axis—which tells him where the eye is pointing—but also with the orientation of a certain fixed plane in the eye—the *retinal horizon* (Fig. 151). Imagine the eye in the primary position looking straight ahead; a horizontal

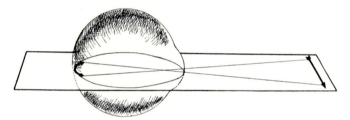

FIG. 151. The retinal horizon. The image of the arrow, fixated in the primary position of the eye, falls on the horizontal meridian.

plane through the pole of the cornea is the retinal horizon and the image of any point in space lying on this plane falls on a horizontal line on the retina—the *horizontal meridian*. The retinal horizon, being fixed in relation to the eye, moves with it. Now we shall see that the appreciation of direction—of a line for example—depends in large measure on the directions the images of external objects make on the retina, and if the orientation of the retina is upset, estimates of direction can become erroneous. Thus a horizontal line is appreciated as such because its image falls on, or is parallel to, the horizontal meridian; if the retina is twisted round, the horizontal line appears to be inclined unless the twist is compensated psychologically (p. 335).

We have thus to take into account the influence of movements of the eye on the orientation of the retina, or what amounts to the same thing, the orientation of the retinal horizon. So long as this plane keeps a definite orientation in space the images of horizontal lines in a frontal plane fall on the horizontal meridian or are parallel to it; the problem is how to define a position of the retinal horizon which we may consider normal—*i.e.* where there is no "twist" of the retina;

_____
* This is, indeed, an approximation; it would seem from the most recent work on this subject that the "centre of rotation" varies within a range of about 2 mm according to the nature of the eye movement; in Van der Hoeve's view, this variability permits a more accurate adjustment of the eyes than would be possible with a fixed centre of rotation.

for the primary position of the eye this is easy, the retinal horizon must be horizontal and, if the eye rotates about its antero-posterior axis (the y-axis) from this position, the retinal horizon becomes inclined to the horizontal and the eye is said to have *rolled* or to have attained an *angle of rolling* or *torsion*. For other positions of the eye we cannot use the horizontal as our reference plane, *e.g.* if the eye is directed vertically upwards the retinal horizon is not twisted round but it is not horizontal. The normal position of the retinal horizon can be defined in relation to a fixed plane in space—the *median plane*, a vertical

FIG. 152. The median plane.

plane through the nose (Fig. 152); so long as the retinal horizon remains perpendicular to this, its position is normal and there is no torsion. Thus in Fig. 153 the eye is represented as looking up and to the right; the retinal horizon is inclined upwards, but it remains at right-angles to the median plane; there is no torsion and a horizontal line on the wall is parallel with the retinal horizon. In Fig. 154 the retinal horizon has been twisted, *i.e.* there has been torsion; it is now no longer at right-angles to the median plane and a horizontal line on the wall is not parallel with the retinal horizon; its image on the retina is there-fore not parallel with the horizontal meridian.*

Rotations about Intermediate Axes. Rolling is brought about by rotation of the eye around its antero-posterior axis; it is not difficult to see that a combined elevation and rolling can be achieved by rotating the eye first about the x-axis and then about the y-axis, or alternatively by rotating about a horizontal axis intermediate between the two. A motion consisting of all three types, *e.g.*

* The definition of the primary position can now be modified to take into account the orientation of the retina; it is the position when the eye is looking straight ahead with head erect and the retinal horizon horizontal.

FIG. 153. The eye is inclined up and to the right. No rolling has occurred and the arrow produces an image coinciding with the horizontal meridian.

FIG. 154. The eye is inclined up and to the right. Torsion has occurred so that the horizontal arrow produces an image inclined across the horizontal meridian.

elevation, adduction, and rolling, can be obtained by choosing an axis with components along each of the three primary x-, y-, and z-axes.

Actions of the Individual Muscles

We are now in a position to analyse the actions of the individual muscles.

The Medial and Lateral Recti. In Fig. 155 is shown a horizontal meridional section through the eye; the medial and lateral recti are indicated by the heavy lines; they run over the surface of the globe but the pull takes place where the muscle is tangential to this surface, at T, the *tangential point*, and the direction of pull is along the *tangential line of force*, TT'. The *muscle plane* is defined as the plane containing the tangential line of force, TT', and the centre of rotation C, *i.e.* it is the plane of the paper in Fig. 155. If C, the centre of rotation, is to remain fixed in space, a pull along TT' must result in a rotation about an axis through C projecting vertically through the paper; in general we may state that *any muscle will rotate the eye about an axis perpendicular to the muscle plane concerned*. The muscle planes of the medial and lateral recti may be taken as horizontal and they thus rotate the eye about a vertical axis through C which has already been defined as the *z*-axis. Such a rotation leads, as we have seen, to a simple movement of adduction or abduction.

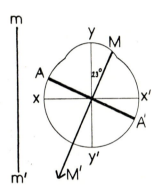

FIG. 155. The actions of the medial and lateral recti. T, tangential point; TT', tangential line of force; C, centre of rotation. The muscle plane is the plane of the paper.

FIG. 156. Action of the superior and inferior recti (right eye). The muscle plane intersects the horizontal section of the eye in MM'. AA' is the axis of rotation. *mm'* is the intersection of the median plane with the plane of the paper.

The Superior and Inferior Recti. The muscle planes of the superior and inferior recti are vertical and approximately identical; however they do not pass through the antero-posterior axis of the eye but are inclined at about 23° to it. The axis of rotation for these muscles is perpendicular to this plane and therefore lies horizontally but, as a result of this inclination, it does not correspond with the transverse horizontal *x*-axis but is inclined 23° away from it. The position is indicated in Fig. 156, which shows a horizontal section through a right eye. The vertical muscle plane intersects this section in the line MM' inclined at an angle of 23° to the antero-posterior axis, *yy'*. The axis of rotation is the line AA' inclined at an angle of 23° to the transverse horizontal axis, *xx'*.

Rotation of the eye about *xx'* causes pure elevation or depression; rotation about *yy'* causes pure rolling; hence rotation about the intermediate axis AA' causes a movement involving both these effects; thus the superior rectus causes a rotation such that M rises out of the paper and its action is therefore *elevation and inward rolling*, the movement of the retinal horizon being clockwise; the inferior rectus causes *depression and outward* rolling.

ADDUCTION

Besides causing elevation (or depression) and rolling, the superior and inferior recti act as adductors, causing the fixation axis to move towards the median plane. This is not immediately evident since it is clear that there can be no rotation about the vertical z-axis, the axis of rotation AA' being perpendicular to it; this third action results from referring the orientation of a fixed direction in the eye—the fixation axis—to a plane outside the eye—*e.g.* the median plane through the head.

Thus in Fig. 156 let us imagine that the superior rectus acts; yy' corresponds to the fixation axis, which in the primary position remains parallel to the median plane, mm'; when the eye is elevated, y moves out of the plane of the paper and moves through a circle which is clearly not parallel to mm'; hence y becomes closer to mm' whilst y' moves farther away, and this can only result in the line yy', the fixation axis, being directed towards the median plane, mm', *i.e.* the superior rectus causes adduction. The inferior rectus causes y to move downwards, but it still moves towards mm' whilst y' moves away; hence both superior and inferior recti cause adduction.

The difficulty arises from the physiological necessity of referring a direction in the eye, the fixation axis for example, to a plane outside it, the median plane; if the axis of rotation is parallel with, or perpendicular to, this plane of reference the inclination of this direction in the eye is unchanged during rotation; thus rotation about xx' gives pure elevation because the axis of rotation is at right angles to the reference plane, mm'; similarly rotation about yy' causes pure rolling because yy' is parallel to mm'; AA', the axis of rotation for the superior and inferior recti, is neither parallel with, nor perpendicular to mm', hence the inclination of the fixation axis to mm' must alter during rotation, *i.e.* adduction must occur.

MODEL EXPERIMENT

The problem becomes very much clearer with a model; a tennis ball may be used; a point is marked to represent the pole of the cornea and a knitting needle is inserted through the centre to represent any desired axis of rotation. If the needle is passed vertically through the ball, rotation causes adduction or abduction; a horizontal needle through the equator permits elevation and depression; a horizontal one through the pole of the cornea causes pure rolling. A horizontal needle passed in a direction intermediate between these two positions, which gives us the axis of rotation for the superior and inferior rectus muscles, causes both rolling and elevation or depression, and it will be seen also that the direction in which the pole of the cornea points, referred to a vertical plane parallel to the original direction of the fixation axis, changes during the rotation. It becomes quite clear that this change of direction is not brought about by rotation about a vertical axis since the knitting needle is held horizontally all the time.

The Superior and Inferior Obliques. The muscle planes of the superior and inferior obliques may be considered to be vertical, as with the recti, but to run at an angle of about 50° to the antero-posterior axis, and on the opposite side, as in Fig. 157. The axis of rotation, AA' is likewise inclined at 50° to the transverse horizontal axis. Contraction of the inferior oblique causes rotation about AA' such that y moves up out of the paper; the eye is thus elevated and rolled outwards; moreover, since the axis of rotation is inclined towards the median plane, the direction of the fixation axis, yy', does not remain constant in respect to this median plane; as *y* comes up out of the paper it clearly moves away from *mm'* and thus the inferior oblique causes *abduction*; the superior oblique causes depression, inward rolling and abduction.

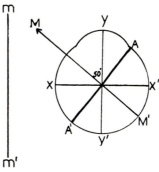

FIG. 157. Actions of the obliques. (Right eye.) *AA'* is the axis of rotation.

Summary. The individual actions of the muscles, thus deduced, may be summarized as follows :

Muscle	Main action	Secondary action
Lateral Rectus.	Abduction.	None.
Medial Rectus.	Adduction.	None.
Superior Rectus.	Elevation.	Inward Rolling and Adduction.
Inferior Rectus.	Depression.	Outward Rolling and Adduction.
Inferior Oblique.	Outward Rolling.	Elevation and Abduction.
Superior Oblique.	Inward Rolling.	Depression and Abduction.

Combined Actions of Muscles

As we shall see, a given movement involves activity in, or inhibition of, several if not all of the six extraocular muscles. It is therefore important to consider their combined actions. Furthermore, we have so far only discussed the direction of pull of a muscle from the primary position of the eye; since this must change frequently as the eye moves out of the primary position, the theoretical axis of rotation must also alter.

Effect of Changed Position of Eye. The simplest example of the effects of moving out of the primary position on the action of a muscle is given by Fig. 158 which illustrates the effects of abduction of the right eye on the direction of pull of the superior rectus. Obviously the rolling and adduction will decrease as the antero-posterior axis of the eye approaches the plane of the muscle, whilst the elevating action will increase. An exactly reverse relationship must exist with the obliques. The variations in the degree of elevation or depression exerted by the superior and inferior rectus, according as the eye is caused to adduct or abduct before the muscle acts, are shown in Fig. 159 after Boeder. Here we imagine that we are looking into a sphere concentric with the left eye, and the lines are those that would be traced out by the fixation axis when the superior or inferior rectus acted alone, and caused a rotation of 50° about the axis of rotation. It is seen that, as the initial position becomes more and more one of

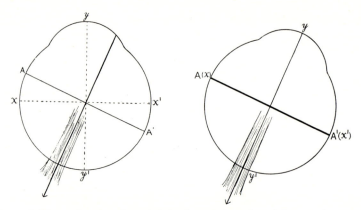

FIG. 158. Illustrating the effect of abduction on the action of the superior rectus. Abduction causes the *x*-axis of the eye to approach the axis of rotation, AA', so that rolling and adduction are decreased.

ABDUCTION ⟵ ⟶ ADDUCTION

FIG. 159. Trace of line of fixation on a sphere concentric with the eye when the superior and inferior recti act individually from positions of adduction or abduction. If we imagine we are viewing inside the sphere the diagram corresponds to a left eye. Each complete curve represents rotation of 50° about the axis of rotation. Small cross-lines indicate cyclotorsion with respect to the objective vertical at every 10° of rotation. (After Boeder, *Amer. J. Ophthal.*)

adduction, the elevation caused by a given degree of rotation about the axis of rotation becomes smaller and smaller, whilst it increases with abduction.*

* This assumes of course that the insertion of the muscle remains the same during abduction; in fact the effective insertion of an extraocular muscle varies very little because it is wide with its tendinous fibres fanning out; hence the axis of rotation tends to remain in the same *position in space* and therefore different in respect to the antero-posterior axis of the eye.

Diagnostic Positions of Gaze. These essentially theoretical considerations on the change in the direction of pull with adduction and abduction, according to which the superior and inferior recti become more efficient in abduction whilst the inferior and superior obliques become more efficient in adduction, have led to the clinical concept of the *diagnostic positions of gaze*. In most movements of elevation and depression the obliques and the recti cooperate; thus a pathologically reduced ability to elevate could be due to paresis of either the superior rectus or the inferior oblique. If, however, the defect is accentuated when the eye is caused to abduct to the extent that the elevating action of the inferior oblique is very small, then the superior rectus is probably the defective muscle. As Boeder has shown, however, because the axes of rotation of the eyes, due to single muscle-pairs, vary so considerably as elevation or depression takes place, this simple view may well be illusory, so that in fact the superior and inferior recti probably always contribute more to elevation and depression than their synergistic obliques. According to Boeder's calculation, their proportionate contractions remain always in the ratio of about three to two. This is borne out by the observations of Breinin (1957) and of Tamler, Jampolsky & Marg (1959) that when the eye is looking upwards in strong adduction and then moves horizontally to abduction, *e.g.* if the left eye starts by looking up and to the right and then looks up and to the left, the superior rectus actually shows increased activity in the electromyogram although, on the classical view, the reverse would be expected since the eye is passing into a position where the action of the superior rectus becomes more and more efficient and therefore, presumably, requires less powerful contraction of its fibres.

Evidence from the Electromyogram (EMG). Until the application of the electromyograph to the extraocular muscles the decision as to what muscles were concerned in a given act was largely based on speculation, although the general principle of reciprocal innervation, whereby during a given movement the antagonist was inhibited during the activation of the agonist, was established by the classical experiment of Sherrington. This investigator cut the nerve supply to an eye so that only the lateral rectus could respond to a cortical stimulus (p. 261); the eye was deviated outwards owing to the unopposed tonic action of the lateral rectus. On stimulating the motor cortex in such a way as to produce adduction in the normal eye, the eye moved inwards to the mid-line as a result of an active inhibition of the tonic impulses to the lateral rectus.

Electromyogram

The activity in a muscle may be measured by the action potentials of its muscle fibres recorded from a needle-electrode inserted into the muscle; the more intense the contraction the greater will be the frequency of the spike discharges in individual units and the larger will be the number of units active. Because of the danger of various artefacts, the results of any study must always be interpreted with caution, but in the hands of experienced workers the EMG has been a valuable tool in assessing the contributions of individual muscles to given eye movements.*

* The technique and many of the pitfalls in interpretation of the EMG have been described in some detail by Marg, Jampolsky & Tamler (1959).

Reciprocal Innervation

Björk & Kugelberg showed that, when the eye looked straight ahead, a given extraocular muscle showed a steady tonic discharge, single units firing with frequencies as high as 50/sec.* This is in marked contrast with skeletal muscles which are usually almost or completely silent during relaxation. With needles in the medial and lateral recti, reciprocal innervation was very well demonstrated; thus on abduction, there was an increased discharge in the lateral rectus associated with a simultaneous inhibition of the tonic discharge in the medial rectus. This is illustrated by Fig. 160; the records marked A are obtained with

FIG. 160. Electromyograms of human medial and lateral recti during steady fixation (A) and a lateral movement (B). The upper record of each pair is from the lateral rectus, the lower is from the medial rectus. A. The gaze is maintained in the straightforward direction; note intense activity in both muscles. B. Slow following movement from 40° inward to 40° outward showing continuous diminution of activity in medial rectus and corresponding increase in the lateral rectus. The dot below the traces in record B indicates the moment at which the gaze passes the midline. Records read from right to left. (Björk & Kugelberg, *EEG clin. Neurophysiol.*)

steady fixation, whilst B shows the discharges in the medial (top) and lateral (bottom) recti during a slow following movement from 40° inward to 40° outward, reading from right to left. The gradual diminution in activity in the medial rectus (top record), accompanied by the increase in activity of the lateral rectus, is well brought out. With this slow type of movement there was never a complete inhibition of the antagonist, by contrast with the rapid "saccade" (p. 249) where the antagonist becomes quite silent (Fig. 161).

Co-Contraction

The EMG has also permitted a solution of the problem of co-contraction, the simultaneous contraction of agonist and antagonist that is a feature of certain

* This is true of all the extraocular muscles, so that all three antagonistic pairs are constantly pulling against each other at rest; the oblique muscles are less active than the recti. According to Björk & Wåhlin (1960) the resting activity is absent in sleep and general anæsthesia.

acts involving the skeletal musculature. The phenomenon of reciprocal inhibition shows that in the execution of any movement of the eyes agonist and antagonist do not work against each other, and this applies even to the point at which the movement terminates; thus the movement of abduction, say, is not arrested by activity in the medial rectus, the reciprocal inhibition observed at the beginning and during the course of the movement being maintained to the end, at which time the muscle exhibits a discharge that is characteristic for the particular position of the eye. Thus the movement is not *ballistic*, as a movement arrested by active contraction of antagonists would be called (Miller, 1958). Nevertheless it might be argued that the movement would be steadied by co-contraction of the elevator and depressor pairs (Boeder), but Breinin

FIG. 161. Electromyograms from lateral rectus (upper tracing) and medial rectus (lower tracing) during quick changes of fixation from 10° outward to straight ahead and back to 10° outward, showing brief acceleration of activity in the agonist accompanied by abrupt cessation of activity in the antagonist. (Björk & Kugelberg, *EEG clin. Neurophysiol.*)

and later workers have shown that there is no increase over the normal tonic resting activity in these muscle-pairs during a lateral movement; similarly, during a pure elevation or depression, the medial and lateral recti fail to show augmented activity.

Proprioception and Position Sense

An important element in the mechanism of reciprocal innervation is the sensory message received from the muscles involved, messages that are initiated by spindles and tendon-organs. Thus, the contraction of the agonist would stretch the antagonist, and the resulting sensory discharge from the spindles and tendon-organs might be the basis for the reflex inhibition of this muscle. The presence of spindles and tendon-organs, as well as several other types of apparently sensory terminations in extraocular muscles, has already been described, but the exact function of these sensory elements has been a matter of dispute that even now is not resolved. This is because of the confusion between two possible roles of muscle sensory organs; as classically regarded, the main role of such an organ as a muscle spindle was to act as the sensory pathway for position sense, whereby the individual is aware of the position of a limb in relation to the rest of the body; the second, and much better understood role, is that of being the sensory element in the myotatic reflex—whereby a stretched muscle contracts actively—or in the clasp-knife response, whereby a muscle will, if stretched beyond a certain point, be caused to relax. Modern studies, moreover, have shown that the muscle spindle, by virtue of its "gamma efferent" system, represents an extremely valuable feedback system that permits an accurate control of the length of a muscle in any given act (Merton, 1951). It may well be, then, that position sense is not served by spindles or Golgi tendon-organs, but rather by other sensory elements.

Position Sense. The absence of proprioceptive sensory information from the muscles of the eye was argued because there is no "position sense" of the eyes (Irvine & Ludvigh); if a subject is placed in the dark and sensation from the conjunctiva is abolished by application of a local anæsthetic, then the subject is unaware of his involuntary eye movements as recorded by the EOG (Reinecke & Poser), whilst artificial movements, caused by experimentally pulling on a muscle, fail to be appreciated (Brindley & Merton). As we shall see, it is the absence of this "position sense" that is the basis for illusions of movement and false projection (p. 333). This absence of position sense, however, simply limits the function that we must attribute to the sensory end-organs in the extraocular muscles; we must regard them as feedback receivers, indicating the degree of contraction or stretch of the muscles and thereby permitting rapid adjustments during the course of a given eye movement. That sensory information is conveyed from the muscles, during stretch, was shown without doubt by Cooper, Daniel & Whitteridge for the goat where spindles were identified, and also for the cat and monkey in which spindles were not found (Fillenz); action potentials being recorded from the brainstem, or from the nerve supplying the muscle, *e.g.* the oculomotor nerve (N III), on stretching the inferior oblique (thus proving that this nerve is not purely motor, incidentally).

Gamma Efferents. Again, it will be recalled that the sensitivity of a muscle spindle to stretch can be augmented greatly by stimulating the small motor fibres (gamma-efferents) innervating the intrafusal fibres. In the goat and sheep Whitteridge (1959) isolated fibres in the IVth nerve that, when stimulated, increased the discharge of a muscle spindle. Thus the spindles in the extraocular muscles are exactly similar in electrophysiological behaviour to those found in the limb muscles, and it is therefore impossible to ignore their role in adjusting the force of contraction through a feedback mechanism that indicates the length of a muscle at any moment.

Sensory Pathway. The evidence relating to the pathway for this sensory information has been summarized by Rogers and Whitteridge. There seems little doubt that there are connections between the muscle-nerves and the trigeminal (N V), often within the orbit; recording from these branches, in the goat, Whitteridge (1955) obtained spindle-responses on stretching the eye-muscle. In the cat, destruction of the eye-muscle nuclei completely denervated the muscles, according to Corbin & Oliver, so that it may well be that in this species the sensory neurones have migrated from N V to the motor nuclei.

Electromyographic Evidence. According to Breinin (1957) the resting activity of a muscle falls to practically nothing on cutting its tendon, suggesting that the normal resting activity is a reflex response to stretch; however, the failure to augment the discharge on pulling the muscle rather discountenances this view of the origin of *tonic* activity, which is therefore probably central in origin. The participation of the spindles in a feed-back mechanism is indicated, however, by Breinin's failure to observe the finely graded reciprocal innervation of agonists and antagonists in the muscles of an enucleated eye; thus, under these conditions, the antagonist is abruptly inhibited as soon as the agonist acts instead of showing the gradual decrease illustrated by Fig. 160. More recently Sears, Teasdall & Stone have shown that pulling on the agonist or on the antagonist during a movement causes a decrease in the spike discharge measured electromyographically, whilst mere cutting the insertion of the muscle had no effect on spontaneous activity. On balance, then, the electromyographic evidence suggests that the motor discharge to the muscles is influenced by sensory messages from the muscles themselves, but more work is obviously required.

Torsion and Listing's Law

We have indicated (p. 226) that a rolling movement of the eye—*e.g.* by rotation about its antero-posterior *y*-axis, would upset the individual's estimate of direction in space unless psychologically compensated. It has been seen that the associated actions of the superior oblique with the inferior rectus tend to cancel out any rolling motion, and in actual fact a study of the movements of the eyes shows that they are executed in such a way as, in general, if not to exclude rotations about the antero-posterior axis, to reduce them to a minimum. This is the basis of *Listing's Law* which will be enunciated more exactly later; for the moment we need only note that since rotations about this third, antero-posterior, axis are apparently excluded, there are virtually only two degrees of freedom in the motions of the eyes, *i.e.* the motions can be resolved into rotations about the horizontal *x*- and vertical *y*-axes. Can we conclude, therefore, that there is no torsion during all movements of the eyes, so that the image of a horizontal line

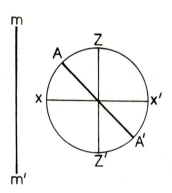

FIG. 162. Illustrating torsion. A vertical frontal section through the right eye. Rotation about AA′ brings *z* nearer to *mm*′ and takes *z*′ farther away.

in the frontal plane always falls on the horizontal meridian or parallel with it? We have seen, in the analysis of the actions of the superior and inferior recti, that the latter adduct the eye even though they rotate it about an axis perpendicular to the vertical, *i.e.* in spite of the fact that there is no rotation about the vertical *z*-axis, and it can be shown that rolling or torsion will occur in spite of the exclusion of rotations about the antero-posterior axis.

Torsion in the Tertiary Position. In Fig. 162 a vertical section through the equator of the eye in the primary position is shown, so that the plane of the paper corresponds to Listing's plane; *xx*′ is the transverse horizontal axis, rotation of the eye about which causes pure elevation or depression; *zz*′ is the vertical axis, rotation about which causes adduction or abduction. *xx*′ coincides in direction with the horizontal meridian and may be considered as the intersection of the retinal horizon with the plane of the paper; it is at right-angles to the median plane, *mm*′, coming out of the plane of the paper; in this, the primary position, there is no torsion and, so long as the retinal horizon, passing through *xx*′, remains at right-angles to this plane, torsion will be absent.

Rotation about *xx*′ obviously does not alter its inclination, and therefore that of the retinal horizon, to *mm*′, so that with pure elevation from the primary position there is no torsion; similarly, rotation about *zz*′, causing adduction or abduction, does not change the inclination of the retinal horizon to the plane *mm*′.

Rotation about the intermediate axis, AA′, lying in the plane of the paper (Listing's plane), causes a combined movement of adduction and depression or abduction and elevation; during this rotation the point *x*′, for example, moves in a circle which is obviously not parallel with the plane *mm*′ nor at right angles to it, consequently the retinal horizon passing through *xx*′ becomes inclined to the plane *mm*′ and the eye experiences torsion in spite of the fact that the axis of rotation, AA′, is in Listing's plane, at right-angles to the antero-posterior axis. If we imagine that we are looking into the eye from behind, a rotation that brings x' up out of the paper corresponds to looking up and to the right; in this event the inclination of the retinal horizon towards mm' follows an anti-clockwise direction and if the eye is a right eye it may be said to have undergone inward rolling. (It is perhaps easier to visualize the events by considering a median plane through zz', corresponding to the vertical meridian of the retina; on rotation about AA' z clearly moves closer to mm'.)

TORSION AND ROLLING

Thus rotation of the eye about an axis intermediate between the horizontal and vertical, whereby the eye passes from the primary position to a tertiary one, results in an angle of torsion; it is customary, but confusing, to draw a distinction between the two general ways of producing this deviation of the retinal horizon from perpendicularity to the median plane; if this is caused by rotation about the antero-posterior axis, or an axis with a component along this direction, it is said to be due to *rolling;* if it is a consequence of rotation about an axis in Listing's plane, it is called *torsion* or *false torsion.* No one has suggested a similar differentiation between adduction or abduction caused by rotation about a vertical axis and that caused by rotation about an axis perpendicular to this (p. 230), and the differentiation between the two processes is entirely unnecessary; the physiologist is chiefly concerned with the position of the retinal horizon in respect to the median plane, and the degree to which it deviates from perpendicularity may be called the angle of torsion or angle of rolling indifferently. Rather than increase the already existing confusion, however, it is probably advisable to retain the distinction ; thus, with Quereau (1955) we may define rolling as a rotation about an antero-posterior axis and torsion (or false torsion as it is often called) as the consequence of oblique rotations about an axis in Listing's Plane.

So long as the head is vertical and no torsion has occurred, the retinal horizon will intersect a vertical frontal plane, *e.g.* the wall of a room, in a horizontal straight line (Fig. 153); if the eye fixates any horizontal line in this plane, therefore, its image will fall on the horizontal meridian of the retina so long as no torsion has been experienced during the movement of fixation.

Donders' Law. The position of the horizontal meridian of the eye in relation to the median plane, *i.e.* the degree of torsion present, can be ascertained by after-image experiments. If the eye, in the primary position, is directed at a horizontal straight line, the image of the latter falls on the horizontal meridian; if the stimulus is strong, an after-image may be evoked and the sensation is projected outwards, so that wherever the gaze is directed the line is perceived in the position it must have if its image is to fall on the horizontal meridian. If this projected after-image coincides with a true horizontal line, it can be said that the truly horizontal line produces an image on the horizontal meridian, *i.e.* that no torsion is present. If, on the other hand, torsion has occurred, the projection of the horizontal meridian appears inclined to a truly horizontal line, and the angle between the after-image and the horizontal gives the angle of torsion.

With the eye in the primary position, a black horizontal line is fixated for a time and the eye is then moved over a screen with horizontal lines on it. If the eye moves vertically upwards or downwards, or horizontally to the left or right, the after-image is found to coincide with the lines on the screen, indicating that there is no torsion. If the eye is moved to a tertiary position, the after-image no longer coincides with the horizontal lines; *e.g.* if the eye looks up and to the right, or down to the left, the after-image is inclined over to the left, as we should expect if rotation took place about an intermediate axis in Listing's plane. The actual directions, in which the projected after-image lies for different movements are indicated in Fig. 163. It is found that no matter how the eye is moved to any position—whether in several steps or as a result of a single rotation—the torsion is the same; this is the basis of *Donders' Law* which states: "*When the position of the line of fixation is given with respect to the head, the angle of torsion will have a perfectly definite value for that particular adjustment; which is independent not only of the volition of the observer but of the way in which the line of fixation arrived in the position in question.*"

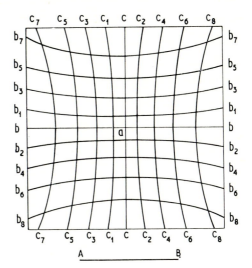

FIG. 163. The inclination of the projection of the after-image of a horizontal line, fixated in the primary position of the eye, on moving the latter into various other positions. *a* is the original fixation point and AB represents the relative distance of the eye from this point. (Helmholtz, *Physiological Optics*.)

Projection of Vertical Lines. With vertical lines, the position is more complicated; a vertical after-image is found to be inclined as though the eye had twisted in the opposite sense, *i.e.* on looking up and to the right the vertical line after-

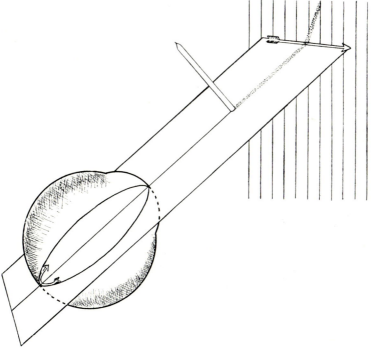

FIG. 164. Illustrating the projection of the vertical meridian of the retina. The eye is looking up and to the right, and it is supposed that torsion has been corrected. The image of the pencil thus falls on the vertical meridian of the retina; its projection against the frontal plane is nevertheless inclined over to the right.

image is tilted over to the right instead of to the left; since the eye cannot exhibit torsion in two ways at once, and since the twist of the horizontal line agrees with theory, this apparent torsion in the opposite sense must be due to some other cause. Suppose now the eye is moved from the primary position upwards and to the right, and the torsion is corrected by an appropriate rolling movement. The after-image of a horizontal line, fixated in the primary position, now corresponds in direction with the truly horizontal line through the new point of fixation; the vertical meridian of the retina is at right angles to the retinal horizon so that we might expect that its projection outwards would be at right angles to a horizontal line on the wall, coinciding with a vertical line. This, however, is not true; the retinal horizon is inclined upwards and to the right and a line perpendicular to it— which represents the projection of the vertical meridian in the absence of torsion— is inclined over to the right when projected on the screen (Fig. 164).

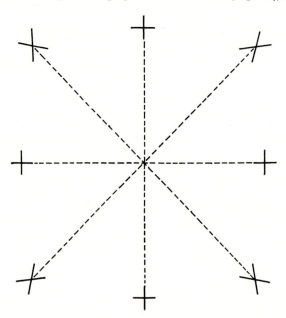

FIG. 165. Approximate appearances of the projections of the after-image of a cross, fixated in the primary position of the eye, for various directions of the fixation axis.

We are now in a position to explain the opposite appearances of horizontal and vertical after-images; due to torsion the horizontal and vertical meridians are tilted over to the left in the case examined. Owing to the characteristics of the projection of the vertical meridian on a vertical frontal plane in space, the after-image of a vertical line, fixated in the primary position, appears tilted over to the right, and more so than the tilt to the left due to torsion.

As a result of these combined effects, therefore, the after-image of a cross, fixated in the primary position, will have the appearances shown in Fig. 165 when the eyes are moved into various tertiary positions.

Listing's Law. It is clear that if, during a rotation of the eyes from the primary position, there is to be no component of rolling about the antero-posterior axis, then the axis of rotation must be perpendicular to this axis, *i.e.* it must lie in Listing's plane (Fig. 150). According to Listing this is, indeed, true so that movements of the eye are confined to two, instead of three, degrees of freedom. Given this limitation—which is the basis of Listing's Law—the experimental finding of Donders that the torsion of the eye is characteristic for its position however this was achieved, follows at once, since the torsion due to rotation about an axis in Listing's plane is predictable on geometrical grounds. More recent experimental studies on the subject have shown that Listing's Law is only an approximation; thus, when the eye is made to look up and outwards, Quereau found that some rotation about an antero-posterior axis occurred so that the resulting torsion was not that predictable on geometrical grounds on the assumption of a rotation about an axis in Listing's plane.*

BINOCULAR MOVEMENTS

Hering's Law. The movements of the two eyes are so co-ordinated as to permit them to operate as a single entity; this unity in behaviour is the basis for *Hering's Law of the Ocular Movements* which states: "The movements of the two eyes are equal and symmetrical."

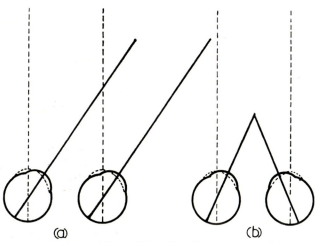

FIG. 166. Conjugate (*a*) and disjunctive (*b*) movements of the eyes.

A movement is said to be *conjugate* when the fixation axes are parallel and the movements of the separate eyes are equal in all respects (Fig. 166, *a*). When the fixation axes are not parallel, as in convergence or divergence, the movement is said to be *disjunctive* (Fig. 166, *b*); in this case the movements of the two eyes are symmetrical, and, as we shall see, they may well be equal in extent even though it can appear that one eye does not move at all (*e.g.* when converging on a point directly in front of one eye).

The Position of Rest. We have so far defined a primary position of the eyes as a reference point from which movements may be described; when the eyes are free from any stimulus determining their mutual orientation (accommodation, fusion of images, etc.) they adopt the so-called "*fusion-free position*" or *physiological position of rest* and it generally happens that in this position the fixation axes diverge slightly (physiological heterophoria) and are thus not in

* This account of torsion is a slightly abbreviated version of that in the first edition of this book; in writing it I relied almost exclusively on Helmholtz's account. Since then several writers have contributed papers designed to clear up the confusion that enters once one departs from Helmholtz (Quereau, 1954, 1955; Marquez, 1949; Moses, 1950). Since I find it very difficult to believe that Helmholtz was wrong in his geometry I have not been tempted to alter my first version.

their primary positions; hence, even for a distant point, the act of fixation requires a tonic action of the extraocular muscles whereby the fixation axes are maintained parallel. As we shall see, this "tonic" action is the result of the operation of the fixation reflex that ensures that both eyes will fixate a given point accurately and thereby prevent the diplopia that would occur were this accurate binocular fixation not maintained (p. 265). To determine this fusion-free position various optical devices are employed to remove the tendency to binocular fixation; thus if a red spot on a green background is viewed by one eye through a red glass and by the other through a green one, the two eyes see quite different pictures and there is no tendency to fuse these, so that the fixation reflex is not operative and the eyes adopt their "natural positions". The muscle balance of the eyes would be said to be perfect if the two eyes maintained accurate alignment with the same point; if they tended to converge they would be said to be *esophoric*; if they diverged *exophoric*, and so on.

Conjugate Movements

Conjugate Innervation. In conjugate binocular movements both eyes must move to the same extent if diplopia is not to result from any shift of the gaze, and it is therefore reasonable to suppose that there is some sort of conjugate innervation of the principal actors in any binocular movement, in the sense that the passage of impulses to one is accompanied by the facilitated passage of impulses to the other. Broadly speaking, we may expect that for a conjugate deviation to the right the left medial rectus will be associated with the right lateral rectus; for a movement up and to the right, the right superior rectus (the elevator with the stronger action in abduction) will be associated with the left inferior oblique (the elevator with the stronger action in adduction). The muscles of the two eyes may thus be classified in pairs, or "associates," such that in any general type of movement a pair may be designated as the chief actors. The clinician makes use of this classification in order to assess a muscle deficiency; the "diagnostic directions of gaze," classified below, are chosen so that any defect in binocular fixation may be related to the muscle associates chiefly acting :

Diagnostic Direction	Chief Actors	
	R.E.	L.E.
Right	L. rectus	M. rectus
Left	M. rectus	L. rectus
Up and right . .	S. rectus	I. oblique
Up and left . .	I. oblique	S. rectus
Down and right . .	I. rectus	S. oblique
Down and left . .	S. oblique	I. rectus

That this linkage is real is proved by the phenomenon of the secondary deviation of a squinting eye. For example, if the left lateral rectus is partially paralysed, when the eyes look left the eyes squint because the left eye fails to make the necessary movement (Fig. 167, *b*). If, however, a special effort is made by the left eye to fixate the point, then the right eye, by overaction of its medial rectus, squints, giving what is called a *secondary deviation* (Fig. 167, *c*).

Limits of Movements. For practical purposes, the limits of binocular conjugate movements are given by the "*field of binocular single vision*," *i.e.* one determines the position, for any direction of the gaze, at which one eye can

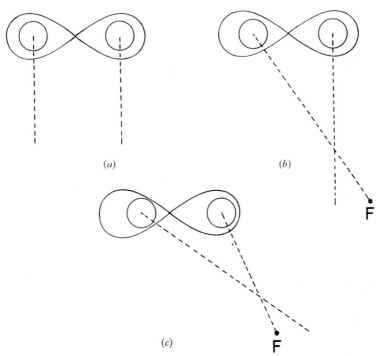

(*a*)   (*b*)

(*c*)   F

Fig. 167. Illustrating primary (*b*) and secondary (*c*) deviations due to paresis of left lateral rectus.

no longer keep pace with the other, as evidenced by an insuperable diplopia. Duane's measurements have shown that this field extends to at least 40° in any given direction and usually up to 50° or more, in fact he states that most individuals retain binocular single vision up to the very limits of the excursions of the eyes, so that it may happen that the binocular field of single vision is larger than either monocular field of fixation taken separately. Thus it appears that, no matter what the maximum excursion of each eye separately is, the excursion of both together is, in normal cases, such that one eye keeps pace with the other and diplopia is avoided even in extreme deviations of the eyes.

Disjunctive Movements

Converging Power. When a near object is fixated, the eyes converge as a result of the combined contractions of the medial recti. There is, of course, a limit to which the fixation axes can be deviated inwards so that if, for example, a pencil in the median line is moved closer and closer to the eyes, a point is reached where the two eyes can no longer fixate the pencil and it appears double. This point, the nearest consistent with single vision, is called the *near point of convergence* (Fig. 168); in 80 per cent of normal individuals it lies between 5 and 10 cm in front of the eyes and is not greatly affected by age as with the near point of accommodation. The *far point of convergence* is given by the point of intersection of the fixation axes in the physiological position of rest; since the eyes in this condition are usually divergent, this point is generally behind the eyes (Fig. 168), its distance being given a negative value.

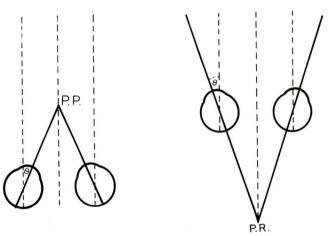

FIG. 168. The near point (P.P.) and far point (P.R.) of convergence.

METRE-ANGLE

By the *converging power* of the eyes, for any given point of fixation in the median line, is meant the angle through which *either* fixation axis moves from the primary position when the convergence takes place (Fig. 168); this angle can, of course, be represented in degrees but Nagel introduced the *metre-angle* as a convenient unit. The metre-angle is the angle through which each eye has rotated from the primary position in order to fixate an object 1 metre away in the median line. If the eyes converge on an object 2 metres away, clearly the angle is approximately halved, and the convergence of each eye is said to be 0·5 metre-angle; if the object is 10 cm away the angle is approximately ten times as large and the convergence is 10 metre-angles. In general, the converging power of each eye is given by the reciprocal of the distance of the fixation point in metres. For an average interpupillary distance of 6 cm the metre-angle corresponds to the convergence angle of 1·7°. It will be noted that the accommodative power in dioptres for any point is given by the same reciprocal (p. 421), so that in some respects this is a convenient notation; nevertheless, because the actual angle of convergence depends on the interpupillary distance, this equality can be misleading. Thus for an emmetrope converging on a point 1/3 metre away the convergence and accommodation are respectively 3 metre-angles and 3 dioptres. With interpupillary distances of 5, 6 and 7 cm the actual convergences are, however, 15, 18 and 21 prism-dioptres respectively. This is an important point when considering accommodative convergence (Breinin, 1957).

AMPLITUDE OF CONVERGENCE

The *amplitude of convergence* is given by the difference in the converging powers of the eyes for the near and far points; hence with a near point of + 8 cm and a far point of − 1 metre, the amplitude is :—

$$1/0\cdot08 - 1/-1 = 12\cdot5 + 1 = 13\cdot5 \text{ metre-angles.}$$

A prism alters the apparent direction in which an object is seen (p. 391); if it is base-out, the object appears to be deviated inwards and the eye adducts

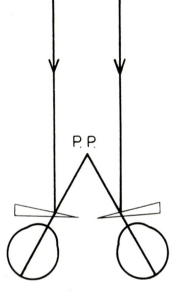

FIG. 169. The use of adducting prisms to cause maximum convergence. (P.P., near point of convergence.)

P. P.

in order to fixate it (a base-out prism is called an *adducting prism*). Theoretically, then, the near point of convergence may be determined by placing pairs of base-out prisms in front of the eyes until a distant object can no longer be seen single (Fig. 169). The strength of the prisms required to achieve this could be converted into metre-angles of convergence by the formula:

Strength of prism in dioptres = No. of metre-angles × ½ interpupillary distance in cm.

Thus with a near point of 12·5 m.a. and an interpupillary distance of 6 cm the prism strength would be given by:

$$\text{Prism strength} = 12\cdot5 \times 3 = 37\cdot5\varDelta \text{ (or } 18\cdot75^\circ\text{d).*}$$

In practice, however, this would be an unreliable measure of convergence-power since the ability to converge in response to prisms varies from moment to moment, and with practice.

* The terminology of convergence is so varied that it is also necessary to be able to convert a convergence distance into an angle of convergence; the formula supplied by Duane is:

$$\text{Convergence angle} = \frac{\text{I.P.D. (mm)} \times 25}{\text{Convergence distance}} + 1\cdot5^\circ.$$

It is stated that the desire for fusion permits a stronger convergence than that obtained without this stimulus; if an object is fixated at the near point of convergence and one eye is then covered up, the other deviates a little; the extra degree of convergence obtained when the stimulus for fusion is present is called the *fusion supplement*.

"See-Saw" Movements. Disjunctive vertical movements—"see-saw" movements—in which one eye moves up and the other down, are not normally produced voluntarily; in the interests of single vision, however, the eyes are able, on the average, to overcome the effects of a 2Δ prism base-up or base-down in front of one eye, *i.e.* they can exhibit a "supervergence" of 1°.

Convergence as a Function of the Two Eyes. It must be appreciated that disjunctive movements are a function of both eyes so that if a distant object

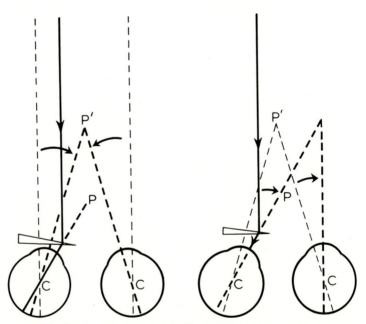

FIG. 170. The fixation axes were originally parallel. A strong adducting prism has been placed in front of the left eye so that it must be directed to P if it is to maintain fixation of the distant point. Both eyes converge to P′ and then make a conjugate deviation to the right. As a result, the left eye is directed at P whilst the right eye re-assumes its original direction of fixation.

in the median line is fixated and the strongest tolerated adducting prism is put in front of one eye, on placing a prism, however weak, in front of the other, diplopia results, *i.e.* no further convergence is possible. The near point of convergence is thus measured by half the strength of the strongest prism tolerated by one eye (when the other has none) or the strength of equal prisms tolerated by both eyes. The explanation for this, according to Hering, was that both eyes shared in the convergence although the direction of one fixation axis might remain finally unchanged. Thus in Fig. 170 the fixation axes of the left and right eyes were initially parallel; a prism has been placed in front of the left eye so that it adducts maximally towards P. The right eye, during this process, was said not to remain fixed and the motions of the two eyes were analysed into an initial convergence to a point P′, such that the convergence of each eye is half the angle necessary for the left fixation axis to move through to fixate P, followed by a conjugate deviation to the right through the same angle; this leaves the right fixation axis pointing in its original direction, whilst the left is directed at P.

In a similar way the asymmetrical convergence to a point P, on the fixation axis of one eye when it is looking straight ahead (Fig. 171), was said to be

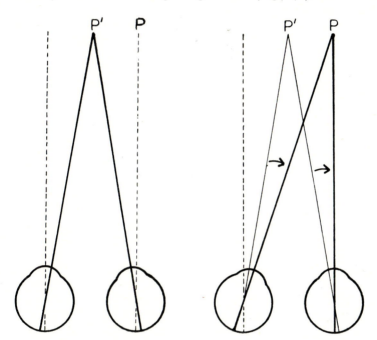

Fig. 171. Illustrating asymmetrical convergence on the point P. The two eyes converge on the point P′ and then make a conjugate movement to the right. The direction of the right fixation axis is thus finally unchanged.

achieved by an initial convergence to a point P′ in the median line, followed by a conjugate deviation. Since convergence is equally shared by the two eyes, we can obtain the convergence of *each* eye for any position of the fixation point by halving the sum of the angles moved through by the two fixation axes from their primary positions.

EXPERIMENTAL EVIDENCE

The asymmetrical convergence illustrated by Fig. 171 need not take place in the gross steps illustrated, and the process may consist in a series of convergence and conjugate lateral movements that may escape observation in the absence of an accurate means of measuring either the movements of the eyes or activity in their muscles. Alpern & Wolter, employing the electro-oculogram (EOG,

p. 249) to record the eye movements found that they were, indeed, compound, but apparently the conjugate movement preceded the convergence, *i.e.* the eyes tended to look to the right of P and subsequently to converge on it. As Alpern & Wolter emphasized, the speed of the conjugate type of movement, namely about 400°/sec, is so much greater than that of convergence (about 25°/sec) that the former might be missed. By measuring the eye movements by photographing the light reflected from the cornea, Westheimer & Mitchell were able to confirm Hering's view exactly, the asymmetrical convergence consisting of a rapid "saccade", *i.e.* a conjugate version, followed by convergence. Using the electromyograph, Tamler, Jampolsky & Marg (1958) showed that the apparently stationary eye in asymmetrical convergence showed activity in both its medial and lateral rectus; this certainly confirms Hering's view of conjugate innervation of both medial recti, and suggests that either the tendency for the apparently stationary eye to adduct is balanced by the pull of the lateral rectus, or that the eye does adduct and then abducts in a conjugate version as illustrated by Fig. 171.

Rolling

When the eyes are in the primary position they cannot be rolled voluntarily; however, the stimulus for fusion can cause such a movement. It is possible, with the aid of 90° prisms placed in front of one eye, to cause the image of an object on the retina to rotate about the fixation axis, *e.g.* the image of a cross may be tilted over. The two eyes are thus presented with different images that can only be fused if the eyes are rolled in opposite directions; the stimulus for fusion causes such a rolling, which may amount to as much as 10°–14°, divided between the two eyes, but is generally much smaller. Convergence is said to be associated with a certain degree of outward rolling of the two eyes, so that their vertical meridians make an angle with each other which, in extreme instances, may amount to as much as 25°. This rolling must produce a rotation of the two retinal images in respect to each other, so that points in space formerly seen single might now be seen double (p. 346); on converging on a line of print, for example, diplopia should result from this asymmetrical torsion; in practice this does not occur so that it would seem, as Harms has pointed out, that when there is a stimulus for fusion, rolling does not take place during convergence; only when the object fixated has adequate symmetry about the fixation axis, so that its retinal image is not seriously modified by rotation about this axis, does rolling occur. For example, if an individual fixated a circle binocularly, rolling of one or both eyes would make no difference to the two retinal images; with a cross, on the other hand, the images would tilt in opposite directions and the individual would have to fuse dissimilar images; the rolling that occurs during convergence is therefore probably largely countered by a corrective fusion movement. As we shall see, the eyes execute a conjugate rolling movement when the head is tilted towards the shoulder; this is a reflex response to the altered pull of gravity on the head, and to the stretch of neck muscles (p. 269).

Analysis of the Movements

It was Dodge in 1903 who made the first serious quantitative attempt to analyse the movements of the eyes; subsequent work has depended for its fruitfulness on improvements in the technique for recording eye movements. Probably the most satisfactory method consists of reflecting light from the cornea, or a contact glass fitting snugly on the eye, and focusing it on to a moving photographic film. By suitable calibration the movements of the reflected light may be converted into angular movements of the eye quite accurately.

Electro-Oculogram. When an electrode is placed on the cornea and another on the posterior pole of the eye or elsewhere on the head, a "standing potential" is recorded of about 1 mV, the cornea being positive. Illumination of the eye gives alterations of this standing potential which we call the electroretinogram (ERG); thus the ERG is really superimposed on the "standing potential." Because of this potential the eye behaves like a dipole orientated along its antero-posterior axis, and if electrodes are placed at right-angles to this axis, *e.g.* in the two canthi, then movements of the eye will cause changes of potential between the electrodes because the dipole's orientation with respect to these electrodes changes. This is the basis of *electro-oculography*, (EOG), an indirect method of recording eye movements, which can be employed even with the eyes closed.* Methods specially adapted to record the small involuntary movements that take place during maintained fixation are those of Rashbass and Ginsborg & Maurice.

The two easily recognizable types of movement concerned in changes of fixation are the *saccade* and *vergence movement*. Saccade was the name originally given by Dodge to the rapid movements between fixation-pauses that occur in reading, but it is now applied more generally to the conjugate shifts of gaze from one fixation point to another. By contrast, the adduction of the eyes during convergence is characteristically different and has been described as a tonic movement. The tracking movements that occur when the eyes follow, or attempt to follow, a moving target are more complex, as we shall see.

The Saccade. The saccade has been studied by Westheimer (1954), the subject being told to fixate a light when it suddenly appeared in the peripheral field. There is a reaction-time of 120–180 msec, after which both eyes move simultaneously. There is a definite overshoot, and the whole operation is over within about 90 msec for an excursion of 20°. The maximum velocity increases with the extent of the movement, being 500°/sec for 30° and 300°/sec for 10°. As indicated earlier, the electromyogram fails to reveal any checking action of the antagonist as the saccade is completed; in fact the electromyograms remained remarkably constant during the whole movement.† (Tamler *et al.* 1959).

Convergence. This is characterized by its slowness, the angular velocity being of the order of 25°/sec comparing with some 500°/sec for a saccade; relaxation of convergence is likewise slow. The reaction time is about the same as for a saccade. The great difference in speed of the saccade and vergence movement has led Alpern & Wolter to suggest that the two movements are executed by different muscle fibres, the saccade being carried out by the large fibres, innervated by large myelinated nerve fibres with characteristic end-

---

* Marg (1951) has given an interesting historical account of the development of electro-oculography, whilst Shackel has investigated the normal potential under a variety of conditions.

† Miller (1958) described an initial burst of activity followed by a much less intense steady discharge during a saccade; according to Tamler *et al.* (1959) Miller's initial burst corresponded with the discharge during the whole saccade, the slower activity being the steady discharge appropriate to the maintained position of the eye after the saccade. Tamler *et al.* measured both eye movement and EMG whereas Miller only measured the EMG.

plates, whilst the vergence would be executed by the fine fibres which, according to Alpern & Wolter, might be innervated by the autonomic system.

ACCURACY OF CONVERGENCE

Many workers have shown an apparent failure of the eyes to converge accurately on to a given fixation point; thus they have measured the binocular movements during an act of convergence and have found them to be greater or less than the required excursions by a degree or more. Such inaccuracies, which would surely lead to double vision, are probably the result of errors inherent in the measurement since Riggs & Niehl, using the light reflected from a tightly fitting contact lens, have shown that the errors are remarkably small, less than 2 minutes of arc on the average; since Panum's area (p. 361) extends over at least 10 minutes at the fovea, this is consistent with the maintenance of single vision.

Movements during Steady Fixation

It has been known for a long time that the eyes do not maintain a steady fixation of a point for any length of time; instead, fixation is interrupted by

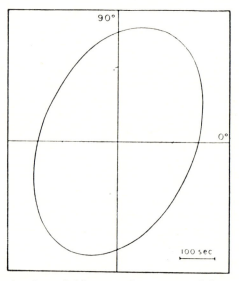

FIG. 172. Indicating the probable range of movements of the eye over a period of steady fixation. The solid line bounds the region within which a point retinal image will be found projected in space 68 per cent of the time during 30-sec. fixation intervals. (After Nachmias, *J. Opt. Soc. Amer.*)

rapid jerks at irregular intervals. The actual movements that take place have been analysed by several workers using modern methods of recording, usually employing the reflexion of light from the cornea.* They have been resolved into three types, as follows: (1) Irregular movements of high frequency (30–70/sec) and small excursion (ca. 20 sec). (2) Flicks, or saccades, of several minutes of arc occurring at irregular intervals of the order of 1 sec. (3) Between saccades there are slow irregular drifts, extending up to 6 minutes of arc. Fig.

* Of the recent contributors to this subject mention may be made of Riggs and his colleagues (Ratliff & Riggs, 1950; Cornsweet, 1956; Riggs & Niehl; Krauskopf, Cornsweet & Riggs, 1960); Barlow (1952); Ditchburn & Ginsborg (1953); Drischel & Lange (1956); Nachmias (1959).

172 illustrates the region in which the fixation point would be 68 per cent of the time during a 30 seconds fixation period, and it will be seen that the range of excursion is not large, certainly not large enough to bring the image of the fixated point off the fovea. All workers are agreed that the saccade is a corrective movement that brings the image back when, as a result of a drift or previous saccade, it is in danger of moving off the central fovea. This is deduced from statistical studies that show that the chance of a saccade occurring in a given direction correlates well with the degree of deviation from central fixation.

Binocular Fixation. When the involuntary movements in the two eyes are studied together during binocular fixation, it is found that the slow drifts take place independently in the two eyes, leading to small degrees of fixation-disparity; *i.e.* if the eyes are looking at a distant point the fixation axes will tend to converge or diverge at random. On the other hand, the rapid saccades take place simultaneously and in the same direction, and corrections for convergence-errors result from the circumstance that the saccades in the two eyes are not always equal in extent. According to Krauskopf, Cornsweet & Riggs, the eyes apparently behave as independent detectors of fixation error, and in correcting their own errors they cause conjugate movements of the other eye that may not necessarily be in the right direction for correction of this eye's error. Since the chance of initiating a saccade by either eye is proportional to the magnitude of its fixation error, we may expect the eye with the larger error to initiate the corrective saccade; if the movement of the other eye in this saccade is a little smaller than that of the initiator, then on a statistical basis we may expect a reasonably accurate binocular fixation. Thus it appears that it is not the error in convergence that is detected, and corrected for, but simply the error of fixation by either eye acting as an independent unit from the viewpoint of detection.

Tracking

If a moving light suddenly appears in the field of view, and if its rate of movement is less than about 30°/sec, the response of the eyes is remarkably efficient; a saccade brings the eyes on target and they follow the motion at almost exactly the same angular velocity as that of the target; inaccuracies in following lead to corrective saccades. When the rate of movement of the target is greater than about 30°/sec, these corrective saccades become more obvious since now smooth following is not possible; the eyes make constant-velocity movements but the velocity rarely matches that of the moving target so that there must be frequent corrective saccades. The studies of Westheimer and others have shown that the following movements are highly integrated and must involve a feedback system whereby errors are used to modify the performance. The feedback information is obviously visual, but there is every reason to believe that sensory information from the muscle receptors plays a role in the smooth execution of the movements—the so-called parametric feedback (Ludvigh).

GENERAL REFERENCES

ALPERN, M. (1962). Movements of the Eyes. In *The Eye*. Ed. Davson. Vol. III. Pt. I. London and New York: Academic Press.

COGAN, D. G. (1956). Neurology of the Ocular Muscles. 2nd Ed. Springfield: C. C. Thomas.

HELMHOLTZ, H. VON (1925). Physiological Optics. Vol. III. Ed. Southall. *Optical Soc. Amer.*

WHITTERIDGE, D. (1960). Central control of eye movements. In Handbook of Physiology. Ed. Field, Magoun & Hall. Washington: *Amer. Physiol. Soc.*, pp. 1089–1109.

SPECIAL REFERENCES

ALPERN, M. & ELLEN, P. (1956). A quantitative analysis of the horizontal movements of the eyes in the experiment of Johannes Muller. *Amer. J. Ophthal.*, **42**, Pt. 2, 289–296.

ALPERN, M. & WOLTER, J. R. (1956). The relation of horizontal saccadic and vergence movements. *Arch. Ophthal.*, **56**, 685–690.

BARLOW, H. B. (1952). Eye movements during fixation. *J. Physiol.*, **116**, 290–306.

BJÖRK, A., & KUGELBERG, E. (1953). Motor unit activity in the human extraocular muscles. *E.E.G. clin. Neurophysiol*, **5**, 271–278.

BJÖRK, A., & KUGELBERG, E. (1953). The electrical activity of the muscles of the eye and eyelids in various positions and during movement. *E.E.G. clin. Neurophysiol.*, **5**, 595–602.

BJÖRK, A., & WAHLIN, A. (1960). Muscular factors in enophthalmos and exophthalmos. *Acta ophthal. Kbh.*, **38**, 701–707.

BOEDER, P. (1961). The co-operation of extraocular muscles. *Amer. J. Ophthal.*, **51**, 469–481.

BREININ, G. M. (1957). Electromyographic evidence for ocular proprioception in man. *Arch. Ophthal.*, **57**, 176–180.

BREININ, G. M. (1957). Quantitation of extraocular muscle innervation. *Arch. Ophthal.*, **57**, 644–650.

BREININ, G. M. (1957). The nature of vergence revealed by electromyography. *Arch. Ophthal.*, **58**, 623–631.

BREININ, G. M., & MOLDAVER, J. (1955). Electromyography of the human extraocular muscles. *Arch. Ophthal.*, **54**, 200–210.

BRINDLEY, G. S., & MERTON, P. A. (1960). The absence of position sense in the human eye. *J. Physiol.*, **153**, 127–130.

BROWN, G. L., & HARVEY, A. M. (1941). Neuro-muscular transmission in the extrinsic muscles of the eye. *J. Physiol.*, **99**, 379–399.

COOPER, S., & DANIEL, P. D. (1949). Muscle spindles in human extrinsic eye muscles. *Brain*, **72**, 1–24.

COOPER, S., DANIEL, P. D., & WHITTERIDGE, D. (1955). Muscle spindles and other sensory endings in the extrinsic eye muscles. *Brain*, **78**, 564–583.

COOPER, S., & FILLENZ, M. (1955). Afferent discharges in response to stretch from the extraocular muscles of the cat and monkey and the innervation of these muscles. *J. Physiol*, **127**, 400–413.

CORBIN, K. B., & OLIVER, R. K. (1942). The origin of fibres to the grape-like endings in the insertion third of the extra-ocular muscles. *J. comp. Neurol*, **77**, 171–186.

CORNSWEET, T. N. (1956). Determination of the stimuli for involuntary drifts and saccadic eye movements. *J. opt. Soc. Amer.*, **46**, 987–993.

DANIEL, P. D. (1946). Spiral nerve endings in the extrinsic eye muscles of man. *J. Anat. Lond.*, **80**, 189–192.

DITCHBURN, R. W., & GINSBORG, B. L. (1953). Involuntary eye movements during fixation. *J. Physiol.*, **119**, 1–17.

DRISCHEL, H., & LANGE, C. (1956). Uber unwillkürliche Augapfelbewegungen bei einäugigen Fixieren. *Pflüg. Arch.*, **262**, 307–333.

DUKE-ELDER, W. S., & DUKE-ELDER, P. M. (1930). The contraction of the extrinsic muscles of the eye by choline and nicotine. *Proc. Roy. Soc. B.*, **107**, 332–343.

FEINDEL, W., HINSHAW, J. R., & WEDDELL, G. (1952). The pattern of motor innervation in mammalian striated muscle. *J. Anat. Lond.*, **86**, 35–48.

FILLENZ, M. (1955). Responses in the brainstem of the cat to stretch of extrinsic ocular muscles. *J. Physiol.*, **128**, 182–199.

GINSBORG, B. L., & MAURICE, D. M. (1959). Involuntary movements of the eye during fixation and blinking. *Brit. J. Ophthal.*, **43**, 435–437.

HINES, M. (1931). Innervation of the extrinsic eye muscles of the rabbit. *Amer. J. Anat.*, **47**, 1–53.

IRVINE, S. R., & LUDVIGH, J. E. (1936). Is ocular proprioceptive sense concerned with vision. *Arch. Ophthal.*, **15**, 1037–1049.

JAMPOLSKY, A., TAMLER, E., & MARG, E. (1959). Artifacts and normal variations in human ocular electromyography. *Arch. Ophthal*, **61**, 402–413.

KRAUSKOPF, J., CORNSWEET, T. N., & RIGGS, L. A. (1960). Analysis of eye movements during monocular and binocular fixation. *J. opt. Soc. Amer.*, **50**, 572–578.

KUPFER, C. (1960). Motor innervation of extraocular muscle. *J. Physiol.*, **153**, 522–526.

LUDVIGH, E. (1952). Control of ocular movements and visual interpretation of environment. *Arch. Ophthal.*, **48**, 442–448.

MARG, E. (1951). Development of electro-oculography. *Arch. Ophthal*, **45**, 169–185.

MARG, E., JAMPOLSKY, A., & TAMLER, E. (1959). Elements of human extraocular electromyography. *Arch. Ophthal.* **81**, 258–269.

MARQUEZ, M. (1949). Supposed torsion of the eye around the visual axis in oblique directions of gaze. *Arch. Ophthal.*, **41**, 704–717.

MERTON, P. A. (1951). The silent period in a muscle of the human hand. *J. Physiol.*, **114**, 183–198.

MERTON, P. A. (1956). Compensatory rolling movements of the eye. *J. Physiol.*, **132**, 25–27 P.

MILLER, J. E. (1958). Electromyographic pattern of saccadic eye movements. *Amer. J. Ophthal.*, **46**, Pt. 2, 183–186.

MILLER, J. E. (1959). The electromyography of vergence movement. *Arch. Ophthal.*, **62**, 790–794.

MOSES, R. A. (1950). Torsion of the eye on oblique gaze. *Arch. Ophthal.* **44**, 136–139.

NACHMIAS, J. (1959). Two-dimensional motion of the retinal image during monocular fixation. *J. opt. Soc. Amer.*, **49**, 901–908.

QUEREAU, J. V. D. (1954). Some aspects of torsion. *Arch. Ophthal.*, **51**, 783–788.

QUEREAU, J. V. D. (1955). Rolling of the eye around its visual axis during normal ocular movements. *Arch. Ophthal.*, **53**, 807–810.

RASHBASS, C. (1960). New method for recording eye movements. *J. opt. Soc. Amer.*, **50**, 642–644.

RATLIFF, F., & RIGGS, L. A. (1950). Involuntary motions of the eye during monocular fixation. *J. exp. Psychol.*, **40**, 687–701.

REINECKE, R. D., & POSER, C. M. (1961). Subjective evaluation of ocular proprioception monitored with the use of the electro-oculograms. *Arch. Ophthal.*, **66**, 130–132.

RIGGS, L. A., & NIEHL, E. W. (1960). Eye movements recorded during convergence and divergence. *J. opt. Soc. Amer.*, **50**, 913–920.

ROGERS, K. T. (1957). Ocular proprioceptive neurons in the developing chick. *J. comp. Neurol.*, **107**, 427–437.

SEARS, M. L., TEASDALL, R. D., & STONE, H. H. (1959). Stretch effects in human extraocular muscle. *Bull. Johns Hopk. Hosp.*, **104**, 174–178.

SHACKEL, B. (1960). Pilot study in electro-oculography. *Brit. J. Ophthal.*, **44**, 89, 337, 608.

TAMLER, E., JAMPOLSKY, A., & MARG, E. (1958). An electromyographic study of asymmetric convergence. *Amer. J. Ophthal.*, **46** Pt. 2, 174–182.

TAMLER, E., JAMPOLSKY, A., & MARG, E. (1959). Electromyographic study of following movements of the eye between tertiary positions. *Arch. Ophthal.*, **62**, 804–809.

TAMLER, E., MARG, E., & JAMPOLSKY, A. (1959). An electromyographic study of coactivity of human extraocular muscles in following movements. *Arch. Ophthal.*, **61**, 270–273.

TAMLER, E., MARG, E., JAMPOLSKY, A., & NAWRATZKI, I. (1959). Electromyography of human saccadic eye movements. *Arch. Ophthal.*, **62**, 657–661.

TORRE, M. (1953). Nombre et dimensions des unités motrices dans les muscles extrinsiques de l'oeil et, en general, dans les muscles squelettiques. *Schweiz. Arch. Neurol.*, **72**, 362–378.

WESTHEIMER, G. (1954). Mechanism of saccadic eye movements. *Arch. Ophthal.*, **52**, 710–724.

WESTHEIMER, G. (1954). Eye movement responses to a horizontally moving visual stimulus. *Arch. Ophthal.*, **52**, 932–941.

WESTHEIMER, G., & MITCHELL, A. M. (1956). Eye movement responses to convergence stimuli. *Arch. Ophthal.*, **55**, 848–856.

WHITTERIDGE, D. (1955). A separate afferent nerve supply from the extraocular muscles of goats. *Quart. J. exp. Physiol.*, **40**, 331–336.

WHITTERDIGE, D. (1959). The effect of stimulation of intrafusal muscle fibres on sensitivity to stretch of extraocular muscle spindles. *Quart. J. exp. Physiol.*, **44**, 385–393.

WOLTER, J. R. (1952). Uber Nervenendigungen in der äusseren Augenmuskulature. *Acta neuroveg.*, **4**, 343–353.

WOLTER, J. R. (1955). Morphology of the sensory nerve apparatus in striated muscle of the human eye. *Arch. Ophthal.*, **53**, 201–207.

WOOLLARD, H. H. (1927). The innervation of voluntary muscle. *J. Anat. Lond.*, **61**, 498–499.

NERVOUS CONTROL OF THE EYE MOVEMENTS

General Considerations

The activities of the muscles of the neck and trunk are ultimately determined by the discharges in the motor neurones of the ventral horns of the spinal cord, which are described as the *final common path*. These neurones are acted upon by sensory neurones, and by interneurones localized in all levels of the central nervous system, from the various segments of the cord to the cerebral cortex. Thus the activity of any given muscle is determined by nervous activity in practically the whole of the central nervous system; nevertheless the activity of an organism may be resolved into certain stereotyped patterns of behaviour—the *reflexes*—which may be evoked independently of many regions of the central nervous system; thus the flexor reflex may operate in the spinal animal, *i.e.* the animal whose spinal cord has been severed from the brain; whilst a large variety of reflex responses may be achieved in the decerebrate animal, the animal whose cerebral hemispheres and basal ganglia have been removed. In general, we may say that these patterns of behaviour may be controlled and modified by activity in brain centres that are located higher in the system than those required for the performance of the reflex activity. This is manifest especially in the voluntary control of muscular activity mediated by the frontal motor cortex and along the pyramidal tracts.

The movements of the eyes form no exception to these general principles; well established reflex patterns of behaviour are present and these may be largely controlled, or at any rate influenced, by voluntary activity initiated, it is presumed, also in the frontal cortex. The final common path is given by motor neurones in the brain, rather than the spinal cord, whilst higher coordinating centres are found in the *superior colliculi* and in the *occipital cortex*. These reflex centres are well established; somewhat more problematical are certain regions of the brain stem, notably the tegmentum of the midbrain, pons and medulla, stimulation of which electrically gives rise to well coordinated patterns of eye movement.

In this short, and necessarily somewhat elementary, discussion of the nervous control of the eye movements we shall be concerned with the reflexes and their nervous pathways—the *reflex arcs*. It must be strongly emphasized, however, that most reflexes are only exhibited reproducibly and in the "pure" form under artificial conditions, for example, in the decerebrate animal; any actual movement in the normal individual represents the final outcome of the antagonistic interplay of numerous reflexes which, in their turn, may be modified to a greater or less extent by the voluntary centres. For example, we shall see that a bright light in the periphery of the visual field evokes a *fixation reflex* whereby the eyes are turned towards the light so as to bring its image on the fovea; this does not mean, however, that the eyes are invariably turned to any light in the peripheral visual field. The reflex, defined as the response of the individual to a stimulus, must be considered, especially in man, as a component in behaviour; under special conditions it may be elicited with the utmost regularity, whilst in the normal intact animal the response to the same stimulus may be greatly different according to the conditions prevailing.

THE FINAL COMMON PATH

The motor neurones activating the eye muscles are derived from the cranial nuclei as follows :—

NIII. (*Oculomotor nerve*). Superior rectus. Inferior rectus. Medial rectus. Inferior oblique.

N IV. (*Trochlear*). Superior oblique.

N VI. (*Abducens*). Lateral rectus.

These nerves represent essentially the axons of cell bodies collected in the grey matter of the mid-brain and pons—the *eye-muscle nuclei*.

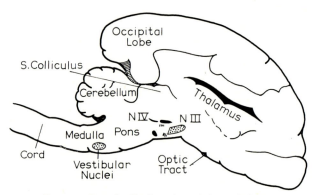

FIG. 173. Longitudinal section of the cat's brain.

The Nucleus of Nerve III. This lies in the tegmentum in the central grey matter in the upper part of the mid-brain below the superior colliculus, beneath and running parallel to the aqueduct of Sylvius (Fig. 173). It is some 5 to 6 mm long and extends between the third and fourth ventricles. It has been conventionally divided into a series of discrete zones each concerned with a pair of muscles; thus according to Brouwer it is divided primarily into a principal (lateral) nucleus providing the motor neurones to the levator palpebræ and four extraocular muscles; the *median nucleus of Perlia*, considered to be a coordinating centre for activating the medial recti during convergence; and the *Edinger-Westphal nucleus*, containing the autonomic motor neurones controlling the ciliary muscle and sphincter pupillæ. The principal lateral nucleus was divided into zones from above downwards (rostrocaudally) each zone representing the motor neurones for the levator, superior rectus, medial rectus, inferior oblique and inferior rectus in this order. Subsequent work, notably that of Warwick, has shown that the organization is not so simple. Thus, although the individual eye muscles are indeed operated by localized groups of neurones within the principal nucleus, the simple rostro-caudal arrangement postulated by Brouwer apparently does not pertain. Moreover, Warwick showed that in monkey and man, the two species in which convergence of the eyes is a prominent feature of the movements, the median nucleus of Perlia is difficult to find, and, when present, its neurones are not internuncial, as one would expect of a coordinating centre, but rather they are motor neurones supplying the superior rectus and inferior oblique. Hence we must assume that the act of convergence is organized at a higher level. The Edinger-Westphal nucleus is well established as the autonomic division of the oculomotor nucleus.

The Nucleus of Nerve IV. This is a small clump of cells lying caudally to the nucleus of Nerve III, being situated in the central grey matter in the floor of the aqueduct of Sylvius and at the level of the lower part of the inferior colliculus.

The nerve fibres, which represent the motor pathway for the superior oblique, undergo an almost complete decussation in the anterior medullary velum, emerging on the dorsal aspect of the brain stem.

The Nucleus of Nerve VI. This nucleus lies in the pons, in the floor of the fourth ventricle.

Medial Longitudinal Fasciculus. A conjugate lateral movement requires a coordinated response on the part of the medial rectus of one eye, innervated by N III, and the lateral rectus of the other, innervated by N VI. This coordination

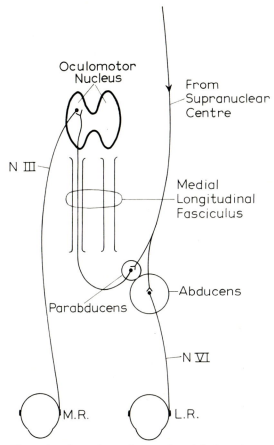

Oculomotor Nucleus

From Supranuclear Centre

N III

Medial Longitudinal Fasciculus

Parabducens

Abducens

N VI

M.R.

L.R.

FIG. 174. Illustrating the conjugate innervation of the lateral rectus of one side and the medial rectus of the other.

is brought about by interneurones running from the nucleus of N VI or a nearby region—the so-called *parabducens nucleus* of Crosby. These interneurones run to the nucleus of N III in the medial longitudinal fasciculus (also called posterior longitudinal bundle), a tract associated with the brain-stem reticular formation which connects the three motor nuclei bilaterally. Thus the initiation of a conjugate lateral movement may be illustrated by Fig. 174, the primary stimulus reaching the parabducens and abducens nuclei; an interneurone in the latter passes up in the median longitudinal fasciculus to activate a motor neurone in N III which passes to the medial rectus.*

* Reciprocal innervation demands, of course, that inhibitory impulses pass to the antagonists; thus the parabducens nucleus would have to send inhibitory impulses to

Lesions in the median longitudinal fasciculus may well be responsible for the so-called internuclear ophthalmoplegia; the loss of the power to adduct the eye in conjugate lateral movements with its retention in convergence. Certainly this syndrome may be evoked by bilateral section of the fasciculus (Hyde & Slusher).

COORDINATING CENTRES

So much for the nuclei of the nerves controlling the eye movements; these nuclei may possibly be regarded as "centres" integrating, in a limited way, the activities of the individual muscles so that a given movement is carried out smoothly and efficiently, but it is probably safer to regard them as the final common path for the necessary movements elaborated at higher levels of the nervous system. Certainly the intimate connection of the eye movements with bodily activity, and the dependence of the eye movements on visual impressions, demand centres at a higher level capable of integrating these associated activities on a wider scale. Centres that are considered to be important for these integrative activities are the superior colliculi, certain regions of the brainstem tegmentum, the occipital cortex and the frontal cortex.*

Superior Colliculi

The functions of these two bodies, often called the *optic tectum*, are not completely known, especially in man, but there is little doubt that they constitute an important centre in the organization of movement. This is clear from their anatomical connexions since they receive afferent impulses from the medial and trigeminal lemnisci, whilst the bulk of their efferent impulses pass to the eye-muscle nuclei by way of the fountain decussation of Meynert and the medial longitudinal fasciculus and to the motor nuclei generally by way of the tectobulbar and tectospinal tracts. In lower animals, such as the cat, moreover, we may conclude that the colliculi are centres for *visually directed movements*. The anatomical basis for this is provided by fibres from the optic tracts that terminate directly in the colliculi, which are thus called *primary optical centres*; in general, the higher the animal phylogenetically the larger the proportion that pass to the lateral geniculate body and thence to the cerebral cortex. In man and the higher apes, therefore, only very few fibres terminate in the colliculi.

Response to Stimulation. Electrical stimulation of the superior colliculi with electrodes implanted in the waking and freely moving cat by Hess' technique causes a movement of the head towards the opposite side; a careful study of the eyes shows that the movement of the head is preceded by a conjugate

N III of the same side besides excitatory impulses to N III of the opposite side. We may note that opinions differ as to whether the fibres related to conjugate deviation cross at once to ascend in the contralateral median longitudinal fasciculus, as indicated in the diagram, or whether they ascend on the same side as the deviation and decussate within the nucleus of N III (see Crosby, 1953, p. 440).

* The literature contains frequent allusions to *gaze centres*, the one controlling lateral movements and corresponding to the so-called *parabducens nucleus*, the other, near the superior colliculi, supposed to control vertical movements. The parabducens nucleus is best regarded as a relay-station on the motor pathway in conjugate lateral movements, and not as a coordinating centre. The movements evoked by stimulation of the colliculi usually have a strong vertical component and it is doubtless for this reason that the hypothetical gaze centre for vertical movements has been sited near these bodies. According to Szentágothai, the interstitial nucleus of Cajal may be regarded as a vertical gaze centre because of its connexions with the eye-muscle nuclei concerned with elevation and depression, whilst a region $\frac{1}{2}$ mm lateral to this nucleus he regards as a horizontal gaze centre by virtue of its connexions with the abducens nucleus and that part of the oculomotor nucleus concerned with the medial rectus.

movement of the eyes (Burgi). Usually there is an upward or downward component in the movement, according to the part of the colliculus stimulated; and
in the rostro-median region a pure upward movement can be obtained. In the
anæsthetized cat, stimulation of the retina by light does not evoke any eye
movements; if, however, the excitability of the superior colliculus is enhanced
locally by the application of a crystal of strychnine, then light causes a prompt
movement of the eyes directed to a definite spot in space characteristic for the
particular region of the colliculus that has been made thus sensitive. By systema-
tically changing the position of the strychninized area, a map of the surface of
the colliculus may be plotted indicating regions of the visual field towards which
the eyes will be directed when a given point is rendered hypersensitive. Presumably there is a reflex path from the retina through the colliculus that determines
that the eyes will move towards the point in the visual field that stimulates the
retina; in the anæsthetized animal this reflex is inhibited, but treatment with
strychnine removes the inhibition and reveals the reflex (Apter).

Probable Roles. Thus in lower animals we may regard the colliculi as centres
that bring about reflex movements of the eyes in response to a visual stimulus.
In man and apes the number of visual fibres passing to the colliculi is small,
and it is unlikely that these mediate any reflex activity since, in man at any rate,
eye movements in response to visual stimuli cannot be evoked in the absence
of visual cortex. However, as the number of visual fibres terminating in the
colliculi decreases, there is a corresponding increase in the number of fibres
running from the occipital cortex to the colliculi, so that on phylogenetic grounds
we may assume that the colliculi retain their function as stations for executing
eye movements, but they become subordinated to the occipital cortex (Crosby &
Henderson). We must now consider, therefore, the regions of the cerebral cortex
that are concerned with eye movements.

Cortical Centres

Occipital Motor Centre. The occipital lobe is differentiated into three
areas on histological grounds; area 17, the *striate area*, is where the visual
fibres terminate, whilst areas 18 and 19, the *peristriate* and *parastriate areas*,
are intimately associated with area 17, neurones passing from Area 17 to Area
18, and from Area 18 to Area 19 and back to Area 17. The classical investigators
of the cerebral cortex by electrical stimulation observed contralaterally directed
conjugate movements of the eyes in response to stimulation of Area 17 in
primates, the movements being apparently directed to the parts of the visual
field that are projected on to the cortex. More recent work has largely confirmed
this; Fig. 175 illustrates the regions of the occipital cortex of the macaque
that gave movements in the experiments of Crosby & Henderson, whilst Fig. 176
illustrates the results obtained by Wagman, Krieger & Bender. According to
these last workers, the occipital cortex may be divided into four quadrants by
two planes; a midsagittal vertical plane dividing the cortex into a right and
left half, and a roughly horizontal plane through the calcarine fissure. Two of
these quadrants are illustrated in Fig. 176. The movements of the eyes were
such as to direct the gaze away from the quadrant stimulated.* In man, Foerster

* Crosby & Henderson found two separate areas in Area 19, an upper one giving
upward movements and a lower one giving downward movements, but Wagman *et al.*
were unable to confirm this, the upper area giving downward movement as with the rest
of the occipital lobe.

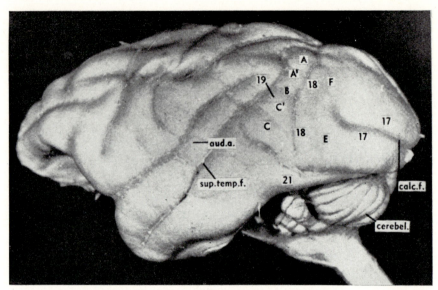

FIG. 175. A photograph of the left side of the brain of *Macaca mulatta* (× 1·8). On area 19 the various points from which eye movements were elicited are indicated by letters. Stimulation of A produced conjugate upward deviation of the eyes, of A′ conjugate deviation obliquely upward toward the right, of B conjugate horizontal deviation toward the right, of C′ conjugate deviation obliquely downward to the right, and of C, conjugate downward deviation. Stimulation in the region of E (area 17) caused oblique conjugate deviation of the eyes upward and toward the right, and in the region of F, conjugate deviation obliquely downward to the right. (Crosby & Henderson, *J. comp. Neurol.*)

FIG. 176. Contralateral conjugate eye movements elicited upon stimulation of the dorsal, lateral and lateral inferior surfaces of the occipital lobe of *Macaca mulatta*. The solid circles indicate the points that were actually stimulated, whilst the lines originating at these circles indicate the direction of the contralateral eye movement in response to this stimulation. The dots outline the region from which obliquely downward and contralateral deviations were obtained, whilst the shaded area indicates the region from which obliquely upward and contralateral deviations of the eyes were obtained. (Wagman, Krieger & Bender, *J. comp. Neurol.*)

obtained eye movements by stimulating Area 19. Wagman *et al.* raise the point as to whether the movement of the eyes is the result of stimulating a sensory region, evoking a sensation of light to which the animal responds, or whether the stimulus does, indeed, activate a motor centre. This question is probably somewhat academic since the modern tendency is to treat many areas of the brain as both sensory and motor. The finding that certain occipital lesions may impair motor activity without impairing vision (Bender, Poatel & Krieger), and that in human subjects eye movements that are not always associated with visual sensation may be evoked by electrical stimulation suggests that there are, indeed, motor regions in the occipital cortex (Bickford *et al.*).

Frontal Motor Centre. In man and other primates there is a region in the frontal cortex, stimulation of which gives rise to movements of the eyes. In

FIG. 177. Diagram of the human cerebral hemisphere seen from the left side illustrating the areas, electrical stimulation of which is followed by movement or sensation. The numbers of the areas are those of Vogt. (Herrick, *Introduction to Neurology*.)

man the region is close to the precentral gyrus, stimulation of which gives rise to discrete movements of the parts of the body as indicated in Fig. 177 (Area 8 $\alpha\beta\delta$); in apes the region lies farther forward. Movements of the eyes following stimulation of this area in the chimpanzee were described by Grünbaum & Sherrington in 1903, and similar movements in man by Foerster and Penfield & Boldrey. In the monkey, Graham Brown described movements of two kinds; in the first place, stimulation of the middle frontal convolution caused a conjugate movement of the eyes to the opposite side, the head remaining still; in the second place, stimulation of the superior frontal convolution caused a turning of the head, the eyes remaining fixed in their sockets. In both cases, therefore, the animal "looked" to the opposite side, but in the former

FIG. 178, *a*. Drawing of left human fronto-parietal area exposed at operation in which cortical stimulation resulted in movements at the following points: 1, conjugate deviation of the eyes upward and to the other side; 2, horizontal conjugate gaze to the other side; 3, divergence of the eyes; 4, conjugate deviation of the eyes downward and toward the other side; 5, no response; 6, hand movement and flexion of the fingers on the right side; 7, flexion of the right thumb; 8, retraction of the right lower lip; 9 indicates longitudinal sinus.

FIG. 178, *b*. Diagram of the left hemisphere of the macaque showing eye deviations from stimulation of the frontal eye fields at the following points: 1, eyes up to the right; 2, deviation to right; 3, divergence; 4, eyes down to right. (After Crosby.) (Lemmen, Davis & Radnor, *J. comp. Neurol.*)

instance the eyes were employed whilst in the latter the muscles of the neck. Interestingly, if the head was prevented from turning, then the eyes moved. More recently the frontal centre has been studied by Crosby in the macaque and Lemmen, Davis & Radnor in man; comparison of Figs. 178 *a* and *b* shows that the results are essentially similar.

VOLUNTARY CENTRE

It is considered that the frontal region is the centre for voluntary eye movements in contrast to the occipital regions which are thought to be concerned with purely reflex movements of the eyes in response to a visual stimulus. At any rate, a stimulus applied to the frontal area is said to be prepotent over a simultaneous one applied to the occipital area. Thus stimulation of the left occipital lobe causes a conjugate movement to the right; stimulation of the right frontal centre causes a deviation to the left. If both areas are stimulated simultaneously, the eyes move to the left. Surgical removal of the "ocular responsive cortex" in man leads to the failure of the individual to direct his eyes voluntarily to the side opposite the lesion. In monkeys and apes stimulation of the ocular responsive cortex causes head movements, opening of the palpebral fissures, and dilatation of the pupils, besides eye movements. In general, as with man, the lateral movements are most frequent; if, however, the medial and lateral recti are cut, cortical stimulation leads to upward and downward movements. Simultaneous stimulation of both sides of the cortex can lead to the fixation of the gaze directly forward.

Efferent Pathways. The pathways by which cortical impulses determining eye movements reach the eye-muscle motor neurones are not completely worked out. The pathway from the frontal centre is independent of the occipital centre, since ablation of the latter does not abolish voluntary eye movements. Fig. 179

FIG. 179. Pathways for the cortical control of the eye movements.
(Slightly modified from Crosby, *J. comp. Neurol.*)

illustrates Crosby's views. According to this, the pathway from the frontal centre is by way of the corticobulbar tract, *i.e.* the tract that carries the voluntary impulses to the musculature generally and to which the name *pyramidal* is given in its course through pons, medulla and cord. Thus the fibres run in the internal capsule and cerebral peduncle; at about the midbrain level, fibres to the nucleus of nerve VI leave the main tract to enter the medial lemniscus, descending in this to the abducens and parabducens nuclei; the remaining eye-muscle nuclei are thought to be indirectly activated by way of the median longitudinal fasciculus. The occipital centres in Areas 17, 18 and 19 are thought to activate the abducens and parabducens nuclei indirectly through the colliculi by way of the internal cortico-tectal tract and directly through the corticotegmental tract. The reason for imputing this double pathway is the old observation of Graham Brown that damaging the colliculi left eye movements intact but, as Whitteridge has pointed out, this evidence is not conclusive since the frontal pathway is known to be independent of the colliculi and the eye movements observed might have been mediated by the frontal centre.*

Brain Stem Stimulation. A systematic exploration of the brain stem in anæsthetized *encéphale isolé* cats† by Hyde has revealed a number of regions, in particular the tegmentum of the midbrain, pons and medulla, from which conjugate movements may be evoked on electrical stimulation. It is unwise to describe these regions as "centres" controlling the execution of eye movements, however, since they may simply contain the pathways from the cortex to the eye-muscle nuclei. Nevertheless it must be appreciated that, in lower animals at any rate, there are regions of the brain stem in which specific types of movement are organized; these are

FIG. 180. Direction-specific types of movement resulting from electrical stimulation in the region of the interstitial nucleus of Cajal by means of electrodes implanted in the otherwise intact brain. (Hassler & Hess, *Arch. Psychiat.*)

called by Jung & Hassler *direction-specific movements*, and they cause the animal to turn in a characteristic direction. Thus, stimulation of the interstitial nucleus of Cajal, which is close to the nucleus of N III, causes a rotation of the head about its longitudinal axis as illustrated by Fig. 180. In higher animals, such as the apes and man, turning of the eyes rather than of the head is the more prominent feature of a change of gaze, and it would not be surprising if direction-specific movements of the eyes were organized at midbrain levels.

THE REFLEXES

Psycho-Optical Reflexes

The most important group of reflexes involving eye movements in man are those in which the incidence of light on the retina acts as the primary stimulus; it is as a result of these reflexes that the eyes are (*a*) directed to objects of

* We may note that' the eye movements evoked by occipital cortex and superior colliculus may be affected differently by lesions in the brain stem, once again indicating separate pathways (Hyde, 1962); furthermore, Hyde & Slusher found that discrete lesions in the median longitudinal fasciculus could abolish adductions in response to some forms of stimulation but not to others. This looks as though the concept of a parabducens centre, controlling lateral movements through a final common pathway up the median longitudinal fasciculus, postulated by Crosby, is unsound.

† This preparation is obtained by a section of the brain stem at about the level of C1, leaving intact the nucleus of N V; in this condition the animal has many of the features of the waking state by contrast to the *cerveau isolé* preparation, where the section is higher, at the collicular level.

interest and (*b*) maintained in the necessary orientation to ensure that the images formed by the two eyes fall on the foveæ. We are accustomed to think of reflexes as being executed without the intervention of awareness on the part of the individual; these visual reactions, however, definitely involve awareness and are therefore classed as *psycho-optical reflexes*; as we shall see, there can be no doubt of their essentially involuntary nature.

The Fixation Reflex. All psycho-optical reflexes may be regarded as manifestations of the more general *fixation reflex*—the reflex which brings the images of an object on to the foveæ of the two eyes and maintains them there. The fixation reflex develops early, since an infant a few days after birth will fixate a bright light; binocular fixation, however, does not develop for some months.

The reflex exhibits itself in two aspects—(*a*) the response to a peripheral stimulus and (*b*) the maintenance of fixation; the mechanism involved in the two processes is nevertheless the same. Thus let us imagine that the eyes are stimulated by a bright object in the peripheral field. Attention is aroused and the eyes move so that the images of the object approach the foveæ—suppose that the nervous response grows in intensity as the images approach closer and closer to the foveæ and reaches a maximum when they fall actually on them. The eye muscles can then be considered to behave as a tuning system, causing movements of the eyes until a maximum nervous response is obtained, just as the knob of a tuning dial is turned to obtain maximum sound from a wireless set. Fixation is thus achieved when maximum nervous discharge is reached. If the head moves slightly, the images are displaced and the nervous response falls off; immediately the tuning mechanism comes into play and the eyes are readjusted to maintain perfect fixation. Thus the same principle, the movement of the eyes to maintain a maximum nervous response, operates both to initiate and to maintain fixation. This principle may also explain the neural basis for the frequent small movements of the eyes that take place even during attempts at steady fixation (p. 250). As studies on the stabilized retinal image have shown (p. 176), the perceived image becomes rapidly indistinct in the absence of a shift of this image on the retina, so that the nervous discharge, postulated above, tends to decrease as the eye remains stationary. The eyes presumably respond to this falling off with a movement which shifts the images on the retinæ sufficiently to excite a new set of cones and the discharge again becomes maximal. The constant, small movements of the eyes in fixation may thus be regarded as the restless groping of the oculo-motor centres for a position that gives maximum nervous discharge. *Ocular nystagmus*—a pendular to-and-fro movement of the eyes—may be regarded as an exaggeration of this groping; if fixation is difficult, as in amblyopia, the eyes move excessively in a vain attempt to find a clear image. The nystagmus of miners working for long periods in the dark is a complex syndrome; nevertheless an element in the ætiology must be the necessity for using peripheral vision; under these conditions fixation on the fovea reduces the visual acuity rather than enhances it, so that the "best position" for the retinal image is much more vaguely defined and this might well result in a ceaseless search for it over relatively large areas of retina to give a pendular type of nystagmus. It must be appreciated, however, that this point of view represents a crude simplification of what must be a more complex process; the factors of attention and meaning cannot be ignored; for example, corrective fusion movements, to be described below, are brought about as a result of a changed orientation of the retinal images, *e.g.* when one eye rolls, and the intensity of the "nervous discharge" remains unaltered.

Other manifestations of the fixation reflex are given by:—

(i) the following movements in *optokinetic nystagmus*;

(ii) the *corrective fusion movements* made in the interests of single vision;

(iii) the movements of the eyes concerned with the *visual righting reflexes*.

Optokinetic Nystagmus. This describes the movements of the eyes when the body is in motion and the subject is gazing at the environment, as when he looks out of a railway carriage (train-nystagmus) or alternatively when the subject is still and his environment, or a prominent part of it, moves around him, as in the clinical test when a rotating striped drum is gazed at steadily. Here the stimulus is the movement of the image of the fixation point on the retina, the eye responding, during the slow phase of the nystagmus, by movements designed to keep the image on the fovea. At a certain moment, fixation of this point ceases and the eyes make a rapid saccade in the opposite direction, to fixate a new stripe on the drum, and the slow movement begins again. The slow movement is obviously a following movement, but the rapid movement is difficult to categorize. It was originally thought that it occurred simply because the eyes were unable to maintain fixation on the fixated stripe, *i.e.* because the stripe had moved out of the field of binocular fixation. In fact, however, the rapid movement usually takes place long before this limit has been reached; moreover, it is not apparently due to a deliberate attempt to fixate a new stripe appearing in the periphery since optokinetic nystagmus occurs in homonymous hemianopia when, because of a lesion in the visual pathway (p. 325), the eye is blind to half the visual field (Fox & Holmes; Pasik, Pasik & Krieger). Thus the eye makes a rapid movement into its blind side. We must conclude, therefore, that the unusual stimulus-condition, namely the apparent rotation of the visual environment, activates a *nystagmus centre* that triggers off these involuntary rhythmical movements (Rademaker & Ter Braak).* The involuntary nature of this movement in man is best revealed when he is surrounded by the moving drum so that practically the whole visual field moves; in this case it is impossible to avoid the nystagmus so long as the eyes are open. When only a small part of the visual field moves, as when the subject looks at a small striped drum, then the subject may avoid the nystagmus by "looking through" the drum, *i.e.* by refusing to fixate any given stripe (Carmichael, Dix & Hallpike).

CORTICAL AND SUBCORTICAL NYSTAGMUS. In animals, such as the rabbit and dog, an optokinetic nystagmus may be evoked even in the absence of cerebral hemispheres, and for this reason it is called *subcortical*. Visual reactions in man, in the absence of a cortex, are, as we have seen, impossible, presumably because of the relative insignificance of the visual projection to the colliculi. It is unwise, therefore, to transpose studies on lower animals to man, and certainly unwise to speak of a *subcortical nystagmus* as such, although the presence of a nystagmus-centre in the lower parts of the brain is not an unreasonable hypothesis. In

---

* The *rhythm* of the nystagmus will be largely determined by the amplitude of the excursions for a given speed of rotation; the fact that this alters under a variety of experimental conditions is further proof that the initiation of the fast movement, which puts an end to the slow movement, is not due to the eyes reaching the maximal extent of the field of fixation. We may note that, according to Ter Braak, the eyes lag slightly behind the movement of the drum during the slow phase; consequently there is a slight drift of the retinal image over the retina.

man this would be activated by the cortical visual stimuli, but in lower animals the colliculi might suffice. Under pathological conditions in man, involving lesions in the cerebral hemispheres, optokinetic nystagmus may be impaired, frequently with the appearance of a *directional preponderance*, in the sense that the reflex is normal when the drum moves one way, and reduced when it moves in the other. In the case of optokinetic nystagmus in man the preponderance is seen when the drum rotates away from the affected side, so that the study of this nystagmus may be a valuable diagnostic tool (Fox & Holmes). According to Carmichael *et al.* the regions of the cortex influencing the optokinetic nystagmus are in the supramarginal and angular gyri of the temporal lobe, the right hemi-

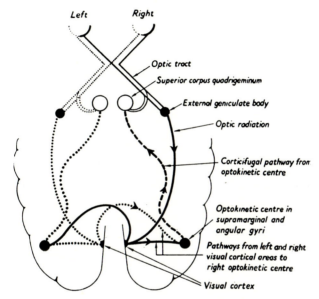

FIG. 181. Suggested schema of optokinetic mechanisms.
(Carmichael, Dix & Hallpike, *Brit. med. Bull.*)

sphere, for example, facilitating nystagmus on moving the drum to the left, and inhibiting that on moving the drum to the right.* A schematic pathway for the nystagmus is illustrated in Fig. 181; it should be noted, however, that Pasik *et al.* do not agree with the location of the cortical centres in the supramarginal and angular gyri.

* In the macaque Henderson & Crosby abolished optokinetic nystagmus by bilateral des-truction of areas 18 and 19; unilateral destruction abolished the nystagmus on rotating the drum away from the injured side, *i.e.* there was a directional preponderance *towards* the injured side, by contrast with man where it is *away* from the lesion. The frontal eye fields (area 8) exerted an inhibitory action so that on ablation of these the nystagmus was more marked.
   We may note the danger of confusion according as the direction of the nystagmus is described in terms of the quick component or the direction of rotation of the drum; thus when Carmichael, Dix & Hallpike (1954) say that nystagmus to the healthy side is suppressed, they are referring to the quick phase of the nystagmus, so that there is suppression of nystagmus when the drum rotates away from the healthy side, *i.e.* towards the lesion.

SINGLE MOVING POINT

We may note that when a single object moves across the stationary visual field, there is no optokinetic nystagmus unless the field is otherwise empty; thus according to Rademaker & Ter Braak, we may think of two opposing tendencies, the shifting of the images of stationary objects on the retina, tending to inhibit the following movement, and the shifting of the image of the single moving point that incites to movement. According to the relative preponderance of the moving or fixed field, one or other of the tendencies will determine the result, *i.e.* whether the eye remains fixed or follows the moving point. This was well demonstrated by Ter Braak who immobilized one eye of a rabbit and examined the movements of the other, which was blinded. Moving a single point across the visual field of the immobilized eye now caused the other eye to give a genuine nystagmus; because the stimulated eye was immobilized, there was no movement of images of stationary objects over its retina, and so the normal inhibition of the nystagmus was released. A similar experiment on a human subject, with one eye immobilized by paralysis of its extraocular muscles, is described by Mackensen (1958).

OPTOKINETIC AFTER-NYSTAGMUS

When a rotating drum is stopped after the subject viewing it has experienced a nystagmus for some time, there is an after-nystagmus lasting for two or three beats only; it has been studied in some detail by Mackensen. It is best evoked if the eyes are presented with a uniform field, *i.e.* in the dark.

Corrective Fusion Movements. The orientation of both eyes so as to produce images of the same object on corresponding parts of the two retinæ requires continuous adjustments, which are brought about by this reflex. Here the effective stimulus is diplopia.

Visual righting reflexes. In man and the ape the eyes play a very important part in the maintenance of posture. It is quite clear that the movements of the eyes must be closely attuned to the posture of the animal; in lower forms this is achieved by a rigid association of the eye muscles with the vestibular apparatus so that the position of the eyes is completely determined by the orientation of the body in relation to gravity and the parts of the body in relation to each other (Fig. 182). Here, then, the labyrinth dominates eye movements. The

FIG. 182. Showing the rigid relationship between the positions of the eyes and the parts of the body in fishes. A and C illustrate the positions of the fish when at rest. B shows the compensatory movement of the eyes that occurs during swimming or on bending the tail into the position indicated. D illustrates the compensatory movement that occurs on rotating the fish about its longitudinal axis (Bard, *Macleod's Physiology in Modern Medicine.*)

visual impressions alone, however, can clearly provide information as to the orientation of the head, and therefore of the body. Thus if a subject is falling forward, his original point of fixation moves upwards and, as a result of the fixation reflex, his eyes move upwards to maintain fixation; the necessary postural adjustments for recovery can be made in the light of impressions provided by the eyes and their adjustments. In this case proprioceptive impulses from the superior recti demand a movement of the head upwards so that the eyes can re-assume the primary position. The proprioceptive impulses from the neck muscles now demand postural changes that will permit the head to re-assume its normal erect position. In man and the ape posture can be maintained quite adequately by means of the visual righting reflexes when the labyrinths have been destroyed.

Vestibular and Proprioceptive Reflexes

The primary stimulus for these reflexes is not visual but arises from the vestibular apparatus or the proprioceptive stretch receptors in the neck muscles. They are classed as *static (or tonic) reflexes* and *kinetic reflexes*; by the first class a definite orientation of the eyes is evoked and maintained for a given position of the head in relation to the trunk and the pull of gravity, whilst by the latter a definite *movement* of the eyes follows a movement or acceleration of the head.

FIG. 183. The positions of the semicircular canals in the head viewed from the side. (After Quix.)

The Vestibular Apparatus. A brief description of the vestibular apparatus would be useful at this point. In man it consists essentially of three semicircular canals in mutually perpendicular planes, and two sacs, the *utricle* and *saccule* (Figs. 183 and 184). Each canal widens at one end into an *ampulla* containing a sense organ—the *crista ampullaris* or *crista acustica*, which bears as an auxiliary structure a jelly-like *cupula* which encloses the sense hairs protruding from the surface of the crista (Fig. 185). The utricle and saccule contain sensory organs called *maculæ*, with a similar type of sense cell but with shorter hairs. The sense hairs of the macula are embedded in an otolith membrane which is encrusted with numerous concretions of lime crystals (*otoconia*) (Fig. 186). The membranous labyrinth, the cavities of which are filled with endolymph, is surrounded by cartilage or bone, the space between it and the surrounding tissues being filled with perilymph.

FIG. 184. Positions of the semicircular canals in the head viewed from above. (After Quix.)

FIG. 185. The cupula of the crista ampullaris. (After Kolmer.)

FIG. 186. Section through the macula utriculi and the ampulla of a vertical semicircular canal in man. *C.*, cupula; *C.A.*, crista ampullaris; *E*, endolymph; *M.U.*, macula utriculi; *O*, otoconia; *O.M.*, otolith membrane; *P*, perilymph; *R.A.*, ramus ampullaris; *R.U.*, ramus utricularis of N VIII. (Lowenstein, after Kolmer, *Biol. Rev.*)

The Utricle

The macula of the utricle is most probably stimulated by a gravitational pull on the otolith membrane which alters the tension in the hair cells; the macula lies normally in a horizontal plane, and under these conditions the tension is at a minimum; if the head is held upside down the stimulus is at a maximum. The utricle is thus a receptor which can respond to alterations in the orientation of the head in relation to the direction of gravity; it can therefore mediate the static class of reflex, *i.e.* compensating poses of the eyes, head, etc. It is worth noting, however, that a sudden linear acceleration of the head could exert an inertial pull on the hairs of the macula and give rise to a kinetic type of reflex response.

The Semicircular Canals

The semicircular canals are receptor organs responding to acceleration of the head; opinion on the manner in which the crista ampullaris is stimulated by an acceleration has fluctuated, but the experiments of Steinhausen and Dohlman

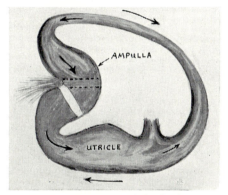

FIG. 187. Illustrating movements of the cupula in the ampullæ of the horizontal canals on accelerating the head to the right. In the left canal the inertial flow of fluid is away from the ampulla, whilst in the right canal it is towards the ampulla.

have now firmly established the original notion of Mach that it is the inertial movements of the endolymph that deform the cupula and stimulate the hair-fibres embedded in it. As Fig. 187 shows, when the head is accelerated the endolymph within the membranous canal tends to be "left behind" and so produces an inertial force that deflects the cupula, which moves in much the same way as a rotating door. When the acceleration ceases there is an inertial movement of fluid in the opposite direction. The function of the macula of the saccule in man is unknown; all the evidence suggests that the utricle and semicircular canals are responsible for all the adapting reactions to acceleration and gravity.

Static Vestibular Reflexes. These reflexes, mediated by the utricle, serve to maintain a normally orientated field of vision despite changes in the position of the head. Thus when the body is tilted towards the prone position the eyes move upwards; when the body is inclined sideways, the eyes roll; it should be emphasized, however, that in man the rolling of the eyes by no means compensates entirely for the altered position of the head; psychological adjustments are necessary (p. 335). Movement of the body or the head about a vertical axis will clearly have no influence on the direction of gravitational pull on the otolith membrane, hence any compensatory movement of the eyes that takes place must be mediated by another type of receptor. It is here that the proprioceptive impulses from the neck muscles are involved.

PROPRIOCEPTIVE NECK REFLEXES

Bending the head forward and backwards towards or away from the chest, besides activating the utricle, will stretch the neck muscles, and it may be shown that the compensatory movements of the eyes that are elicited may be caused by both of these receptive mechanisms. Thus movement of the trunk, keeping the head fixed, gives the same reflex, but now by virtue of the stretched neck muscles. Lateral movements in response to moving the head about a vertical axis are mediated exclusively by the neck mechanism. Hence cutting the cord in the cervical region may reduce an animal's ability to maintain orientation (Cohen).

Kinetic Reflexes. Kinetic eye reflexes are compensatory effector movements called forth chiefly by angular acceleration of the head. As illustrated by Fig. 184, the canals are arranged in the head in three mutually perpendicular planes. We may distinguish on each side a horizontal or external canal, both lying in the same plane which, in effect, is not horizontal when the head is erect but slopes backwards at 30°, hence they only come into the horizontal plane when the head is tilted forward through this angle. Rotation of the head about a vertical axis has its main effect on this pair of canals, which we may describe as a *synergic pair*. When the head is rotated about its vertical axis, *e.g.* when the head looks to the right, the reflex movement of the eyes in the opposite direction that maintains fixation on a point that was originally straight ahead of the eyes will be mediated by the inertial stimuli in the horizontal canals. The anterior vertical canal of one side is in the same plane as the posterior vertical canal of the other, so that we may distinguish two more synergic pairs, namely left anterior-right posterior, and left posterior-right anterior. When the head is moved forwards and backwards, towards and away from the chest, the compensatory rapid movements of the eyes upwards and downwards are mediated by the synergic pair whose planes lie in a sagittal plane, whilst when the head is moved towards and away from the shoulder the other vertical pair, lying in the frontal plane, parallel to the forehead, will mediate the rolling movement that takes place.

ELECTROPHYSIOLOGY

Studies of the action potentials in fibres from the ampullæ made by Lowenstein and his collaborators have shown that there is normally a tonic discharge from them all when the head is at rest; on accelerating the head about a vertical axis, for example, the discharge from the ampulla of one horizontal canal is increased, whilst that of the other is inhibited. The inhibited ampulla in this case is the one that "leads" the canal, *i.e.* on rotating the head to the right the left ampulla is inhibited; with the vertical canals the leading ampulla gives the increased discharge. Thus the message sent to the central nervous system, when the head is accelerated in looking round horizontally, is double, consisting of an increased discharge in some vestibular nerve fibres and a descreased discharge in others. Furthermore, when the movement ceases, the deceleration of the head causes inertial currents in the opposite direction, so that the cupulas in the horizontal canals will be deflected in the opposite way, and this will lead to a new message, in which those fibres that had shown the increased discharge will now show inhibition, whilst the inhibited fibres will give the discharge. It is presumably this second message that brings the compensatory eye-movement to a stop.

Vestibular Nystagmus. The mechanism of the semicircular canals is best investigated in the intact animal or man by the study of the nystagmus that occurs on rotating about a given axis. If a human subject is rotated about a vertical axis when he is seated in a rotating chair with his head bending forward to bring his horizontal canals into the plane of rotation, then his eyes go into a *rotatory nystagmus*; it is as though they were making repeated attempts at maintaining fixation of an object in front, but they are not visual responses since they occur when the eyes are closed, the eye-movements being recorded electrically. The nystagmus consists in a slow movement of the eyes in the opposite direction to that of rotation, followed by a rapid saccade in the direction of rotation. The speed of the slow movement is that of the speed of rotation. The direction of the nystagmus is named after the direction of the fast movement; hence the direction of a rotatory nystagmus is the same as that of the rotation. If the rotation is maintained for about 20–30 sec the nystagmus ceases.

MECHANISM

Why should the eyes go into a nystagmus on rotation? That is, what is there in the stimulus-conditions that results in this repetitive type of motion? We may answer the last question first. It will be recalled that for any abrupt movement of the head there are an acceleration and a deceleration, and therefore there are two sets of messages sent to the central nervous system, determined by two types of inertial fluid movement. The cupula is deflected one way and then the other. By contrast, when the rotation is sustained, the initial acceleration is not followed by a deceleration, and consequently no inertial force is brought into play to return the cupula to its mid-position. Instead the cupula must rely on its own elasticity, and experiments have shown that it behaves as a heavily damped pendulum, requiring some 20–30 sec to return to its mid-position after maximal deflection, *i.e.* it requires as long as the nystagmus lasts. Thus a sustained deflection of the cupula, with its accompanying pattern of nervous discharges, gives rise to rhythmic nystagmoid movements, whilst a deflection followed by a rapid return gives rise only to a compensatory deflection of the eyes. Experimentally this was demonstrated by Steinhausen who showed that if he applied a transitory pressure to a canal, through a tube inserted into it, the effect was only a simple movement of the eyes; if he maintained a constant pressure, so that the cupula remained deflected, the eyes went into a nystagmus which lasted as long as the pressure was maintained.

POST-ROTATORY NYSTAGMUS

We may imagine that our human subject has been rotated at a steady speed for some 20–30 sec; the cupulas have returned to their mid-positions and the rotatory nystagmus has ceased. We now abruptly cease the rotation There is now an inertial flow of endolymph such as to deflect the cupulas in the opposite direction. Moreover, these deflections will be maintained until the natural elasticity brings the cupulas back to their mid-positions. Hence the conditions are such as to induce another nystagmus, lasting another 20–30 sec, but differing only in the direction; thus the slow component will be in the direction of rotation. It is this nystagmus that is easy to demonstrate; the subject is rotated at an even speed for some 20–30 sec and then the rotation is abruptly stopped and the experimenter observes the nystagmoid movements.

THE VERTICAL CANALS

The effects of stimulating the vertical canals are more complex. Studies of the discharges in the nerve fibres from the ampullæ indicate that, whereas rotation in the plane of the horizontal canals only stimulates the horizontal ampullæ, rotation in other planes causes a complex group of inhibitory and stimulatory responses in the ampullæ of *all* the canals. The final compensatory movement of the eyes, resulting from a rotation in a plane other than that of the horizontal canals, represents the integrated response to stimuli arising in all the ampullæ. It must be appreciated, moreover, that the macula of the utricle may be stimulated by these rotatory accelerations, and thus make its contribution to the general response of the eyes.*

Compensatory Rolling. The rolling of the eyes that takes place when the head is tilted towards the shoulder has attracted considerable interest. It is clear that both otolith and semicircular canals may act as receptors, but if the compensatory rolling is to be sustained for any length of time clearly it is only the otolith, or neck proprioception mechanism, that will operate. Merton's studies have emphasized the much greater effectiveness of the semicircular canals in producing a rolling. When a subject is swung from side to side on a swing hung from a ball-bearing, such that the axis of rotation corresponds to the visual axis of the eye, then it is found that the eyes roll in the opposite direction to that of the movement of the head; the rolling movement lags behind the head movement, so that the compensation is never complete; in other words, the vertical meridians of the eyes do not remain vertical. The compensation amounts to about a quarter of the actual movement of the head. When a head movement is sustained, however, this partial compensation is not maintained, so that the vertical meridian returns almost completely to the position it would have had if no rotation had occurred. According to Woellner & Graybiel, for example, at a tilt of 15° the rolling is only 1·5°, whilst with a tilt of 70° it is only 4°. As Merton has explained, the partial compensatory movements during rotation are of value in reducing the angular movements of the retina, and thereby permitting a reasonable visual acuity even when the head is swinging through quite large angles.

Reaction of Labyrinth to Artificial Stimuli

Caloric Nystagmus. A current of warm water (40°–45°) or cold water (22°–27°) through the auditory meatus causes a nystagmus of vestibular origin; the slow movement is towards the stimulated side, with cold water, and away from

---

* The effects of electrical stimulation of the ampulla of a single canal have been described by Fluur, but as he points out, this is an exceedingly artificial procedure, since, under normal conditions of stimulation, there are reactions in both sides of the head simultaneously. Stimulation of the left lateral canal caused a conjugate movement to the right; the left anterior vertical canal a conjugate movement upwards, and the left posterior vertical canal a conjugate movement downwards. Combined stimulation of the left anterior and posterior canals caused a conjugate counter-clockwise rolling.

this side with warm water. The fact that the nature of the nystagmus depends on the position of the head suggests that the cause is associated with thermal currents in the endolymph.

Galvanic Nystagmus. Passing a direct current from one ear to the other causes a nystagmus, the slow phase being towards the positive pole. The nature of the nystagmus is independent of the position of the head.

Compression Nystagmus. Experimental increase in the pressure in the middle ear causes a nystagmus.

Unilateral labyrinthectomy causes a nystagmus for a few days with the slow phase directed towards the operated side; injection of cocaine has a similar effect. It will be recalled that in the normal animal at rest there are tonic discharges from both ampullæ of a synergic pair. Accelerations, requiring compensatory movements, cause an imbalance in this system, the discharge from one ampulla increasing and that from the other being inhibited. Clearly, then, extirpation of one labyrinth creates an imbalance that will be interpreted by the central nervous system as an acceleration, and some compensatory movements of the eyes will be initiated. In this way we may explain the effects of extirpation; with irritative lesions in the vestibular apparatus or in its nervous pathway the balance is upset once again, but this time in the opposite sense (see, for example, Cranmer).* After a time the necessary central compensations take place and the nystagmus subsides.

The Nervous Pathways in the Labyrinthine Reflexes

Vestibular Reflex Arc. The labyrinth is supplied by the vestibular branch of N VIII ; as with other sensory nerves, the fibres have their cell bodies outside the central nervous system, in this case the *ganglion of Scarpa* (Fig. 188); the fibres terminate in four main nuclei in the medulla, namely, *Deiter's nucleus*, *Bechterew's nucleus*, *Monakow's nucleus*, and the *triangular nucleus*. Secondary neurones pass:

(*a*) to the cord as the vestibulo-spinal tract,

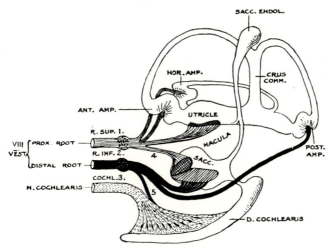

FIG. 188. Innervation of the membranous labyrinth. (De Burlet, *Anat. Anz.*)

* Because of the involvement of proprioceptive impulses from the neck muscles in eye movements, we might expect irritative lesions in the cervical cord to cause nystagmus; in fact they do. Presumably impulses pass up the cord in the spino-vestibular pathways which connect the proprioceptive centres of the cord with the inferior vestibular nuclei; within the vestibular areas there is a transfer of impulses to pathways connecting with the oculomotor nuclei (Crosby, 1953).

(*b*) to the cerebellum,

(*c*) to the mid-brain eye-muscle nuclei by way of the median longitudinal fasciculus. Tentatively, then, we might illustrate a vestibular reflex arc by Fig. 189, where the parabducens nucleus is treated as a relay station to bring about coordinated activity between abducens (N VI) and oculomotor (N III) nuclei. However, there is no doubt that some fibres from the vestibular nucleus pass directly up the median longitudinal fasciculus to the eye-muscle nuclei, so that the intervention of the parabducens nucleus is not an anatomical necessity.

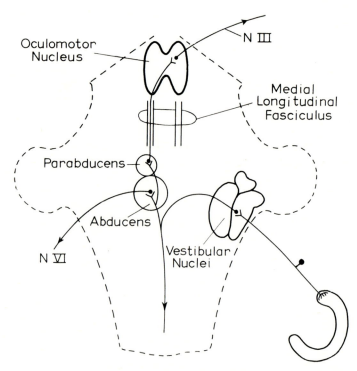

FIG. 189. Possible reflex arc in the response of the eyes to a labyrinthine stimulus. (After Crosby, *J. comp. Neurol.*)

Nystagmus Centres. There is by no means any certainty as to the existence of one or more specific centres controlling nystagmus, either optokinetic or vestibular, or both. According to de Kleyn, the vestibular nystagmus may be elicited in a rabbit from which the cerebral hemispheres and cerebellum have been removed, and the brain stem has been sectioned just anterior to the abducens nucleus, so that the nuclei of N III and IV are out of action, whilst a further section through the medulla, just behind the vestibular nuclei, reduces the amount of the brain involved practically to the vestibular nuclei. Under these conditions the lateral rectus exhibits a slow contraction and quick relaxation on stimulating the labyrinth. For vestibular nystagmus to occur, therefore, little more than a three-neurone arc, involving the vestibular nucleus, seems to be necessary.

With optokinetic nystagmus, obviously visual centres are involved, and the question arises as to whether and how the vestibular centre may also become involved in optically induced nystagmus, since there is no doubt that vestibular nystagmus may be influenced by higher centres. According to Ohm, for example, optokinetic and vestibular nystagmus were able to interact in the vestibular nuclei, which were therefore the centre through which both types of nystagmus operated. This view seems to have been disproved, however, by the observation that in cases of streptomycin lesions of the vestibular nuclei, severe enough to abolish caloric nystagmus, optokinetic nystagmus could be elicited normally (Dix, Hallpike & Harrison). The situation has not been completely clarified yet but some recent work of Lachmann, Bergmann & Monnier (1958) on the rabbit is of interest. These workers discovered a mesodiencephalic region, stimulation of which would cause a nystagmus; the most sensitive region was near the thalamus and was thus considerably rostral to the vestibular nuclei. By studying the interaction of this "central nystagmus", evoked by electrical stimulation of the brain, with vestibular nystagmus obtained by mechanical stimulation of the labyrinth, these workers came to the conclusion that the two forms of nystagmus had a common meeting ground in the midbrain, since there was no doubt of their mutual reaction, both subtractive and additive effects being obtained (Bergmann, Lachmann, Monnier & Krupp). Presumably, then, vestibular nystagmus is normally mediated through this midbrain centre, although de Kleyn's experiments show that this is not necessary. Optokinetic nystagmus presumably also uses the centre, but whether this is obligatory or not remains to be conclusively proved.

The Visual, Labyrinthine and Proprioceptive Postural Mechanisms

The visual righting reflex enables the animal to maintain posture independently of the gravistatic labyrinthine mechanism; as we have seen, the primary stimulus is a disorientation of the visual fields from normal. The gravity reflexes tend to maintain normal posture, utilizing as primary stimulus the abnormal gravitational pull on the body; these reflexes also tend to maintain the visual fields normal, independently of the visual stimulus, since they can be evoked in the decerebrate animal. The actual response of man, for example, to a disorientating influence, is therefore the result of these two main groups of reflexes working together, and it is of interest to speculate on their relative contributions to any given postural righting movement.

Suppose then that a human subject is carefully poised on one foot and his equilibrium is suddenly disturbed. The changed pull of gravity in relation to his long axis, and the acceleration of his head, cause rapid labyrinthine reflex adjustments of the body, and also eye movements calculated to maintain a normal orientation of the visual field in the new position of the body. The first phase, then, is the re-establishment of correctly orientated visual fields. This has been done, however, on the basis of crude sensory data—gravitational—and for the eyes, which require a careful adjustment for both to fixate the same point, this reflex compensation is probably grossly inadequate. The fixation reflex now ensures the correct adjustment of the eyes, *i.e.* use is made of more precise sensory data. We now have the eyes directed accurately so as to maintain a normal orientation of the visual fields in both eyes; the centres controlling postural mechanisms can now receive data from three sources—the labyrinth, proprioceptive receptors of the muscles of the body generally and proprioceptive receptors of the eye muscles.*

* The problem of proprioceptive impulses from the extraocular muscles has been discussed earlier (p. 235); the term will be used to avoid laborious circumlocutions,

The data from the last-named source, in view of the extreme delicacy of adjustment possible with the eye muscles, are doubtless of major importance and they indicate the exact movements of the head necessary to permit the eyes to return to their primary position and still retain a normally orientated visual field. The head righting response is thus largely controlled with the aid of eye-muscle proprioceptive impulses, although labyrinthine and neck-muscle proprioceptive impulses contribute as well. The visual reflex thus reinforces and gives precision to the much cruder gravitational type of reflex.

Cortical Control of the Eye Movements

The fixation reflex operates by way of the occipital cortex; that this reflex—although an important component in behaviour—does not dominate the eye movements is clear from the fact that an individual does not respond to every peripheral stimulus by a movement of the eyes; similarly, on turning the head, more often than not the eyes move *with* the head and not against as would happen if purely labyrinthine or proprioceptive impulses determined the eye movements. There is thus an over-riding control over the eye movements capable of inhibiting the more primitive reflex patterns; the centre for this control in man is in the frontal lobe of the cortex.

Impairment of Voluntary Control. The importance of the voluntary frontal centre is revealed by the defects in patients suffering from lesions in this area or, more usually, in the projection fibres in the internal capsule or anterior part of the midbrain. As described by Holmes, the patient cannot move his eyes in response to a command although an obvious effort is made to obey, accompanied often by great distress. There is no paralysis of eye movements since a slowly moving object may be followed; if the movement is at all rapid, however, following is unsuccessful. Reading may be carried out slowly provided that the letters are not too far apart. When the eyes are deviated by following a moving point, great difficulty may be experienced in bringing them back to their primary position. When the head moves, the eyes generally move in the opposite direction. Clearly the oculomotor behaviour of the patient is now determined by reflex patterns—primarily the fixation reflex. The following movements are responses of the eyes to a movement of the image off the fovea; if the point moves too quickly the eyes become the prey to fixation reflexes initiated from other points in the visual field and so cease to follow—the following movements in the normal human subject therefore represent the combined effects of voluntary control and the fixation reflex; the voluntary centre inhibits other reflexes which, if permitted to operate, would prevent the full execution of the primary intention, and it is thus only when this centre is unimpaired that true purposive movements of the eyes can be carried out.

The powerful nature of the fixation reflex is revealed in lesions of the sort described; the caloric or galvanic nystagmus is a labyrinthine reflex regularly evoked in the normal subject; in these patients, however, such responses can only be elicited when the patient is in the dark—in the light, the fixation reflex, operating without any inhibitory control from the frontal centre, can and does dominate oculo-motor behaviour to the extent of inhibiting vestibular reflexes. Again, when the patient has fixated an object, great difficulty is experienced

---

but we need not commit ourselves to the view that such sensory impulses really are utilized in this context; the motor discharge required to achieve and maintain a given fixation point could, of itself, provide the information.

in removing the gaze from it and many expedients are used to achieve this, such as jerking the head or covering the eyes with the hand.

The fact that a patient can follow a row of letters in reading indicates that the fixation reflex implies not only a visual stimulus but also interest and attention; after reading the first group of letters interest in them ceases and the occipital centre is ready to respond to the letters in the peripheral field; in the normal subject this response is immediate since the primary reflex response to the first group is readily inhibited by the frontal centre; in the sufferer from a frontal lesion the new response is slow and is only brought about if the new stimulus falls close to the fovea. That the patient reads in the right direction shows the importance of attention and interest even when the voluntary centre is not active.

Impairment of Fixation Reflex. A disturbance in the fixation reflex in which vision is unimpaired is rare; however, cases of lesions of the cortico-tectal tract—the efferent pathway in the reflex—have been described. In these patients the movements of fixation are normal but the maintenance of fixation is defective, especially if strong deviation of the eyes is necessary. If the eyes are in their position of rest—and fixation is most easily maintained in this position—the voluntary effort is quite adequate to sustain normal fixation; with the eyes deviated, fixation requires a more complex and continuous muscular effort and it is then that the fixation reflex becomes important—the automatic pilot which keeps the plane on its course while the pilot attends to other things. When the head, or the object of fixation, is moving, maintenance of fixation becomes likewise a complex act and the patient fails to follow a moving object and complains of being unable to "focus" objects while he is moving, as in a vehicle. The phenomena of defects in the fixation reflex thus fit in well with the general conception of its function and relation to the voluntary frontal centre.

Other Reflex Responses. The abrupt turning of the eyes to an unexpected sound—the *acoustic reflex*—or towards a stimulus applied to the body, primitive as it may appear, involves integrations of a high order since spatial localization enters into the response; it would seem that the frontal cortex is involved (*i.e.* that this part of the brain is not exclusively concerned with voluntary acts). In other movements implying judgment of the nature of the stimulus, such as blinking and aversion of the eyes as a result of a threatening gesture, much wider regions of the cortex are concerned, and the pulvinar of the thalamus—phylogenetically related to the lateral geniculate body—is regarded as a possible "lower visual centre" intimately associated with these and related responses, since it has close connections with the precuneus, angular gyrus, parieto-occipital and occipito-temporal lobes.

THE CEREBELLUM

This region of the brain is off the main ascending and descending pathways from cord to midbrain and cortex, and may be regarded essentially as a regulating device for the smooth execution of the motor activity of the organism. It may be described as a "feed-back centre", in the sense that it receives information from all regions of the body and from the parts of the brain directly concerned in motor activities; because of its reciprocal connections with these parts, including the regions of the cortex concerned with voluntary movements, it is able to modify their activities continuously in the light of this information. The control of the eye movements, both reflex and voluntary, therefore involves activity of this part of the brain. The direct connections of the flocculonodular lobe with the vestibular nuclei in the medulla suggest a very intimate connection between vestibularly evoked eye reflexes and this, the so-called paleocerebellum. Certainly ablation of this portion of the cerebellum causes nystagmus—of a transient kind, however.

GENERAL REFERENCES

CAMIS, M., & CREED, R. S. (1930). Physiology of the Vestibular Apparatus. *Oxford.*

COGAN, D. G. (1956). Neurology of the Extraocular Muscles. 2nd. Ed. Springfield: C. C. Thomas.

HOLMES, G. (1938). The cerebral integration of the ocular movements. *Brit. Med. J.* ii, 107–112.

ROELOFS, C. O. (1954). Optokinetic nystagmus. *Doc. Ophthal.* 7–8, 579–650.

SZENTAGOTHAI, J. (1943). Die zentrale Innervation der Augenbewegungen. *Arch. f. Psychiat.*, 116, 721–760.

WHITTERIDGE, D. (1960). Central control of the eye movements. In Handbook of Physiology. Ed. Field, Magoun & Hall. Vol. II. pp. 1089–1109. Washington: *Amer. Physiol. Soc.*

SPECIAL REFERENCES

APTER, J. T. (1945). Projection of the retina on superior colliculus of cats. *J. Neurophysiol.*, 8, 123–134.

APTER, J. T. (1946). Eye movements following strychninization of the superior colliculus of cats. *J. Neurophysiol.*, 9, 73–86.

BERGMANN, F., LACHMANN, J., MONNIER, M., & KRUPP, P. (1959). Central nystagmus. III. Functional correlations of mesodiencephalic nystagmogenic centre. *Amer. J. Physiol.*, 197, 454–460.

BICKFORD, R. G., PETERSEN, M. C., DODGE, H. W., & SEM-JACOBSEN, C. W. (1953). Observations on depth stimulation of the human brain through implanted electrographic leads. *Proc. Staff Meetings Mayo Clin.*, 28, 181–187.

BROWN, T. G. (1922). Reflex orientation of the optical axes and the influence upon it of the cerebral cortex. *Arch. néerl. Physiol.*, 7, 571–578.

BURGI, S. (1957). Das Tectum opticum. Seine Verbindungen bei der Katze und seine Bedeutung beim Menschen. *Deutsch. Z. Nervenheilk.*, 176, 701–729.

CARMICHAEL, E. A., DIX, M. R., & HALLPIKE, C. S. (1956). Pathology, symptomatology and diagnosis of organic affections of the eighth nerve system. *Brit. med. Bull.*, 12, 146–152.

CARMICHAEL, E. A., DIX, M. R., & HALLPIKE, C. S. (1954). Lesions of the cerebral hemispheres and their effects upon optokinetic and caloric nystagmus. *Brain*, 77, 345–372.

COHEN, L. A. (1961). Role of eye and neck proprioceptive mechanisms in body orientation and motor coordination. *J. Neurophysiol.*, 24, 1–11.

CRANMER, R. (1951). Nystagmus related to lesions of the central vestibular apparatus and the cerebellum. *Ann. Otol.*, 60, 186–196.

CROSBY, E. C. (1953). Relations of brain centres to normal and abnormal eye movements in the horizontal plane. *J. comp. Neurol.*, 99, 437–479.

CROSBY, E. C., & HENDERSON, J. W. (1948). Pathway concerned in automatic eye movements. *J. comp. Neurol.*, 88, 53–91.

CROSBY, E. C., YOSS, R. E., & HENDERSON, J. W. (1952). The pattern for eye movements on the frontal eye field etc. *J. comp. Neurol.*, 97, 357–383.

DE BURLET, H. M. (1924). Zur Innervation der Macula sacculi bei Säugetieren. *Anat. Anzeiger*, 58, 26–32.

DIX, M. R., HALLPIKE, C. S., & HARRISON, M. S. (1949). Some observations upon the otological effects of streptomycin intoxication. *Brain*, 72, 241–245.

DOHLMAN, G. (1935). Some practical and theoretical points in labyrinthology. *Proc. roy. Soc. Med.*, 28, 1371–1380.

FLUUR, E. (1959). Influences of semicircular ducts on extraocular muscles. *Acta otolaryngol. Suppl.*, 149.

FOERSTER, O. (1931). The cerebral cortex in man. *Lancet* (2), 309–312.

FOX, J. C., & HOLMES, G. (1926). Optic nystagmus and its value in the localisation of cerebral lesions. *Brain*, **49**, 333–371.

GRÜNBAUM, A. S. F., & SHERRINGTON, C. S. (1903). Observations on the physiology of the cerebral cortex of the anthropoid ape. *Proc. Roy. Soc. B.*, **72**, 152–155.

HASSLER, R., & HESS, W. R. (1954). Experimenteller und anatomische Befunde über die Drehbewegungen und ihre nervösen Apparate. *Arch. Psychiat.* **192**, 488–526.

HENDERSON, J. W., & CROSBY, E. C. (1952). An experimental study of optokinetic responses. *Arch. Ophthal.*, **47**, 43–54.

HYDE, J. E. (1960). Facilitation and addition of electrically evoked eye movements in cats. *J. Neurophysiol.*, **23**, 583–591.

HYDE, J. E. (1962). Effect of hindbrain lesions on conjugate horizontal eye movements in cats. *Exp. Eye Res.*, **1**, 206–214.

HYDE, J. E., & SLUSHER, M. A. (1961). Functional role of median longitudinal fasciculus in evoked conjugate ocular deviations in cats. *Amer. J. Physiol.*, **200**, 919–922.

JUNG, R., & HASSLER, R. (1960). The extrapyramidal motor system. In *Handbook of Physiology*. Ed. Field, Magoun & Hall. Vol. II, pp. 863–927. Baltimore: American Physiological Society.

DE KLEYN, A. (1939). Some remarks on vestibular nystagmus. *Confin. Neurol.*, **2**, 257–292.

LACHMANN, J., BERGMANN, F., & MONNIER, M. (1958). Central nystagmus elicited by stimulation of the meso-diencephalon in the rabbit. *Amer. J. Physiol.*, **193**, 328–334.

LACHMANN, J., BERGMANN, F., WEINMAN, J., & WELNER, A. (1958). Central nystagmus. II. Relationship between central and labyrinthine nystagmus. *Amer. J. Physiol.*, **195**, 267–270.

LEMMEN, L. J., DAVIS, J. S., & RADNOR, L. L. (1959). Observation on stimulation of the human frontal eye field. *J. comp. Neurol.*, **112**, 163–168.

LOWENSTEIN, O. (1936). The equilibrium function of the vertebrate labyrinth. *Biol. Rev.*, **11**, 113–145.

LOWENSTEIN, O. (1956). Comparative physiology of the otolith organs. *Brit. med. Bull*, **12**, 110–114.

MACKENSEN, G. (1958). Zur Theorie des optokinetischen Nystagmus. *Klin. Mbl. Augenheilk.*, **132**, 769–780.

MACKENSEN, G. (1959). Untersuchung zur Physiologie des optokinetischen Nachnystagmus. v. Graefes' *Arch. Ophthal.*, **160**, 497–509.

MERTON, P. A. (1956). Compensatory rolling movements of the eye. *J. Physiol.*, **132**, 25–27 P.

OHM, J. (1936). Ueber Interferenz mehrerer Arten von Nystagmus. *Proc. Acad. Sci. Amst.*, **39**, 549–558.

PASIK, P., PASIK, T., & BENDER, M. (1960). Oculomotor function following cerebral hemidecortication in the monkey. *Arch. Neurol.*, **3**, 298–305.

PASIK, P., PASIK, T., & KRIEGER, H. P. (1959). Effects of cerebral lesions upon optokinetic nystagmus in monkeys. *J. Neurophysiol.*, **22**, 297–304.

PENFIELD, W., & BOLDREY, E. (1937). Somatic motor and sensory representation in the cerebral cortex of man as studied by electrical stimulation. *Brain*, **60**, 389–443.

RADEMAKER, G. G. J., & TER BRAAK, J. W. G. (1948). On the central mechanism of some optic reactions. *Brain*, **71**, 48–76.

STEINHAUSEN, W. (1933). Uber die Beobachtung der Cupula in den Bodengangsampullen des Labyrinths des lebenden Hechts. *Pflüg. Arch.*, **232**, 500–512.

TER BRAAK, J. W. G. (1936). Untersuchungen ueber optokinetischen Nystagmus. *Arch. néerl. Physiol.*, **21**, 309–376.

WAGMAN, I. H., KRIEGER, H. P., & BENDER, M. B. (1958). Eye movements elicited by surface and depth stimulation of the occipital lobe of macaque mulatta. *J. comp. Neurol.*, **109**, 169–193.

WARWICK, R. (1953). Representation of the extra-ocular muscles in the oculomotor nuclei of the monkey. *J. comp. Neurol.*, **98**, 449–503.

WARWICK, R. (1955). The so-called nucleus of convergence. *Brain*, **78**, 92–114.

WOELLNER, R. C., & GRAYBIEL, A. (1959). Counterrolling of the eyes and its dependence on the magnitude of gravitational or inertial force acting laterally on the body. *J. app. Physiol.*, **14**, 632–634.

THE PUPIL

Sphincter and Dilator Muscles

The aperture of the refracting system of the eye is controlled by the iris which behaves as a diaphragm, contracting or expanding as a result of the opposing actions of two muscles of ectodermal origin, namely the *sphincter pupillæ* and the *dilator pupillæ*. As classically described, the sphincter is an annular band of smooth muscle, 0·75–0·8 mm broad in man, encircling the pupillary border, which on contraction draws out the iris and constricts the pupillary aperture. The dilator is made up of smooth muscle fibres running radially between the stroma and the pigment epithelium; some distance from the pupillary margin the fibres blend with those of the sphincter, whilst at the ciliary margin prolongations are sent off into the ciliary muscle and trabecular meshwork. On contraction the muscle folds up the iris and dilates the pupil. This view of the dual muscular control of the pupil has not been accepted by all workers in this field, however. For example Apter has argued that the radial fibres, to which dilator action is ascribed, do not in fact respond to electrical stimulation or to application of adrenaline, and she considers that the ciliary muscle fibres in the root of the iris may well be responsible for some of the dilator actions that may be observed as the result of nervous and drug action. To prove this she excised portions of iris from the pupillary, ciliary and intermediate regions. The portion nearest the pupil was considered to contain sphincter fibres, the middle portion purely radial fibres, and the root the ciliary fibres. In no case could she obtain any muscular activity from the middle region. On the other hand, there seems little doubt, from Loewenfeld's critical review of the subject, that we may indeed speak of a dilator activity that is not a mere inhibition of the sphincter, and in this account we shall adhere to the classical terminology of a sphincter and a dilator muscle.

Both muscles are ectodermal in origin, developing from the anterior epithelial layer of the primitive optic cup. The sphincter separates from this layer and develops into true muscle tissue, whereas most of the dilator cells remain in their original position and fail to develop fully, remaining in a state intermediary between true muscle and true epithelial tissue—so-called *myoepithelial cells*.

Innervation. The sphincter is innervated by parasympathetic fibres from N III by way of the ciliary ganglion and the short ciliary nerves; the dilator is controlled by the cervical sympathetic, the fibres relaying in the superior cervical ganglion; post-ganglionic fibres enter the eye in the short and long ciliary nerves (Fig. 6, p. 5).

Functions of the Pupil. A pupil of varying size performs three main functions :—

(*a*) It modifies the amount of light entering the eye, thus permitting useful vision over a wide range of luminance levels. The amount of light entering the eye is directly proportional to the area of the pupil; under conditions of night vision the absolute amount of light entering the eye is of great importance and a sixteenfold increase of sensitivity of the eye to light should be obtained by an increase of pupil diameter from 2 mm to 8 mm. At the other end of the scale, excessive luminance reduces visual acuity; the strong pupillary constriction occurring in these circumstances mitigates this condition and thus extends the range of useful vision. In nocturnal animals this aspect of pupil-size is of greater importance and it is probable that the slit of the fully constricted pupil of the cat is an adaptation permitting a greater restriction of the amount of light penetrating the eye in daylight.

(*b*) As a result of constriction, the pencils of light entering the eye are smaller and the depth of focus of the optical system is increased (p. 299). When the eye is focused for distant objects, the depth of focus is large and the pupil-size is relatively unimportant; when the eye is focused for near objects, on the other hand, the depth of focus becomes small and a constricted pupil contributes materially.

(*c*) By the reduction in the aperture of the optical system aberrations are minimized. In the dark these aberrations are unimportant, since form is only vaguely perceived, so that the advantage accruing from the increased light entering a dilated pupil far outweighs the effects of aberrations; in daylight, however, the reverse is true; and we have already seen how, at varying luminances, the size of the pupil is adjusted to give optimum visual acuity (p. 175).

THE PUPILLARY REFLEXES

The accurate adjustment of the pupil-size to the optical requirements of the eye implies a reflex response to illumination; this is the basis of the *light reflex* under which term we may include the constriction of the pupil when the luminance is increased, and the dilatation when the luminance is decreased. The other important reflex, from the optical point of view, is the *near reflex*, the constriction of the pupil that takes place during the focusing on a near object. Additional reflexes are the *lid-closure reflex*, a constriction in response to closure of the lid, and the *psycho-sensory reflex*, a dilatation of the pupil in response to a variety of sensory and psychic stimuli.

Experimental Measurement—Pupillography. The experimental study of the size of the pupil—*pupillography*—has been carried out by a variety of techniques; since the pupil responds to visible light the method of measurement must dispense, if possible, with illumination unless this involves flash-light photography where the duration of the flash is so short that the pupil has no time to respond. For continuous studies flash-photography is obviously of no use, since the flashes have their effects, although delayed; by the use of infra-red photography, however, a cinematographic record of the pupil in the dark may be obtained and this is the method that has been most commonly employed. More recently Lowenstein & Loewenfeld have developed a method of "electronic pupillography" based on infra-red scanning of the pupil, the reflected light from the scanned pupil being brought on to an infra-red sensitive photo-tube. The scanned image is made visible by the usual television principles, if this is required; alternatively the size of the pupil may be recorded less directly on a cathode-ray screen. Thus when the scanning spot crosses from the iris to the pupil there is an abrupt decrease in the reflected light, and this shows up as a sudden fall in the signal on the oscilloscope. The larger the pupil the longer the portion of a given scan will give the low signal.

The Light Reflex

When the light falling on one eye is increased, the pupil of this eye constricts—the *direct light reflex*; at the same time the pupil of the other, unstimulated, eye also contracts—the *indirect* or *consensual light reflex*. A record of the changes in pupil-size in the two eyes during exposure to a bright light is shown in Fig. 190, where the pupil-diameter is given as the ordinate and is plotted against time of exposure. The record is shown in three parts; at the arrow on the top, the light is switched on to illuminate the right eye, whose pupillary diameter is indicated by the full line. Both pupils contract down to about 3 mm, and the sizes oscillate together whilst, as time progresses, there is an increase in size on which the oscillations are imposed; this is seen by the middle record, the mean pupil-size being about 4 mm. At the arrow in the bottom record the light

O·1 SEC.

FIG. 190. Effect of exposure of right eye to a bright light. Ordinate: pupillary diameter in mm. Abscissa: time of exposure. Record in full line applies to right eye; in broken line to left eye.
First line: the pupils were large and quiet in darkness. At the arrow the right eye was exposed to a steady illumination.
Second line: this shows the pupillary oscillations after the right eye had been exposed for 3 min to the light.
Third line: when the light was turned off, at the arrow, the pupils dilated and the oscillations disappeared. (Lowenstein & Loewenfeld, *Amer. J. Ophthal.*)

was turned off, and the pupils return slowly to their original diameters. The increase in diameter that occurs during sustained illumination may be regarded as an effect of light-adaptation. On flashing a light into the eye, then, the response is a constriction of the homolateral and contralateral pupils, the extent of the constriction depending on the intensity of the light and the state of adaptation of the eye. If the light-stimulus is prolonged, the pupil dilates slowly and reaches a size which, for a given individual, depends on the intensity of the light. When both eyes are stimulated there is a summation of the individual responses so that both pupils constrict rather more than when one alone is stimulated with the same intensity of light; conversely if, when both are being subjected to a light stimulus, one eye is closed, the contralateral pupil dilates slightly.

Effect of Luminance. The magnitude of the initial constriction caused by a light-stimulus depends, as we should expect, on the intensity of the light.

This is demonstrated by Fig. 191 where the constriction, in millimetres, is represented by the heights of the black bars, whilst the relative luminances of the stimuli are plotted logarithmically as abscissæ. At the arrow marked *a*, the intensity is some millionth of that required to evoke the 3 mm response, and this corresponds to the threshold for colour vision, *i.e.* the cone threshold. At the arrow marked *b*, the intensity is some 10^{-9} to 10^{-10} of that required to produce the 3 mm response; this is the threshold for rod vision, and it will be seen that under the conditions of these experiments the threshold for pupillary response is higher than that for the visual response.

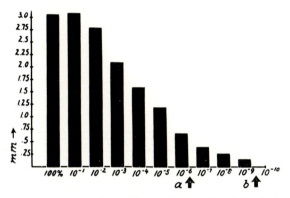

FIG. 191. Average extent of pupillary reflexes elicited by light-stimuli of decreasing intensity. The heights of the columns indicate the average degree of constriction, whilst the abscissa shows the intensities of the light-stimuli (duration 1 sec.). The arrow *a* shows the threshold for colour vision and the arrow *b* the absolute threshold. (Lowenstein & Loewenfeld, *Amer. J. Ophthal.*)

Rods and Cones. The receptors for the pupillary response to light are obviously the rods or cones or both; in fact, many studies have shown that both receptors may bring about the reflex. At threshold intensities for pupillomotor activity the visual sensation is colourless, proving that the rods are mediating the response; on plotting the sensitivity to the different wavelengths a typical scotopic sensitivity curve is obtained with maximum in the region of 5000 Å (Schweitzer). If the response of the pupil is plotted against intensity of the light-stimulus, as in Fig. 192, there appears an obvious break in the curve when white or blue light is employed, a break corresponding to the transition from rod to cone vision. When red light is employed there is no break, and the threshold is higher because the red light is very ineffective as a rod stimulator (p. 132). In general, the cone response to a flash has a shorter latency (0·2–0·3 sec) and is more rapid and longer-lasting than the rod response, which has a latency of 0·45–0·6 sec.

Summation. Schweitzer has studied the effects of increasing the area and duration of the stimulus. It will be recalled that the visual stimulus shows a limited amount of spatial summation, in the sense that if the thresholds for a small patch of light and a larger patch are compared, the threshold is lower for the larger patch; this is due, as we have seen, to the convergence of rods and cones on to ganglion cells (p. 150). The area over which summation of the visual response occurs is relatively small by comparison with that for the pupillographic response; thus Schweitzer found complete summation up to an area subtending 4° in the periphery and 0·5° at the fovea, whilst partial summation extended over much wider areas. This means that to make the most efficient use of light in the pupillomotor response we must stimulate a large area of retina; when this is done we find that the visual and pupillomotor thresholds are equal, but Schweitzer was unable to push the

FIG. 192. Pupillary contraction as a function of the intensity of the light-stimulus for three different types of light. Solid line and dots: curve for white light. Broken line and crosses: curve for blue light obtained by placing filter in front of white source; the apparent increase in the threshold is due to the absorption of light by the filter. Dotted line and squares: curve for red light obtained by placing red filter in front of the white source. The black bar above the abscissa indicates values below the absolute threshold; the hatched bar indicates the range of scotopic vision. Note that with red light pupillary responses are only obtained at intensity levels corresponding to photopic vision. (Lowenstein & Loewenfeld, *Amer. J. Ophthal.*)

sensitivity of the pupillomotor response beyond this point, *i.e.* he could not obtain a contraction of the pupil in the absence of visual sensation.* As a result of the operation of the light reflex, the size of the pupil tends to adopt a characteristic value for each level of luminance; according to De Groot & Gebhard the diameter, d, in mm, is related to the luminance, B, in mL, by the empirical equation:

$$\log d = 0.8558 - 0.000401 (\log B + 8.1)^3$$

In the completely dark-adapted eye the mean pupillary diameter is given variously as 6·6 to 7·6 mm.

The Near Reflex

By the near reflex is meant the constriction of the pupil accompanying the convergence of the eyes on to a near object; associated with these two actions of convergence and miosis, there is, of course, the act of accommodation

---

* It is commonly stated that the threshold for pupillomotor activity is higher than that for vision, and this is true for small test-fields; thus if this subtended 1° 50′, the ratio of thresholds varied from 8 to 1000; when the Ulbricht integrating sphere was employed, permitting exposure of a very large field, the thresholds became equal because of the greater degree of summation in the pupillomotor response. Temporal summation, whereby two stimuli, following each other rapidly, are more effective than a single one, depends essentially on the photochemical characteristics of the receptors (Bunsen-Roscoe Law) rather than on any neural organization; it is not surprising, therefore, that temporal summation is the same for the pupillomotor and visual responses (Schweitzer, 1956).

all three being mediated by N III. The response is bilateral and the maximal constriction obtained with this reflex is approximately equal to that obtained with the light reflex; the two reflexes may summate their responses.

The Lid-Closure Reflex

This is a homolateral pupillary constriction associated with closure of the lid; it is evoked if the lid is held open whilst the effort of closure is made. The effect is not large. The mechanism is probably central, and the innervation of the orbicularis by fibres from the IIIrd nucleus may be a factor in the reflex.

Psycho-Sensory Reflex

This is a dilatation of the pupils evoked by stimulation of any sensory nerve or by strong psychical stimuli. Pupillary dilatation thus occurs during the induction stage of anæsthesia, in extreme fear and in pain; in sleep, on the other hand, when these stimuli are lacking, the pupils are generally constricted. The mechanism is clearly a cortical one and is apparently mediated both by way of the cervical sympathetic, which activates the dilator pupillæ, and by way of N III which inhibits the tonus of the sphincter pupillæ. The reaction is not seen in the newborn, but appears in the first few days of life, developing fully at the age of six months.

NERVOUS PATHWAYS

The receptors of the light reflex are the rods and cones; the afferent pathway is therefore through the optic nerves and tracts; the pupillary fibres leave the optic tract before the lateral geniculate body is reached, and for many years it

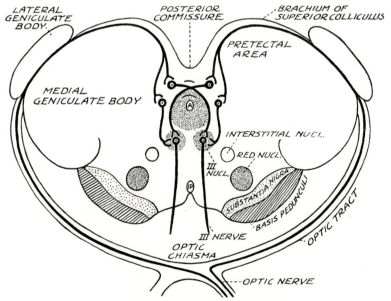

FIG. 193. Diagram of the path concerned in the pupillary light reflex.
(Magoun & Ranson, *Arch. Ophthal.*)

was thought that they relayed in the superior colliculus. Magoun & Ranson showed, however, that in cats and monkeys the fibres pass through the medial border of the geniculate body and then run, by way of the brachium of the superior colliculus, into the *pretectal nucleus*, a group of cells occupying a position at the junction of the diencephalon and the tectum of the mid-brain; here they have their first synapse. In the cat the majority of the secondary fibres cross in the posterior commissure and terminate in the Edinger-Westphal nucleus; in primates the crossing is not so extensive. Destruction of the superior colliculus, therefore, leaves the light reflex intact; stimulation of the pretectal area gives a bilateral constriction of the pupils; conversely, destruction of this area gives a dilated and fixed pupil. From the Edinger-Westphal nucleus the pupillo-constrictor fibres pass with the IIIrd nerve fibres to the ciliary ganglion. The reflex arc for the direct and indirect light reflexes is indicated in Fig. 193; the diagram indicates quite clearly how a light stimulus, falling on one eye, gives rise to pupillary constriction in both eyes.

Reflex Inhibition. On the basis of Sherrington's principle of reciprocal innervation we might expect the pupilloconstrictor activity to be accompanied by an inhibition of the normal tonic activity of the dilator. Nisida, Okada & Nakano measured the normal resting activity in the long ciliary nerve of the cat, this being the sympathetic pathway to the eye and thus to the dilator pupillæ; the spontaneous discharge in many of the fibres was inhibited when light was shone into the eye. Other fibres were unaffected and were presumably concerned with the control of the blood vessels. According to Okada *et al.*, the central pathway in this reflex inhibition is essentially similar to that illustrated by Fig. 193 although the final motor pathway is by way of the nerve cells of the lateral column of the cervical and thoracic segments of the cord, the so-called *ciliospinal centres of Budge*, between C6 and T4.

Cortical Centres. Since the pupil is subject to psychical influences it is reasonable to expect cortical connections with the pretectal centre; furthermore, the intimate connection between pupillary, ciliary and convergence activities in the "near response" demands the presence of an integrating centre, which, according to Jampel, is unlikely to be at subcortical levels. In the monkey Jampel has described a region at the junction of areas 19 and 22, *i.e.* in the occipito-temporal region, stimulation of which causes a constriction of the pupils together with accommodation and convergence. It is here, therefore, that the integration of the pupillary, ciliary and convergence mechanisms in the "near response" probably takes place. The general scheme for pupillary control, postulated by Jampel, is indicated in Fig. 194, where the preoccipital centre is marked PAC; this is influenced by the entire cortex, indicated by X, (accounting for psychosensory responses) and by visual stimuli. Impulses pass down to the pretectal nucleus whence they are relayed to the Edinger-Westphal nucleus to activate the sphincter pupillæ and ciliary muscle. Influences from the spinal cord are shown by neurones from Z. The pathway for the light reflex has not been incorporated in the diagram, to avoid confusion; presumably the near and light reflexes interact in the pretectal nucleus. The phenomenon of the *Argyll Robertson pupil*—abolition of the direct and indirect light reflexes with retention of the near reflex—suggests that the motor pathways to the iris muscles are different in the two reflexes, and Lowenstein (1956) has presented some experimental evidence in favour of this hypothesis.

Fig. 194. A diagrammatic scheme, illustrating the three levels of function in the nervous system involved in the near response (see text). (I) This indicates the functionally specific area for the near response in the pre-occipital cortex. (II) This indicates the level of the tectum and pretectum. (III) This indicates the final common pathway for impulses to the ciliary muscle, medial rectus, and iris sphincter. (X) This represents the input of nervous activity from the entire cerebral cortex that modifies the output of the functionally specific areas for the near response in the preoccipital cortex. (Z) This represents the input of nervous activity from the spinal cord and brain stem which modifies the impulses discharged from the cerebral cortex into the tectum and pretectum. A.G., accessory ganglion; AB. NU., abducens nucleus; CAUDAL E. W. NU., caudal Edinger Westphal nucleus; CIL. GANG., ciliary ganglion; CIL. M., ciliary muscle; CORT.-TEG. TR., cortico-tegmental tract; INT. CORT.-TECT. TR., internal cortico-tectal tract; LAT. GEN. B., lateral geniculate body; MED. RET., medial rectus; MED. RECTUS NU., medial rectus nucleus; OC. N., oculomotor nerve; OC. NU., oculomotor nucleus; POST. CIL. N., posterior ciliary nerves; ROSTRAL E.W. NU., rostral Edinger Westphal nucleus; SUP. COL., superior colliculus; TECT.-OC. TR., tecto-oculomotor tract. (Jampel, *Amer. J. Ophthal.*)

Other Pupillomotor Centres. The sphincter pupillæ undoubtedly dominates pupil activity so that the pretectal and cortical pupilloconstrictor centres have received most attention. The strong association of dilatation of the pupil with emotional states would indicate the presence of dilator centres in those parts of the brain that have been shown to be strongly associated with emotional states, namely the hypothalamus and the limbic system generally. In fact, electrical stimulation in the hypothalamus, over quite a wide region, causes dilatation of the pupil (Hess). The pathway from the brain in dilator responses involves the sympathetic system, the pupillomotor fibres leaving the cord from the first and second thoracic segments and relaying in the superior cervical ganglion. Stimulation of the cord between the VIth cervical and IVth thoracic segments causes dilatation of the pupil and it is customary to speak of spinal dilator centres, but it seems most likely that the stimulus merely activates the sympathetic motor neurones in the cord.

The Peripheral Mechanisms

Reflex Dilatation. Stimulation of the cervical sympathetic trunk in the neck causes a pronounced dilatation of the pupil. If the sympathetic trunk is cut there is an initial dilatation, due to the irritative effect of the cut, and this is followed by a constriction so that the pupil on the cut side is smaller than the other; this is presumably due to the fact that normally the size of the pupil is determined by a balance of forces between sphincter and dilator; putting the dilator out of action allows the sphincter to take control. The same phenomenon is manifest in the reflex response to light; in the sympathectomized eye the response is generally larger. Reflex dilatation, brought about by some sensory stimulus, is mainly due to active dilatation, mediated by the sympathetic, since when the sympathetic trunk is cut there is only a small dilatation, due to inhibition of sphincter tone. Some time after removing the sympathetic supply to the iris it becomes hypersensitive to adrenaline and this gives rise to what has been called "paradoxical pupillary dilatation". Thus a sensory stimulus causes, in this sympathectomized eye, a small dilatation due to relaxation of sphincter tone, and this is followed by a much larger dilatation due, presumably, to the liberation into the blood of adrenaline as a consequence of the sensory stimulus.

Stimulation of N III, or the ciliary ganglion, causes constriction of the pupil; damage to the ciliary ganglion or IIIrd nerve reduces the reflex responses to light very considerably, such constriction as occurs being due to inhibition of sympathetic tone.* Weak psycho-sensory stimuli result in reflex pupillary dilatation in both normal and ciliary ganglionectomized eyes, the effect being a little larger in the normal eye, as we should expect.

THE EFFECTS OF DRUGS

The main effects of drugs on the pupil are largely what one would expect of a system innervated by both parasympathetic and sympathetic fibres.

Parasympathetic Drugs. It will be recalled that parasympathetic activity is mediated by the liberation of acetylcholine, so that this substance and drugs with a similar chemical constitution will behave in the same way as parasympathetic stimulation, causing a constriction of the pupil. Thus acetylcholine, pilocarpine, muscarine and many synthetic compounds are *parasympathomimetic*, by virtue of their chemical similarity to the parasympathetic chemical mediator. Another group mimics the parasympathetic by virtue of their inhibitory action on cholinesterase, the enzyme that destroys acetylcholine at its site of action and thus prevents the chemical mediator from acting indefinitely. They are said to *potentiate* the action of acetylcholine. Eserine, physosostigmine and many modern synthetic drugs, such as diisopropylfluorophosphate (DFP), act in this way causing a prolonged pupillary constriction by preserving from

---

* In the cat, in contrast to man and monkey, the sympathetic supply to the iris does not pass through the ciliary ganglion; hence in this animal damage to, or removal of, the ganglion does not influence sympathetic activity.

destruction the acetylcholine, liberated by the tonic and reflex activity of the parasympathetic nerve endings. Another group of substances block the action of acetylcholine by competing for its sites of activity on the muscle; an example of this *parasympatholytic* action is given by atropine, and various synthetic drugs such as homatropine. These drugs, by blocking the tonic parasympathetic activity, leaving sympathetic activity normal, cause a long-lasting dilatation of the pupil, which is now unresponsive to light.

Sympathetic Drugs. The sympathetic chemical mediator is noradrenaline, whilst adrenaline, liberated by the adrenal medulla in response to stress, has an essentially similar action. These substances cause dilatation of the pupil. Several drugs, such as ephedrine, cocaine and Marsalid, potentiate the action of the sympathetic system, and it was considered that they did this by inhibiting an enzyme, amine oxidase, which was thought to destroy adrenaline and noradrenaline. Recent work has shown that the position is more complex, and it seems more likely that the actions are mimetic, their chemical similarity to adrenaline and noradrenaline being sufficient to permit them to have a direct action on the muscle fibres. Certain substances block the action of the sympathetic transmitter, *e.g.* ergotamine, 933 F, yohimbine, dibenzyline, and are thus described as *sympatholytic*. They cause a constriction of the pupil by blocking the tonic sympathetic activity.

In general, then, the pharmacology of the pupil is what one might predict on general pharmacological principles.

Other Drugs. Certain drugs act directly on smooth muscle, and since the sphincter is the stronger of the two iris muscles, their action on the pupil is largely determined by whether they cause this muscle to relax or contract. Thus *histamine* causes a powerful miosis which overcomes the mydriasis of atropine. *Morphine* and *veratrine* cause a miosis by direct action on the plain muscle; the pin-point pupil of morphia addicts is thought to be due, however, to the action of the drug on the central nervous system. The ions *barium*, *strontium* and *potassium* stimulate smooth muscle and cause miosis. We may note that stimulation of the peripheral end of N V, the sensory nerve to the eye, causes a constriction of the pupil that would seem to be due to the liberation of a substance that may be extracted from the iris and has been called by Ambache *irin*; up to date its constitution has not been completely established.

Isolated Muscles. By cutting away the pupillary and ciliary regions of the iris, Heath & Geiter studied the actions of drugs on the muscles separately; in general the results largely confirmed expectation, except that atropine antagonized the action of adrenaline; moreover, the dilator not only responded to adrenaline but also to acetylcholine (Sachs & Heath). Again Apter who, as we have seen, separated the iris into three components, found no response of her "dilator portion" to adrenaline. As Loewenfeld has argued, the reactions of iris muscles *in vitro* cannot be compared with those of living tissues in the intact animal.

Pupillary Unrest

It is clear from the above that the state of the pupil at any moment is determined by a variety of synergic and antagonistic nervous influences; in general, external circumstances—light, and proximity of the fixation point—tend to cause constriction whilst the internal factors of sensation, and psychic activity generally, cause dilatation. The continual interplay between these opposing forces results in a constant state of pupillary activity—the pupil is restless—and the size of the pupil under any given conditions is a fluctuating quantity. The fact that both pupils fluctuate in size in harmony shows that the phenomenon of pupillary unrest is determined centrally, and is not merely an example of the independent rhythmic activity so frequently seen in smooth muscle (Stark, Campbell & Atwood). The pathological condition in which this activity is abnormally great is called *hippus*.

GENERAL REFERENCES

LOEWENFELD, I. E. (1958). Mechanisms of reflex dilatation of the pupil. *Doc. Ophthal.*, **12**, 190–448.

LOWENSTEIN, O., & LOEWENFELD, I. E. (1962). The Pupil. In *The Eye*. Ed. Davson Vol. III, Pt. 2. London & New York: Academic Press.

SPECIAL REFERENCES

AMBACHE, N. (1959). Further studies on the preparation purification and nature of irin. *J. Physiol.*, **146**, 255–294.

APTER, J. T. (1959). Distribution of radial contractile forces in the iris of cats. *Amer. J. Ophthal.*, **48** Pt. 2, 317–321.

APTER, J. T. (1960). Responses and distribution of the human intraocular muscles. *Amer. J. Ophthal.*, **49**, 1178–1183.

DE GROOT, S. G., & GEBHARD, J. W., (1952). Pupil size as determined by adapting luminance. *J. Opt. Soc. Amer.*, **42**, 492–495.

HEATH, P., & GEITER, C. W. (1939). Some physiologic and pharmacologic reactions of isolated iris muscle. *Arch. Ophthal.*, **21**, 35–44.

HEATH, P., & SACHS, E. (1940). Antagonism between adrenergic drugs and atropine in the isolated iris dilator. *Arch. Ophthal.*, **24**, 142–148.

HESS, W. R. (1957). The Functional Organization of the Diencephalon. New York: Grune & Stratton.

JAMPEL, R. S. (1959). Representation of the near-response on the cerebral cortex of the macaque. *Amer. J. Ophthal.*, **48**, Pt. 2, 573–582.

LOWENSTEIN, O. (1956). The Argyll Robertson pupillary syndrome. *Amer. J. Ophthal.*, **42**, Pt. 2, 105–121.

LOWENSTEIN, O., & LOEWENFELD, I. E. (1950). Role of sympathetic and parasympathetic systems in reflex dilatation of the pupil. *Arch. Neurol. Psychiat.*, **64**, 313–340.

LOWENSTEIN, O., & LOEWENFELD, I. E. (1950). Mutual role of sympathetic and parasympathetic in shaping of the pupillary reflex to light. *Arch. Neurol. Psychiat.*, **64**, 341–377.

LOWENSTEIN, O., & LOEWENFELD, I. E. (1958). Electronic pupillography. *Arch. Ophthal.*, **59**, 352–363.

LOWENSTEIN, O., & LOEWENFELD, I. E. (1959). Scotopic and photopic thresholds of the pupillary light reflex in normal man. *Amer. J. Ophthal.*, **48**, Pt. 2, 87–98.

LOWENSTEIN, O., & LOEWENFELD, I. E. (1959). Influence of retinal adaptation upon the pupillary reflex to light in normal man. *Amer. J. Ophthal.*, **48**, Pt. 2, 536–550.

MAGOUN, H. W., & RANSON, S. W. (1953). The central path of the light reflex. *Arch. Ophthal.*, **13**, 791–811.

NISIDA, I., & OKADA, H. (1960). The activity of the pupillo-constrictor centres. *Jap. J. Physiol.*, **10**, 64–72.

NISIDA, I., OKADA, H., & NAKANO, O. (1960). The activity of the cilio-spinal centres and their inhibition in pupillary light reflex. *Jap. J. Physiol.* **10**, 73–84.

OKADA, H., NAKANO, O., OKAMOTO, K., NAKAYAMA, K., & NISIDA, I. (1960). The central part of the light reflex via the sympathetic nerve in the cat. *Jap. J. Physiol.*, **10**, 646–658.

SACHS, E., & HEATH, P. (1941). "Cholinergic" behaviour of the dilator iridis. *Amer. J. Ophthal.*, **24**, 34–39.

SCHWEITZER, N. M. J. (1956). Threshold measurements on the light reflex of the pupil in the dark adapted eye. *Doc. Ophthal.*, **10**, 1–78.

STARK, L., CAMPBELL, F. W., & ATWOOD, J. (1958). Pupil unrest: an example of noise in a biological servomechanism. *Nature, Lond.*, **182**, 857–858.

ACCOMMODATION

THE change in the refractive power of the eye, when the image of a near object is brought into focus on the retina, is described as accommodation; such a process must involve an *increase* in the dioptric power of the system (p. 412).

Scheiner's Experiment. Scheiner, as long ago as 1619, demonstrated that the eye changes its dioptric power on viewing a near point. Fig. 195 illustrates his experiment. A near object was viewed through a screen in which two holes were bored sufficiently close together so that light, passing through both, entered the pupil. The near object was seen single as we should expect (Fig. 195,

FIG. 195. Scheiner's experiment. (*a*) The eye is focused on a point close to the eye; this point is seen single. (*b*) The eye is focused for infinity; a double blurred image of the point is now formed on the retina.

a); on focusing the eye on a distant object, however, the near object immediately appeared double. In this case the image of the near object is formed behind the retina (Fig. 195, *b*) and since two separate pencils of light are concerned with each point, a double blurred image is formed.

Theory of Accommodation

According to the modern theory of accommodation, which is largely based on Helmholtz's ideas, the capsule has sufficient elasticity to mould the lens into a more strongly curved system than is necessary for distant vision. The elasticity of the capsule is held in check by the normal tension in the zonule, so that accommodation consists in a relaxation of the tension in the zonule which permits the capsule to mould the lens into a more strongly curved system. The relaxation of the zonule follows a *contraction* of the ciliary muscle.

The Ciliary Muscle. The ciliary muscle is classically described as containing three types of unstriped muscle fibre:

(*a*) *Meridional fibres* arising from the epichoroid and attaching to the scleral spur.

(*b*) *Radial fibres*, situated more internally and anteriorly, arranged in the manner of a fan.

(*c*) *Circular fibres*, continuous with, and inseparable from the radial fibres, running round the free edge of the ciliary body just behind the root of the iris.

However, Fincham has shown that this formulation is rather too rigid; the fibres take origin from the epichoroid, and in the outer part of the muscle (nearest the sclera) they run a purely meridional course, to be inserted in the scleral spur.

More internally, the fibres make up a branching meshwork and it is this part that has been incorrectly called the radial portion—the fibres are not arranged in a regular radial manner but, as indicated, in a reticular meshwork. As a result of the branching of the bundles of fibres, a number acquire a more or less circular direction, a tendency that becomes more pronounced towards the inner edge of the muscle. Thus the innermost edge consists essentially of circular fibres— the so-called *sphincter muscle of Müller*—but they are not to be regarded as making up a separate muscle. The circular elements give off short tufts of fibres which are inserted into a ring of elastic tissue (A of Fig. 196) at the base of the iris. Another layer of elastic tissue (B) is situated between the muscle and the pigment epithelium of the ciliary body. The elastic elements presumably resist the tension of the zonule.

Fig. 196. The ciliary muscle. A and B indicate elastic tissue.
(Fincham, *Brit. J. Ophthal.*)

EFFECTS OF CONTRACTION

The general anatomical characteristics of the ciliary muscle indicate that its contraction must relax the zonule; the meridional fibres pull on the epichoroidal tissue and drag the ciliary body forward. The circular fibres, probably the most important in accommodation, must, on shortening, decrease the radius of the circle that they constitute; this can only be achieved by a radial extension of the ciliary body which must reduce the tension in the zonule (Fig. 197). These anatomical considerations are confirmed by the observation that during accommodation the external surface of the ciliary body moves forward by 0·5 mm. Moreover, careful observation of the lens during accommodation shows that it becomes tremulous as though its normal taut suspension had been relaxed; again, the equator of the capsule of the unaccommodated lens shows fine wrinkles, proving that it is held under tension; during accommodation these wrinkles are smoothed out.

Changes in the Lens. The actual changes in the lens during accommoda-

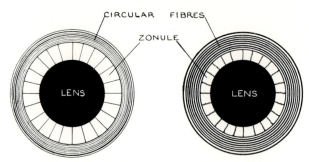

FIG. 197. Illustrating the action of the circular fibres in relaxing the tension of the zonule.

tion were studied by Helmholtz by means of the Purkinje images (p. 454); during accommodation image III, formed by the anterior surface of the lens, became smaller, indicating an increase in the curvature of this surface (Fig. 198). Studies on individuals with congenital aniridia have shown that the lens does become smaller (1·25 mm) and thicker (1·3 mm) as Helmholtz's theory would demand, and it seems from Fincham's work that the central zone of the anterior surface becomes more convex in relation to the peripheral parts—the surface becomes what Fincham calls a "conoid." More recently, Nordenson has emphasized

 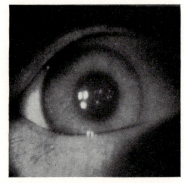

FIG. 198. The change in the size of the Purkinje image, formed by the anterior surface of the lens, following accommodation. The object, whose image was formed by the reflecting surfaces of the eye, consisted of three bright lamps arranged in a triangle. Left: unaccommodated eye. Right: accommodated eye. (Fincham, *Brit. J. Ophthal.*)

that the flattening of the periphery is not necessarily associated with accommodation; in the resting state he found the radius of curvature in the central zone to be 9·5 mm, whilst in the periphery it was 16·2 mm, *i.e.* the periphery was relatively flat in the unaccommodated lens; during accommodation the radius of the central zone fell to 7·4 mm and that of the periphery to 10·6 mm, *i.e.* both centre and periphery increased in curvature.

Whatever the exact changes may be, they must involve a rearrangement of the lens substance since this is quite incompressible; the general increase in curvature must mean a decrease in the surface of the lens and this must mean that the shape approaches more closely to that of a sphere (in the sphere we have the condition of maximum volume for minimum area; if we decrease the surface of a body and maintain its volume the same, we must make it more nearly spherical). The effects of this rearrangement may be observed with the slit-lamp microscope when there are mobile opacities in the lens; the movement consists generally of an axial flow from the periphery, as we should expect.

EXCISED LENS

It follows from the theory of accommodation that the excised lens must be in a state of maximum accommodation; Hartridge demonstrated the truth of this proposition in a remarkably neat manner. He estimated the dioptric power of the cat's eye *in situ* by measuring the magnification of a portion of the fundus observed through a modified ophthalmoscope. On removal of the lens its curvatures were measured and its dioptric power calculated. He showed that the combined power of the cornea and excised lens amounted to 12 dioptres more than the power of the eye *in vivo*, *i.e.* the lens, with the curvatures it possessed in the excised state, would provide the eye with an extra 12 dioptres of refractive power. Incidentally, this represents in effect the theoretical amplitude of accommodation of the cat's dioptric system; it would seem, however, that the cat can only use some 3·5 dioptres of this accommodative power.

THE LENS CAPSULE

According to Fincham, the shape of the lens is largely determined by the structure of the capsule; where the capsule is thinnest it might be expected that the lens contents would bulge out, thus giving the larger curvature of the

FIG. 199. The lens capsule. (Fincham, *Brit. J. Ophthal.*)

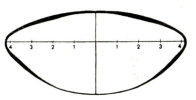

posterior surface where the capsule is, indeed, thinnest (Fig. 199). The greater curvature of the central zone of the anterior surface might be explained in the same manner. It might be objected, however, that the theory fails to explain why it is that the *anterior* surface increases in curvature strongly during accommodation, whilst the posterior surface remains almost unchanged (Gullstrand gave radii of curvature of 6 mm and 5·3 mm for the relaxed and maximally accommodated states). If, nevertheless, as Fincham argues, the posterior part of the capsule is already stretched to the limit of its elasticity, then any change in tension must be reflected by bulging in those other parts which are not initially so stretched.

The Change in Accommodation with Age. The amplitude of accommodation decreases progressively with age (presbyopia); in a child of ten years it is, on the average, about 14 D; at forty it is 6 D; and at 60 it is only 1 D. It is known that the lens substance becomes sclerosed in old age and there is every reason to believe that the loss of accommodative power is essentially due to the progressive failure of the capsule to mould the lens into a more spherical shape when the zonule is relaxed. Presbyopia is thus not due to a defective power of the ciliary muscle to contract. This view is borne out by Fincham's observation that the curvature of the excised senile lens is considerably less than that of a juvenile one; apparently the senile lens tends to "set" in its unaccommodated shape.

The Nervous Mechanism

Parasympathetic. Contraction of the ciliary muscle is brought about by the activity of the parasympathetic fibres of N III, with their origin in the Edinger-Westphal nucleus; the fibres relay in the ciliary ganglion. Stimulation of N III causes an increase in the refractive power of the eye (the eye becomes myopic), an effect that is inhibited by blocking the ciliary ganglion or by the application of atropine to the eye. Eserine, which potentiates the action of acetylcholine, causes a spasm of accommodation.

Sympathetic. Opinions have varied as to whether the sympathetic plays any role in accommodation (see, *e.g.* Cogan, 1937); the action of the ciliary muscle is antagonized by the elasticity of the capsule, and fine adjustments are therefore possible by means of the interplay of these opposing forces; an antagonistic muscle, innervated by the sympathetic, whose contraction tightens the zonule and therefore flattens the lens, may be thought to be unnecessary in man on this account. Some studies of Olmsted and Morgan and their colleagues have suggested, however, that the sympathetic nerves might cause an active flattening of the lens, stimuli likely to cause generalized sympathetic stimulation, such as a tap on the nose of a rabbit, being said to cause an increase of the animal's normal hypermetropia by about 1 D; stimulation of the cervical sympathetic in the anæsthetized cat and dog caused large changes in refractive condition, especially if the parasympathetic division to the eye was cut. Again, Biggs, Alpern & Bennett found a decrease in accommodative power in humans after subconjunctival injections of adrenaline. These effects could, conceivably, be due to the presence of genuine radial fibres, innervated by the sympathetic, whose action would be, in contraction, to tighten the zonule.

VASCULAR EFFECTS

However, Fleming & Olmsted have shown that the transient myopia, *i.e.* increased refractive power of the eye, that occurs on cutting the sympathetic runs a parallel course to the transient dilatation of the blood vessels, and they have concluded that the effects of sympathetic stimulation are the result of the constriction of the ciliary blood vessels with a consequent decrease in volume of the ciliary body which might possibly increase the pull on the zonule.

The Stimulus for Accommodation

It might be thought that the effective stimulus for accommodation would be the blurring of the retinal image, but if this were the only clue, the centre responsible would be unable to determine whether the object had come nearer or moved farther away, since in both cases the image would be blurred. We should therefore expect the eye to "grope" for the correct change in power, whereas it was found by Fincham that when the eye observes an object, and the vergence* of the light is altered, the accommodative effort is correct; that is, if the vergence is changed so that the object is apparently closer, the eye increases its power, and *vice versa*. There is no oscillation, as we should expect in an instrument unable to distinguish the nature of the vergence-change.

Aberrations. What then is the stimulus? Fincham's experiments indicated that in many subjects the chromatic aberration of the retinal image provided the necessary clue, the aberration rings being theoretically different according to the nature of the out-of-focus image. Thus, if the object were too close, the image of a point would be a light disc surrounded by a red fringe, whilst if it were too far away the disc would be surrounded by a blue fringe. By using monochromatic light many subjects were unable to make correct adjustments. A certain number of subjects were able to do so, however, and it would seem that spherical aberration provides a clue (Campbell & Westheimer) since reducing the spherical aberration of the eye reduced the subject's accuracy in accommodating in monochromatic light.†

Fluctuations. When a subject views a near object steadily his accommodation fluctuates through a range of about 0·25 D with a dominant frequency of the order of 2 cycles/sec (Campbell, Robson & Westheimer); this is presumably analogous with pupillary unrest, and with the high-frequency tremor in the eye movements although here the frequency is in the range of 75 cycles/sec. Since the unrest is considerably reduced when the subject views an empty field it is possible that these oscillations are determined by variations in the clarity of the image—retinal feedback.

Depth of Focus of the Eye

In a lens system there is theoretically only one position of the object that will give an image at a definite distance from the principal plane; hence with the eye, where the position of the retina is fixed, there is only one position, for a given state of the dioptric power, where an object will produce a distinct image. For the emmetropic eye, this is at infinity. When the object is brought nearer to the eye, the image of a point on it becomes a "blur-circle" because the true image is behind the retina. If the blur-circle is not large, however, it is not recognized as differing from a point and the object may thus be brought within a finite distance of the eye before the blur-circle becomes so large that the image is appreciated as "indistinct." The extent to which the object may be moved before the points on it appear out of focus is called the *depth of focus*.

* By *vergence*, in this context, is meant the degree of divergence or convergence of the rays of light in a pencil as they strike the principal plane of a refracting system; the closer an object, the greater the vergence of its rays, hence the reciprocal of its distance from the principal plane may be used as a measure of vergence; if this is in metres the unit of vergence is the dioptre; thus the vergence of the light from an object is the *dioptric value of the object-distance*. We may note that the term vergence is also applied to the degree of convergence or divergence of the fixation axes; this often leads to ambiguities and confusion. Thus by "vergence-induced accommodation" a writer could mean accommodation induced by convergence or by changed light-vergence.

† Fincham (1951) observed that if a subject, who failed to accommodate correctly in monochromatic light, was allowed to scan the object in view, correct accommodation became possible, and he pointed out that when the eye turns through a small angle from the point of fixation the rays of light at the opposite sides of the blur-circles on the retina acquire different degrees of obliquity to the surface, this difference being opposite in direction when the image is out of focus due to being too close and too far away. The different degrees of obliquity will be translated into different sensations of brightness by the operation of the Stiles-Crawford effect.

As Fig. 200 shows, the depth of focus obviously depends on the pupil-size. It will also depend on the distance of the fixation point from the eye; if this is large (*e.g.* 100 m) the point may be moved many metres closer to the eye before it goes out of focus; if it is small (*e.g.* 25 cm) a movement of a centimetre or two

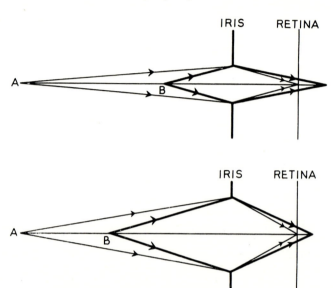

FIG. 200. Illustrating the influence of the size of the pupil on the depth of focus. With the small pupil (above) B produces a blur-circle of fixed size when it is closer to the eye than with the large pupil (below). The depth of focus (AB) is smaller with the larger pupil.

is enough to blur the image. For the human eye the figures obtained by Campbell were as follows:—

Pupil Diameter	Depth at Infinity	Depth at 1 Metre
1 mm	From infinity to 1·25 m	5·0 m to 56 cm
2 mm	,, ,, ,, 2·33 m	1·8 m to 70 cm
3 mm	,, ,, ,, 2·94 m	1·5 m to 75 cm
4 mm	,, ,, ,, 3·57 m	1·4 m to 78 cm

Visual Acuity. Ogle & Schwartz presented the subject with a chart and changed the vergence of light from it by means of a lens, keeping the image-size constant. At a certain point the visual acuity was decreased and the change of vergence was recorded. This amounted to 0·6 dioptres and Ogle & Schwartz defined the depth of focus in terms of this amount of vergence. The depth of field, on the other hand, could be defined as the equivalent distance through which the chart would have been moved to produce this change of vergence. The *hyperfocal distance* was defined as the distance of the fixation point at which objects beyond this all appear in focus.

Tolerated Change of Vergence. Adamson & Fincham measured the change of vergence tolerated by the eye, *i.e.* if an object was made to appear closer or farther away, by means of lenses, a point was reached when the eye adjusted its accommodation, and this was indicated by a change of its refracting power as measured with an optometer. The average change in vergence tolerated by the eye was found to be $\pm$ 0·25 D. An object 1 m away (vergence $-$ 1 D) may be moved so that the vergence changes to $-$ 0·75 D or to $-$ 1·25 D without blurring of the image; *i.e.* it can be moved to 1·33 m or 0·80 m, giving a depth of focus of 53 cm. If the object is 25 cm away (vergence $-$ 4 D) the limits of tolerance are $-$ 3·75 D and $-$ 4·25 D, representing a depth of focus of 3·0 cm (26·6 $-$ 23·6 cm). The difference between the values found by Ogle & Schwartz and Fincham depends on their different criteria.*

GENERAL REFERENCES

ALPERN, M. (1962). Accommodation. In *The Eye*. Ed. Davson. Vol. III. Pt. 2. London & New York : Academic Press.

FINCHAM, E. F. (1937). The mechanism of accommodation. *Brit. J. Ophthal.*, Mon. Suppl. No. 8.

SPECIAL REFERENCES

ADAMSON, J., & FINCHAM, E. F. (1939). The effect of lenses and convergence upon the state of accommodation of the eye. *Trans Ophthal., Soc. U.K.*, **59**, 163–179.

BIGGS, R. D., ALPERN, M., & BENNETT, D. R. (1959). The effect of sympathomimetic drugs upon the amplitude of accommodation. *Amer. J. Ophthal.*, **48**, Pt. 2, 169–172.

CAMPBELL, F. W., ROBSON, J. G., & WESTHEIMER, G. (1959). Fluctuations in accommodation under steady viewing conditions. *J. Physiol.*, **145**, 579–594.

CAMPBELL, F. W., & WESTHEIMER, G. (1958). Sensitivity of the eye to difference in focus. *J. Physiol.*, **143**, 18 P.

CAMPBELL, F. W., & WESTHEIMER, G. (1959). Factors influencing accommodation responses of the human eye. *J. opt. Soc. Amer.*, **49**, 568–571.

COGAN, D. G. (1937). Accommodation and the autonomic nervous system. *Arch. Ophthal.*, **18**, 739–766.

FINCHAM, E. F. (1951). The accommodation reflex and its stimulus. *Brit. J. Ophthal.*, **35**, 381–393.

FLEMING, D. G., & OLMSTED, J. M. D. (1955). Influence of cervical ganglionectomy on the lens of the eye. *Amer. J. Physiol.*, **181**, 664–668.

MORGAN, M. W., OLMSTED, J. M. D., & WATRUS, W. G. (1940). Sympathetic action in accommodation for far vision. *Amer. J. Physiol.*, **128**, 588–591.

OGLE, K. N., & SCHWARTZ, J. T. (1959). Depth of focus of the human eye. *J. opt. Soc. Amer.*, **49**, 273–280.

OLMSTED, J. M. D., & MORGAN, M. W. (1939). Refraction of the rabbit's eyes in the unexcited and excited state. *Amer. J. Physiol.*, **127**, 602–604.

OLMSTED, J. M. D., & MORGAN, M. W. (1941). The influence of the cervical sympathetic nerve on the lens of the eye. *Amer. J. Physiol.*, **133**, 720–723.

OSHIMA, S. (1958). Studies on the depth of focus of the eye. *Jap. J. Ophthal.*, **2**, 63–72.

* Campbell & Westheimer (1958) prevented their subjects from accommodating with atropine and they were asked to recognize the rhythmic blurring of the image of an object brought nearer and farther from the eye; when this rhythmic excursion was too small, no change was experienced, and on increasing it a point was reached when the rhythmical changes were noted. The average "sensitivity to difference of focus" was 0·2 D. Oshima (1958) found a much higher sensitivity, 0·02 $-$ 0·06 D.

THE NEAR RESPONSE

Convergence, Accommodation and Miosis

When a near object is focused, three events occur simultaneously—convergence, accommodation and pupillary constriction (miosis). The motor pathway for all three activities is through the nucleus of N III, accommodation and miosis being mediated by the autonomic division of this motor nucleus—the Edinger-Westphal nucleus; and there is no doubt that these pathways, along the oculomotor nerve, are separate since the three reactions may be abolished selectively by appropriate treatment of the nerve or ciliary ganglion. As we have seen, the central coordination of this triad of responses is probably at a higher level of the brain, in the cerebral cortex. The question naturally arises as to the extent to which these responses to the near stimulus are independent of each other. Is it possible to converge without accommodating? Can one accommodate without converging? If the answers to these questions are yes, is pupillary constriction tied preferentially to the convergence or the accommodation? These questions, so important for the theory of squint, have been examined and discussed intensively, whilst in recent years Fincham in England and Alpern in America have submitted them to exact quantitative study.

Accommodation and Convergence. Suppose first we examine a normal young subject and measure his accommodation, by means of an objective optometric test, whilst he converges on an object that is brought closer and closer

Fig. 201. The relation between accommodation and convergence. The curve marked AC represents accommodative convergence, *i.e.* the convergence that takes place when the eyes accommodate under conditions where altered convergence does not lead to diplopia. The curve marked CA represents the accommodation that takes place when the eyes converge, the arrangement being such that altered accommodation does not lead to blurring of the image. (Fincham & Walton, *J. Physiol.*)

to his eyes. Clearly, if he is to see single and distinctly the convergence and accommodation must "match", one dioptre of accommodation occurring with one metre-angle of convergence. The results of such a measurement are shown by the line marked "normal" in Fig. 300; it will be seen that accommodation does not match exactly; and since diplopia does not occur, we may attribute this to an "accommodation lag", the eye tolerating a certain degree of blurring of the image that is important for depth of focus (p. 300).* The line marked "normal" of Fig. 201 thus gives us a standard of reference, telling us how convergence and accommodation go together when the stimuli for these responses match, and presumably reinforce each other.

Accommodative Convergence. Next we may allow the two eyes to view separate objects independently by a haploscopic device; under these conditions there is no compulsion for fusion and the eyes may adopt any degree of convergence without experiencing diplopia. The apparent nearness of the test-chart, seen by the right eye, is now varied by means of lenses, so that in order for it to be seen distinctly the right eye must accommodate. The line in Fig. 201 marked AC shows that the eyes converge as a result of the accommodation of the right eye; this *accommodative convergence* matches the accommodation over a certain range; but not exactly, so that with 6 dioptres of accommodation the convergence is only a little over 4 metre-angles.†

Convergence-Induced Accommodation. Next, we may measure the changes of accommodation that take place when the eyes are *made* to converge whilst the object remains at the same apparent distance—the *vergence* of the light (p. 299) is said to be fixed.‡ The *convergence-induced accommodation* is indicated in the line of Fig. 201 marked CA. Once again the linkage between the two processes is manifest, and in this case, too, the accommodation lags behind the convergence. This is because of the age of the subject who was 32 years old, and the lag is a sign of presbyopia, subjects under 24 years old showing an almost perfect match between convergence and accommodation. *In a young subject, therefore, the stimulus to convergence automatically induces an accommodation of the right order of magnitude for distinct vision.*

Conflict between Reflexes. In the experimental arrangements so far employed there has been no conflict between the two stimuli, an alteration in the degree of convergence, for example, being compatible with single vision over the whole range. If we cause a subject to fixate a test-chart some 0·33 metres away, his accommodation for distinct vision is 3 D whilst his convergence is 3 m.a. By means of prisms, or other devices, we may make it necessary for him to converge further, or diverge, in order to maintain single vision. We may ask, What happens to his accommodation? If the linkage were still maintained, an increase in convergence would be accompanied by an increased accommo-

---

* It has been argued, *e.g.* by Ogle, that a certain degree of "fixation disparity" is tolerated, in which case, of course, the failure of accommodation to match convergence could be due to errors in binocular fixation, the resultant physiological diplopia (p. 346) being in some way suppressed or tolerated. Not all workers are willing to accept the existence of a significant fixation disparity, however.
† The ratio of the accommodative convergence, indicated by AC, over the accommodation, indicated by A, is called the AC/A ratio, and is considered a valuable diagnostic measurement. It has been examined in great detail by Alpern and his collaborators.
‡ Convergence was stimulated by bringing the object closer, but the effective vergence of the light was held constant by the use of very narrow pencils of light so that the rays entering the eye were effectively parallel for all distances of the object from the eye.

dation, but since the vergence of the light has not been altered the chart would become blurred by the unnecessary increase in power. There would be thus a conflict between the accommodation reflex, which demands that the accommodation remain unchanged, and the convergence-induced accommodation that operates through the link. Fig. 202 shows that the link has some flexibility. The line through the circles shows the convergence-induced accommodation that occurred under the earlier conditions where there was no compulsion to maintain any degree of accommodation. The curve through the crosses shows the convergence-induced accommodation during the present experiment; the arrow indicates the initial condition, the subject converging on an object 0·33 m

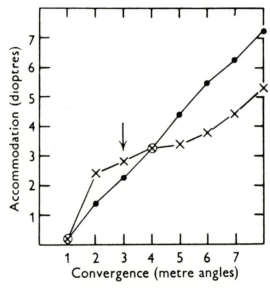

Fig. 202. Illustrating the convergence-induced accommodation that occurs when alterations of accommodation will lead to blurring of the image. The line through the circles shows the normal relationship between accommodation and convergence, whilst the line through the crosses shows the convergence-induced accommodation taking place when the subject views an object 0·33 m away whilst the degree of convergence is varied by a haploscopic device. (Fincham & Walton, *J. Physiol.*)

away, showing 3 m.a. of convergence and 3 D of accommodation. As convergence increases, accommodation does indeed follow it, but to a much smaller extent, an increase of convergence from 3 to 7 m.a. being associated with an increase of only about 1 D, by contrast with an increase of 3 D that would have occurred under the "free conditions". Thus some blurring of the image has occurred, but this has acted as a "brake" on the convergence-induced accommodation. This experiment thus reveals, once again, the presence of a link between convergence and accommodation, but also demonstrates that the link is not rigid and may be relaxed when its effects militate against distinct vision.

RELATIVE AMPLITUDE OF ACCOMMODATION

The converse experiment is carried out by fixing the convergence and placing

lenses in front of the eyes to alter the degree of accommodation. Any accommodative convergence, under these conditions, will cause diplopia, so that the compulsion for fusion operates as an inhibitor of this linked convergence. In fact
we do indeed find that convergence is maintained to give single vision over quite
a wide range of accommodation, but the conflict between the two requirements
leads to a restriction of the amount of accommodation that can be exercised,
in other words the *relative amplitude of accommodation* is less than the amplitude
when the eyes are free to converge and diverge in accordance with the nearness
or farness of the object.

Convergence-Accommodation Link. In general, then, we may conclude
that accommodation and convergence are linked together by a common nervous
mechanism that activates the two together. Because the stimulus of diplopia
is more effective than that of blurred vision, we may consider that the response
to nearness is primarily one of convergence; in a young person the associated
activation of the accommodation mechanism is accurate enough to make the
image fairly distinct, whilst the fine adjustment is provided by the accommodation reflex *per se*, which adjusts the focal power of the eye more exactly,
using as clues the alterations of chromatic aberration etc. that take place when the
image is not accurately focused. In older persons the convergence-induced
accommodation is less adequate and the reflex response must be larger.

Pupillary Response. Finally we may ask how the pupillary reflex is involved.
When the eyes are made to converge, with accommodation kept fixed, there is
usually some pupillary constriction, but very small by comparison with that
which would occur were accommodation permitted to occur to match the
convergence (Knoll). Thus the inhibition of the convergence-induced accommodation has been associated with inhibition of the near pupillary reflex.
By contrast, the relationship with accommodation is very strong (Marg &
Morgan), in fact, according to Alpern, Ellen & Goldsmith, the pupil continues
to constrict even when the amplitude of accommodation has been exceeded;
thus the increased effort to accommodate is apparently sufficient to cause
pupillary constriction. In a similar way, with presbyopic subjects, the stimulus
to accommodation is sufficient to cause pupillary constriction, so that presenting
a near object, even if accommodation is inadequate, causes a constriction of a
magnitude that would be expected had the accommodation taken place (Alpern,
Mason & Jardinico).

GENERAL REFERENCES

ALPERN, M. (1962). Movements of the eyes. In *The Eye*. Ed. Davson. Vol. III, Pt. 1.
London & New York: Academic Press.
BREININ, G. M. (1957). Relationship between accommodation and convergence. *Trans.
Amer. Acad. Ophthal.*, **61**, 375–382.

SPECIAL REFERENCES

ALPERN, M. (1958). Vergence and accommodation. I and II. *Arch. Ophthal.*, **60**, 355–
357; 358–359.
ALPERN, M., ELLEN, P., & GOLDSMITH, R. I. (1958). The electrical response of the
human eye in far-to-near accommodation. *Arch. Ophthal.*, **60**, 592–602.
ALPERN, M., KINCAID, W. M. & LUBECK, M. J. (1959). Vergence and accommodation.
III. Proposed definitions of the AC/A ratios. *Amer. J. Ophthal.*, **48**, Pt. 2, 141–148.

ALPERN, M., MASON, G. L., & JARDINICO, R. E. (1961). Vergence and accommodation. V. Pupil size changes associated with changes in accommodative convergence. *Amer. J. Ophthal.*, **52**, Pt. 2, 762–766.

FINCHAM, E. F. & WALTON, J. (1957). The reciprocal actions of accommodation and convergence. *J. Physiol.*, **137**, 488–508.

KNOLL, H. A. (1949). Pupillary changes associated with accommodation and convergence. *Amer. J. Optom.*, **26**, 346–357.

MARG, E. & MORGAN, M. W. (1950). The effect of accommodation, fusional convergence and the proximity factor on pupillary diameter. *Amer. J. Optom.*, **27**, 217–225.

THE PROTECTIVE MECHANISM

THE eyes are protected from mechanical insults by two mechanisms—blinking and the secretion of tears; by the latter process irritating particles and fumes are washed away from the sensitive cornea and the surface of the globe is maintained in a normally moist condition. Blinking, besides its obvious protective function, also operates to prevent dazzle by a blinding light, to maintain the exposed surface of the globe moist by spreading the lacrimal secretions and, during sleep, by preventing evaporation. Finally the act of blinking assists in the drainage of tears. The pathological condition of *keratitis sicca* may thus result from either defective lid closure or defective lacrimal secretion.

BLINKING

Orbicularis Oculi. Closure of the eyes is brought about by contraction of the orbicularis oculi muscle, associated with a reciprocal inhibition of the levator palpebri of the upper lid. The orbicularis oculi is an oval sheet of concentric

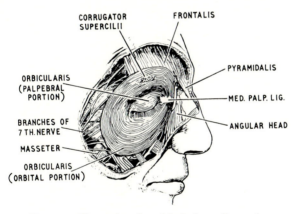

FIG. 203. Illustrating the orbicularis oculi muscle.
(After Wolff, *Anatomy of the Eye and Orbit.*)

striped muscle fibres extending from the regions of the forehead and face surrounding the orbit into the lids (Fig. 203). Although a single muscle, with its origin mainly in the medial canthal region of the orbit, it is customary to divide it into a number of separate muscles, or parts, the main divisions being the *pars orbitalis* and *pars palpebralis*. The pars palpebralis is divided itself into the upper and lower pretarsal and upper and lower preseptal muscles (Fig. 204). All the palpebral muscles insert into the lateral palpebral raphe and thus, by contracting, act as tensor muscles to the lids, moving the nasal end of each lid towards the nose.

Blinking is normally an involuntary act, but may be carried out voluntarily. The more vigorous "full-closure" of the lids involves the orbital portion of the muscle; this act may be evoked as a reflex response, *e.g.* the blepharospasm consequent on a painful corneal stimulus, or it may be carried out voluntarily. Associated with the blink there is a movement of the eyes, its exact nature depending on the initial position (Ginsborg & Maurice).

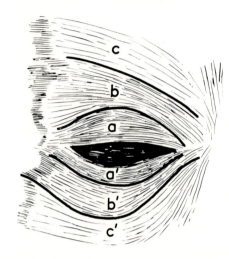

FIG. 204. Illustrating the subdivisions of the orbicularis muscle. *c* and *c'* represent the pars orbitalis; *b* and *b'* are the pretarsal, and *a* and *a'* the preseptal muscles. (After Jones, *Trans. Amer. Acad. Ophthal.*)

Reflexes. Reflex blinking may be caused by practically any peripheral stimulus but the two functionally significant reflexes are (*a*) that resulting from stimulation of the endings of N V in the cornea, lid or conjunctiva—the *sensory blink reflex*, or *corneal reflex*, and (*b*) that caused by bright light—the *optical blink reflex*. The corneal reflex is rapid (0·1 sec reflex time) and is the last to disappear in deepening anæsthesia; it is mediated by N V, impulses being relayed from the nucleus of this nerve to N VII. The reflex is said to be under the control of a medullary centre. The optical reflex is slower and, in man, the nervous pathway includes the visual cortex; the reflex is absent in children of less than nine months.

The blink- or wink-responses to a tap on the face, for example on the supra-orbital region, have been described as a group of *facial reflexes* to which various names, after their discoverers, have been attached (McCarthy, v. Bechterew, etc.). The name *orbicularis oculi reflex* has been suggested to cover them all since their reflex paths are essentially the same, and they apparently consist of two phases—a *proprioceptive* response due to stretch of the facial musculature, followed by a *nociceptive* response which may be regarded as protective in function (Rushworth).

Normal Rhythm. In the waking hours the eyes blink fairly regularly at intervals of two to ten seconds, the actual rate being a characteristic of the individual. The function of this is to spread the lacrimal secretions over the cornea, and it might be thought that each blink would be reflexly determined by a corneal stimulus—drying and irritation. As a result of extensive studies by Ponder on human subjects, it would appear that this view is wrong; the normal blinking rate is apparently determined by the activity of a "blinking centre" in the globus pallidus of the caudate nucleus. This is not to deny, however, that the blink-rate is modified by external stimuli, particularly through N V and N II, and also by the emotional state of the individual; Ponder's work shows this most clearly—for example, the blink-rate of an individual in the witness-box went up markedly during cross-examination; that of another decreased on ingestion of a large dose of alcohol, and so on; the fact remains, however, that when any given route for sensory impulses is blocked, *e.g.* by cocainization of the cornea, the blink-rate is, on the average, unchanged, *i.e.* characteristic of the individual.

Movements of Eyes. In conclusion, attention should be drawn to the strong association between blinking and the action of the extraocular muscles. A movement of the eyes is generally accompanied by a blink and it is thought that this aids the eyes in changing their fixation point. It will be remembered that in lesions of the frontal motor centre the fixation reflex asserts itself so strongly that a change in the fixation point becomes very difficult but may be brought about by cutting off the visual stimulus by closing the eyes or jerking the head. It is possible that blinking in the normal individual is an aid, although not a necessary one, in inhibiting the fixation reflex preparatory to the adoption of a new point of fixation.

LACRIMATION

The surface of the globe is kept moist by the tears, secreted by the lacrimal apparatus, together with the mucous and oily secretions of the other secretory organs and cells of the conjunctiva and lids.

Lacrimal Glands. The lacrimal gland, proper (Fig. 205), lies in the upper and outer corner of the orbit, just within the orbital margin. It is divided by the lateral horn of the aponeurosis of the levator muscle into two lobes, *orbital* and *palpebral*. About twelve ducts gather the secretion of the entire gland and open through the palpebral conjunctiva, some 4–5 mm above the upper border

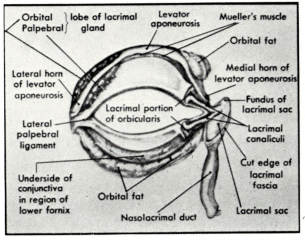

FIG. 205. Tarsal plates and lacrimal system. (Kronfeld, McHugh & Polyak, *The Human Eye in Anatomical Transparencies.*)

of the tarsus. It has a typical serous gland structure, and is supplied mainly by the lacrimal branch of the ophthalmic artery, the lacrimal vein draining the blood into the superior ophthalmic vein. The glands are supplied by the *lacrimal nerve*, which is the smallest terminal twig of the ophthalmic division of the trigeminal (Fig. 206).

Accessory Lacrimal Glands. In addition to the lacrimal gland, there are numerous microscopical *accessory lacrimal glands* in the conjunctiva—the glands of Krause and Wolfring—structurally organized in an essentially similar fashion but on a very much smaller scale.

Sebaceous and Mucous Secretions. An oily fluid is secreted by the glands of Zeiss and the Meibomian glands, in the eyelids, whilst goblet cells in the conjunctiva secrete mucus.

Precorneal Film. The fluid layer on the cornea is called the precorneal film and is said by Wolff to consist of an innermost layer of mucus, a middle layer of lacrimal secretions and an outer oil film which serves to reduce evaporation of the underlying watery layer (Mishima & Maurice) as well as preventing overflow at the lid-margin.

Normal Output. The normal daily output of tears was estimated by Schirmer in 1903 in subjects with their lacrimal ducts and sacs removed; the time for a drop to form was measured; the amount of evaporation that had occurred was estimated by a separate experiment, and knowing the weight of the drop the formation during this period was computed. Schirmer estimated a secretion of 0·5 to 0·75 g in 16 hr. He concluded that there was no secretion during sleep. Schirmer also devised tests for normal lacrimation; these consisted of hooking a strip of filter paper over the lower lid margin and measuring the length of wetting that occurred in a fixed time. In some tests the presence of the filter paper was the stimulus for secretion, whilst in adaptations of this test the nasal mucosa was stroked with a brush, or the subject was asked to look into the sun. Applying this test de Roetth observed a considerable decrease in the magnitude of this lacrimation-response with age, the secretion at 80 years being only about a fifth that at 20 years.

Chemistry of the Lacrimal Secretion

The fluid collecting in the lacus lacrimalis is a mixture of mucus and secretions of the lacrimal glands—the tears proper—and is thus slightly opalescent. According to Krogh, Lund & Pedersen-Bjergaard, the tears are isosmolar with blood plasma, but the precise relationship between the two fluids will obviously depend on the degree of evaporation that the fluid undergoes before collection, and, presumably, on the rate of secretion of the fluid. Thus Giardini & Roberts found the concentration of chloride to fall from 135 mM to 110 mM as the rate of secretion was increased by exposing the human eye to larger and larger concentrations of tear-gas. Essentially similar changes were found by Balik for chloride, sodium, urea and phosphate, whilst Thaysen & Thorn found the concentrations of urea, sodium, potassium and chloride to be independent of rate of secretion. Balik defined a "secretion ratio", F, being the ratio of the concentrations of a given substance in tears over plasma; with urea, sodium and phosphate this was greater than unity with normal rates of flow, suggesting possible active accumulation in the tears, although evaporation as the main cause of these ratios cannot be ruled out. The concentration of glucose in the tears is remarkably low, being only a few per cent of that in plasma (Giardini & Roberts). The pH is about 7·2 becoming more alkaline with continued lacrimation (Swan, Trussell & Allen).

Proteins. The concentration of proteins in the tears is low, being of the order of 0·1 to 0·6 per cent by comparison with 6–7 per cent for plasma; they have been resolved into a number of components by the technique of paper-electro-phoresis.*

LYSOZYME

Thus Brunish described an albumin, representing some 39 per cent of the total, 3 globulins representing 45 per cent, whilst the rest was made up of *lysozyme*, an antibacterial substance first described by Fleming in 1922 which is responsible for the low bacterial count of normal human tears. Lysozyme is a strongly basic protein, of molecular weight 14–25,000; with an iso-electric point of 10·5 to 11·0 it has a net positive charge at physiological pH and thus migrates to the cathode by contrast with the other proteins which have a net negative charge. It is an enzyme, and owes its bactericidal activity to its power of dissolving the mucopolysaccharidic coats of certain bacteria. It is not peculiar to human tears, being widely distributed in the plant and animal kingdoms, egg-white and fig-tree latex being rich sources, for example.

OTHER FRACTIONS

Although it is usual to designate the globulins as α-, β- and γ-, it is unlikely that the protein fractions of tears are identical with their plasma analogues, so that it is better to indicate them by non-committal names; thus U. Krause isolated six fractions which he denoted by arabic numerals, 1 to 5 in descending order of speed of migration in the electric field. His fraction 1 would corres-pond to "tear-albumin" of Erickson (1956); fraction 2 to a globulin with a speed of migration close to that of a_2-globulin, and so on.

It would seem that the tear proteins differ from their plasma analogues by virtue of the larger amounts of mucopolysaccharide in combination with them; at any rate, according to McEwen, Kimura & Feeney, they stain strongly with the PAS reagent (p. 54).

Drainage of Tears

When the secretion of tears exceeds the loss due to evaporation the excess fluid, if it is not to overflow—*epiphora*—must be drained away. The passage for this drainage consists of the *canaliculi*, the *lacrimal sac* and the *naso-lacrimal duct*. The lacrimal *puncta* are the openings of the canaliculi in the lid-borders of the inner canthus; the canaliculi course at first vertically and then more or less horizontally to the lacrimal sac, which is continued inferiorly as the naso-lacrimal duct emptying into the inferior meatus of the nose (Fig. 205). The sac and the duct may be regarded as essentially a continuous structure, the term "sac" really applying to *that part of the duct lying within the orbit*. Any theory of the mechanism of conduction of the tears must take into account the common experience that the act of blinking favours drainage and prevents overflow; certainly the dimensions of the canaliculi and puncta are so small (about 0·5 mm diameter) as to make it unlikely that an adequate drainage could be maintained

---

* The literature on the protein fractionation of tears is large and has been summarized recently by U. Krause (1959) and McEwen (1962). The first description is that of Miglior & Pirodda (1954); other outstanding contributions are from the laboratories of McEwen, Erickson and Brunish, to name only a few. We may note that François (1959) has shown that, by contrast with aqueous humour and lens, the use of agar in place of paper for electrophoresis is contra-indicated; at any rate the fractions obtained by this technique are so different as to suggest interaction of the proteins with the agar.

by the unassisted action of gravity (siphoning would of course be necessary for the upper canaliculus).

The Lacrimal Pump. The mechanism has been analysed most recently by Jones, and is described by him as the *lacrimal pump*. Essentially the pumping action consists in an alternate negative and positive pressure in the lacrimal sac caused by the contraction of the orbicularis muscle. Because of the anatomical relationships of this muscle, in particular that part called Horner's muscle, to the palpebral ligament and lacrimal sac, contraction during blinking causes a dilatation of the sac. At the same time, the muscular contraction also causes the the canaliculi to become shorter and broader. Finally contraction of the orbicularis also tends to invert the lower lid, thus ensuring that the punctum dips in the lacus lacrimalis. Negative pressure in the nose during inhalation, and gravity, are also factors in emptying the sac.

The Nervous Mechanism

Tears are secreted reflexly in response to a variety of stimuli, *e.g.* irritative stimuli to the cornea, conjunctiva, or nasal mucosa; thermal stimuli, including peppery foods, applied to the mouth and tongue; bright lights, and so on. In addition it occurs in association with vomiting, coughing and yawning. The secretion associated with emotional upset is described as *psychical weeping*. Section of the sensory root of the trigeminal prevents all reflex weeping, leaving psychical weeping unaffected; similarly the application of cocaine to the surface of the eye, which paralyses the sensory nerve endings, inhibits reflex weeping, even when the eye is exposed to potent tear-gases. The afferent path in the reflex is thus by way of N V. The motor pathway to the main lacrimal gland is more complex.

Parasympathetic. The parasympathetic supply is from the *facial nerve* (N VIII); preganglionic fibres arise from the *lacrimal nucleus* in the pons; they run in the *nervus intermedius*, through the *geniculate ganglion* (without relaying), to the *sphenopalatine ganglion* as the *greater superficial petrosal nerve*. Post-ganglionic fibres enter the *zygomatic nerve* and thence the *lacrimal* (Fig. 206). The sympathetic pathway is by way of the *deep petrosal nerve* which arises from the cervical sympathetic plexus; it joins the greater superficial petrosal nerve to form the *nerve of the pterygoid canal*, or *Vidian nerve*, which ends in the sphenopalatine ganglion; thence the fibres run with the parasympathetic as described above. Other fibres reach the gland by way of the lacrimal

FIG. 206. Innervation of the lacrimal gland. G.G., Gasserian ganglion; F.G., facial ganglion. (After Mutch, *Brit. J. Ophthal.*)

artery. Innervation of the lacrimal gland is not always complete at the time of birth; thus Sjögren found a complete lack of reflex secretion of tears in 13 per cent of normal full-term babies and in 37 per cent of premature babies during the first three days of extra-uterine life. Since this condition was not associated with any dryness of the cornea—keratitis sicca—it might be suspected that normally the secretions of the accessory lacrimal glands, which are not involved in reflex secretion, are adequate to keep the cornea moist. This suggestion is supported by the relative absence of corneal symptoms after complete removal of the lacrimal gland. Thus the reflex secretion may be regarded as an emergency response.

Sympathetic. The function of the sympathetic in the secretion of tears is problematical; section of the superficial petrosal nerve—a procedure often concomitant with operative removal of the Gasserian ganglion—or blocking of the sphenopalatine ganglion, causes a failure of reflex and psychical lacrimation, suggesting that the parasympathetic only is concerned with reflex secretion. Furthermore, there is no apparent interference with weeping as a result of bilateral section of the cervical sympathetic. According to Whitwell, therefore, it is the sympathetic innervation that is responsible for a tonic secretion adequate to keep the eye moist, but the possibility must be considered that the main gland is normally at rest, whilst the accessory glands operate continuously and independently of any innervation. In this event the sympathetic would play no role in the formation of tears.

Crocodile Tears. Some human subjects lacrimate strongly when eating, and the syndrome has been given the name of "crocodile tears"; there is usually a history of facial nerve paralysis, and it would seem that there generating fibres to the salivary glands, after an injury to the VIIth nerve, run an errant course into the lacrimal gland.

GENERAL REFERENCES

McEWEN, W. K. (1962). Secretion of tears and blinking. In *The Eye*. Ed. Davson. Vol. III, Pt. 3. London & New York : Academic Press.
MUTCH, J. R. (1944). The lacrimation reflex. *Brit. J. Ophthal.*, **28**, 317–336.
RUSHWORTH, G. (1962). Observations on blink reflexes. *J. Neurol. Neurosurg. Psychiat.*, **25**, 93–108.
VEIRS, E. R. (1955). The Lacrimal System. London & New York: Grune & Stratton.

SPECIAL REFERENCES

BALIK, J. (1959). Uber die Ausscheidung von Natrium in die Tränen. Ophthalmologica, *Basel*, **137**, 95–102.
BALIK, J. (1959). Uber die Ausscheidung von Harnstoff in die Tränenflüssigkeit bei Keratoconjunctivitis sicca. *Klin. Mbl. Augenheilk.*, **135**, 533–537.
BALIK, J. (1959). Uber die Ausscheidung von Natrium in die Tränen bei trockener Keratoconjunctivitis v. *Graefes' Arch. Ophthal.*, **160**, 633–657.
BALIK, J. (1960). Secretion of inorganic phosphorus in tears. *Amer. J. Ophthal.*, **49**, 941–945.
BRUNISH, R. (1957). The protein components of human tears. *Arch. Ophthal.*, **57**, 554–556.
ERICKSON, O. F. (1956). Albumins in lacrimal protein patterns. *Stanf. med. Bull.*, **14**, 124–125.
FLEMING, A. (1922). On a remarkable bacteriolytic element found in tissues and secretions. *Proc. Roy. Soc. B.*, **93**, 306–317.

FRANÇOIS, P. (1959). Micro-electrophorèse sur gélose des larmes humaines. *Bull. Soc. belge d'Ophthal.*, **122**, 343–351.

GIARDINI, A., & ROBERTS, J. R. E. (1950). Concentration of glucose and total chloride in tears. *Brit. J. Ophthal.*, **34**, 737–743.

GINSBORG, B. L., & MAURICE, D. M. (1959). Involuntary movements of the eye during fixation and blinking. *Brit. J. Ophthal*, **43**, 435–437.

JONES, L. T. (1958). Practical fundamental anatomy and physiology (of lacrimal apparatus). *Trans. Amer. Acad. Ophthal.*, **62**, 669–678.

KRAUSE, U. (1959). A paper electrophoretic study of human tear proteins. *Acta ophthal. Kbh.*, **53**, Suppl. pp. 67.

KROGH, A., LUND, C. G., & PEDERSEN-BJERGAARD (1945). The osmotic concentration of human lacrymal fluid. *Acta physiol. scand.*, **10**, 88–90.

McEWEN, W. K., KIMURA, S. J., & FEENEY, M. L. (1958). Filter-paper electrophoresis of tears. III *Amer. J. Ophthal.*, **45**, 67–70.

MIGLIOR, M., & PIRODDA, A. (1954). Indagini elettroforetiche sulla composizione proteica delle lacrime umane normali. *Giorn. ital. Oftal.*, **7**, 429–439.

MISHIMA, S., & MAURICE, D. M. (1961). The oily layer of the tear film and evaporation from the corneal surface. *Exp. Eye Res.*, **1**, 39–45.

PONDER, E., & KENNEDY, W. P. (1928). On the act of blinking. *Quart. J. exp. Physiol.*, **18**, 89–110.

DE ROETTH, A. (1953). Lacrimation in normal eyes. *Arch. Ophthal.*, **49**, 185–189.

SCHIRMER, O. (1903). Studien zur Physiologie und Pathologie der Tränenabsonderung und Tränenabfuhr. *v. Graefes' Arch. Ophthal.*, **56**, 197–291.

SJÖGREN, H. (1955). The lacrimal secretion in newborn, premature and fully developed children. *Acta ophthal. Kbh.*, **33**, 557–560.

SWAN, K. C., TRUSSELL, R. E., & ALLEN, J. H. (1939). pH of secretion in normal conjunctival sac determined by glass electrode. *Proc. Soc. exp. Biol. Med. N.Y.*, **42**, 296–298.

THAYSEN, J. H., & THORN, N. A. (1954). Excretion of urea, potassium and chloride in human tears. *Amer. J. Physiol.*, **178**, 160–164.

WHITWELL, J. (1961). Role of the sympathetic in lacrimal secretion. *Brit. J. Ophthal.* **45**, 439–445.

SECTION IV

Visual Perception

INTRODUCTION

Sensation and Perception

IN Section II we have investigated the "mechanism of vision" in the limited sense of attempting to understand the elementary processes in the retina that result in discharges in the optic nerve, and of attempting to correlate these with the sensations. To this end, very simple visual phenomena were chosen—the sensation of luminosity, the discrimination of flicker, colour and form. In respect to this last category, we confined ourselves to the very element of form discrimination—the resolution of points and lines—and in visual acuity studies we indicated that the recognition of letters was an unsuitable basis for the study of resolution since it involved activities at a higher level than those we were immediately concerned with. In this section we must consider some of the manifestations of this higher form of cerebral activity.

The Perceptual Pattern. Essentially we shall be concerned with the modes in which visual sensations are interpreted; the eyes may gaze at an assembly of objects and we know that a fairly accurate image of the assembly is formed on the retinæ of the two eyes, and this is "transferred" by a "point-to-point" projection to the occipital cortex. This is the basis for the visual sensation evoked by the objects but there is a large variety of evidence, derived from everyday experience, which tells us that the final awareness of the assembly of objects involves considerably more nervous activity than a mere point-to-point projection of the retina on the cortex would require. As a result of this activity we appreciate a *perceptual pattern*; the primary visual sensation, resulting from stimulating the visual cortex, is integrated with sensations from other sources presented simultaneously and, more important still, with the memory of past experience. For example, a subject looks at a box; a plane image is produced on each retina which may be represented as a number of lines, but the perceptual pattern evoked in the subject's mind is something much more complex. As a result of past experience the lines are interpreted as edges orientated in different directions; the light and shade and many other factors to be discussed later are all interpreted in accordance with experience; its hardness is remembered and its uses, and the original visual sensation is *interpreted as a box*, not a series of lines. It is impossible, in practice, to separate the sensation of seeing from the perceptual process; the sensation is essentially an abstraction—what we think would be the result of a visual stimulus if this higher nervous integrative activity had not happened. In the case of a flash of light the influence of higher nervous activity is very small and the sensation is virtually identical with the final perception. With a written word, on the other hand, the final perceptual pattern presented to consciousness is something far different from the bare visual sensation. We shall be considering some of the psychological aspects of this difference between the sensation and the perceptual pattern in consciousness later in this section; lest we should be misled into thinking of it as a mere philosophical word-play, however, it is important that we first consider its possible physiological and anatomical basis.

THE VISUAL PATHWAY

Optic Nerve and Tract

The ganglion cells of the retina (p. 81) are the second-order neurones in the transmission of retinal impulses to the cerebral cortex; the axons of these cells constitute the *optic nerves* (N II) and *optic tracts*, passing either to the *lateral geniculate bodies* or the *superior colliculi* (the pupillary fibres, it will be remembered, pass to the pretectal centre of the midbrain). The general plan of the visual pathway is indicated in Fig. 207; the fibres from the nasal halves of the retinæ decussate in the *optic chiasma*, so that each optic tract contains fibres from the

FIG. 207. The visual pathway. Fibres from the nasal retina, including the nasal half of the macula, decussate in the chiasma to join the uncrossed fibres of the temporal half of the retina. (Wolff, after Traquair.)

temporal half of one retina and the nasal half of the other. A visual impulse, arising from the right half of the field, is therefore conveyed exclusively along the left optic tract and thus to the left cerebral hemisphere. Section of the optic tract thus gives rise to what is called *homonymous hemianopia*, or half-blindness—one half of the visual field of each eye, the temporal half of the opposite side and the nasal half of the other, being obliterated. The degree of decussation varies from species to species and is obviously a function of binocular vision; thus in the guinea pig some 99 per cent of the optic nerve fibres cross to the opposite side, leaving only 1 per cent uncrossed; in the rat some 10 per cent remain uncrossed; in the opossum 20 per cent, whilst in the cat and primates, with frontally directed eyes, about equal numbers of fibres are crossed and uncrossed.

Arrangement of Fibres. The fibres are grouped in the nerve in three bundles according to the retinal fields from which they originate as follows:

(*a*) Uncrossed temporal fibres.
(*b*) Crossed nasal fibres.
(*c*) Macular fibres.

Half of the macular fibres undergo decussation in the chiasma, so that half of the macula is represented in each tract. The relative positions of the bundles in the optic nerve and tract are indicated in Fig. 208.

The fibres vary in size, being divided roughly into coarse and fine; since the speed of conduction in a nerve fibre increases with its diameter, this variation in size must be associated with different conduction rates in the visual pathway. It is interesting that in the cat the fine, slowly conducting, fibres pass to the midbrain visual centres whilst the coarse fibres go to the visual cortex. So great is the difference in calibre of the fibres, that a visual impulse can be transmitted to the lateral geniculate body, relayed here to the cortex, and the cortical

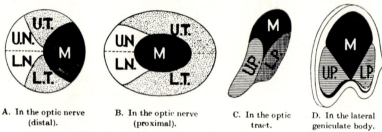

A. In the optic nerve (distal). B. In the optic nerve (proximal). C. In the optic tract. D. In the lateral geniculate body.

The crescents below U.P. and L.P. are the uniocular fibres.

FIG. 208. Distribution of the fibres in optic nerve, optic tract, and lateral geniculate body. U.T., upper temporal; U.N., upper nasal; L.N., lower nasal; L.T., lower temporal; U.P., upper peripheral; L.P., lower peripheral. (Wolff, *Anatomy of the Eye and Orbit*.)

response may pass to the midbrain before the impulse reaches this region by way of the fine fibres directly. It is theoretically possible, therefore, for midbrain reflex activities to be anticipated and modified by cortical influences initiated by the same stimulus. In fact Doty states that the evoked potential recorded from the midbrain, in response to a light stimulus, appears some 12 msec after that recorded from the cerebral cortex of the cat.*

Non-Geniculate Pathways

Collicular Fibres. In all species, including man, a portion of the optic tract fibres avoids the lateral geniculate body and goes to the superior colliculus in what has been called the *mesencephalic root of the optic tract*, to distinguish it from the *diencephalic root* running to the lateral geniculate body. According to the position of the animal in the phylogenetic scale, the proportion of optic fibres travelling to the midbrain station changes; in birds there is very little cortical

* Recent studies with the electron microscope have shown that the number of small unmyelinated fibres in the optic nerve is vastly greater than had been estimated on the basis of light-microscopical measurements, so many of these fibres being beyond the limits of resolution of the light-microscope. For example, Maturana has counted some 470,000 unmyelinated fibres in the frog's optic nerve and 12,000 thicker myelinated fibres, whereas earlier counts had shown a total of only about 14,000.

representation of retinal impulses, the vast majority of the optic tract fibres running to the optic tectum or superior colliculus; in rodents the collicular projection is less, but still very significant, whilst in apes and man it is very small. The fact that there is a projection of retinal fibres on the superior colliculus in man might suggest that visual responses to light would occur in the absence of an occipital cortex; in fact, however, only pupillary responses, which, as we have seen, are mediated by fibres relaying in the pretectal nucleus, are obtained in the absence of a functioning cortex.

Basal Optic Root. A further projection of the optic tract is given by the *posterior accessory optic tract*; it has been described in all species, including man, although not all workers are agreed as to its existence. The fibres end in grey matter (called the *nucleus opticus tegmenti* in the rabbit) at the mesial end of the substantia nigra ventral to the red nucleus. The function of this projection may conceivably be to activate Magoun's reticular activating system in the so-called *arousal response* (Moruzzi & Magoun). Thus sensory stimuli, besides having specific effects mediated by the thalamus and cortex, have also what has been called a non-specific activity that apparently prepares the brain for the reception of impulses by the specific pathway. This non-specific pathway makes use of certain regions of the brain included under the general term of the reticular formation. Visual stimuli are certainly capable of eliciting responses in the reticular formation (Ingvar & Hunter), but it is not certain that these responses arise from a direct projection from the optic tract, since they may be evoked secondarily from the occipital cortex, this region being known to send corticofugal fibres to the reticular formation (Jasper, Ajmone-Marsan & Stoll).

Lateral Geniculate Body

In primates and man the cells of the dorsal nucleus of the lateral geniculate body are arranged in six laminæ, and the fibres of the optic tract make synaptic connections with these cells. It was shown by Glees & LeGros Clark that the crossed optic fibres end in layers one, four and six, whilst the uncrossed, temporal, fibres synapse with cells in layers two, three and five (Fig. 209). There thus seems to be a rigid separation of the fibres arriving from the two eyes, so that the fusion of the two retinal images required by binocular vision cannot apparently take place at this level. In this respect, then, we may regard the lateral geniculate body as a sorting centre that rearranges the crossed and uncrossed fibres that had become quite mixed in the optic tract. By noting the distribution of transneuronal atrophies* following small retinal lesions, Penman and LeGros Clark showed that there is a virtual "point-to-point" representation of the retina in the lateral geniculate body, thereby ensuring that the one-to-one relationship between cones of the fovea, bipolar and ganglion cells is carried through as far as this stage in the visual pathway.

Each nerve fibre of the optic tract, after entering its lamina, breaks up into a number of terminals, each ending in a "bouton" applied to a lateral geniculate body cell; each cell has only one bouton applied to it, so that there is no overlapping of impulses from different retinal receptors. (In the cat, on the other hand, there are a large number of boutons to each cell—in this animal visual acuity is subservient to sensitivity to light.) The terminal branches of each optic tract fibre end on up to thirty lateral geniculate cells. Since each geniculate cell receives a bouton from only one optic tract fibre, there should

---

* When a neurone is injured, the degeneration is not necessarily confined to this cell; thus the destruction of primary visual neurones in the retina causes the cell bodies of geniculate cells to degenerate, a phenomenon described as *transneuronal degeneration*; apparently the geniculate neurone depends for its viability on receiving impulses from the ganglion cells of the retina.

Ipsilateral retinal ganglion cells

Contralateral retinal ganglion cells

FIG. 209. Illustrating the segregation of the optic tract fibres into the separate
laminae of the lateral geniculate body in primates. Fibres from the contralateral retina, *i.e.* the crossed fibres, relay in layers 1, 4 and 6. (Glees, In
The Visual System.)

be some 10–30 times as many geniculate cells as optic tract fibres, yet the numbers appear to be about equal.

Feedback. Modern neurophysiology has brought out the reciprocal nature
of the connexions between any two stations in the central nervous system.
Traditionally the lateral geniculate body has been regarded as a relay-station
from retina to cerebral cortex, and, as such, doing little more than pass the
visual messages on. However, there is some evidence that the message is modified,
and this modification is effected not only by activity on the part of geniculate
cells, but also by *corticofugal fibres, i.e.* by fibres originating in the occipital
cortex which, by either excitatory or inhibitory activity, modify the responses
of the geniculate cells to the retinal impulses. By this feedback arrangement the
cortex is able to modify and control the messages it receives (Widén & Ajmone-
Marsan). Inhibition of geniculate cells following light stimuli may also be
achieved by activity on the part of the geniculate cells themselves. According to
Vastola, the mechanism might be that illustrated by Fig. 210; here the principal
cell, activated by an optic tract fibre, sends its message up to the cerebral
cortex but also, by a collateral fibre, it activates a short-axon neurone in the
lateral geniculate body, and this in turn inhibits the activities of neighbouring
principal geniculate cells. According to Vastola, the cells that are most strongly
inhibited are those that receive the weakest excitatory stimuli from the optic
tract. Such an inhibition of the weakly stimulated cells by the more strongly
excited ones is of obvious value in sharpening up the retinal image, as we have
seen when considering the basis of visual acuity. The lateral geniculate body

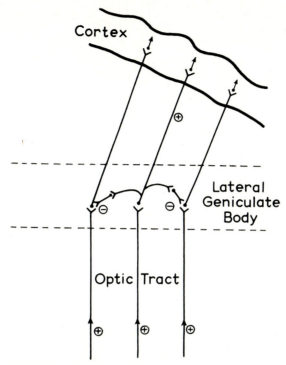

Fig. 210. Illustrating inhibition within the lateral geniculate body. The middle one of the three geniculate cells relays an excitatory influence to the cerebral cortex and also to short-axon inhibitory cells which, as a result of this activation, inhibit the neighbouring geniculate cells.

thus continues a process that has already been begun in the retina itself, namely, a process of accentuating the differences in response to light taking place in neighbouring receptors.

Significance of Lamination. The segregation of the cells of the lateral geniculate body into six layers has aroused some speculation as to its significance; the lamination seems to be a measure of the position of the animal in the phylogenetic scale since in rodents, such as the rabbit, it is either absent or, at any rate, very difficult to see. In the cat there are three obvious laminæ, called, A, A₁ and B; fibres from the contralateral eye relay in A and from the homolateral eye in A₁, whilst fibres relaying in B probably do not lie on the cortical pathway, the neurones in this layer probably running to the thalamus (Bishop & Clare). Recent studies indicate, however, that the homolateral and contralateral fibres are not rigidly separated; thus Fillenz describes two interlaminar layers, A₁B and A₁A, in which fibres from both eyes synapse; moreover, since degenerating and normal synapses may be seen in a single geniculate cell in these layers after cutting one optic nerve, it would seem that fibres from both eyes may converge on a single geniculate cell, *i.e.* interaction between the eyes is possible at this level in the cat. In primates, as we have seen, there are six layers, three for the contralateral eye and three for the homolateral. LeGros Clark pointed out that the smallest retinal lesion always caused degeneration in three layers of the lateral geniculate body, suggesting that the unit of conduction to the cortex is a three-neurone one, and he thought that this might be related to the trichromatic nature of vision (p 186) whereby colour responses seem to be determined by mixtures of three primary sensations. Certainly the recent studies of De Valois (1960) lend some support. He found that the responses of single cells of the monkey's lateral geniculate body depended on the layer in which they were situated; thus the dorsal pair of layers gave responses when the light was flashed on to the retina (ON-responses, p. 202), whilst the cells of the intermediate layer gave responses either at ON or at OFF, according to the wavelength of the light employed; the ventral pair of layers gave responses only when the light was switched off (OFF-responses), so that light projected on to the retina caused only a cessation of spontaneous activity followed by a spike discharge when the light was switched off.

Ventral Nucleus. The significance of the unlaminated, ventral or *pregeniculate* nucleus of the lateral geniculate body is not clear; it has been stated that its prominence decreases as we ascend the phylogenetic scale, so that in primates it is only vestigial, but Polyak (1957) disagrees, showing that many optic tract fibres relay here in the monkey, and pass thence to the midbrain, relaying in the Edinger-Westphal nucleus and thus providing a second pathway, in addition to the pretectal fibres already described, mediating pupillary responses to light. De Valois has shown that single cells in this nucleus give relatively simple responses to illumination, by contrast with the much more complex behaviour shown by the cells of the dorsal nucleus.

The Visual Cortex

From the lateral geniculate body, the third-order neurones pass as the *optic radiation* to the surface of the occipital pole, arborizing round the cells of the fifth, or granule, layer of the cortex. The cortex in this area is characterized

FIG. 211. The cortical visual areas. Striate area marked with vertical lines; the parastriate area with crosses and the peristriate area with dots. C, calcarine sulcus; C.L., collateral sulcus; S, sagittal sulcus of the gyrus lingualis (L); O, optic nerve; T, optic tract; E, lateral geniculate body; P, pulvinar; S, superior colliculus; *i*, inferior colliculus. (Whitnall, *Anatomy of the Human Orbit*.)

by the presence of a thick granule layer of cells with a dense plexus of medullated fibres, situated in the fifth layer, which gives rise to a white line, visible with the naked eye, the *white line of Gennari*. It is here that the visual fibres end. The area is named the *striate area* because of this white line; the region over which it extends is indicated in Figs. 211 and 212.

Retinal Projection on the Cortex. Small lesions in the striate area lead to blindness in well-defined regions of the visual fields, and a systematic study of the effects of gun-shot wounds in this region of the cortex has led to the definite picture of the projection of the retina on the visual cortex reproduced in Fig. 213 from Gordon Holmes. In general the projection may be represented by picturing one half of the retina spread over the surface of one striate area, the macular region being placed posteriorly, the periphery anteriorly, the upper margin along its upper edge and the lower on its inferior border. The macula, as one might expect, is projected over an area out of all proportion to its size, just as with the motor representation of Area 4, where the cortical centres concerned with the hand are much larger than those connected with movements of the proximal segments of the arm. More recent studies of head injuries by Spalding have largely confirmed the picture presented by Gordon Holmes.

"Point-to-Point Projection". Anatomical and physiological investigation has confirmed this general plan of the retinal projection and has brought out the existence of a virtual "point-to-point" relationship between retinal stimulus

Fig. 212. Lateral view of the right hemisphere. Striate area marked with cross lines; the parastriate and peristriate areas by large and small dots respectively. PO, parieto-occipital; L, lunate; T, transverse occipital; Lt, lateral sulcus. A is placed on the angular gyrus, which surrounds the upturned end of the superior temporal sulcus. S, S, S is the lateral cerebral fissure (fissure of Sylvius). R, R is the central sulcus (fissure of Rolando). FS, FM, FI are placed on the posterior parts of the superior, middle and inferior frontal convolutions respectively; between them and the sulcus are the pre-central sulcus and convolution. (Whitnall, *Anatomy of the Human Orbit*.)

FIG. 213. The projection of the retina on the visual cortex. On the left the striate area of the left hemisphere of the brain is shown, the calcarine fissure being opened up to reveal that portion of it which lines its walls. On the right is the right half of one visual field. The correspondence of the markings indicates the representation of different segments of the visual field on the cortex. (Gordon Holmes, *Proc. Roy. Soc.*)

and cortical representation. For example, in the monkey, a definite projection map can be plotted by stimulating the retina with a point source of light and determining the exact locus of the electrical potential evoked in the cortex (Talbot & Marshall). From a strictly anatomical point of view this point-to-point projection, in the sense of a single cone being connected to a single bipolar cell, which is connected to a single ganglion cell, and so on, is not possible; in the retina the one-to-one relationship between cone and optic nerve fibre only holds good in the central fovea, and even here it is only a functional relationship since impulses from a single cone have subsidiary paths which permit a spread of their responses outwards to several ganglion cells. Similarly, as we have just seen, in the lateral geniculate body, although there are no internunciary neurones, each fibre of the tract ends on a number of geniculate cells, and a further dispersion is possible in the cortex by intracortical association cells. The point-to-point relationship is therefore a functional one, in that there is a preferential path from one cone, say, to one cortical cell. This point-to-point relationship between retinal light-stimulus and cortical evoked response may be found, moreover, only under highly artificial conditions, involving deep anæsthesia. In the intact animal, with implanted electrodes in different regions of the cortex, it is found that the evoked response to discrete stimuli is by no means so highly localized. In a similar way, the more elaborate study of visual sensitivity in human subjects with lesions in their visual pathway has shown that portions of the visual field that are apparently "spared", in the sense that they respond to light, are not necessarily completely normal (Battersby *et al.*).

Cortical Lesions and Lateral Geniculate Body. Lesions in the visual cortex are reflected in regions of degeneration in the lateral geniculate body of the same side; the smallest cortical lesion, leading to degeneration, always involves cells in all six layers of the geniculate body; the conducting unit of the optic radiation is therefore apparently six fibred, and impulses from corresponding regions of the six cell layers are brought into relation in the cortex; fusion of the temporal field of one eye with the nasal field of the other is therefore possible at this level. Lesions in the optic radiation, *i.e.* in the geniculate fibres on their way to the cortex, such as those encountered in temporal lobe injuries, do not give rise to such discrete visual defects as do lesions in the visual cortex; this indicates that the cortex is acting as a sorting office for the fibres in the optic radiation, which have become mixed after leaving the lateral geniculate body.

The "Sparing of the Macula." The fact that lesions in the optic radiation, or in the visual cortex, frequently do not involve the macula (the "sparing of the macula") has led many to suppose that fibres from the lateral geniculate body do not pass exclusively to the cortex of the same side, but that some macular fibres cross in the corpus callosum, or alternatively by way of mesencephalic connections, and therefore give rise to a bilateral cortical representation of the macula. In primates and man, however, complete destruction of one occipital lobe is followed by complete cellular atrophy of the homolateral geniculate body, hence the cells of this body project exclusively on to the occipital cortex of the same side. Moreover, such damage leads to loss of half the retinal fields including half of each macula (Spalding; LeGros Clark). The apparent sparing of the macula is probably essentially a result of its large cortical representation by comparison with that of the peripheral retina; moreover, the part of the cortex involved in this projection lies in the margins of distribution of the middle and posterior cerebral arteries so that, when one of these is occluded, a portion of it, at least, may receive sufficient blood from the other to remain functional. The possibility that macular sparing may be due to a crossing of macular fibres in the chiasma is rulled out by Gordon Holmes on the grounds that lesions in the optic tract cause a complete hemianopia extending into the fovea.

Areas 18 and 19

The point-to-point relationship between peripheral stimulus and cortical response, observed with the visual sensations, is probably not so rigid in other cerebral systems; in the motor cortex, for example, the response to stimulation of a localized area is not by any means invariable and may be reversed. Rigid relationships are more characteristic of the lower parts of the central nervous system, and Gordon Holmes has suggested that it is essentially because the visual sense was the first, phylogenetically speaking, to obtain cortical representation that these relationships partake somewhat of the rigid character of the reflex responses of the midbrain. The more plastic visual centres, needed to account for the extreme importance of vision in human perceptions, are subserved by areas of the occipital cortex immediately adjoining the striate area, the *peristriate* and *parastriate areas* (Areas 18 and 19; Fig. 177). On stimulation of these areas visual auras and hallucinations are evoked as well as eye movements. According to Gordon Holmes the functions of the striate area are limited to the primary visual sensations, including colour vision, relative localization in space (in the sense that so long as the striate area is intact the relative positions of objects in the visual field are correctly interpreted but not their positions in relation to the observer), and the perception of form. The more complex and highly evolved perceptions, developed by the integration of visual with other sensory impressions, involve, besides the striate area, the nearby Areas 18 and 19. Evidence in favour of this is largely clinical; thus the identification by vision of familiar objects may be disturbed or abolished by injuries of the lateral portion of the posterior part of the left hemisphere, though the recognition of the form of the objects may be preserved.

Identification and Localization. The power of identifying objects is acquired by the different senses to different extents; thus even though we habitually identify objects by seeing them alone, this perceptual process involves memory of the application of the other senses before the object acquired a significance; the red-hot poker is identified as such by vision alone but the complete perception of it as an entity depends on the earlier use of the sensations of touch and temperature besides vision. The letters of the alphabet are mere arbitrary symbols, in the learning of which visual impressions are predominantly concerned, and Holmes describes a case in which complete agnosia of letters occurred as a result of a lesion in the lateral and inferior surface of the occipital lobe close to the striate area. Vision, as such, was almost unimpaired, but letters meant nothing to the individual, after the stroke, and could only be identified (with blocks) by the aid of touch. He could write correctly but not read what he had written. The identification by sight of other objects was unimpaired. Colour agnosia, in which colour vision was virtually unimpaired, has been described as a result of similar lesions; here colour has ceased to have significance and is not associated with objects; an artist, for example, following a lesion of this sort, was unable to *state* the colours of the sky or familiar objects, although he could identify colours as such. Somehow, as a result of the lesion, he had lost the ability to connect his colour sensation with the object evoking it.

Absolute spatial localization—the identification of the position of objects in relation to oneself—is a visual perception in which the extra-calcarine areas are involved; it is disturbed by bilateral injuries of the posterior portion of the parietal and lateral part of the occipital lobes, chiefly by those that involve the angular gyrus. Thus an individual, whose angular gyri were injured by a bullet passing through his brain, was unable to grasp an object without groping for it, as he was unable to estimate its distance from him. Topographical memory was lost too.

Cortical Associations. The higher visual functions involving complex associations, must, in the first place, involve the striate area, since in man cortical visual impulses pass to this region alone; it was originally thought that there were long association tracts connecting the visual cortex with the more remote parts of the cerebral mantle; recent work has shown, however, that no long-fibre connexions are made by the striate areas. The cells of the striate area are connected only by short neurones to the immediately adjoining Area 18 (peristriate area). From Area 18 short fibres relay to Area 19 (parastriate area) and back to the striate area.

The integration of visual sensations with activity in other and more distant parts of the cortex is thus carried out by way of Areas 18 and 19; these areas are possibly a sorting house or marshalling yard for visual impressions which, in conjunction with other sensory impulses, subserve more highly integrated functions.

Corpus Callosum

This is an inter-hemispherical tract that provides connexions between a given point on one hemisphere with a symmetrical point on the other. By stimulating discrete points on the cortex, Curtis recorded electrical responses on symmetrical points on the cortex of the other hemisphere. In primates, the only area that did not give a response was Area 17, showing the probable absence of interhemispherical connexions between these two areas. The integration of the two halves of the visual field is thus subserved by the peri- or para-striate areas, which have these callosal connexions between the two sides.

Callosal Transfer of Visual Habit. If a cat is placed in a box from which there are two exits, it may be trained to discriminate between two signs, for example between a vertical and a horizontal bar, if these are placed over the respective exits and the animal is rewarded with food when choosing the one exit and not when choosing the other. If one eye is covered while the animal is trained in this pattern-discrimination, it is found that when the animal is made to use the other eye for the discrimination it succeeds as well as if both eyes had been open during the training. In other words, we may say that there has been transfer of the learned habit from one eye to the other; if the left eye is trained the right eye can also execute the task, and vice versa. If the optic chiasma is sectioned by a sagittal incision, so that all visual impulses from one eye are only carried to one hemispere, it is found that the animal is still able to make the transfer, in the sense that the task learnt with the left eye can still be executed by the right eye. Finally, if both the chiasma and corpus callosum are separated by sagittal incisions, the animal must now learn this habit separately with each eye. Thus, one cat, operated on in this way, required respectively 80, 170 and 850 trials to learn three different types of visual discrimination with the left eye, whilst on covering this and testing it with the other eye open it required 70, 160 and 830 trials in order to relearn the discriminations. Furthermore, the animals could be taught to make contradictory discriminations with the two eyes; for example, the left eye could be trained to respond positively to the vertical bar whilst the right eye could be trained to respond negatively to this, and positively to the horizontal bar. Hence its choice of exit depended on which eye it was using (Sperry, Stamm & Miner).

In monkeys, too, with their optic chiasma sectioned, there is interhemispheral transfer of learned visual discrimination, which is abolished by section of the commissures (Downer). This author studied the "handedness" of his experimental monkeys under these conditions and showed that, according to which eye was open, they employed the contralateral arm, *i.e.* the arm controlled by that side of the brain to which the visual information was restricted by the section of the chiasma. If they were prevented from doing this, by binding the arm, then the animal groped with its free arm as though it were blind.

Phylogenetic Significance

The phylogenetic significance of the striate and associated cortical areas has been well summarized by Holmes:

"In the evolution of the brain, vision is the first sense organ to obtain a representation in the cortex of the forebrain. Even in birds, fibres carrying retinal impulses reach what is regarded as the neopallium; it is only later in evolution that other sense organs attain cortical connexions and it is still later that so-called 'motor centres' appear. With vision, too, localization in the cortex reached its acme, for every point of the retinæ is represented rigidly in it; then the brain, if we may speak teleologically, decided that such a rigid machine was unsuitable to its further development and adopted a more plastic organization for its later-evolved functions. It is consequently not surprising that cortical visual reactions are more highly organized, and possibly organized on a simpler plan, than other cerebral activities. Even in birds, the original visual cortex is connected with the roof of the mid-brain by efferent fibres—the *tractus occipito-mesencephalicus* of Kappers—which are probably the homologue of the occipito-mesencephalic fibres of mammals, and by means of these the cortex may be able to influence reactions, including ocular movements and postures, in response to retinal stimuli. As the cortex became the main, and finally the exclusive organ for visual perceptions, the primary visual reactions—as reflex direction of the eyes to light, accommodation, fusion when binocular vision was acquired, and fixation—were transferred to it till in man they can be evoked through it only. The next step in development was the appearance of associational areas around the visual cortex which enable it to co-operate with other sense impressions and to elaborate further the faculties of spatial perception, discrimination, and recognition."

Encephalization of Visual Function. There has thus been an "encephalization" of visual function in phylogenetic development; this is revealed by the effects of extirpation of the occipital lobes in different orders. In fishes and amphibians, vision is not represented in the fore-brain, so that removal of the latter has no effect on vision. In reptiles and birds vision is barely, if at all, affected by such treatment. In rabbits, removal of the occipital lobes causes a definite impairment of vision but the animals can discriminate brightness differences and recognize the positions of objects sufficiently well to permit the avoidance of obstacles, to jump, climb and recognize food by sight. The extensive researches of Lashley on the rat have revealed an essentially similar picture in this rodent. Early experiments on dogs seemed to reveal a complete blindness as a result of extirpation of the occipital lobes; more recent work has shown, however, that in this species, and even in the ape, there is a certain residual sensitivity to light and an ability to discriminate differences in intensity (Marquis). In man, only pupillary responses are obtained.

HIGHER INTEGRATIVE ACTIVITY

Inadequate Representation. We may now consider some examples which appear to illustrate the importance of higher integrative activity in the interpretation of visual stimuli. *Schroeder's staircase* (Fig. 214) shows how the same visual stimulus may evoke different meanings in the same subject; to most people the first impression created by Fig. 214 is that of a staircase; on gazing at it intently, however, the observer may see it as a piece of overhanging masonry. (If the reader has any difficulty in seeing Fig. 214 as a piece of overhanging masonry, he has only to turn the page upside down by slowly rotating the book, keeping the eyes fixed on the drawing.) *Rubin's vase* (Fig. 215) may be seen either as a vase or two human profiles. In general, diagrams of this sort are called *inadequate representations* of the object they are intended to copy, or *ambiguous figures*. The lines, as such, can be interpreted with more or less ease in two different ways and the fact that they are perceived in one or other definite manner emphasizes the arbitrary element of interpretation in the visual process. Helmholtz quotes in this connexion the case of a windmill, observed against the night sky; according as the observer fancied that the sails were in front of, or behind, the body of the mill he saw them revolving in different directions. Careful experimentation with ambiguous figures has shown that, over a period of time, the fluctuations in meaning exhibit a periodicity character-istic of the observer. This is not to deny, however, that with an effort of will, by moving the eyes, blinking, etc., the meaning of the pattern may be made to

FIG. 214. Schroeder's staircase.

FIG. 215. Rubin's vase.

change. Nevertheless, if the subject merely regards the figure for several minutes and the times during which it is seen in its two meanings are recorded, it is found that the fluctuations are definitely not random in nature. It is interest-ing that the periodicity may be affected by drugs.

Reading. The reading process is an instance of the arbitrary attachment of meaning to symbols; with practice the meaning becomes associated not with the complete picture of a word but with its general shape and thus the practised reader can be imposed on easily with mis-spelt words; the context leads him to expect a certain word and he actually sees it even though it is not on the page. Here the perceptual process is imposing a meaning on the visual stimulus that does not correctly belong to it, and many examples of this arbitrary activity of the higher centres may be cited; for example most people read the word "vicegerent" as "viceregent" because the latter is the word they expect even though it does not occur in the dictionary. The filling up of the blind spot and the failure of the hemianopic subject to realize his defect are further instances.

Colour Perception. The vagaries in the perception of colour have provided the psychologist with a great deal of material for speculation; in general, it seems fairly evident that we associate colours with objects; the colour becomes one of an object's attributes, and experiments seem to indicate that there is a strong tendency to perceive that colour in the object even when the physical conditions have been chosen to make this impossible. For example, a red letter-box may be illuminated with blue light so that far more blue light is reflected off it than red, yet the subject continues to call it red, and his *perception* is that of a red object. If the object, so illuminated, is looked at through a tube, so that its colour may be divorced from its shape, it is said to appear blue. Experiments of this sort have led to the following classification of colours as applied to objects of everyday experience. The colour of an object is probably first learnt to be associated with it under conditions of diffuse daylight; this is called the *true colour*. As a result of its continual association with the object it becomes the *memory colour*—the colour we expect the object to have—and this colour imposes itself on perception even when the optical conditions are unfavourable. If the colour of the object is stripped of all accessory stimuli and associations, *e.g.* on viewing it through a tube, it then becomes the *plane colour*. Unfortunately a great many of the experiments of this sort ignored the effects of induction; thus on looking at an extensive coloured object through a tube, only a portion of the retina is stimulated and the inductive effects associated with a complete visual field are cut out. We must therefore expect a change in the perception of colour on looking through a tube because the *physical stimulus*, and therefore the sensation, have changed.

Tone Constancy. Similar perceptive effects are described for the blacks, greys and whites. A grey wall may be compared with a grey piece of paper on a table reflecting the same amount of light; the wall appears white whilst the paper appears grey, presumably because we associate lightness with the walls of a room. These phenomena are classified under the heading of *tone constancy*, but it is possible that inductive effects play an important part. For example, it is argued that the black of this type, seen on a fine day, reflects more light than does the white of the paper in dim illumination, and yet the black is seen as black in both circumstances. The psychologist "explains" this as tone constancy; the physiologist, however, would merely state that the black sensation is evoked by a certain area of the retina being stimulated less intensely than another, adjoining, area; he would be the last to suggest that there is an absolute black sensation depending on some critical level of retinal stimulation. We know, moreover, that the sensitivity of the retina is enormously affected by light-adaptation (p. 207), so that it is impossible to expect that the same sensation will be evoked by the same stimulus under widely differing states of adaptation. We must therefore be careful of attributing to the activities of higher centres phenomena that properly belong to the retina.

Having clarified our position in relation to the difference between a perception and a sensation, we can now proceed to analyse some of the simple mechanisms concerned in the perceptual processes.

MONOCULAR PERCEPTION

The Projection of the Retina

Objects are perceived in definite positions in space—positions definite in relation to each other and to the percipient. Our first problem is to analyse the physiological basis for this spatial perception or, as it is expressed, the *projection of the retina into space.*

Relative Positions of Objects. The perception of the positions of objects in relation to each other is essentially a geometrical problem. Let us confine the attention, for the present, to the perception of these relationships by one eye—*monocular perception.* A group of objects, as in Fig. 216, produces images on the retina in a certain fixed geometrical relationship; for the perception of the fact that A is to the left of B, that B is to the left of C, etc., it is necessary that the incidence of images at *a, b, c* on the retina be interpreted in a similar, but, of course, inverted geometrical relationship. The neural requirements for this interpretation are (*a*) that the retina should be built up of elements which

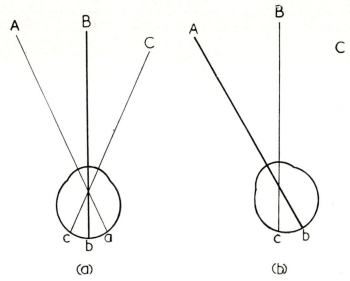

FIG. 216. (*a*) A group of objects, A, B, C, produces images on the retina, *a, b, c*; the retinal images are projected outwards in space towards the points evoking them. (*b*) The eye has moved to the left so that the image of A falls on *b*. *b* was previously projected to B but it is now projected to A.

behave as units throughout their conducting system to the visual cortex and (*b*) that the retinal elements should have "local signs." The local sign could represent an innate disposition or could result from experience—the association of the directions of objects in space, as determined by touch, etc., with the retinal pattern of stimulation. However they arise, the local signs of the retinal elements provide the complete information as to the relative positions of A, B and C.

The retinal stimuli at *a, b* and *c* are appreciated as objects outside the eye—the retina is said to be *projected* into space, and the field of vision is thus the projection of the retina through the nodal point. It will be seen that the geometrical relationship between objects and retinal stimuli is reversed; in the retina *a* is to the right of *b*, and so on; it is customary to speak of the "psychological erection of the retinal image"; this is thoroughly misleading since it suggests an awareness, on the part of the higher centres, of the actual points on the retina stimulated. This of course is untrue; *a* and *c* are projected to the left and right of B, not because the higher centres have learnt the laws of geometrical optics but because such a projection corresponds with experience.

Position in Relation to Observer. The recognition of the directions of objects in relation to the observer is more complex. If the eye (Fig. 216, *b*) is turned to the left, the image of A falls on the retinal point *b*, so that if *b* were always projected into the same direction in space, A would appear to be in B's place. In practice we know that A is perceived as fixed in space in spite of the movements of the eye; hence the direction of projection of a retinal point is constantly modified to take into account movements of the eye—we may call this *"psychological compensation."* It will be seen that correct projection is achieved by projecting the stimulated retinal point through the nodal point of the eye. Movements of the eye due to movements of the head must be similarly compensated. As a result, any point in space remains fixed in spite of movements of the eye and head. Given this system of "compensated projection," the recognition of direction in relation to the individual is now feasible. B may be said to be due north, or more vaguely "over there"; when the head is turned, since B is perceived to be in the same place, it is still due north or "over there."

False Projection. Under some conditions the human subject will make an error in projecting his retinal image so that the object giving rise to this image appears to be in a different place from its true one; the image is said to be *falsely projected.* If the eye is moved passively, for example by pulling on the conjunctiva with forceps, the subject has the impression that objects in the outside world are moving in the opposite direction to the movement of the eye. The exact nature of this false projection is illustrated in Fig. 217. The eye is

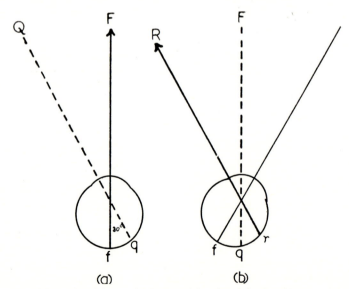

(a)   (b)

FIG. 217. Illustrating false projection resulting from the forcible movement of the eye. (*a*) The point F is fixated. (*b*) The eye has been moved forcibly 30° to the right. The image of F falls on *q*, and the projection of *q* is made on the assumption that the eye has not moved, *i.e.* towards R.

fixated on an object F, whose image falls on the fovea, *f*.* The eye is moved forcibly through 30°, so that the image of F falls on a new point, *q* (Fig. 217, *b*). The correct projection of *q* would be through the nodal point out to F; however, projection takes place as though the eye had not moved. The image falls 30° to the right of the fovea; with the eye in its original position, such a retinal stimulus would correspond to an object 30° to the left, the point Q in Fig. 217, *a*, so that the stimulus on *q*, in the new position of the eye, is projected 30° to the left, along the line *r*R. Consequently, as the eye is moved to the right, the retinal image of F is projected progressively to the left.

INFORMATION FROM MOTOR DISCHARGE

Quite clearly, under these abnormal conditions, the necessary information as to the position of the eye is not being sent to what we may call a *"space representation centre"* (Ludvigh), so that interpretation of the retinal image is made on the basis of inadequate information. The tension in the spindles and tendon-organs will undoubtedly be altered as a result of this passive movement, and the fact that no use is made of this proprioceptive information indicates that normally the space representation centre employs a different type of information on which to base its estimates of the position of the eye. This information could be provided by the motor discharge from the voluntary and reflex centres controlling the movements of the eyes; thus when the subject moves his eyes to the left to fixate point A in Fig. 216, the centre that initiates the motor discharges to the medial and lateral recti, besides sending its impulses to the motor neurones of the nuclei of N III and VI, may also send a message to the space representation centre indicating the intensities of these discharges, and thus the approximate extents of the eye movements. The space representation centre thus interprets the shifting images of A, B and C over the retinæ not as a movement of these points but as a movement of the eyes to fixate A. The proprioceptive messages from the muscle spindles and tendon-organs operate on a completely unconscious level, simply serving to moderate the strengths of the contractions of individual fibres in accordance with variations in local conditions—the so-called *parametric feedback* (Ludvigh). In the case of the eye that has been moved passively, the space representation centre has obviously not been informed of the eye movement, and the interpretation of the shifting retinal images is now what would be expected had the eyes remained stationary, *i.e.* the interpretation is that of a moving of the external objects from right to left, with its consequent false projection.

OCULOGYRAL ILLUSION

Another example of false projection is given by the oculogyral illusion described by Graybiel & Hupp in 1946. A subject is seated in a rotatable chair in the dark, and he fixates a small source of light which is attached to the chair and rotates with it. When the chair is rotated the light appears to move in the same direction. In this case the rotation has stimulated the semicircular canals, and the space representation centre has been informed that the body has rotated. The subject is unaware that the fixation light has also moved, so that the station-

* In this section the term "fovea" will be used very loosely to indicate the position of the image of a centrally fixated point; it will be the intersection of the visual axis with the retina.

ary retinal image is reinterpreted; clearly, if the head moves whilst the image of a point remains stationary, the point must have moved to the same angular extent as the head. Hence the retinal image is projected as though the object had moved in relation to the observer. Thus, if the chair is rotated to the right, the light will be falsely projected to the right of the observer, although it has remained fixed in relation to him.

AUTOKINETIC ILLUSION

Humboldt in 1799 noticed that after watching a faint star for a short time it would start to move around in various directions. An obvious explanation for this apparent movement may be the occurrence of involuntary eye movements, the space representation centre being inadequately informed of them, whilst the relatively uniform background against which the light is viewed fails to provide adequate retinal information of the eye movements. There is still some disagreement as to whether such movements could always account for the phenomenon, so that other factors have been invoked as well. The subject has been reviewed recently by Grosvenor.

Apparent Movement of an After-Image. The apparent movement of an after-image, when the eye moves, is an excellent illustration of psychological compensation. A retinal stimulus, being normally projected through the nodal point, is projected into different points in space as the eye moves; an after-image can be considered to be the manifestation of a continued retinal impulse, and its projection changes as the eye moves. The after-image thus appears to move in the same direction as that of the movement of the eye. Whether or not the gradual drift of an after-image across the field of view is entirely due to eye movements, it is difficult to say. One certainly has the impression that the eye is "chasing" the after-image.

Visual Estimates

The Directions of Lines. We have so far considered the problem of estimating the positions of points, in relation to each other and to the percipient. The estimate of the directions of lines involves no really new principles, since if two points, A and B, are exactly localized, the direction of the line AB can be appreciated. The perspective distortion, however, and the torsion of the eye resulting from a change in the direction of fixation, can modify the estimate of the direction of a line, referred to a fixed line in space—*e.g.* the horizontal or vertical—unless some psychological compensatory process is introduced.

RETINAL MERIDIANS

A horizontal line—fixated in the primary position of the eye—is recognized to be horizontal because its image falls on a set of receptor elements on the retina lying on the horizontal meridian. Similarly a vertical line is recognized because its image falls on the vertical meridian. When the eye moves to the right, into a secondary position, a horizontal line still falls on the meridian because there has been no torsion. On looking up and to the right, however, the image of a horizontal line is inclined at a certain fixed angle, depending on the position of the eye, to the horizontal meridian of the retina. Because of the torsion a psychological compensation must be made so that an image, inclined across the horizontal meridian, is perceived as the image of a truly horizontal line.

The full significance of Donders' Law (p. 238) now becomes evident. Movements of the eye involve torsion—this cannot be avoided—and torsion involves a disturbance of orientation of lines unless psychologically compensated. The higher centres, in order to compensate, must know the degree of torsion, and this information becomes physiologically simple to acquire if the torsion is characteristic of the position of the eye. Thus the motor innervation bringing about a given position of the eyes is "reported" to the space representation centre, and this centre, in interpreting the retinal image, works on the assumption that this movement has brought about a characteristic degree of torsion. Donders' Law states that the torsion is a definite quantity for a given position of the eyes ; and this regularity is achieved by the eyes rotating about an axis in Listing's plane (Listing's Law).

Vestibular Influences

Movements of the head are associated with compensatory reflex movements of the eyes, mainly of vestibular origin, designed to keep the visual fields normally orientated. In man, however, the rolling necessary to compensate for an inclination of the head towards the shoulder is quite inadequate, amounting to only one-tenth to one-fifth of the inclination of the head; since horizontal lines appear horizontal even when the head is strongly inclined, psychological compensation must be involved here; presumably the information required is provided by the labyrinth. That this labyrinthine information is not entirely adequate is shown, however, by *Aubert's phenomenon*. A subject regards a bright vertical slit in a completely dark room; on bending the head over to the side, the slit appears to incline in the opposite direction. When the lights are switched on the slit becomes vertical. If, in the dark, the head is inclined suddenly the slit remains vertical for a while but finally tilts over; it would seem that the abrupt movement stimulates the semicircular canals (p. 269) which cause adequate compensation. If the higher centres have to depend on the tonic receptors only—utricle and proprioceptive neck impulses—the compensatory mechanism becomes inadequate (Merton). It would appear, therefore, that the tonic receptors must be reinforced by the visual sensation; the observer knows that the bars of the window, for example, are not usually tilted over and so a compensation is initiated.

Accuracy of Estimates

The power of appreciating whether a line is horizontal or vertical is very highly developed in man. Volkmann describes experiments in which he repeatedly set a line to what he considered to be the true horizontal; his mean error was only $0 \cdot 2°$ with his left eye, the left-hand end of the line was too low; with his right eye the right-hand end was too low. We may say that Volkman's *"apparently horizontal meridians"* were slightly inclined to the true horizontal. With vertical lines his error was greater—more than $1°$—but it was a constant error indicating an inclination of his *"apparently vertical meridians"*. More recent work, notably that of Gibson, bears out the findings of Volkmann; vertical lines are, on the average, estimated to within $0 \cdot 28°$ and horizontal lines to within $0 \cdot 52°$; when an attempt is made to adjust a line to a fixed angle with the vertical, *e.g.* $60°$, the error is much greater ($1 \cdot 74°$) a finding which suggests that the vertical and the horizontal act as a frame of reference to which all other directions are referred. It is interesting that, as a result of an "adaptation" process, retinal orientation values may be disturbed; thus on looking at a line inclined at an angle of 5 degrees to the vertical, after about five minutes it appears truly vertical whilst a vertical line appears tilted.

Comparison of Lengths. The influence of the movements of the eyes in the estimation of length was emphasized by Helmholtz. An accurate comparison of the lengths of the lines AB and CD (Fig. 218) can be made, whereas if an attempt is made to compare the lines A′B′ and C′D′, quite large errors occur. According to Helmholtz, the eye fixates first the point A and the line AB falls along a definite row of receptors, thereby indicating its length. The eye is now moved to fixate C, and if the image of CD falls along the same set of receptors the length of CD is said to be the same as that of AB. Such a movement of the eye is not feasible with the lines A′B′ and C′D′. Similarly the parallelism, or otherwise, of pairs of lines can be perceived accurately because on moving the eye over the lines the distance between them must remain the same.

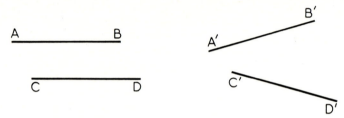

Fig. 218. AB and CD, being parallel, can be compared in length with accuracy whereas A′B′ and C′D′ cannot.

Fairly accurate estimates of relative size may be made, nevertheless, without movements of the eyes. If two equal lines are observed simultaneously, the one with direct fixation and the other with peripheral vision, their images fall, of course, on different parts of the retina; if the images were equally long it could be stated that a certain length of stimulated retina was interpreted as a certain length of line in space. It is probable that this is roughly the basis on which rapid estimates of length depend; a white line stimulating, say, twenty-five retinal elements being considered to have the same length as another line stimulating the same number of elements in another part of the retina. It is easy to show, however, that the matter is not quite so simple; the retina is curved so that lines of equal length in different parts of the visual field do not produce images of equal length on the retina; the distortion in the image resulting from the use of oblique pencils of light also complicates the matter, so that it is unlikely that such a simple relationship between size of image and projected size is achieved. The problem of the estimation of absolute size is closely linked with that of the estimation of distance and will be discussed under that heading (p. 341).

Estimates of Angles. Two angles may be compared with accuracy if eye movements are permitted and if the sides are parallel. The errors in comparison increase greatly if the sides are not parallel. Essentially we are dealing with the same problem—the superimposition of the retinal pattern on another. In the estimation of right-angles some characteristic errors are encountered. Thus the cross made by the lines *ab* and *cd* (Fig. 219) appeared to Helmholtz to be truly rectangular, whereas it is correctly given by the line-segments γ and δ. This error is an expression of the fact that the apparently horizontal and vertical meridians of the retina (p. 335) are not exactly at right-angles. When the cross was turned at an angle of 45° the error in assessing the right-angles became much greater; the true right-angles to the right and left appeared to be 92° whilst those lying above and below appeared to be 88°.

FIG. 219. The cross *abcd* appeared correct to Helmholtz, whereas the true cross is given by the line-segments γ and δ.

Optical Illusions. There are innumerable instances in the psychological literature of well-defined and consistent errors in visual estimates under special conditions; there is probably no single hard-and-fast rule by which they can be explained, but an important element may be the tendency for distinctly perceptible differences to appear larger than those more vaguely perceived. Thus the line AB of Fig. 220 has been correctly bisected at C, but because AC is divided into easily perceptible parts, whilst the line CB is not, the former

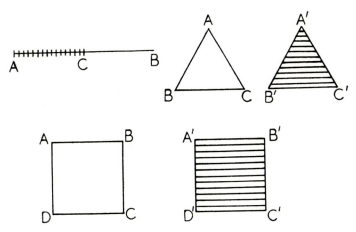

FIG. 220. Some optical illusions. AC appears greater than CB. The angles B′ and C′ of the equilateral triangle A′B′C′ appear to be greater than A′. The sides A′D′ and B′C′ of the square A′B′C′D′ appear to be greater than the sides A′B′ and C′D′.

appears longer. The triangles ABC and A′B′C′ are both equilateral but, because of the division of the lines A′B′ and A′C′, the triangle A′B′C′ appears taller and therefore the angles at the base appear greater than 60°. Similarly, ABCD and A′B′C′D′ are squares yet the height of the latter figure appears to be greater than its breadth.

FIG. 221. Hering's illusion.

In Fig. 221 (after Hering) the lines *ab* and *cd* are truly parallel and yet they appear to converge on each other on moving away from A (above) and diverge on moving away from B (below). It may be shown that the illusion results from

FIG. 222. An optical illusion; the letters are in fact all correctly orientated.

the tendency of an angle to appear greater when lines are drawn through it parallel to one of the sides (thus the angles B′ and C′ in the triangle A′B′C′ of Fig. 220 appear too large). The illusion created by Fig. 222, in which the letters

FIG. 223. The thin line appears to be bent where it joins and leaves the thick line.

appear to slope in different directions, is created by the disorientating effect of the background-lines. In Fig. 223 the thin line, although it is continuous and straight, appears to be bent in towards the thick line; no satisfactory explanation of this illusion has so far been given.

Summary. To summarize, we may say that the pattern of objects in the outside world is perceived as a result of the interpretation of the geometrical pattern of the image on the retina. It is not sufficient, however, to know merely the pattern of objects in space, it is useful also to relate *direction* on the retina with certain fixed directions in space. Primarily these are the vertical and the horizontal, the most frequently recurring directions of contours in the outside world. The retina has therefore become specialized by the development of apparently vertical and horizontal meridians; these act as a pair of rectangular co-ordinates through the fovea to which the position of any point or line is referred. In order that the interpretation of the retinal pattern be independent of the movements of the fixation axis, and of the inclination of the apparently horizontal meridian (torsion), a compensated system of projection into space is necessary. As a result of this compensation, the *absolute* position of an object in space is always correctly interpreted and the directions of lines, in relation to the horizontal and vertical, are also accurately estimated.

There is a great deal of evidence, that the tendency to project the retina is "innate" although few would deny that accurate projection is only acquired with experience. Presumably the development in evolution of an innate tendency to project the retina in accordance with certain geometrical rules had survival value; the "rules" turn out to be similar to those that would be followed if the individual learnt to project the retina in accordance with his own experience.

The Monocular Perception of Depth

From purely geometrical considerations, the estimation of the relative positions of objects in three dimensions by a single eye is not feasible; the points A, B

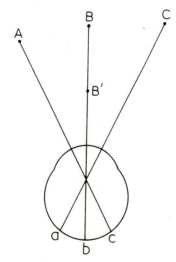

FIG. 224. With uniocular projection the relative positions of B and B′ cannot be distinguished.

and C in space (Fig. 224) produce images, *c*, *b* and *a* on the retina which are projected outwards along the lines *c*A, *b*B, and *a*C, but there is nothing in the geometry of this projection system to enable it to differentiate between the points B and B′ for example. The projection of the retinal image of a single eye is thus two-dimensional and objects in space are presented to consciousness as a plane pattern. Nevertheless, the individual may *perceive* depth with a single eye by making use of a variety of clues, whose significance has been ascertained by accumulated experience. These clues are:

"Aerial Perspective." As a result of the scattering of light by the atmosphere the colours of distant objects give some clue to their distance; the scattered light is predominantly blue and violet and the eye views a distant object through a "wall" of blue light. The thicker this wall, the bluer will the object appear to be; distant mountains thus appear blue, a fact exemplified in the well-known lines:

> "T'is distance lends enchantment to the view
> And robes the mountain in its azure hue."

It must be appreciated, however, that a self-luminous object, such as a lamp, is visible because its own emitted radiations reach the eye; since blue light is scattered preferentially to red, a distant white light appears yellow or red when seen through a hazy atmosphere; the red light penetrates the atmosphere whilst the blue is scattered on the way. It might be objected that a mountain reflects light and that we see it because of this reflected light; this reflected light suffers scattering and so the mountain should appear yellow or red. Distant objects, however, are seen largely through contrast with the brighter sky; it is because they reflect less light than that emitted by the background that they are discriminated; the reflected light is therefore not important in perception and it is the wall of scattered light that determines the colour sensation. (When the brightness of "wall" plus the brightness of the mountain due to reflected light becomes equal to the brightness of the background, the mountain becomes invisible. For this reason, the visibility of distant points in the landscape constitutes a good measure of the atmospheric haze.)

The scattering of light also blurs the outlines of objects and thus gives another clue to their distance from the observer; the apparent closeness of mountains in a very clear atmosphere is an illusion based on the normal association of clearly defined objects with proximity to the observer.

Relative Sizes of Objects. The apparent size of an object may be represented by the angle it subtends at the nodal point of the eye; thus AB and A'B' (Fig. 225) appear to have the same size because they subtend the same angle and they are the same distance away; CD, moreover, appears as big as AB because it subtends the same angle although its real size is twice as great as that of AB. If the observer knows that CD is twice as large as AB, *e.g.* if AB is a bicycle and CD is a car, he can say that CD is twice as far away from him as AB, *i.e.* he can estimate their *relative* distances in the third dimension. A fair estimate of the *absolute* distance away can be made if the object viewed is familar, *e.g.* a man or a cottage. When a man walks away from an observer the image on the latter's retina becomes smaller and smaller; this is interpreted as a more and more distant, not as a smaller and smaller, man. In gunnery, the visual estimation of range is made almost entirely on this basis.

The association of size with distance can give rise to common illusions; in a thick fog a figure "looming up" looks very large because the figure is assumed to be farther away than it actually is. Similarly objects seen through binoculars appear to be very close whereas their images, seen through the instrument, are at infinity.

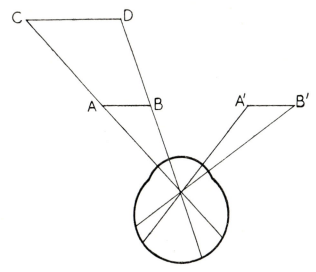

FIG. 225. Illustrating the value of relative size in estimating depth.

ABSOLUTE SIZE

The determination of *absolute size* is thus closely interwoven with that of distance; any rigid formulation of this process on the basis of the number of retinal elements stimulated by the image of an object is therefore doomed to failure. A given retinal distance represents an absolute size of an object in space only for one distance of the object from the observer. A change in this distance must necessitate a revaluation of retinal distance. When an object is recognized to be far away, a small retinal distance is interpreted as a certain unit of "absolute size" in space; if the same object is brought much closer, its image becomes larger so that a larger retinal distance now becomes equivalent to the same unit of "absolute size" in space. The close linkage between this revaluation process and the acts of convergence and accommodation is shown by the condition of *"paresis micropsia."* As a result of a defective convergence mechanism, for example, a strong effort of convergence is made in order to fixate a near object; this effort, being out of all proportion to the resulting convergence, is associated with much too great a change in retinal dimension values; the object converged upon appears smaller because it is treated as being much closer and the retinal dimension values have been scaled down too far.

THE MOON ILLUSION

The assignment of a size to objects very far away, such as the sun and moon, must be entirely arbitrary, and so it is not surprising that the assigned size varies, although the reasons for the variations are not apparent. Thus the sun and moon, when seen on the horizon appear very much larger than when viewed at the zenith.

Form. The contours of objects give some idea as to their relative positions in the third dimension. Thus in Fig. 226 the cottage is in front of the tree which is

FIG. 226. The value of the overlapping of contours in the estimation of depth.

in front of the windmill which itself is perceived to be in front of the hill, entirely because of the overlapping of the contours.

Perspective. The projected retinal image of an object in space may be represented as a series of lines on a plane, *e.g.* a box; these lines, however, are not a unique representation of the box since the same lines could be used to convey the impression of a perfectly flat object with the lines drawn on it, or of a rectangular, but not cubical, box viewed at a different angle. In order that

FIG. 227. Full side view.

FIG. 228. Three-quarters view. The front wheel appears smaller than the back; both appear elliptical.

a three-dimensional object be correctly represented to the subject on a two-dimensional surface, he must know what the object is, *i.e.* it must be familiar to him. Thus a bicycle is a familiar object; viewed flat-on it has the appearance of Fig. 227; if it is turned away from the observer it appears as in Fig. 228; the wheels, for example, are elliptical and the front one is smaller than the rear one. Because the observer knows that the wheels are actually circular and of the same size he can state that the bicycle is directed into the third dimension, *i.e.* he perceives depth in a two-dimensional pattern of lines. The perception of depth in a two-dimensional pattern thus depends greatly on exerience—the knowledge of the true shape of things when viewed in a certain way. The limitations of two-dimensional representation become evident when we look at the photograph of an unfamiliar object, such as a complex crystal; the picture is almost meaningless because we have no idea of the actual shapes of its component parts.

Light and Shade. A sphere always appears in a two-dimensional pattern as a circle, however viewed; perspective can therefore give no clue to its solidity. The light and shade on its surface, however, immediately give it a three-dimensional appearance (Fig. 229); in general, it is important that the origin of the source of light be known and then the relations of the shadows of objects to each other indicate their mutual arrangement in space. The protective

FIG. 229. Illustrating the value of light and shade in giving the appearance of depth to a sphere.

colouring of a large number of animals is designed to offset the appearance of solidity resulting from uneven illumination. Thus the back of an animal receives more light than the belly and if the back reflected the light just as efficiently as the belly it would appear much brighter and convey the impression of solidity (Fig. 230). However, the white belly of the donkey, for example, increases the amount of light reflected by it so as to make it approximate in brightness to its back, which is grey. As a result the animal appears, at a distance, to be fairly uniformly bright over its whole surface and therefore appears flat (Fig. 230), a characteristic that helps it to merge with its background. Under certain conditions of illumination, light and shade can give valuable clues to the length of a room, for example, in the third dimension; if the source of illumination is close to the observer, the luminance of the walls decreases progressively with their distance away. As a result of the process which results in "tone constancy," the walls generally appear to be evenly illuminated, the actual change in luminance being interpreted as an *increase in distance* from the observer. In this case the phenomenon of "tone constancy" is essentially similar to that of "size constancy"—the tendency to interpret a diminishing retinal image as an object of constant size moving away from the observer.

Parallactic Displacement. On movement of the head from side to side, the objects nearer to the observer appear to move, in relation to more distant points, in the opposite direction. Similarly, when the observer moves forward, the nearer objects appear to move past him whilst the more distant objects appear to move with him. Helmholtz remarks that if one sits in a wood with one eye closed and the head motionless, the picture presented is quite flat; on moving the head, however, the environment springs to life due to the parallactic displacements which indicate the essentially three-dimensional nature of the scene.

FIG. 230. Protective shading of an animal (see text).

Accommodation. Within a limited range, the accommodative effort required to see an object clearly might be expected to give a clue as to its absolute distance from the observer, but although opinions differ, it seems safe to conclude that the kinæsthetic sensations from the ciliary muscle do not contribute materially to the power to assess distance, and the same would appear to be true, in binocular vision, for the process of convergence (Zajac, 1960). The extreme difficulty in separating the factor of accommodation from all the other factors concerned reveals that depth perception is a complex process whose components are so interwoven as to make it a somewhat academic exercise to attempt to separate them and measure their individual contributions.

This description of the monocular factors in depth perception shows that there are many ways in which the one-eyed person can perceive depth in his environment; nevertheless his perceptions are grossly inadequate when compared with those of a normal subject, and we may now inquire into the general characteristics of binocular vision.

BINOCULAR PERCEPTION

The two eyes behave, in so far as their motor taxis is concerned, as a single unit; binocular vision is likewise integrated, so that in many respects the perception can be described in terms of a single eye.

The "Cyclopean Eye." If its two images on the retinæ were projected independently into space, an object would appear to be differently orientated in

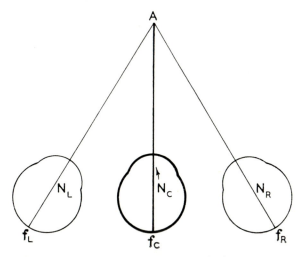

FIG. 231. The Cyclopean projection.

relation to the individual according as its direction was referred to the primary position of one or the other eye. For example, in Fig. 231, the point A is fixated by both eyes, and it is correctly projected into space at A; to the left eye, however, it is to the right of the fixation axis in its primary position, whilst to the right eye it is to the left. Since it is symmetrically disposed in regard to the two eyes, the object is considered to be straight ahead of the observer—neither to the right nor to the left—so that binocular projection can be represented by the "*Cyclopean eye,*" as in Fig. 231, an imaginary eye in the forehead to which all directions are, in fact, referred. The point A is considered to be straight ahead of the observer because it lies on the fixation axis of the Cyclopean eye in its "primary" position.

Binocular Double Vision. The Cyclopean projection is represented by transposing the images on the two retinæ to the single, median, eye as in Fig. 231. When the images on the two retinæ are not symmetrically disposed about the fixation point, however, such a transposition leads to a double projection, and it is found, in fact, that when the same object can be projected in two directions by the Cyclopean eye double vision does actually occur. In Fig. 232, the two eyes fixate the point A, as before. A point B, closer to the eye, on the median line, produces images at b_L and b_R; the problem is to determine how the observer projects these images. In Fig. 232, the Cyclopean eye, occupying a mean position between the two eyes, is drawn in. The image of A falls on the fovea of each eye and hence its projection by the Cyclopean eye is given by projecting

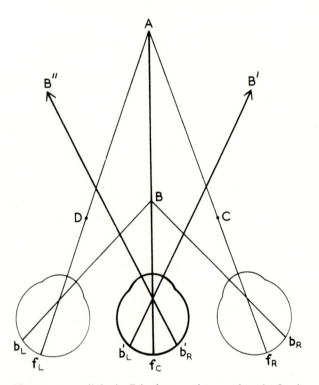

Fig. 232. Heteronymous diplopia. B is closer to the eyes than the fixation point. By the left eye the image of B is projected to B′; by the right to B″.

f_c through the nodal point, *i.e.* it coincides with the true direction of A. The image of B on the left retina, b_L, occurs to the left of f_L and must be put in a similar position on the Cyclopean retina; b_L is thus projected to B′. On the right retina, B forms an image, b_R, to the right of f_R, which, when transposed to the Cyclopean eye, gives a projection to B″. Since B is projected to B′ and B″ at the same time, it is seen double; the diplopia is called *heteronymous diplopia* because on closing one eye the image appears to move away from the fixing eye, *e.g.* on closing the left eye the image of B appears to be at B″, *i.e.* away from the right, fixing, eye. The *homonymous diplopia*, caused by an object farther away from the fixation point, is indicated in Fig. 233. The normal presence of double images in the binocular field of vision is not usually noticed; they are easily demonstrated, however, by placing a pencil close to the eyes in the median line; when a distant object is fixated, the pencil is seen double.

Binocular Alignment. On a binocular projection, the point B is aligned with the point A, so that if an observer places a pencil in front of him so as to coincide with a distant object when both eyes are open, he really puts the pencil in such a position that its double images lie at equal distances to the left and right of the distant object—B' and B'' of Fig. 232. Such a Cyclopean alignment is, in general, not accurate; the careful alignments necessary for sighting

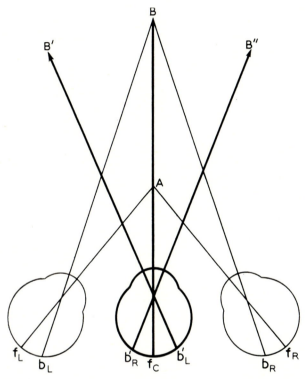

FIG. 233. Homonymous diplopia. B is farther away from the eyes than the fixation point A. By the left eye the image of B is projected to B'; by the right eye to B''.

a rifle, for example, are made with one eye; if the alignment were made with the right eye a point C, on the fixation axis, would be correctly aligned with A; for the left eye, the point D (Fig. 232). (The reader should try rapidly pointing with a pencil at a distant object; keeping the pencil fixed, he should inspect the double images of the pencil while he fixates the distant object; if the latter lies between the double images, the pointing has been carried out on a Cyclopean projection; if, on the other hand, one of the double images coincides with the distant object, the pointing has been carried out on the basis of a monocular projection.)

Diplopia due to Squint or Prisms. In Fig. 232 the point A was seen single, on a Cyclopean projection, because the lines joining it to the nodal point of each eye met the retinæ in the foveæ. B was seen double because the lines from it through the nodal points met the retinæ on opposite sides of the fovea. A similar state of affairs occurs in squint. Fig. 234 represents a divergent squint. A is fixated by the right eye, but the left visual axis diverges from A; the image of A on the left retina thus falls at a_L. If the images on the two retinæ are transposed to the Cyclopean eye, the image of A is projected towards A and towards A′, to the right of A. A heteronymous diplopia is therefore caused by this divergent squint.

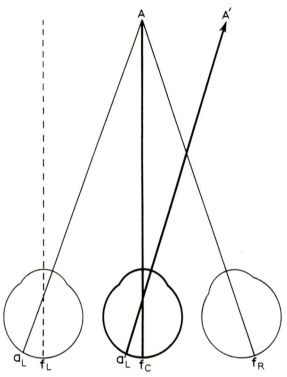

Fig. 234. Heteronymous diplopia due to divergent squint. The image of A is correctly projected by the left, fixating, eye to A; by the right eye it is projected falsely to A′.

PRISM

A prism may cause diplopia, provided that the eyes do not compensate for the change of apparent direction of the object caused by the prism. In Fig. 235, a base-out prism has been placed before the left eye. The image of A falls on f_R the fovea of the right eye, but in the left eye it falls on a, to the left of the fovea f_L. On the Cyclopean projection, the images of A are projected in two directions, A and A′. In Fig. 236, the eye has compensated for the prism by adducting; both images now fall on the foveæ, and the Cyclopean projection indicates single vision. It is interesting that a single projection is obtained in this instance; the left eye has adducted, so that on the basis of our earlier arguments (p. 332) an image falling on the fovea should be projected through

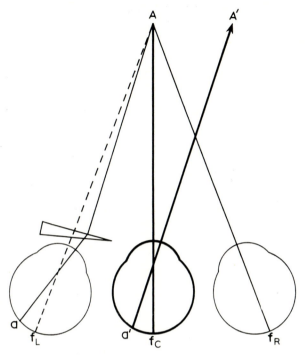

FIG. 235. Diplopia due to a prism.

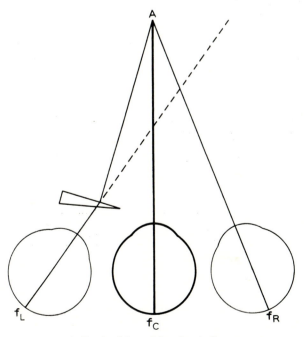

FIG. 236. Single vision with prism before one eye.

the nodal point—to the right of A. If the left eye, only, were being used, such a projection would occur—a *false projection*, in the sense that the image of A is not projected towards A. The fact that with binocular vision the two images of A are correctly projected to a single point indicates that the Cyclopean projection is determined by the projection of the eye that has not been interfered with.

When prisms are placed in front of both eyes, if the necessary oculo-motor adjustments are possible, single vision is retained, but this time the retinal images of objects are erroneously projected, either closer to or farther away from their true position.

The "False Macula." The diplopia due to squint is an instance of false projection; the squinting eye fails to project a retinal image through the nodal point, *e.g.* the stimulated point a_L of Fig. 234 is not projected through the nodal point to A but its projection may be described as though the point stimulated were to the left of a_L. The fovea of the squinting eye is likewise projected falsely, an image falling on f_L is projected towards A, the fixation point of the other eye. In many cases the false projection may be corrected by the development of a *"false macula,"* that portion of the retina on which the image of the fixation point, A, of the other eye falls, acquiring some of the characteristics of the fovea. The change is a cortical one—it is impossible for the anatomical characteristics of the retina to alter; the development of a false macula represents a change in the significance of the stimulus falling on it; the stimulus becomes the centre of attention, and that falling on the true macula is suppressed; moreover, the false macula is correctly projected into space. We have seen that projection is essentially a matter of localization in space of a retinal stimulus; to do this correctly the positions of the eye and head must be known and psychological compensations for movements of the eye and head are an integral part of the projection mechanism. The development of the false macula requires a re-adjustment of this psychological compensation to take into account the abnormal relationship of the visual axes of the two eyes.[*]

Innate Projection. The existence of false projection following squint reveals that the projection of the eye through the nodal point is an innate characteristic, developed doubtless during the early years of life, but nevertheless an inherited quality. The possibility of a development of a false macula reveals, on the other hand, a certain plasticity in the function of the visual cortex. We have already remarked on the rigidity of the relationship between stimulus and sensation in this area of the cortex, a rigidity which differentiates it from other parts of the cerebral mantle, and it is interesting that the relationship may be modified by experience and is therefore not absolute as with processes occurring at lower levels in the brain.

A condition of *monocular diplopia* may arise from the development of a false macula. Thus the stimulus falling on a_L (Fig. 234) is originally projected to A'; after the development of a false macula it is correctly projected to A. Sometimes both projections take place simultaneously, so that, as a result entirely of cortical activity (there is clearly only one image on the retina), the point A is seen simultaneously at A and A'.

The development of a *"pseudo-fovea"* may result from hemianopia; in this

---

[*] There is unfortunately a serious danger of confusion arising out of the different senses in which "false projection" is regarded. To the neurologist the macula of the squinting eye is falsely projected because the individual grasps wide of the object whose image falls on it (he "past-points"). False projection thus means the projection of a retinal image to some other point in space than that occupied by the object evoking it, and this is the sense maintained in this book. To some ophthalmologists, on the other hand, false projection is synonymous with what is called *"abnormal retinal correspondence"*. With the development of a "false macula," an image, not on the macula of the squinting eye, is projected to the same point in space as the image on the macula of the normal eye; the retinal correspondence (p. 351) has been readjusted to give single binocular vision of an object whose images do not fall on the innate corresponding points of the two retinæ. Thus the neurologist would say that the "false macula" is correctly projected into space, whilst some ophthalmologists would say that it is falsely projected.

condition one half of the foveal image is seen, a condition so annoying that the affected person tends to use an adjacent portion of the retina for fixation. With time this point acquires the characteristics of the true fovea—it is correctly projected into space and the images of objects falling on it become the centre of attention and interest.

Convergence. With two eyes we have the geometrical basis for an estimate of the absolute distance of a point from an observer, since the converging power necessary for binocular fixation is uniquely determined by its distance away in the third dimension of space. The relative distances of different objects are likewise determined by the relative degrees of convergence necessary for binocular fixation. That variations in convergence may cause three-dimensional illusions was shown long ago by Meyer in the so-called *wallpaper phenomenon*. As described by Helmholtz, the illusion is brought about by looking at a wall-paper with a vertical line pattern; by making his eyes cross, so that the two eyes were fixating adjacent lines, Helmholtz found that the wallpaper appeared to float out of the wall, whilst if he made his eyes diverge the paper receded into the wall in the region of the fixation points. The crossing or divergence of the eyes caused no apparent diplopia because the fields of view consisted of only vertical lines. As Helmholtz and others have interpreted the phenomenon, the changed convergence *per se* was responsible for the apparent three-dimensionality of the wallpaper; in other words, the act of convergence contributed to the sensation of depth. However, more modern workers are inclined to deny to the convergence *per se* any significant contribution to depth perception (Stevenson Smith, 1946; 1949; Zajac, 1960); it is because alterations in convergence, by altering the fixation point, change the relative sizes and positions of other objects around the fixation point, that the retinal images are modified and thus the appearance of the fused binocular retinal images.

STEREOSCOPIC DEPTH PERCEPTION

We have so far considered the geometrical consequences of the use of the two eyes in estimating distance—the system has been treated as a range-finder— and the problem of the fusion of the two images in the separate eyes has not been considered. Not only does the fusion of the images provide a unitary perception of the binocular field of view, but it presents the objects in this field in a three-dimensional pattern that is quite impossible of achievement with monocular vision. In the following pages we shall inquire into those characteristics of the two retinal images that (*a*) permit or favour fusion and (*b*) contribute to the three-dimensional percept.

Corresponding Points and the Horopter

Corresponding Points. We have seen, in our discussion of binocular projection, that a single object in space is projected in two different directions when its images, formed by the two eyes, do not both fall on the foveæ (Fig. 232); this results in diplopia, and single vision is only achieved when the retinal stimuli are projected to the same point in space. The foveæ may therefore be described as *corresponding points*; they are points on the two retinæ normally projected to the same point in space.

Every point on the retina of each eye is projected into space to give the field of vision ; where the projections overlap we have the binocular field of vision; the problem is to determine which points in the binocular field of vision are seen single or, more correctly, which pairs of points in the retinæ of the two eyes are projected to the same point in space. The matter is subject to experimental investigation and the following conclusions were drawn by Helmholtz:

(*a*) The apparently horizontal meridians of the two retinæ correspond.

(*b*) The apparently vertical meridians correspond.

(*c*) Points on the apparently horizontal meridians, equally distant from the foveæ, are pairs of corresponding points.

(*d*) Points equally distant from the apparently horizontal meridians, which are on the apparently vertical corresponding lines, are a pair of corresponding points.

In so many words, points equidistant from the apparently horizontal and vertical meridians of the retinæ were said to be corresponding points.

The Vieth-Müller Horopter Circle. Fig. 237 represents a horizontal section through the two eyes, fixating the point F. The points a_L and a_R are

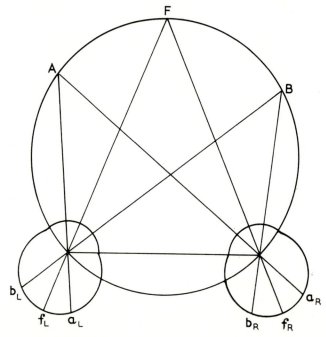

FIG. 237. The Vieth-Müller horopter circle. F is the fixation point. If corresponding points are symmetrically distributed about the foveæ the points in space, in the fixation plane, whose images fall on corresponding points lie on the circle.

equally distant from the vertical meridians of the two eyes and are therefore projected to the same point in space through the respective nodal points, namely, to A. The points b_L and b_R, also symmetrically disposed about the vertical meridians, are projected to B. From the geometry of this binocular projection it is evident that A, F and B lie on a circle passing through the fixation point,

F, and the nodal points of the eyes. All points in space, lying on this circle, so long as they produce images on the two retinæ, produce them on corresponding points provided that the symmetry, postulated by Helmholtz, exists. The circle is called the *Müller* or *Vieth-Müller horopter circle*: it is the locus of points, in a horizontal plane, that produce images falling on corresponding points of the two retinæ when the fixation axes are horizontal, and are directed on the point F. Moreover, if the eyes may be considered to rotate about the nodal points instead of their centres of rotation, the fixation point may move to any point on the circle and all other points will still produce images on corresponding points. With this approximation the Müller horopter circle becomes the locus of points, in a horizontal plane, that produce images on

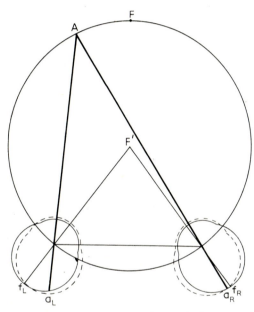

Fig. 238. When F was the fixation point, A lay on the horopter-circle; when F' becomes the fixation point A no longer produces images on corresponding points, so that A is not on the more generally defined horopter.

corresponding points for a given degree of convergence of the eyes when the retinal horizons are horizontal. The Müller circle only indicates the points in space *in a single plane* that produce images on corresponding points. If the circle is rotated about a line joining the nodal points, the surface so produced gives the locus of all points in space whose images fall on corresponding points, for a fixed degree of convergence of the eyes. This is only true if the two retinæ possess strict spherical symmetry and if the corresponding points are symmetrically disposed around the foveæ. As the apparently vertical meridians of the retinæ are not parallel to each other (p. 337) there is no such perfect symmetry and this Müller horopter surface, as we may call it, is only an approximation.

The Horopter. The *horopter* as originally defined is the *locus of points in space whose images fall on corresponding points of the two retinæ, i.e.* no proviso is made as to the fixation point or the degree of convergence. The Müller horopter circle must therefore be regarded as a special case of the horopter when the fixation point has been defined. The number of points in space that will produce images on corresponding points, *however the eyes move*, is strictly limited; thus in Fig. 238, when the eyes move to a new fixation point not lying on the original Müller circle, *e.g.* the point F', the images of A do not lie symmetrically with regard to the foveæ and are therefore not on corresponding points. Hence, although A lies on the Müller horopter circle when the eyes fixate F, it does not lie on the horopter. The horopter was calculated by Helmholtz from experimental data on the positions of corresponding points and the laws of the eye movements; it is a curve of the third degree (a curve that cuts a plane in three points). Under certain conditions the horopter acquires a simpler form; *e.g.* if the eyes are looking straight ahead in the primary position, the horopter becomes a horizontal plane passing through the feet, all points on this plane being seen single. When the point of fixation is either in the median plane of the head or in a horizontal plane with the fixation axes horizontal, the horopter becomes a Müller circle and a vertical line, intersecting in a point.

Longitudinal Horopter

For practical purposes, the so-called *longitudinal horopter* is the most useful. For a given fixation point it is the locus of points in a horizontal plane whose images fall on corresponding points of the two retinæ. Thus, if Müller's assumptions were correct, it would be his horopter circle. In fact, however, the postulated symmetry about the vertical meridians does not hold good, so that the longitudinal horopter is not a circle.

Hering-Hillebrand Deviation. Thus if we wish to find the point corresponding to a_L (Fig. 237) it is, in general, not at a_R such that $f_L a_L = f_R a_R$, but closer to, or farther away from f_R. This so-called *Hering-Hillebrand deviation* causes a characteristic change in the longitudinal horopter, so that not only does it deviate from a circle but its shape changes with the fixation distance. With strong convergence it was found to be concave to the face; at about 2 metres it became approximately a straight line in the frontal plane, whilst beyond this distance it was a curve, convex to the face.

Modern Analysis

Interest in the horopter, up to 1932, was largely academic; in this year, however, Ogle and his associates drew attention to the implications of the horopter from the point of view of the relative sizes of the retinal images. On the basis of certain assumptions, Ogle showed that the shape of the longitudinal horopter should be an index to the degree of discrepancy between the sizes of the retinal images. His interest in the problem of aniseikonia led to a very thorough investigation of the horopter, both from a practical and theoretical aspect; it is impossible in a brief space to do justice to the results or the conclusions of this study. The mathematical analysis confirmed the general conclusions of Hillebrand on the variation of the shape of the horopter with distance. Thus at a certain distance it coincided with the frontal plane whilst at other distances it was curved. The significance of altered image-size, *i.e.* of *aniseikonia*, will be discussed later (p. 364).

The Stereoscope and Depth Perception

The essential feature of stereoscopic perception is the existence on the two retinæ of *different images of the same object*; the object is seen in two aspects because of the different viewpoints of the eyes. Thus Fig. 239 represents two

FIG. 239. Stereoscopic photographs of a book.

photographs of a book as it would be seen by the left and right eyes; if these photographs are viewed separately by the two eyes and their images fused, the book is perceived as a three-dimensional object.

FIG. 240. Optical principles of the Brewster stereoscope.

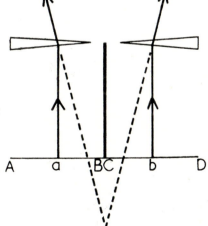

The Stereoscope. The fusion of the two images can be carried out, with a little practice, by holding them directly in front of the eyes, a piece of cardboard in the median plane being used to keep the fields separate. The conditions are, however, artificial in that the eyes normally converge when near objects are viewed, and a convenient instrument, which permits this convergence when the objects viewed are close to the eyes and directly in front of them, is the *stereoscope*, the optical properties of which are shown in Fig. 240. Two pictures, representing different aspects of the same object, AB and CD, are placed about 10 cm from the eyes. They are viewed separately through base-out prisms, so that symmetrically disposed points on the stereograms are projected to the same point, *e.g. a* and *b* are projected to *c*.

Discrepant Images. If the two identical circles of Fig. 241, *a*, are placed in the stereoscope, their images are fused but no sensation of depth is achieved

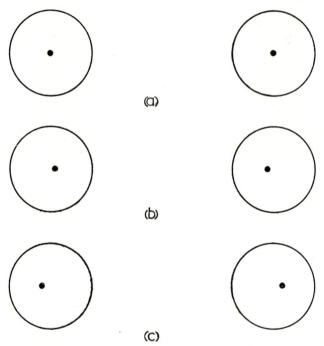

FIG. 241. (*a*) The spots are in the centres of the two circles; the fused image is two-dimensional. (*b*) The spots are de-centred nasally. The spot appears, on fusion of the images, to be nearer the observer than the plane of the circle. (*c*) The spots are de-centred temporally. The spot appears, on fusion of the images, to be farther from the observer than the plane of the circle.

precisely because the pictures are identical and are such as would, in effect, be presented to the eyes were a flat circle viewed. If the dots are placed in the circles, as in Fig. 241, *b*, fusion of the images creates the impression that the dot is floating in space in front of the circle, whereas if the dots are placed as in Fig. 241, *c*, the dots appear to be behind the plane of the circle. The stereograms imitate the appearances to the two eyes of a three-dimensional pattern; thus let us imagine that there is a dot on the surface of a sphere placed symmetrically with regard to the two eyes; viewed with the left eye, the dot appears to the right of the centre of a circle—the outline of the sphere—whilst viewed by the right eye it is to the left. The combined image, as seen in the stereoscope, gives the impression of a point on the surface of the sphere. It will be noted that a sphere, viewed from any angle, appears as a circle; the two aspects of a sphere are therefore identical circles and binocular perception of a uniformly bright sphere can give no impression of solidity. It is essentially because a sphere is normally unevenly illuminated, and has light and dark spots on it, that the aspects presented to the eyes are different; the fusion of these aspects places the lights and shades in their true relationships in three dimensions and so creates the appearance of solidity. The importance of light and shade in stereoscopic vision may be seen by examining photographs of unfamiliar objects which reflect light to varying extents on different parts; stereoscopic vision puts the various high lights in their correct positions in the third dimension and so contributes greatly to the intelligibility of the presentation.

Parallax. The difference in the two aspects of the same object (or group of objects) is measured as the *instantaneous parallax*. In Fig. 242, B is closer to

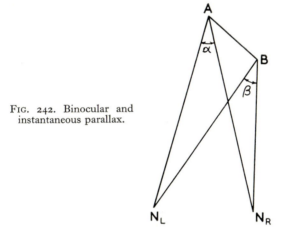

FIG. 242. Binocular and instantaneous parallax.

the observer than A; the fact is perceived stereoscopically because the line AB subtends different angles at the two eyes, and the instantaneous parallax is measured by the difference between the angles α and β. The *binocular parallax* of any point in space is given by the angle subtended at it by the line joining the nodal points of the two eyes; hence the binocular parallax of A is α; that of B is β; the instantaneous parallax is thus the difference of binocular parallax of the two points considered.

Accuracy and Limits of Stereoscopic Perception. The accuracy of stereoscopic perception is remarkable. Andersen and Weymouth and later, Ten Doesschate, placed three wires in front of an observer; the distance the middle wire had to be moved to appear out of the plane of the other two was measured; the parallax was of the order of four seconds of arc, corresponding to a disparity of the retinal images far smaller than the diameter of a single cone. Other values in the literature range from 1·6 to 24 seconds.

With two editions of the same book, it is not possible, by mere inspection, to detect that a given line of print was not printed from the same type as the same line in the other book. If the two lines in question are placed in the stereoscope, it is found that some letters appear to float in space, a stereoscopic impression created by the minute differences in size, shape, and relative position of the letters in the two lines. The stereoscope may thus be used to detect whether a bank-note has been forged, whether two coins have been stamped by the same die, and so on.

It may be shown, on geometrical grounds, that beyond a certain distance from the eyes, the difference of parallax of objects becomes effectively zero; beyond this point, then, objects in the environment appear to be in a single plane; the distance has been computed to be about 450 metres but of course it depends on the figure taken for the smallest perceptible instantaneous parallax.

Effect of Distance. Several studies of the effects of distance on relative depth discrimination have been described. Under these conditions the observer is presented, in the distance, with two similar objects, separated laterally but initially at the same distance from him; one object is moved nearer or farther away until the observer states that he can detect the fact; and the distance between the two objects represents the *linear* depth limen, which may be converted to an angular disparity or parallax. According to Teichner, Kobrick & Wehrkamp, there is an actual improvement in the power to discriminate as the distance increases, although on theoretical grounds we should not expect any change, when the limen is expressed in terms of an angle of parallax. Ogle (1958) has pointed out, however, that the monocular clue given by difference in perceived size, when the two objects are not equidistant from the observer, becomes relatively more important in depth discrimination as distance increases; and it is for this reason that there is an improvement of depth discrimination, the eye being more sensitive to changes of size than to changes of parallax at large distances. This view was confirmed by Jameson & Hurvich.

Duration of the Stimulus. Dove in 1841 observed that stereopsis could be experienced by viewing pictures in a stereoscope when they were illuminated by an electric spark, proving that the experience did not depend on movements of the eyes, such as those involved in convergence. A more systematic study by Ogle & Weil has shown that the accuracy* of stereopsis increases by a factor of four on increasing the exposure-time from 4 to 1000 msec. This suggested to Ogle & Weil that small nystagmoid movements, by contributing to visual acuity, improved stereoscopic acuity, since there is no doubt that these two parameters are related. That this is not the correct explanation, however, is shown by Keesey's study on visual acuity with different exposure-times; this did, indeed, improve as the time increased from 20 to 200 msec, but the same improvement was found when the image on the retina was "stabilized" in such a way that it always remained on the same portion of the retina. Thus the small involuntary scanning movements do not contribute to visual acuity, and the improvement of both visual acuity and stereoscopic acuity with viewing-time implies only that the neural processes concerned with the discrimination require a certain minimum time for their best performance.

Disparate Points and Stereoscopic Perception

Stereoscopic perception results from the fusion of dissimilar images; it follows from this that the fused percept is made up by the integration of stimuli

* The accuracy of stereopsis is determined by measuring the threshold, *i.e.* the smallest instantaneous parallax that is just detected with stereoscopic vision. As with other thresholds, of course, there is a range of uncertainty over which we must speak of a *probability of detection*, and the threshold must be assessed on a statistical basis (Ogle, 1950; 1962).

falling on disparate points on the two retinæ, *i.e.* of points which, on a Cyclopean projection, would be seen double. Thus in Fig. 243, A′B′C′D′ and A″B″C″D″ are the two aspects of a slab, ABCD, inclined to the median plane. If the lines B′D′ and B″D″ correspond, it is quite clear that the lines A′C′ and A″C″ *cannot*, the line XY corresponding approximately with A′C′. Hence, on a purely Cyclopean projection, if the edge of the slab, BD, is seen single, the near edge, AC, is seen double. The fused percept is, nevertheless, that corresponding to

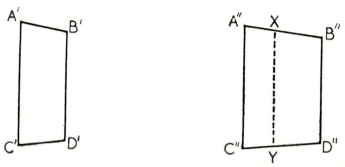

FIG. 243. Illustrating the importance of the incidence of images on non-corresponding points in stereoscopic perception.

a single entity—a slab "floating in space." The existence of images of the same point in space on disparate points of the two retinæ is, therefore, just as much a characteristic of stereoscopic perception as the existence of images on corresponding points; in fact, if all points on an object produced images on corresponding points, there would be no stereoscopic perception.

Corresponding Points Defined. The facts of stereoscopic perception tell us, therefore, that a pair of corresponding points on the two retinæ is not com-

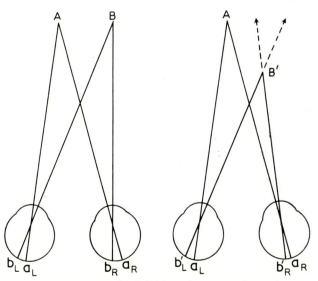

FIG. 244. Illustrating the definition of corresponding points.

pletely defined by the statement that their images are seen single, since disparate points may also be seen single. Let us consider the points A and B of Fig. 244. They are on the horopter and their images fall on corresponding points, a_L and a_R; b_L and b_R. Both points are seen single in binocular vision. Let us now consider the points A and B'; if A is the fixation point, B' is not on the horopter and, on a Cyclopean projection, would be seen double. If, however, A and B' are points on an object, seen single as a stereoscopic percept, B' must be seen single although it is not on the horopter; we must find what it is that differentiates its images b'_L and b'_R from the pair b_L and b_R which enables us to say that they are not corresponding points. It will be seen that when A and B are on the horopter, closing either eye fails to alter their apparent relative positions; on the other hand, when A is on the horopter but B' is not, B' is projected in different directions in relation to A according as one or other eye is closed. Thus with the left eye closed, B' appears closer to A than when the right eye is closed. The actual binocular, or stereoscopic, projection of B' in relation to A is, therefore, different from either of the separate projections. It is essentially this difference that is made use of in the most reliable experimental methods for assessing the positions of corresponding points (*e.g.* the so-called *nonius* method). If the fixation point is used for reference, another point will produce images on corresponding points if its binocular projection is identical with the separate projections of the two eyes.

Nonius Method.

Experimentally the points on the longitudinal horopter may be determined by an apparatus illustrated schematically by Fig. 245. The observer views a fixation point and a vertical horopter-rod through an arrangement of screens that permits both eyes to fixate the fixation point, F, whilst the right eye is able to see only the upper half of the vertical rod, and the left eye only the bottom half. The

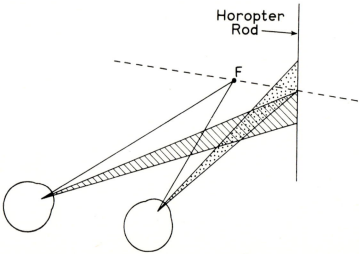

Fig. 245. Nonius method for determining corresponding points. Both eyes are able to fixate F, the fixation point, whilst the right eye sees only the upper half of the horopter rod and the left eye only the bottom half. When the rod is on the horopter its upper and lower halves appear in line. (After Ogle.)

position of this rod is adjusted so that when the eyes are fixating F, upper and lower halves of the rod appear above and below each other. Under these conditions the retinal direction values of the points stimulated by the rod are the same.

Panum's Area. If the stereograms of Fig. 243 are modified so that the lines A′C′ and B′D′ progressively get closer, whilst the equivalent lines of the right stereogram get progressively farther apart, a point is reached where fusion becomes impossible and double vision takes the place of a stereoscopic percept. There is thus a limit to the disparity of retinal points, beyond which they cannot be fused. Panum attempted to define the limiting degree of disparity beyond which fusion becomes impossible. He stated in general that "contours resembling each other, depicted on approximately corresponding points, must be fused together." The circumference that contained those points on the other retina that could be fused with a given point on the first, he called the *corresponding circle of sensation*. This formulation is probably rather too rigid; the ability to fuse contours is determined largely by the possibility of interpreting them as the right- and left-eyed views of a three-dimensional object, and thus the meaning of the final fused percept contributes to some extent to the ability to fuse disparate images. Nevertheless there is reason to suppose that there is a certain contour of finite size such that any point within it will invariably fuse with a single point on the other retina. It is to be noted that the two aspects of any object in space, as seen by the left and right eyes, differ principally in respect to their width, their height being very nearly the same; it is not surprising therefore that it is possible to fuse pairs of vertical parallel lines with quite large discrepancies in their separation, whereas only very small discrepancies in the separation of horizontal lines are tolerated. Panum's "circle" should thus be described as an ellipse with its long axis horizontal. According to Ogle (1950) the length of the horizontal axis of this ellipse varies from one subject to another and, in a given subject, with the position on the retina at which the measurement is made. In one subject it increased from 5 to 30 minutes of arc on passing from central to peripheral vision, and in another from 10 to 40 minutes.

Double Images in Stereoscopic Perception. If a pencil is placed vertically at arm's length, an inch or two to the side and in front of a thin bar, a unitary stereoscopic percept of the two is obtained, with no double images. The images would be said to fall within the Panum circles. On bringing the pencil closer to the eyes, with the bar as a fixation point, a stage is reached at which the double images of the pencil can be distinguished; nevertheless the pencil and the bar may still be perceived as a unitary pattern because one of the double images is ignored. When the pencil is brought very close to the eyes, no accurate perception of it in relation to the bar may be obtained because the double images have now become too obvious. In this experiment the pencil was not on the horopter, which passes through the fixation point; the farther removed from the horopter the pencil becomes, the less accurate and well defined is the stereoscopic percept; fortunately, however, for the unitary perception of the outside world, the more distant an object from the horopter, the more vaguely is it seen, owing to the limitations in the depth of focus of the eye. Thus objects in the environment may produce retinal images of such gross disparity that, if they were distinctly perceived, a unitary perception would be impossible. The vagueness of the double images, however, permits the ready suppression of one, so that all objects in the binocular field of view appear normally single and it requires a careful examination to reveal the actual existence of double images.

In general, the closer the position of an object to the horopter, the more accurate is depth perception; for example if one pin is placed on the horopter and another very close to it, but off the horopter, the eyes can estimate with extraordinary accuracy the displacement in the third dimension. The farther the pins are off the horopter, the grosser the estimate, a fact following from Weber's psychophysical law.

RANGE OF STEREOSCOPIC DEPTH

Finally, we may ask whether stereoscopic perception of depth is achieved when the disparity of the retinal images is such as to give double images, or must there always be "fusion". Helmholtz was in no doubt from his experiments that objects could be quite accurately located as being nearer to, or farther from, a given point by virtue of their double images, and it was presumably the crossed disparity in the one case (cf. Fig. 232) and the uncrossed disparity in the other (cf. Fig. 233) that permitted the perception. More recent studies of Ogle (1953) have confirmed this view, although if the disparity becomes too large the two images become indefinitely localized in space. Thus Ogle divides the region of stereoscopic depth into several parts; for small retinal disparities where fusion takes place, the sensation of depth is compelling and the subject is able to make accurate quantitative estimates of relative depth in accordance with the degree of retinal disparity; beyond this region, where double images may be shown to occur, *i.e.* where fusion is not real, the experience of depth remains, but quantitative estimates of relative depth are poor or non-existent. Finally, when the disparity is still larger, the sense of depth disappears and the two images are indefinitely localized (Ogle, 1962).

Cyclopean and Stereoscopic Projection. The study of stereoscopic perception has revealed a defect in the Cyclopean system of representing the projection of the two eyes in binocular vision. According to this, the point B of Fig. 232 is seen double however close it is to A, whereas we know that, if the separation is not too large, B is seen single. On a *stereoscopic* projection system, therefore, the points b_L and b_R are correctly projected through their respective nodal points to B. The Cyclopean projection of the images of B is unreal, in the sense that it projects the images of a single object to two different points in space simultaneously; the stereoscopic visual process imposes a truer meaning on the two retinal stimuli, not by suppressing one or the other of the two projected images, but by establishing a single projection that corresponds to the true position of B in relation to A. This process extends to retinal images that fall outside Panum's circle, and, even when double images become apparent, it is found that they tend to be projected into space in a direction much closer to the true position of the point giving rise to them than would be expected on a Cyclopean projection.

The Cyclopean projection is not, nevertheless, to be treated as a useless and academic mode of representing the projections of the two eyes; it tells us how the eyes would combine their separate projections if this combination were a simple additive process; thus in Fig. 233 the right eye alone would project its image of B to the right of A, whilst the left eye would project it to the left. The

Cyclopean projection is nothing more than an addition of these two projections. By comparing the Cyclopean with the actual stereoscopic projection we can form an idea of the fundamental revaluation of retinal points that must take place to permit single vision as a result of the stimulation of disparate points.

EXPERIMENTAL DEMONSTRATION

An interesting demonstration of this shift in visual directions has been given by Burian and is illustrated in Fig. 246; the subject views a stereogram consisting of a set of three vertically arranged dots. The images of the upper and lower dots fall on corresponding points, whilst those of the middle dots, 2 and 2', do not, being displaced nasally to give a crossed disparity. When viewed, the appear-

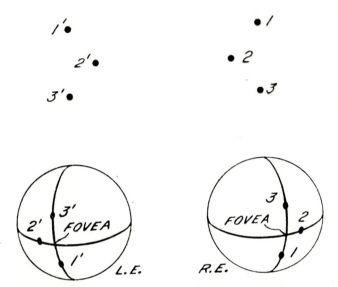

FIG. 246. Illustrating the shift in visual direction of a point by virtue of viewing it stereoscopically. The subject views the stereogram consisting of the sets of dots; on fusion the dots appear in a vertical line. (Burian, *Documenta Ophthalmologica*.)

ance will be that of the dots 1 and 3 lying in a frontal plane with dot 2 closer to the observer (cf. Fig. 241, *b*). What is remarkable, is that the three dots will all appear to be in the same vertical line; consequently the visual directions of the retinal points on which the points marked 2 fall have been altered because of the stereoscopic effect, since we know that if, in the stereograms, the points 2 were placed immediately under points 1 and 3 they would still appear in the same vertical line, but this time, of course, also in the same fronto-parallel plane.

Stereopsis and Perception

It has been customary to treat stereopsis as being the result of a higher perceptual process that interprets the separate fields of view of the two eyes. Thus it has been argued that the two fields "are presented separately to consciousness and that the final percept results from a psychic act". As Ogle has emphasized, however, the experience resulting from fused disparate images is so immediate and compelling that it is difficult to separate it from a visual sensation, as such, and it might well be more correct to describe the experience simply as the response to the falling of disparate images on the two retinæ. Interpretation, in the sense of a conscious analysis of the two retinal images, is of course not an element in the experience. The same may be said of stereoscopic lustre (p. 370); for explanatory purposes we may say that the experience results because it is the only way of interpreting the two images of different luminosity, yet once again the experience is so compelling and immediate that we must treat it as the "response to retinal images of different luminosity".

Reversal of Relief

It will be noted by comparing the stereograms of Fig. 241 *b* and *c*, that the dot in the circle appears to be in front or behind according as it is displaced to the right or left of the centre as viewed by the left eye, and according as the dot is displaced to the left or right of the centre as viewed by the right eye. Thus the pair of stereograms, *c*, is really obtained from the pair, *b*, by interchanging the pictures presented to the left and right eyes. In any pair of stereograms a *reversal of relief* may be obtained by interchanging the pictures presented to the right and left eyes. Such a reversal implies a knowledge by the higher perceptual centres of the contributions of each retina to the final fused image, and yet it is interesting that we are normally not aware as to which eye sees any object not seen by both eyes in the binocular field of view. Thus Rogers describes the following experiment. A tube, about 2 inches in diameter, is held in front of the right eye and directed towards the far left corner of the room. A piece of white paper is placed in front of the left eye so as to screen this eye from the part of the room seen by the right eye. The impression is obtained of seeing the objects in the room with the *left eye* through a hole in the paper.

Size Effects

Horizontal Magnification. The importance of the sizes of the retinal images in determining space perception can best be described with the aid of an example, in which the size of one retinal image is increased with the aid of a lens which modifies the image-size but leaves the dioptric power of the eye almost unchanged (an aniseikonia glass). In Fig. 247 (*left*) we have a line on the longitudinal horopter; it appears to be in the frontal plane and the images on the two retinæ are of the same size. In Fig. 247 (*right*) a lens has been put in front of the right eye; the lens magnifies in the horizontal meridian only, *i.e.* it is a cylinder with axis vertical. The retinal image is now formed at a_R and b'_R and is projected through the nodal point. The intersections of the projections of both eyes give the apparent positions of A and B in stereoscopic single vision, namely, at A and B'. It is clear that a considerable distortion of space values has resulted, AB appearing to lie along AB'. AB therefore no longer lies on the "horopter" of the individual with the aniseikonia glass in front of one eye, and the horopter has thus changed its shape. It has been found that the eye is sensitive to as little as a 0·25 per cent change in the size of one retinal image. This spatial distortion can only be evoked by a magnification in the horizontal meridian; if an ordinary spherical magnifying lens is employed, magnifying in both horizontal and vertical meridians, then the distortion disappears.

Vertical Magnification. If the magnification is confined to the vertical meridian, then we have what Ogle calls the *induced size effect*. The space dimensions are changed, but in the sense that would have been produced by horizontal magnification of the image in the other eye. It is for this reason that simple over-all magnification of the image in one eye, by a spherical lens, has no effect with regard to spatial distortion. Thus the horizontal magnification in the right eye would give the distortion illustrated by Fig. 247, with B appearing at B'; the vertical magnification, by its induced effect, would cause A to move back into the plane of B', and so the distortion disappears.

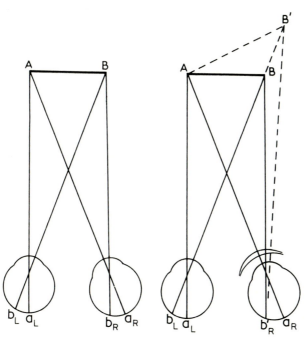

FIG. 247. The effect of an aniseikonia glass on depth perception. *Left:* AB is in the frontal plane and may be said to lie on the longitudinal horopter. *Right:* AB is now projected to AB'.

INDUCED SIZE EFFECT

The induced effect, which is essentially the effect of producing *vertical disparities* in the retinal images, is a most striking phenomenon. The interpretation put forward by Ogle is difficult to present in a short space and this will not be attempted here; suffice it to say that, as with so many stereoscopic and other illusions, the experience may be regarded as a matter of putting the best interpretation on an anomalous set of stimuli. The experience in ordinary viewing conditions where vertical disparities become prominent is in asymmetrical convergence, one eye fixating a point immediately in front of it, whilst the other converges (see, for example Fig. 171, p. 247). Under these conditions certain readjustments in spatial orientation are made; if, now, the vertical disparities are introduced artificially, then the adjustments in spatial orientation that would have been appropriate to asymmetrical convergence are carried out, leading to distortion of space values.

The Pulfrich Phenomenon

If a swinging pendulum with a luminous bob is observed simultaneously through a green glass by one eye and a dark red glass by the other, instead of moving in a plane the pendulum appears to move through an elliptical path. Thus if the left eye wears the red glass, the pendulum on its left-to-right swing appears to move away from the observer and on its reverse swing to move towards him. If the colours are interchanged, the direction of apparent rotation is reversed. Different coloured glasses are unnecessary to evoke the effect,

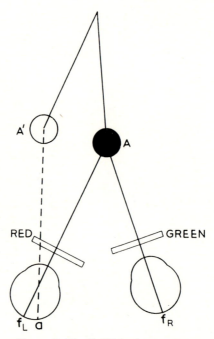

Fig. 248. The Pulfrich phenomenon.

and it is sufficient if the light entering one eye is reducd by placing a neutral filter before it.

Interpretation. The cause of the illusion is the difference in reaction-times of the two eyes in response to the different colours or different luminances. In Fig. 248 let us assume for simplicity that the right eye responds instantaneously to the image of the bob at any point in its path, whilst the left eye responds after a delay. In effect, therefore, when the two eyes are fixating the bob, indicated in its true position in black at A, the left eye is, in effect, seeing it as though it were at A', *i.e.* as though its image on the left retina were at a instead of at f_L. The disparate images are fused to give a stereoscopic effect, so that the bob is actually projected to a point outside the plane of the pendulum. The disparity is uncrossed, so that the bob on its left-to-right swing appears farther from the observer. The degree of disparity will obviously depend on the speed of the bob, and this passes from zero at the extreme of its swing through a maximum at the bottom of its swing; hence the bob will appear in the plane of the pendulum at the extremes of its swing and closest to and farthest from the observer at the bottom of its right-to-left and left-to-right swings respectively. In other words, its motion will be elliptical. Careful experimental studies of the Pulfrich phenomenon, for example those of Lit, have confirmed this explanation.

FURTHER ASPECTS OF BINOCULAR VISION

Retinal Rivalry and Ocular Dominance

Stereoscopic vision is essentially the response to disparate images on the retinæ of the two eyes; if the images are too disparate, as under the artificial conditions of the stereoscope, great difficulty is experienced in obtaining a single fused percept, the double images being so far apart as to force themselves on the awareness and so destroy the unity of the percept. The importance of the *meaning* of the final percept is evident when one attempts to fuse two pictures in the stereoscope; it may be found impossible for a time, but if fusion once takes place to give a three-dimensional representation of some object, then the significance of the two aspects has become clear and the stereograms may be fused rapidly at will.

Retinal Rivalry. If two pictures that cannot possibly be related as two aspects of the same three-dimensional object are presented to the two eyes, single vision *may*, under some conditions, be obtained but the phenomenon of

Fig. 249. The letters **F** and **L** in the stereoscope give simultaneous perception to create the impression of a letter E.

retinal rivalry enters. Thus the two letters **F** and **L** of the stereogram in Fig. 249, when presented to the two eyes separately, can be fused to give the letter **E**; the letters **F** and **L** cannot, however, by any stretch of the imagination be regarded as left and right aspects of a real object in space, so that the final percept is not three-dimensional and, moreover, it is not a unitary percept in the sense used in this discussion; great difficulty is experienced in retaining the appearance of the letter **E**, the two separate images, **F** and **L**, tending to float apart. We are here dealing with a mode of binocular vision that may be more appropriately called *simultaneous perception*; the two images are seen simultaneously, and it is by *superimposition*, rather than fusion, that the illusion of the letter **E** is created.

With the stereograms of Fig. 250, if both patterns were fused or superimposed, the result would be a criss-cross pattern; in actual fact, however, no such perfect superimposition is achieved and the phenomenon of retinal rivalry becomes strongly evident. In different parts of the field one or other set of lines predominates whilst the opposing set is suppressed; sometimes for a brief interval one set of lines will appear all by itself over the entire field; in general the impression is one of fluctuation and Helmholtz stated that the appearance at any moment was largely determined by the attention paid to any aspect, *e.g.* if the observer started to count the lines of one set the others, in the opposite direction, tended to disappear. Helmholtz deduced from this observation that "the content of each separate field comes to consciousness without being fused with that of the other field by means of organic mechanisms, and therefore the fusion of the two fields in one common image, when it does occur, is a psychic act." More recent studies of retinal rivalry, however, indicate that there is a periodicity in the recurrence of one or other field in awareness which appears to be independent of volition; the distinction between fusion by a "psychic act" and an "organic mechanism" is, moreover, not one that would be countenanced by the modern physiologist.

Fig. 250. The stereograms do not give a regular criss-cross pattern in the stereoscope.

Ocular Dominance. Retinal rivalry may be viewed as the competition of the retinal fields for attention; such a notion leads to the concept of *ocular dominance*—the condition when one retinal image habitually compels attention at the expense of the other. Whilst there seems little doubt that a person may use one eye in preference to the other in acts requiring monocular vision, *e.g.* in aiming a rifle, it seems doubtful whether, in the normal individual, ocular dominance is really an important factor in the final awareness of the two retinal images. Where the retinal images overlap, stereoscopic perception is possible and the two fields, in this region, are combined into a single three-dimensional percept. In the extreme temporal fields, entirely different objects are seen by the two eyes and as to which dominates the awareness at any moment depends largely on the interest it arouses; as a result, the complete field of view is filled in and one is not aware of what objects are seen only by one eye. Where the fields overlap, and different objects are seen by the two eyes, *e.g.* on looking through a window the bars may obscure some objects as seen by one eye but not as seen by the other, the final percept is determined by the need to make something intelligible out of the combined fields. Thus the left eye may see a chimney-pot on a house whilst the other eye sees the bar of a window in its place; the final perceptual pattern involves the simultaneous awareness of both the bar and the chimney-pot because the retinal images only have meaning if both are present in consciousness. So long as the individual retinal images can be regarded as the visual tokens of an actual arrangement of objects, it is possible to obtain a single percept and there seems no reason to suppose that the final percept will be greatly influenced by the dominance of one or other eye. When a single percept is impossible, retinal rivalry enters;

this is essentially an alternation of awareness of the two fields—the subject apparently makes attempts to find something intelligible in the combined presentation by suppressing first one field and then the other—and certainly it would be incorrect to speak of ocular dominance as an absolute and invariable imposition of a single field on awareness, since this does not occur.*

When the field of one eye is consistently dominant over that of the other, this generally occurs as a result of a general law that the predominant field along an edge is that field in which the edge lies. Thus if a vertical bar is presented to the left eye and a horizontal bar to the right eye the combined impression may be represented by the cross in Fig. 251, although it must be appreciated that the result is by no means so clear-cut as a simple diagrammatic representation would indicate. At the extremes of the fused cross one eye sees only white

FIG. 251. Schematic representation of the simultaneous perception of a vertical and horizontal bar in the stereoscope. (Helmholtz.)

whilst the other sees the contour, or edge; this eye is "dominant" and the black bar is seen in preference to the white space. Where the bars overlap there is a mixed state of affairs. To the right eye the field above and below the overlap is white and, since this eye is dominant along the horizontal edge, we may expect white above and below the bar; to the left eye the field to the left and right of the overlap is white and since, in this region, the left eye is also "dominant" we expect white to the left and right.

Experimentally the subject of ocular dominance has received more attention than it probably deserves, and attempts have been made to relate it to "handedness". Dolman's peephole test consists of a 13×20 cm card with a round central hole in it of 3 cm diameter. A target 6 m away is looked at through the hole held at arm's length. Under these conditions only one eye can actually see the target, and the one that is found to be doing so is adjudged the dominant eye. Walls has summarized the various tests and placed them in five categories and has stated that in effect they reduce to only two, namely those based on motor control of the eyes and those based on the assessment of subjective visual direction. According to Walls, for instance, the motor taxis of the eyes may be likened

* An interesting observation of Creed's should be recorded here; in studying the retinal rivalry caused by observation in the stereoscope of two postage stamps, differing in colour as well as slightly in design, he noted that the dominance of one colour was not necessarily associated with the dominance of the design belonging to it—thus at a given moment it was quite possible for the design of one stamp to prevail with the colour of the other.

to the steering apparatus of a motor car; one wheel is directly attached to the steering rod whilst the other is guided by the track rod. It is difficult to translate this analogy into physiological terms, however; we know that the muscles to both eyes are innervated at the same time in any movement, and it would be quite incorrect to think of the one eye dragging the other along with it, as this view of ocular dominance would require.

Stereoscopic Lustre

If the stereograms of Fig. 252 are fused, the impression of lustre is created. By lustre is meant the appearance of a surface when some of its reflected light seems to come from within it; it is as though one sees some of the light from the object *through* the rest of the reflected light. The stereograms of Fig. 252 represent the two appearances of a crystal when viewed by the two eyes separately, but the two differ also in being bright and dark at corresponding places. Stereoscopic lustre is therefore the result of stimulating corresponding points of the retinæ to different extents, and the phenomenon suggests an explanation for the lustre in real objects. If the two stereoscopic pictures are to be interpreted

FIG. 252. Stereoscopic lustre.

as tokens of the same object, the surface of the latter must be such that a small change in viewpoint (from left eye to right eye) makes a profound change in the amount of light reflected into the eye. An object with a diffusely reflecting surface could not produce such a change and it therefore appears "flat"; a strongly reflecting surface, on the other hand, would provide the reflected light with a directional quality such that the amount of light entering the eye varied considerably with the viewpoint; such a surface is, in general, lustrous. The chromatic lustre of a bird's plumage, of a thin film of oil, and so on, is due to the variation in the quantity and *quality* of the light entering the eye with change of viewpoint. It must be pointed out, however, that lustre in objects can be appreciated by *one eye only*; Helmholtz has shown, nevertheless, that the *illusion* of lustre may likewise be produced with a single eye; in these circumstances the illusion is created by rapid changes in the brightness of the points in the retinal image, associated with either movements of the eye or of the object; thus on Helmholtz's view essentially the same impression can be gained in one eye by successive stimuli as is gained in two eyes by simultaneous stimuli. Bartley has confirmed this viewpoint; he has shown that successive monocular presentation of two stereograms of different luminance creates the sensation of lustre. The psychological issues involved in such an equivalence of time and space need not concern us here; the important feature of stereoscopic lustre resides in its demonstration that, wherever this is possible, the higher perceptual centres will read such a meaning into two retinal images as to make them the tokens of a single object in space; the simultaneous presentation to the two eyes of a light and a dark view of an object is *interpreted* as the single presentation of a lustrous object in three dimensions, and this happens even though both the light and dark views reflect light diffusely. If the two views cannot be regarded as the tokens of a single object, retinal rivalry takes the place of this perceptual process; in the case of stereoscopic lustre this can be shown by presenting differently coloured views of the same object; if the difference in colour is not very pronounced the impression of lustre is gained on fusion; when the difference is made great lustre gives way to retinal rivalry.

Binocular Aspects of Some Visual Functions

Stereoscopic vision reveals the existence of processes integrating the responses in the two eyes to give a unitary percept quite different from that predictable on the basis of a summation of the separate impressions. Retinal rivalry, on the other hand, provides a condition in which the separate impressions appear, at certain moments, to be unaffected by each other, whilst between these two states we may have a more or less perfect overlap of the visual impressions with, however, dominance of one or other field in certain parts. It is worth inquiring to what extent the simpler aspects of vision discussed in Section II are affected by the use of two eyes. There is, unfortunately, disagreement on many points so that the whole subject merits further investigation.

Light Threshold. If there is the possibility of summation between the two eyes, we may expect that the absolute light threshold, *i.e.* the smallest light stimulus necessary to evoke the sensation of light in the completely dark-adapted eye, will be smaller when the two eyes are employed to view the stimulating patch. There are conflicting claims regarding this possibility; Pirenne has shown that the threshold is definitely lower in binocular vision, but this *does not* indicate a summation between the two eyes. The use of two eyes increases the chance of one eye receiving the requisite number of quanta from a flash of light to stimulate vision. The decrease in threshold, to be expected on this basis of quantum fluctuations, can be calculated; it corresponds to that actually found.

Brightness Sensation. At higher levels of luminance the position is more complex; when the fields presented to the two eyes are equal, there is no obvious summation—this is evident from everyday experience, since the closing of one eye does not make a previously binocularly viewed piece of white paper appear significantly darker. When there is a gross discrepancy in the luminance of the two fields, retinal rivalry appears, although it may most frequently manifest itself as ocular dominance, the bright field determining the binocular sensation. (Under special conditions, it will be remembered, the sensation of lustre may be created.) Under intermediate conditions, there seems to be some fusion of the separate sensations, so that the binocular sensation of brightness is intermediate between that evoked in the monocular fields. *Fechner's paradox*, whereby a monocularly viewed white surface appears brighter than when it is viewed binocularly in such a way that one eye views it directly and the other through a dark glass, is an expression of this binocular fusion. Some measurements of Bartley have shown that the subjective brilliance of an illuminated patch may be increased by a factor of about 1·4 on passing from monocular to binocular fixation.

The liminal brightness increment appears to be the same whether the two halves of the visual field, which have to be discriminated in respect to brightness, are present in the separate eyes or in one eye.

Flicker. The classical experiments of Sherrington would indicate a more or less complete independence of the two eyes in respect to the discrimination of flicker. Thus under conditions where flicker is perceptible at 20 cycles per second, the presentation of separate flickering patches to the two eyes in such a way that the dark period of one eye corresponded to the bright period of the other, did not give fusion although a flicker rate of 40 cycles per second in one eye would have done. Smith has shown that when one eye views a steady light source and the other an intermittent one, the sensation is one of binocular flicker, *i.e.* it is impossible to discriminate between the sensation so evoked and that which would be produced by two flickering sources presented separately to the two eyes. In the region of the critical fusion frequency, however, retinal rivalry occurs, so that the flicker sensation alternates with the impression of a stationary source. The critical fusion frequency, under these conditions, is not entirely determined by the luminance of the flickering patch but on the ratio of this luminance to that of the stationary source. The experimental conditions for the study of binocular flicker are clearly essentially the same as those under which retinal rivalry and ocular dominance are studied; where a unitary percept is possible, as in the special case of the two flickering patches being synchronous, we may expect the binocular flicker sensation to be identical with that evoked in either eye separately. When conditions are different in the two eyes, but not too discrepant, retinal rivalry becomes obvious. When the discrepancy is very strong, rivalry gives place to the dominance of one eye. A study of the tendency for dominance, when different pictures are presented in the stereoscope, shows that the picture with the most contours tends to become dominant; in the case of flicker, it is the flickering field that imposes itself on awareness at the expense of the stationary.

Binocular Colour Mixing. When a pair of stereograms consists merely of two coloured pieces of paper, the condition most frequently encountered is that of retinal rivalry, one or other of the colours dominating awareness for a time to give place to the other. A true binocular mixing can be obtained, however, conforming approximately to the laws of monocular colour mixing, if the conditions are suitable. According to some studies by Johannsen, conditions favouring mixture are low absolute luminance and a small separation of the two colours in the spectrum. When rivalry occurs, the longer wavelength tends to dominate, and where there is a difference in luminosity between the colours, dominance occurs with the brighter of the two. The fact that so careful an experimenter as Helmholtz denied the existence of binocular colour mixing reveals that there are large individual differences in the capacity to mix colours binocularly.

Colour Stereoscopy. The stereoscopic appearance obtained by regarding two differently coloured, but otherwise identical, plane pictures with the two eyes separately, is probably due to chromatic differences of magnification. If the left eye, for example, views a plane picture through a red glass and the right eye views the same picture through a blue glass, an illusion of solidity results.

Chromatic difference in magnification causes the images on the two retinæ to be slightly different in size, so that the images of any point on the picture do not fall on corresponding points; the conditions for a stereoscopic illusion are thus present.

Visual Acuity. If the two eyes had identical visual acuities we might, at first thought, expect to find no difference in visual acuity according as monocular or binocular vision were employed. Measurements of acuity are carried out, however, at the very limit of the subject's resolving power, the observer investigating how frequently a correct answer is made in the discrimination of breaks in successively presented Landolt-C's; there is thus no definite size of Landolt-C that can be invariably resolved whilst a slightly smaller one invariably cannot—the investigator chooses a certain "end-point," *e.g.* five correct answers out of eight, so that he really estimates a probability that the subject will correctly resolve a Landolt-C of a given size. Bárány has shown that merely on a probability basis the apparent visual acuity should be increased in binocular vision, and that the experimentally determined increase conforms to the predictions derived from probability theory.

Adaptation. It would seem from the work of Mandelbaum that the adaptive state of one eye is unaffected by that of the other; thus the absolute threshold of one eye was not altered by adapting the other to a variety of luminance levels. This is an important finding, since it justifies the use of one eye as a control in adaptation studies, *e.g.* those of Wright (p. 105).

THE PERCEPTION OF MOTION

The perception of motion has two elements in it; there is the direct appreciation of movement in consequence of the gliding of the image over the retina when the eye is still (or as a result of the movement of the eye when the image of the object fixated remains stationary on the retina), and there is the more "intellectual" recognition of the fact of movement deduced from the observation that an object is projected to a certain point in space at one moment and at another point after a certain interval of time. Thus we recognize that the large hand of a watch is in motion because at one minute it points at "ten" and at the next minute at "eleven"; there is, however, no real perception of motion, the threshold rate of movement being too low. In experimental studies the measurements are concerned with the direct perception of movement. The sensitivity of the retina to movement is highest at the fovea, as one might expect, since it is here that discrimination, generally, reaches its acme; nevertheless the periphery shows a high sensitivity in comparison with the low order of visual acuity attainable in this region; in the peripheral retina, so great is the difference between visual acuity and motion acuity, that the existence of objects may often only enter awareness when they are moved; as soon as they become stationary they are no longer perceived.*

* This is a somewhat loose way of stating the fact; one becomes aware of an object when it moves in the peripheral field, but this may be an expression of visual acuity rather than motion acuity; owing to adaptation, the awareness of a stationary object in the peripheral field soon ceases, and it requires the stimulation of a new set of receptors to come again into consciousness. The sudden awareness of this fresh stimulation is *interpreted* as a movement of the object, yet experiments seem to show that if the movement of the object is continued there need be no real perception of motion. According to Warden, the direct comparison of visual with movement acuity is beset with difficulties.

Thresholds. The threshold sensitivity to movement can be measured in a number of ways as follows:

(*a*) *The minimum excursion of a moving body necessary for its being in motion to be appreciated.* This minimum depends on the speed of movement, but under favourable conditions it is of the order of ten seconds of arc. This is an extremely small displacement, so small that if two stationary points were separated by this amount they could not be discriminated as separate. The image of the moving point thus need not move over a whole cone before its movement is appreciated. As a result of diffraction and chromatic aberration, the image of a point covers several cones; these are stimulated to different degrees, since the brightness of the image falls off as the periphery of the blur-circle is approached; a very slight movement of the whole image modifies the distribution of light on the several cones and thus modifies the pattern of discharge in their nerve fibres. A movement much smaller than the diameter of a cone could modify the distribution of light on the cones and so provide the peripheral basis for this high degree of acuity. According to McColgin, the threshold increases with increasing distance from the fovea.

(*b*) *The minimum angular speed of a point.* In the absence of stationary reference points, this is of the order of one to two minutes of arc per second.

(*c*) *The minimum duration for a given excursion.* If a point is moved between two stationary points, there is a speed above which the motion cannot be appreciated, *i.e.* the observer sees the point at all points in its path simultaneously; the moving luminous point becomes a "streak." With an excursion of 10°, the minimum duration is of the order of 50 milliseconds, corresponding to a speed of movement of 200 degrees per second.

Illusions. A large variety of illusions of movement have been described; most typical, perhaps, are the motion after-images—the apparent movement of stationary objects after the observer has gazed at moving ones for some time. Again, there is the stroboscopic type of motion, typified by the effects of cinematographic projection; successive photographs representing separate stages in the movement are perceived as a continuous act. The phenomena of apparent movement generally serve to emphasize the higher perceptual element in the appreciation of movement.

GENERAL REFERENCES

BARTLEY, S. H. (1941). *Vision. A Study of its Basis.* New York: Van Nostrand.
HELMHOLTZ, H. VON. (1925). *Physiological Optics* (translated J. P. C. Southall). Optical Soc. Amer.
OGLE, K. N. (1950). *Researches in Binocular Vision.* Philadelphia: Saunders.
OGLE, K. N. (1958). Present state of our knowledge of stereoscopic vision. *Arch. Ophthal.,* **60,** 755–774.
OGLE, K. N. (1962). The optical space sense. In *The Eye.* Ed. Davson. Vol. IV. Chapters 11–18. London & New York: Academic Press.
POLYAK, S. L. (1957). *The Vertebrate Visual System.* Chicago: University of Chicago Press.

SPECIAL REFERENCES

ANDERSEN, E. E. & WEYMOUTH, F. W. (1923). Visual perception and the retinal mosaic. *Amer. J. Physiol.,* **64,** 561–594.
BÁRÁNY, E. (1946). A theory of visual acuity and an analysis of the variability of visual acuity. *Acta ophthal. Kbh.,* **24,** 63–92.

BATTERSBY, W. S., WAGMAN, I. H., KARP, E. & BENDER, M. E. (1960). Neural limitations of visual excitability: alterations produced by cerebral lesions. *Arch. Neurol.*, **3**, 24–42.

BISHOP, G. H. & CLARE, M. H. (1955). Organization and distribution of fibres in the optic tract of the cat. *J. comp. Neurol.*, **103**, 269–304.

BURIAN, H. M. (1951). Stereopsis. *Doc. Ophthal.*, **5–6**, 169–183.

CLARK, W. E. LeGROS. (1959). The anatomy of cortical vision. *Trans. Ophthal. Soc. U.K.*, **79**, 455–461.

CREED, R. S. (1935). Observations on binocular fusion and rivalry. *J. Physiol.*, **84**, 381–391.

CURTIS, H. J. (1940). Intercortical connections of corpus callosum as indicated by evoked potentials. *J. Neurophysiol.*, **3**, 407–413.

DE VALOIS, R. L. (1960). Colour vision mechanisms in the monkey. *J. gen. Physiol.*, **43**, No. 6 (Suppl.), 115–128.

DOTY, R. W. (1961). Remarks on the optic-tectum. In *The Visual System*. Ed. Jung & Kornhuber. pp. 215–217. Berlin: Springer.

DOWNER, J. L. DE C. (1959). Changes in visually guided behaviour following midsagittal division of optic chiasma and corpus callosum in monkey. *Brain*, **82**, 251–259.

FILLENZ, M. (1961). Binocular interaction in the lateral geniculate body of the cat. In *The Visual System*. Ed. Jung & Kornhuber. pp. 110–117. Berlin: Springer.

GLEES, P. (1961). Terminal degeneration and trans-synaptic atrophy in the lateral geniculate body of the monkey. In *The Visual System*. Ed. Jung & Kornhuber. pp. 104–110. Berlin: Springer.

GLEES, P. & CLARK, W. E. LeGROS. (1941). The termination of optic fibres in the lateral geniculate body of the monkey. *J. Anat.*, **75**, 295–308.

GRAYBIEL, A. & HUPP, D. (1946). The oculogyral illusion: a form of apparent motion which may be observed following stimulation of the semicircular canals. *J. aviat. Med.*, **17**, 3–27.

GROSVENOR, T. (1959). Eye movements and the autokinetic illusion. *Amer. J. Optom.*, **36**, 78–87.

HOLMES, G. (1945). Organization of the visual cortex in man. *Proc. Roy. Soc. B*, **132**, 348–361.

INGVAR, D. H. & HUNTER, J. (1955). Influence of visual cortex on light impulses in the brain stem of the unanæsthetized cat. *Acta. physiol. scand.*, **33**, 194–218.

JAMESON, D. & HURVICH, L. M. (1959). Note on factors influencing the relation between stereoscopic acuity and observation distance. *J. opt. Soc. Amer.*, **49**, 639.

JASPER, H., AJMONE-MARSAN, C. & STOLL, J. (1952). Corticofugal projections to the brain stem. *Arch. Neurol. Psychiat.*, **67**, 155–171.

KEESEY, U. T. (1960). Effects of involuntary eye movements on visual acuity. *J. opt. Soc. Amer.*, **50**, 769–774.

LASHLEY, K. S. (1942). The problem of the cerebral organization of vision. *Biol. Symp.*, **7**, 301.

LIT, A. (1960). The magnitude of the Pulfrich stereophenomenon as a function of target velocity. *J. exp. Psychol.*, **59**, 165–175.

LUDVIGH, E. (1952). Control of ocular movements and visual interpretation of environment. *Arch. Ophthal.*, **48**, 442–448.

MANDELBAUM, J. (1941). Dark adaptation. Some physiologic and clinical considerations. *Arch. Ophthal.*, **26**, 203–239.

MARQUIS, D. G. (1934). Effects of removal of the visual cortex in mammals, with observations on the retention of light discrimination in dogs. *Ass. Res. Nerv. Ment. Dis.*, **13**, 558–592.

MATURANA, H. R. (1959). Number of fibres in the optic nerve and the number of ganglion cells in the retina of anurans. *Nature, Lond.*, **183**, 1406–1407.

McCOLGIN, F. H. (1960). Movement thresholds in peripheral vision. *J. opt. Soc. Amer.*, **50**, 774–779.

MERTON, P. A. (1956). Compensatory rolling movements of the eye. *J. Physiol.*, **132**, 25–27 P.

MORUZZI, G. & MAGOUN, H. W. (1949). Brain stem reticular formation and activation of the EEG. *EEG clin. Neurophysiol.*, **1**, 455–473.

OGLE, K. N. (1953). Precision and validity of stereoscopic depth perception from double images. *J. opt. Soc. Amer.*, **43**, 906–913.

OGLE, K. N. (1958). Note on stereoscopic acuity and observation distance. *J. opt. Soc. Amer.*, **48,** 794–798.

OGLE, K. N. & WEIL, M. P. (1958). Stereoscopic vision and the duration of the stimulus. *Arch. Ophthal.*, **59,** 4–17.

PANUM, P. L. (1858). *Physiologische Untersuchungen uber das Sehen mit zwei Augen.* Kiel.

PENMAN, G. G. (1934). The representation of the areas of the retina in the lateral geniculate body. *Trans. Ophthal. Soc. U.K.*, **54,** 232–270.

PIRENNE, M. H. (1943). Binocular and uniocular threshold of vision. *Nature,* **152,** 698–699.

SMITH, S. (1946). The essential stimuli in stereoscopic depth perception. *J. exp. Psychol.,* **36,** 518–521.

SMITH, S. (1949). A further reduction of sensory factors in stereoscopic depth perception. *J. exp. Psychol.,* **39,** 393–394.

SPALDING, J. M. K. (1952). Wounds of the visual pathway. I. The visual radiation. *J. Neurol.,* **15,** 99–107.

SPALDING, J. M. K. (1952). Wounds of the visual pathway. II. The striate cortex. *J. Neurol.,* **15,** 169–183.

SPERRY, R. W., STAMM, J. S. & MINER, N. (1956). Relearning tests for interocular transfer following division of optic chiasma and corpus callosum in cats. *J. comp. physiol. Psychol.,* **49,** 529–533.

TALBOT, S. A. & MARSHALL, W. H. (1941). Physiological studies on neural mechanisms of visual localization and discrimination. *Amer. J. Ophthal.,* **24,** 1255–1264.

TEICHNER, W. H., KOBRICK, J. L., & WEHRKAMP, R. F. (1955). The effects of terrain and observation distance on relative depth discrimination. *Amer. J. Psychol.,* **68,** 193–208.

TEN DOESSCHATE, G. (1955). Results on an investigation of depth perception at a distance of 50 metres. *Ophthalmologica, Basel,* **129,** 56–57.

VASTOLA, E. F. (1960). Monocular inhibition in the lateral geniculate body. *E.E.G. clin. Neurophysiol.,* **12,** 399–403.

VOLKMANN, A. W. (1863). *Physiologische Untersuchungen in Gebiet der Optik.* Leipzig.

WALLS, G. L. (1951). A theory of ocular dominance. *Arch. Ophthal.,* **45,** 387–412.

WIDÉN, L. & AJMONE-MARSAN, C. (1961). Action of afferent and corticofugal impulses on single elements of the dorsal lateral geniculate nucleus. In *The Visual System.* Ed. Jung & Kornhuber. pp. 125–133. Berlin: Springer.

ZAJAC, J. L. (1960). Convergence, accommodation and visual angle as factors in perception of size and distance. *Amer. J. Psychol.,* **73,** 142–146.

SECTION V

Visual Optics

VISUAL OPTICS

THE science of geometrical optics consists in the study of the passage of light through various systems; it assumes as a fundamental proposition that light travels in straight lines. This, of course, is only partially true, the phenomena of diffraction providing instances of the non-rectilinear propagation of light. From the point of view of physiological optics, however, we need only consider these deviations from the point of view of the effect of pupil size on the resolving power of the eye, all other aspects being sufficiently accurately dealt with on the basis of this primary assumption—the rectilinear propagation of light. Light, passing through a medium, may be treated as an infinite number of rays which may be represented as straight lines; accurately defined, a ray of light is the straight line between two points in a uniform medium along which light is propagated.

REFLEXION

Plane Mirrors

When light strikes a surface bounding two media, a part is reflected at the surface. The Law of Reflexion states that the reflected ray lies in the same plane as the incident ray and the normal to the reflecting surface, and that the two rays make equal angles with the normal, *i.e.* the *angle of incidence, i,* is equal to the *angle of reflexion, r* (Fig. 253).

FIG. 253. Reflexion at a plane surface. Point object.

If we consider a luminous point, A, in front of a plane mirror, we may represent the passage of light in the plane of the paper as in Fig. 253, where M is a section of the mirror made by a plane through A at right-angles to it (the mirror would thus project out of the paper at right-angles). Rays of light from A may be represented as straight lines, striking the mirror at B, B′, B″, etc. To determine the course of the reflected rays we must erect normals at B, B′, B″, etc. The angles *i, i′, i″*, etc. are the angles of incidence and, by drawing reflected rays to make angles of reflexion *r, r′, r″*, etc. equal to the angles of incidence, the course of the reflected light is obtained.

It will be seen that the reflected rays diverge from each other, and that if they are produced backwards through the mirror they meet at a point A′; to an eye placed in front of the mirror it appears that the reflected rays are actually emanating from this point so that A′ is called the *image* of A. It can be shown geometrically that A′ is as far behind the mirror as A is in front of it, *i.e.* AC = A′C. This last fact gives us a rapid means of constructing the image of an object formed by a plane mirror, and of tracing the pencils of light during reflexion.

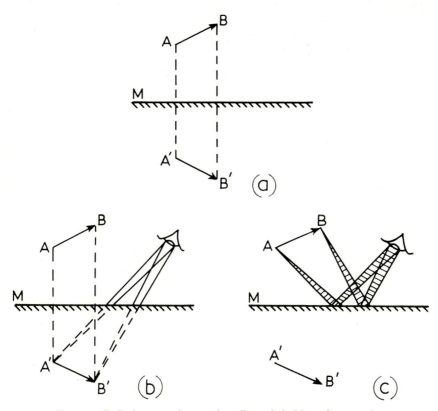

Fig. 254. Reflexion at a plane surface. Extended object. Construction of the pencils of light entering the eye.

Let us consider an object, the arrow AB of Fig. 254, *a*, in front of a plane mirror, M. The position of the image is obtained at once by drawing perpendiculars from A and B to the mirror and producing them behind an equal distance. To the eye, in front of the mirror, all the rays from A and B appear to diverge from A′ and B′ so that the reflected rays entering the eye may be obtained by drawing lines from A′ and B′ to the extremes of the pupil of the eye (Fig. 254, *b*); the actual course of the light from A and B to the eye may then be drawn in (Fig. 254, *c*).

A′ is said to be the image of A because *all* rays from A appear to emanate from A′. It is referred to as a *virtual image* because the rays only *appear* to diverge from it—the eye is unable to distinguish between a real object at A′

or a virtual image, since in both cases the rays of light striking the eye diverge in an identical manner. It will be seen that the image of AB is laterally inverted; thus an observer looking directly at AB would see the head of the arrow on his right; on looking at the image he would see the tail on his right.

Rotation of the Mirror. It is important in retinoscopy to know the effects of rotating the mirror on the position of the image. If M is the mirror (Fig. 255) and A a point source of light, the image A' is obtained as before by dropping a perpendicular and measuring off an equal distance behind. The mirror is now tilted upwards through an angle θ, and the new position of the image, A'', is obtained in the same way. It is easy to show that the line joining the image to the centre of rotation moves through twice the angle of rotation of the mirror.

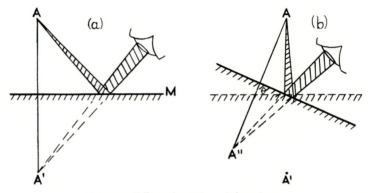

Fig. 255. Effect of rotation of the mirror.

Spherical Mirrors

Construction of the Image. A reflecting surface having the form of a portion of a sphere is termed a spherical mirror (Fig. 256). The *centre of curvature*, C, is the centre of the sphere of which the mirror forms a part; the *pole*, P, is the middle point of the reflecting surface. To represent the path of rays in a single plane we must consider a section of the mirror, and this is chosen so that it passes through the pole and the centre of curvature; it is called a *principal section*. The straight line passing through the centre of curvature and the pole is termed the *principal axis*, to distinguish it from any other line passing through the centre of curvature and striking the mirror, which may be called a *subsidiary axis*.

In Fig. 256, *a*, M is the principal section of a concave mirror, P is the pole, C the centre of curvature, and NP the principal axis. Any ray from a luminous point, O, on the axis, *e.g.* OA, strikes the mirror and is reflected in accordance with the fundamental law of reflexion. The normal at A is given by the line CA, which is a radius of the sphere of which the mirror forms a part, so that the angle OAC equals *i*, the angle of incidence. The reflected ray is given by drawing AI such that the angle CAI equals OAC; it strikes the principal axis in I. Now it can be proved that all rays from O (with certain reservations to be discussed later) pass through I after reflection at the mirror; consequently, to an eye in front of the mirror, the reflected rays appear to come from I, the

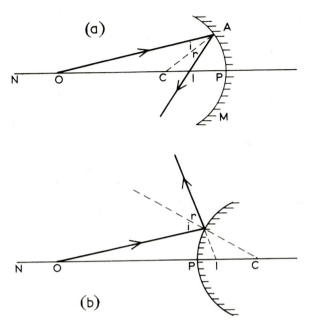

FIG. 256. Reflexion at spherical mirrors. Point object on the axis.

image of O. Since the rays after reflexion *do* actually pass through I, the image is said to be real.

A similar construction may be applied to a convex mirror as in Fig. 256, *b*; the reflected rays, in this case, diverge from the axis instead of cutting it, and it may be shown that they all diverge from the same point I behind the mirror. I is thus the virtual image of the point O.

Position of the Image. For any position of the object, the position of its image formed by a spherical mirror can be calculated with the aid of the formula:

$$1/v + 1/u = 2/r \qquad . \qquad . \qquad . \qquad . \qquad . \ (1)$$

where *u* is the distance of the object from the mirror,
     v is the distance of the image from the mirror,
     r is the radius of curvature of the mirror.

In applying this formula, a convention as to the signs to be applied to the various distances must be adopted; the convention in common use is the following. All distances are measured from the pole of the mirror to the point in question; if, on passing from the pole to the point, one moves *with* the direction of the incident light the distance is said to be positive; if one moves *against* the direction of the incident light the distance is negative. Thus in Fig. 256, *a*, the radius of curvature, *r*, is measured from P, the pole, to the centre of curvature, C; the distance is measured against the direction of the incident light and *r* is given a negative value, *e.g.*—10 cm. Similarly the distances of the object and image, *u* and *v*, are negative. With the convex mirror it will be seen that *r* is positive. Conventionally, light is made to come from the left, so that all distances to the right of the mirror are positive and all to the left are negative.

Example. An object is placed 20 cm in front of a concave mirror of radius 10 cm. Where is the image?

Here u is -20 cm and r is -10 cm.

$$1/v - 1/20 = -2/10$$
Whence $v = -6 \cdot 66$ cm

i.e. the image is $6 \cdot 66$ cm in front of the mirror.

Principal Focus. If the luminous object is placed on the principal axis, as before, but very far away indeed from the mirror, *i.e.* at infinity, the position of the image may be found by substituting in Equation (1):

$$1/v + 1/\infty = 2/r$$
$$i.e. \ 1/v = 2/r$$
$$v = r/2.$$

In words, the distance of the image from the mirror is half the radius of curvature. This position of the image is called the *principal focus* of the mirror, and its distance from the pole of the mirror is said to be the *focal length, f*, which is equal to half the radius.

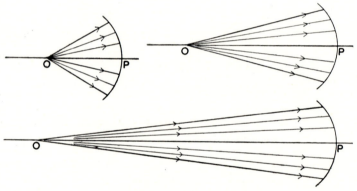

Fig. 257. Illustrating the decreasing divergence of the rays from a point O as the latter is moved farther and farther away from the mirror.

If we consider the rays emanating from a luminous point at various distances from a mirror, as in Fig. 257, we note that when they reach the mirror they diverge from each other, and from the axis, to different extents; the farther the object from the mirror the less the divergence, so that in the limiting case of an object infinitely far away the rays do not diverge but are parallel. Now we have just defined the principal focus of the mirror as the position of the image of a point, infinitely far away on the axis, hence *all rays parallel to the axis pass through the principal focus*. In Fig. 258 the reflexion of rays from a point infinitely far away on the axis, by a convex and a concave mirror, is shown; it will be noted that, in the case of the convex mirror, the reflected rays *appear* to come from the principal focus.

Object Not on the Axis. The position of the image of a point off the axis may be calculated with the mirror formula, but in this event the distances must be measured along a subsidiary axis. Thus if O is the object (Fig. 259, *a*) we may draw an axis through O and C, the centre of the mirror; the image will be formed, say, at I on the axis. When the object is at infinity, but in this case not on the principal axis, the rays will be parallel with each other but not parallel to the axis. The distance of the image will be given by the same formula, *i.e.* it will be $r/2$, but it will be on the subsidiary axis and so not at the principal focus. It will be in the *focal plane* of the mirror, *i.e.* a plane through the principal focus at right angles to the principal axis. In general we may say that parallel rays converge on the focal plane of a concave mirror (or diverge from the focal plane of a convex mirror); when the rays are parallel with the principal axis

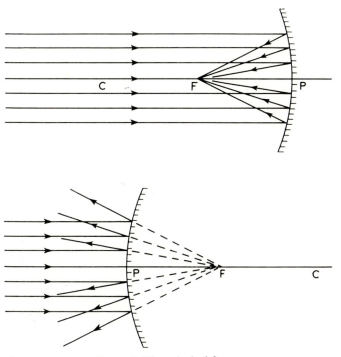

FIG. 258. The principal focus.

they converge on the principal focus; when the rays are parallel, but inclined to the principal axis, they converge on a point in the focal plane, and this point is given by the intersection of the subsidiary axis with this plane (Fig. 259, *b*).

Example. A concave mirror of radius 100 cm is placed vertically; a star is reflected in the mirror. What is the position of the image of the star, if a line joining the centre of curvature of the mirror to the star makes an angle of 30° with the horizontal?

The state of affairs is similar to that represented in Fig. 259, *b*. The star is infinitely far away for optical purposes, on the subsidiary axis OCB, making an angle of 30° with the principal axis, which is horizontal. The rays of light from the star are parallel and come to a focus at a distance of $r/2$ from the mirror on the subsidiary axis, *i.e.* at I, 50 cm from the mirror.

Finite Object. So far we have considered the images of point objects; an object of finite size can be treated as a series of points, and its image may be found as above, but it is simpler to make use of certain principles already derived. Thus in Fig. 260, *a*, AB is the object, and we wish to find the position of the image. It has already been shown that all rays from any point on the object will meet at a single point on the image; hence if we can follow out two rays from a point on the object, and find their point of intersection, we can find the position of the image of this point. Now a ray from A parallel to the principal axis is reflected back through the principal focus (ADF). Another ray from A, through the

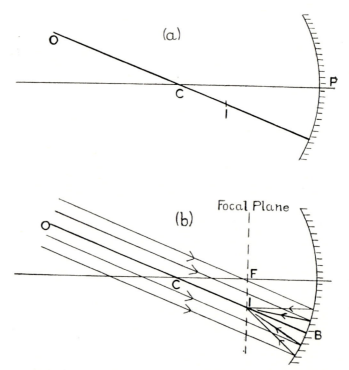

Fig. 259. Reflexion at concave mirror. (*a*) Point object on a subsidiary axis, OC. (*b*) Point object infinitely far away on the same subsidiary axis.

centre of curvature of the mirror, is reflected back along its own path, since it strikes the mirror normally. It intersects the first ray at A′ which is thus the image of A. Similarly by drawing rays parallel to the axis and through the centre of curvature from B, the position of B′ can be established, and thus the image of the object AB. The image in this case is inverted, real, and diminished. The construction for a convex mirror is indicated in Fig. 260, *b*; here the two rays diverge after reflexion and must be produced back to give the position of the virtual image.

The *linear magnification* for spherical mirrors is given by the ratio: *Size of Image/Size of Object*, and it is equal to v/u. If we extend our sign convention so that distances measured above the axis are positive and distances below negative, then the ratio: *Size of Image/Size of Object*, will be positive in the case of an

(a)

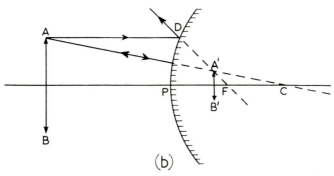

(b)

FIG. 260. Image of a finite object formed by reflexion at concave (*a*)
and convex (*b*) mirrors.

erect image and negative in the case of an inverted one. To make the magnification formula fit in with this convention, a negative sign must be put in front
of the ratio v/u:

$$Magnification = i/o = -v/u \qquad . \qquad . \qquad . \qquad . (2)$$

A Note on Real and Virtual Images. The image formed by a plane or
convex mirror is defined as a virtual image because the reflected rays from the
mirror *appear* to come from it. The image, A'B', formed by the concave mirror

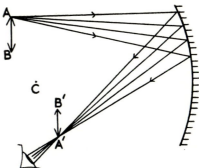

FIG. 261. Showing how a real image may be
viewed by the eye.

of Fig. 260, *a*, is defined as real because the reflected rays actually meet in a point at A′ and at B′ and, of course, at intermediate points on the line A′B′. If a screen is placed at A′B′ a clear image of AB will be formed on it because all light from A, for example, reflected by the mirror, comes to a point at A′ and no light from other parts of the object overlaps it. If the image is viewed directly, it will be seen distinctly, as with a virtual image, provided that the eye is not too close; this is because the rays, converging on A′ for example, cross and start to diverge as in Fig. 261, so that the eye is presented with rays diverging from A′ and treats the latter as a definite luminous point in space.

REFRACTION AT PLANE SURFACES

By refraction is meant the change in direction of light (or bending of the rays) which takes place when it passes from one transparent medium to another. Thus if PQ (Fig. 262, *a*) is the surface separating air above it from water below,

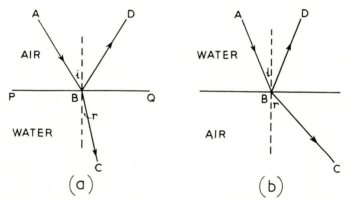

Fig. 262. Refraction and reflexion at an air-water (*a*) and a water-air interface (*b*).

the ray AB is refracted, or bent towards the normal at B; we may note, incidentally, that the ray AB gives rise to two rays on striking the surface, a reflected ray BD and the refracted ray BC. The change in direction of the ray on refraction takes place at the surface of separation.

According to whether the refracted ray is bent towards or away from the normal, the medium in which refraction occurs is said to be more or less *optically dense* than the medium in which the incident ray lies. Fig. 262, *a*, represents the passage of light from a medium of less to a medium of greater density, and Fig. 262, *b*, represents the reverse case, where the refracted ray is bent *away* from the normal. The angles made by the incident and refracted rays with the normal are called respectively the *angles of incidence* (*i*) and *refraction* (*r*).

The law defining refraction is called *Snell's Law*. It states that the refracted ray lies in the plane containing the incident ray and the normal, and that the angles of incidence and refraction are connected by the equation:

$$\text{Sin } i/\text{Sin } r = n \qquad . \qquad . \qquad . \qquad . \qquad . \quad (3)$$

where n depends on the optical characteristics of the two media through which the light passes and is called the *index of refraction*. The index of refraction at the air-water interface should be written: $_{air}n_{water}$ to indicate that the light passes from air to water.

The term *refractive index* is used for the special case where the first medium is a vacuum, *i.e.* the index of refraction at a vacuum-water interface is called the refractive index of water. The index of refraction is thus a characteristic of two media in contact, whilst the refractive index is a characteristic of a single medium. The optical density of air is very little different from that of a vacuum, so that the index of refraction of an air-water interface, for example, is generally treated as though the air were a vacuum, whence the index of refraction is taken as the refractive index of water.

It is often important to be able to derive the index of refraction of an interface from the refractive indices of the two media, *e.g.* if we have crown glass of refractive index 1·52 and flint glass of refractive index 1·66, we want to know how light will behave on passing from crown to flint glass, *i.e.* we want to know the index of refraction: $_{Crown}n_{Flint}$

The answer is given by the ratio :

$$\frac{n_{Flint}}{n_{Crown}}$$

where n_{Flint} and n_{Crown} are the refractive indices of the respective glasses. More generally, on passing from medium (1) to medium (2) the index of refraction: $_1n_2$ is given by the ratio: n_2/n_1. It follows that if we are given the index of refraction for passing from one medium to another, the index of refraction for passing in the reverse direction is the reciprocal of this value; *i.e.* $_2n_1 = 1/_1n_2$.

Parallel-Sided Plate. In Fig. 263, *a*, is shown the passage of a ray of light from air through a parallel-sided plane slab of glass. On passing into the glass the ray is bent towards the normal in accordance with Snell's Law; on emerging it is bent away from the normal to an equal extent, so that it emerges parallel with its original direction. In Fig. 263, *b*, the refraction of a pencil of rays from a luminous point is shown; it will be seen that there is no perfect

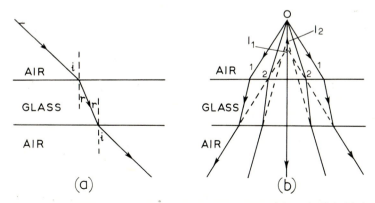

Fig. 263. (*a*) Behaviour of a single ray on passing through a parallel-sided slab of glass. (*b*) Behaviour of several rays.

image of a point, the rays (1) diverge, after refraction, from I_1 and the rays (2) from I_2. These effects of refraction are, however, not large, and with a window-pane, for example, an almost perfect image is obtained which appears to be at the same position as that of the object.

To an eye viewing the object obliquely, there is a lateral displacement of the image; this may be shown experimentally by viewing an iron bar through a

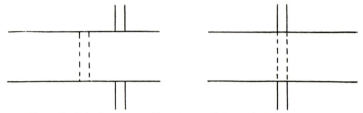

FIG. 264. Displacement of bar by parallel-sided plate glass with oblique vision.

thick glass plate so that part of the bar may be seen as an image through the plate whilst the rest is seen directly. If the line of vision is normal to the surface of the plate, the bar appears continuous—the image and object coincide in direction. With oblique vision, however, that part of the bar seen through the plate glass is shifted laterally (Fig. 264).

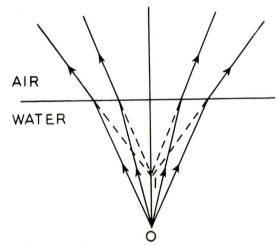

FIG. 265. The object O, viewed by an eye in air, appears to be at I.

When the eye observes an object *in* a different medium, the image appears to be closer to the eye than the object actually is, if the medium surrounding it is more dense than that surrounding the eye; *e.g.* a coin at the bottom of a tank of water appears closer to the eye than it actually is; the formation of the image in this case is shown in Fig. 265. If the pencil of rays is small it appears, after refraction, to diverge from a single point.

Total Internal Reflexion. If the refraction, at a water-air interface, of rays emanating from a luminous point in the water is constructed as in Fig. 266, it is found that as the angle of incidence is made greater and greater the emergent rays are inclined less and less to the surface until a point is reached where the emergent ray just grazes it; if the angle of incidence is increased beyond this value no emergent ray can be constructed, and the ray is said to be *totally internally reflected*; in other words, when this limiting value of the angle of incidence is exceeded, all the light obeys the simple law of reflexion instead

FIG. 266. Total internal reflexion.

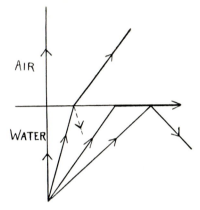

of a portion of it being refracted and a portion reflected. The limiting angle of incidence is called the *critical angle*, which is related to the index of refraction of the surface by the equation:

$$\text{Sin } i = {}_{water}n_{air}$$
$$= 1/{}_{air}n_{water}$$
$$= 1/n_{water} \qquad . \qquad . \qquad . \qquad . \qquad . \quad (4)$$

i.e. the sine of the critical angle is equal to the reciprocal of the refractive index of the medium.

The critical angle for a water-air interface is about 49°; for crown glass and air it is about 42°.

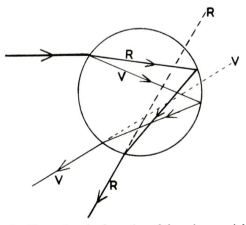

FIG. 267. Illustrating the formation of the primary rainbow.

The formation of rainbows results from total internal reflexion in raindrops; they are seen when the sun shines on falling rain and the observer must have his back to the sun; in favourable circumstances several bows may be seen— the brightest, the primary bow, is red on its outer edge and violet on its inner, and results from rays which have been refracted into and out of a drop of water, suffering a total internal reflexion between the two refractions as in Fig. 267. Because water has a different refractive index for each wavelength of light, the emergent rays from the raindrops make different angles to the eye according to their wavelength. It can be shown that, although the light emerges from many different raindrops in different positions, the final effect must be to make the red rays, for example, appear to come from a different point in the sky than that from which the violet rays appear to come. The secondary bow is formed by rays that have been twice internally reflected by the raindrops.

Prisms

A prism is defined for the purposes of geometrical optics as a figure bounded by three planes intersecting in three parallel straight lines.

The passage of a ray of light through a prism may be constructed on the

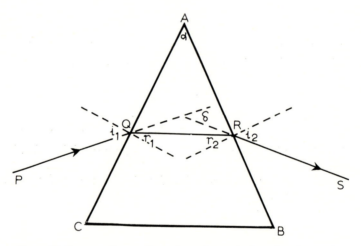

FIG. 268. Passage of a ray through a prism. α is the refracting angle A the refracting edge; δ the angle of deviation.

basis of Snell's Law as in Fig. 268 where the triangle ABC represents a section through a prism; the edge A is called the *refracting edge* and the angle α the *refracting angle*. It is clear that the ray emerging from the prism has been altered in direction, having been bent towards the *base* of the prism, BC. The extent of this change of direction is measured by the *angle of deviation*, δ, formed by producing the incident ray, PQ, forwards and the emergent ray, RS, backwards.

The angle of deviation is determined by three factors:

(*a*) The refractive index of the material of the prism.
(*b*) The angle of the prism (α).
(*c*) The angle of incidence of the ray considered.

When the angle of the prism and the angle of incidence are small, the deviation is given by the equation:

$$\delta = (n - 1)\, a \qquad . \qquad . \qquad . \qquad . \qquad . \ (5)$$

If the prism is made of glass, of refractive index about 1·5, *the deviation is equal to half the refracting angle.*

For a given prism, the smallest value that the deviation may have is called the *angle of minimum deviation*; it can be shown that a ray suffering minimum deviation makes equal angles of incidence and emergence ($i_1 = i_2$; Fig. 268).

Formation of the Image. For a well-defined image of a point object, O, to be seen (Fig. 269) the rays after refraction must appear to diverge from a

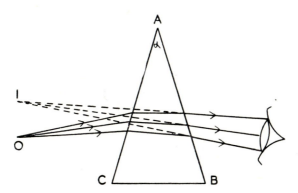

FIG. 269. Image formation by a prism.

single point, I. With a prism of finite angle this is theoretically impossible; the nearest approach to perfect image formation is given by choosing the conditions such that the central ray of the pencil of light forming the image is deviated to a minimum. Ophthalmic prisms are designed so that, as far as is possible, the central rays of pencils are minimally deviated.

Ophthalmic Use of Prisms. A prism may be used to correct a pathological deviation of one eye. Thus if, when the right eye (Fig. 270, *a*) converges on the point O, the left eye looks straight ahead, the images of the object O do not fall on the foveæ of the two eyes and diplopia results. The interposition of a prism between the object and the left eye, however, deviates the rays from O so that they fall on the fovea, F. A prism used in this way to counteract a divergent squint is referred to as a *"base-in"* prism. A *"base-out"* prism is required to correct a convergent squint as in Fig. 270, *b*.

Notation of Prisms. The employment of prisms in ophthalmology has led to the use of a number of different methods of indicating the strength of a prism. From a practical point of view we are interested in the apparent displacement of an object caused by the prism; thus in Fig. 271 the object at O appears to be at I; it has been displaced through an angle θ and this angle can be used to indicate the prism's strength; alternatively the linear displacement, *a*, at a fixed distance may be used. On the *prism dioptre* or *tangent centune* system, a prism of one prism dioptre strength (1$\varDelta$) displaces an object, 1 metre away, through 1 cm. This corresponds approximately to an angle, θ, of $\frac{1}{2}°$ hence on

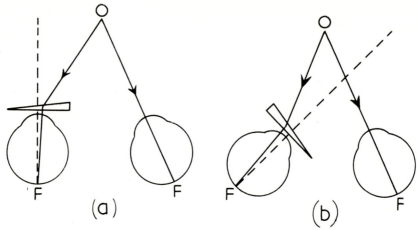

FIG. 270. (*a*) Use of base-in prism to compensate divergent squint.
(*b*) Use of base-out prism to compensate convergent squint.

the tangent centune system the angle of apparent displacement is measured in units of half a degree.

Ophthalmic prisms are used under conditions of minimum deviation, *i.e.* the central ray in the formation of the image is minimally deviated; the angle of minimum deviation can therefore be used as an index to the strength of an ophthalmic prism (expressed as °*d*), and it will be seen from Fig. 271 that δ and θ are approximately equal when the distance of the object from the prism is large (as occurs in practice). Since, however, the prism dioptre, used as the

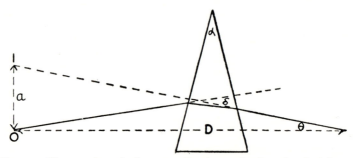

FIG. 271. The notation of prisms. α, refracting angle; δ, angle of minimum deviation; θ, angle of apparent deviation.

unit for measuring θ, is equivalent to half a degree, a prism of 5°*d* is equivalent approximately to one of 10Δ.

Under conditions of ophthalmic practice, equation (5) relating the refracting angle, α, to the deviation, δ, applies; consequently with glass prisms the strength can be indicated by the refracting angle, which is equal to twice the deviation. Thus a prism of refracting angle 10° (referred to as a ten-degree-prism) is equivalent to a 5°*d* prism, which, as we have seen, is equal to a 10Δ prism.

To make the confusion even worse the arc centune system is also employed; on this system the angle θ is indicated in units of a hundredth of a radian (∇);

this unit, however, is approximately equal to half a degree so that the difference between the prism dioptre and arc centune, or *centrad*, as it is called, is negligible.

Example. An object at 6 metres appears to be displaced 5 cm on placing a prism in front of the eye. What is the strength of the prism in $°d$?

1 cm subtends 1 prism dioptre at 1 metre.
5 cm subtend 5 prism dioptres at 1 metre.
5 cm subtend 5/6 prism dioptres at 6 metres.
The apparent deviation is 5/6 prism dioptres.
The strength in $°d$ is thus 5/12.

REFRACTION AT A SINGLE SPHERICAL SURFACE

The behaviour of rays of light on passing from one medium to another, when the surface of separation is spherical, is of great importance not only for the understanding of the properties of a lens, which, as we shall see, constitutes a special case, but for the study of the eye as an optical instrument.

In Fig. 272, *a*, PQR represents the spherical boundary between air and a more dense medium, *e.g.* water. The index of refraction of the surface, $_{air}n_{water}$, can be equated to the refractive index of water, n_{water}, or simply, n.

We may define the *centre, C, radius* of *curvature*, CP, *principal axis*, OPC, *pole*, P, and *principal section* in exactly the same way as for spherical mirrors.

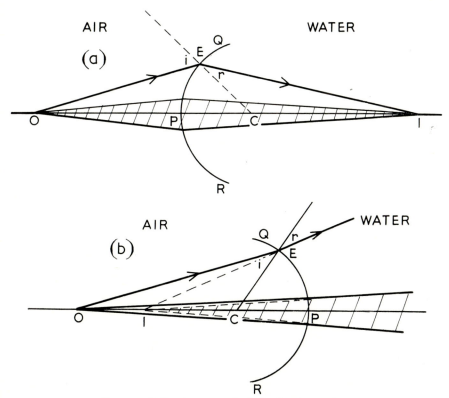

FIG. 272. Refraction at a spherical refracting surface.

If O is a luminous point on the axis, OE can be considered to be a ray emanating from it. This ray strikes the surface making an angle of incidence, i, with the normal (CE being a radius and therefore normal to the surface at the point E). The ray is refracted at E, being bent towards the normal, and strikes the axis at I. Now it may be shown by geometrical reasoning that, provided its angle of incidence is small, *any* ray from O will pass through the same point I; hence I is the real image of the point O provided that the rays from O make a small angle of incidence; this restriction may be conformed with by confining the rays crossing the surface to a thin, axial, pencil as illustrated in Fig. 272, *a*.

If the surface of separation is made concave to the air, the refracted ray OE diverges away from the axis; all other rays behave in the same manner, but so long as the pencil of rays is small they diverge from a definite point, I, the virtual image of the point O (Fig. 272, *b*).

For both convex and concave surfaces, the relative positions of image and object are given by the general formula:

$$n/v - 1/u = (n - 1)/r \qquad . \qquad . \qquad . \qquad . \ (6)$$

where u is the distance of the object from the surface, v the distance of the image, and r is the radius of curvature; the sign convention must be observed as with spherical mirrors

More generally, if the refractive index of the object-space is n_1 and that of the image-space is n_2, the formula becomes:

$$n_2/v - n_1/u = (n_2 - n_1)/r \qquad . \qquad . \qquad . \qquad . \ (6a)$$

Example. An object is placed 25 cm in front of a glass block which presents a convex spherical surface to the object. If the radius of curvature of the surface is 5 cm and the refractive index of the glass is 1·5, find the position of the image of the object formed in the glass block.

The distance of the object, u, is measured against the direction of the incident light and is therefore − 25 cm. r, the radius of curvature, is measured with the direction of the incident light and is + 5 cm.

Substituting in Equation (6) we get :—

$$1·5/v - 1/\text{-}25 = 0·5/5$$

or

$$1·5/v + 1/25 = 0·5/5$$

Whence $v = + 25$ cm, *i.e.* the image is real and 25 cm away from the surface, in the direction of the incident light.

The points O and I in Fig. 272 are described as *conjugate foci* and in any optical system any two points, chosen such that if the object is placed at one the image of it appears at the other, are called conjugate foci. If, in the case of the convex system in Fig. 272, *a*, we imagine that the object is placed at I, its image will be formed at O, since in geometrical optics we can always reverse a ray along its original path. We can thus imagine a divergent beam of rays from I striking this time a *concave* surface of separation and being made, by refraction, to *converge* on O. A convex surface thus causes divergent rays to converge on the axis when the rays pass from a less dense medium to a more dense one; a concave surface causes convergence if the rays pass from a more dense medium to a less dense. In dealing with spherical surfaces, therefore, we cannot state generally that a surface of a particular type, *e.g.* convex, will cause the incident rays to converge on the axis, unless we specify the change in the medium on passing from one side of the surface to the other.*

Principal Foci. With spherical mirrors the position of the principal focus was defined as the position of the image when the point object was infinitely far away on the axis, *i.e.* when the rays emanating from it could be considered parallel to the axis. A similar point can be defined in relation to the spherical refracting surface, and it is called the *second principal focus*; in the case of the convex system in Fig. 273, *a* (the rays are passing from a less dense medium to a more dense), the second principal focus represents a real point image ; with the concave system, on the other hand, the parallel rays after refraction diverge from the second principal focus which is thus on the "object side" of the surface.

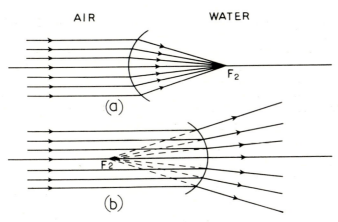

FIG. 273. The second principal focus.

The *first principal focus* is defined as the position a point object must have on the axis such that the rays, after refraction, run parallel to the axis; in this case the image is said to be at infinity. In the case of the convex system (Fig. 274, *a*) the first principal focus represents a real position of an object, whilst with the concave system (Fig. 274, *b*) the position of the object necessary to make the rays from it run parallel to the axis is virtual, in the sense that the rays before refraction must *converge on* the first principal focus. The reader should familiarize himself with this concept of a *virtual object*; the rays from any real point object on the axis will always diverge from this line, hence in order to make them run parallel with the axis after refraction they must meet a converging system as in Fig. 274, *a*; a diverging system can only make the rays diverge even more; in order that rays after refraction by such a divergent system may run parallel with the axis, they must clearly be converging on the refracting surface; the point to which they are converging is called the position of the

* In the concave system represented by Fig. 272, *b*, O and I are conjugate foci, hence an object at I produces an image at O. This does not mean, however, that a *real* object at I will produce an image at O. O and I are conjugate foci because the ray from O may be reversed along its path; when we say that the object is at I, light is considered to be coming from the right, *i.e.* I is the point to which rays *would have* converged in the absence of the spherical surface; they are bent away from the axis and meet at O, a real image. I is called a *virtual object*.

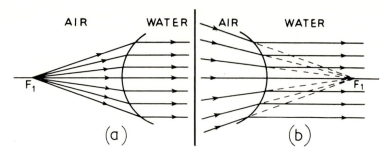

FIG. 274. The first principal focus.

virtual object. With the concave system of Fig. 274, *b*, the first principal focus is therefore on the "image side" of the refracting surface.

The distances of the first and second principal foci from the pole of the refracting surface are called the *first* and *second focal lengths* respectively, and are represented by the symbols f_1 and f_2. They may be evaluated in terms of r and n by substitution in Equation (6). Thus when u is equal to infinity, the distance of the image becomes the second focal length, f_2, *i.e.*:

$$n/f_2 - 1/infinity = (n - 1)/r$$

whence
$$f_2 = nr/(n - 1) \qquad . \qquad . \qquad . \qquad . \qquad . \quad (7)$$

Similarly, f_1 is given by the equation:

$$f_1 = -r/(n - 1) \qquad . \qquad . \qquad . \qquad . \qquad . \quad (8)$$

Inspection of Equations (7) and (8) tells us that f_1 and f_2 are related as follows:

$$f_2 = -nf_1$$

i.e. they are of opposite sign and therefore on opposite sides of the refracting surface, and for the special case considered, namely with the light passing from a less dense to a more dense medium, f_2 is greater than f_1 numerically.

The formula relating object- and image-distances becomes:

$$n/v - 1/u = -1/f_1$$
$$= n/f_2$$

or, more generally, if n_1 is the refractive index of the object-space and n_2 that of the image-space:

$$n_2/v - n_1/u = (n_2 - n_1)/r$$
$$= P' \qquad . \qquad . \qquad . \qquad . \qquad . \quad (9)$$

where P' is defined as the *surface power* and is equal to $(n_2 - n_1)/r$.

Object Off the Axis. As in the case of reflexion by spherical mirrors, the construction for determining the position of the image of a point object, not on the principal axis, is carried out by drawing a subsidiary axis through C, the centre of curvature of the surface, and the object. A narrow pencil of rays from the object converges to a point image (Fig. 275) whose distance from the surface may be calculated from Equation 6.

AIR   WATER

FIG. 275. Formation of the image of a point off the axis.

Finite Object. The position and nature of the image of a finite object may be determined by drawing a ray, AQ, parallel to the axis, which converges on the second principal focus, F_2, in the case of the convex surface (Fig. 276, *a*), or diverges from this point in the case of the concave surface. A second ray, through the centre of curvature, C, strikes the surface normally and hence passes through undeviated. The point of intersection of the rays, A_1, represents the image of A.

In the case of the convex surface the image is real, inverted, and diminished; with the concave surface the image is virtual, erect, and diminished.

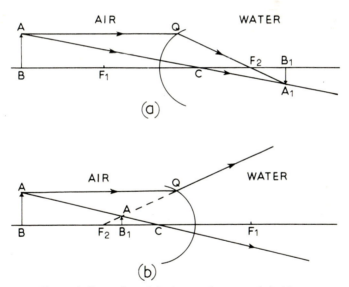

FIG. 276. Formation of the image of an extended object.

The magnification produced by a spherical refracting surface may be calculated from the formula:

$$i/o = v/n.u \qquad . \qquad . \qquad . \qquad . \qquad . \quad (10)$$

The position, nature, and magnification of the image depend on the position of the object; they may be determined by construction or by substitution in Equations (6) and (10); the construction of the image for typical positions of the object represents a useful exercise for the student.

The Aphakic Eye. We are now in a position to investigate the refraction of light by the eye from which the lens has been removed (*aphakic*). The cornea and aqueous humour have almost identical refractive indices, consequently we may treat the aphakic eye optically as a homogeneous medium of refractive index 1·3365, separated from air by a spherical surface of separation (Fig. 277). The radius of curvature of the human cornea may be taken as 7·8 mm.

f_1, the first focal length, is given by:

$$f_1 = -r/n - 1 = -7·8/0·3365 = -23·2 \text{ mm.}$$

f_2, the second focal length, is given by:

$$f_2 = -n.f_1 = 1·336 \times 23·2 = 31·2 \text{ mm.}$$

The first principal focus is thus 23·2 mm in front of the cornea whilst the second principal focus is 31·2 mm behind; this latter point is the position where parallel rays from a point infinitely far away on the axis form an image. The length of the eye, from the anterior to the posterior poles, is given as 24·4

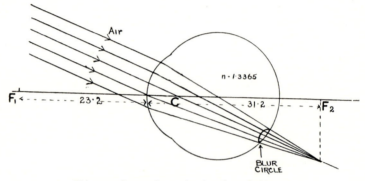

Fig. 277. Image formation by the aphakic eye.

mm, consequently a distant object forms an image some 6·8 mm behind the retina. The image of a distant object on the retina is thus badly blurred in the aphakic eye; this is best demonstrated by considering a pencil of light from a distant object as in Fig. 277; the intersection of the pencil with the retina constitutes a "blur circle" and this circle of finite size represents the image of a point on the object. A distinct image of an object is only obtained if all the rays from any point on it meet in a single point on the image; this is clearly not the case here and the image on the retina is blurred. It will be noted that the size of the blur circle depends on the size of the pencil of light entering the eye, and this depends on the size of the pupil; diminishing the pupil size thus tends to make an out-of-focus image less blurred.

Apparent Position of the Pupil. The pupil, when viewed in the intact eye, is seen as an image formed by refraction at the surface of the cornea. The rays of light, in these circumstances, pass from the more dense medium into the less dense and we must proceed carefully lest we become confused. In Fig. 278, QPR is the surface of the cornea and F_a and F_p are the focal points as calculated by treating the cornea as a spherical refracting surface of radius 7·8 mm.[*] F_a is thus 23·2 mm in front of the cornea and F_p 31·2 mm behind. A ray of light

[*] See footnote p. 411

parallel to the axis, passing from air into the eye, converges on to the second principal focus, F_p; on the principle of the reversibility of rays it follows that a ray, passing *out of the eye* such that it appears to have come from F_p, is refracted parallel to the axis; *i.e.* the ray from A, the top of the pupil, which strikes the surface at D, emerges parallel with the axis. Another ray from A, appearing to come from C, the centre of curvature, strikes the surface normally and passes out undeviated. These two emergent rays diverge from the point A′, obtained by producing them backwards; a similar construction gives the image of B at B′; A′B′ is thus the erect, magnified, virtual image of the pupil, AB.

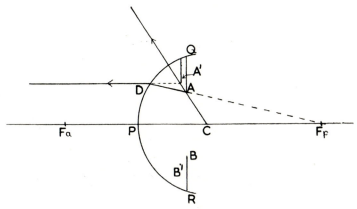

Fig. 278. Apparent position of the pupil. The pupil, AB, is seen as a magnified erect, virtual image, A′B′, closer to the cornea.

It will be seen later that the formation of the image of an object within the eye, as in Fig. 278, has some analogy with the formation of the image of an object within the first principal focus of a convex lens, *i.e.* the images are in both cases magnified and virtual. There is a fundamental difference, however, in that the image formed by the eye is closer to the surface than the object, whereas the reverse happens with the convex lens.

REFRACTION BY SPHERICAL LENSES

Thin Lenses

A spherical lens is a portion of a refracting medium bounded by two spherical surfaces (if one of the surfaces is plane, *e.g.* in a plano-convex lens, it is regarded as part of the surface of an infinitely large sphere). The various possible types of lens are shown in Fig. 279. The refractive properties of the spherical lens may best be deduced by applying the simple principles of ray construction used with a single spherical surface.

The Lens Formula. The simple bi-convex lens of Fig. 280 is bounded by two spherical surfaces of radii r_1 and r_2. The rays of light from a luminous point O, on the common principal axis, are refracted at the first surface and converge towards the point I′, the image of O which would be formed if no further refraction took place. At the second surface, however, the rays are

CONVEX   PLANO   CONVEX   CONCAVE   PLANO   CONCAVE
CONVEX MENISCUS   CONCAVE MENISCUS

FIG. 279. Types of lens.

made to converge further (they meet a concave surface and are passing from a more dense to a less dense medium), and they meet at the point I, the image of the object O formed by the lens as a whole. Now I may be considered as the image, formed by the second surface of the lens, of the virtual object, I′; the position of I′ can be calculated simply from the formula for a spherical surface (Eqn. 6) provided the refractive index of glass and the radius of curvature, r_2, are known; similarly, the position of I, the image of I′, can be calculated, this time making use of r_1. The position of the image O is thus determined by

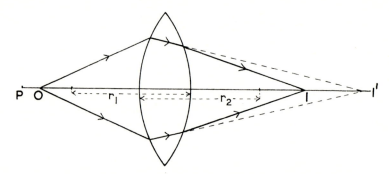

FIG. 280. The formation of the image of a point O by a biconvex lens. I′ is the image that would have been formed if refraction had occurred only at the first surface; I is the image resulting from refraction at both surfaces.

the radii of curvature and the refractive index of the lens. It should be noted that, for an accurate treatment, the thickness of the lens should also be known; if the lens is thin, its thickness is ignored and a simple formula relating the position of the object with the position of the image can be derived:

$$1/v - 1/u = 1/f_2$$

where u and v have the same meaning as before and f_2 is the second focal length of the lens. The second principal focus is defined, as before, as the position of the image of an infinitely distant point on the axis; its distance from the lens is f_2.

The bi-convex lens of Fig. 280 is a "converging lens" in the sense that it tends to bend incident rays, arising from a point object on the axis, towards the axis. The second principal focus is thus a real image of a distant point, and occurs on the right of the lens (Fig. 281, *a*). The first principal focus is the position of a point object on the axis such that its image is at infinity; it is on the left side of the lens and it may be shown that the first focal length is equal to the second focal length, *i.e.* $f_2 = -f_1$.

The bi-concave lens in Fig. 281, *b* is a "diverging lens"; parallel rays from an object infinitely far away on the axis thus diverge from the axis after refraction so that the second principal focus is a virtual image on the *left* of the lens; the first principal focus is the position of a virtual object, to the right of the lens, such that the rays, after refraction, emerge parallel to the axis.

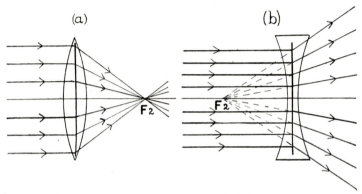

FIG. 281. The second principal focus.

For a converging lens the second focal length is thus, according to our sign convention, a positive quantity; with a diverging lens, on the other hand, it is a negative quantity. *It is customary to characterize a lens by the second focal length*; a converging lens is thus a positive or "plus" lens, a diverging one a negative or "minus" lens. The lens formula is generally written:

$$1/v - 1/u = 1/f \qquad . \qquad . \qquad . \qquad . \qquad . \qquad (11)$$

where *f* implies the second focal length.

Example. A converging lens of focal length 10 cm is placed 5 cm in front of an object. Where is the image ?

Here,
$$u = -5 \text{ cm}$$
$$f = +10 \text{ cm}$$
$$1/v - 1/-5 = 1/10$$
$$1/v = 1/10 - 1/5$$
$$= -1/10$$
i.e.
$$v = -10 \text{ cm.}$$

The image is ten centimetres away from the lens, on the same side as the object, *i.e.* it is virtual.

It is a simple matter to calculate, from the curvature of its surfaces, whether a lens of a given shape will act as a converger or diverger; in general, any lens whose thickness diminishes on passing from the centre to the periphery behaves as a converging lens, whilst a lens whose thickness increases on passing in this direction behaves as a diverging lens; thus lenses 1, 2, and 3 are converging (Fig. 279) whilst, 4, 5 and 6 are diverging.

Construction of the Image. The image of a finite object may be constructed by the methods of ray tracing described for mirrors and for a single spherical refracting surface. In this case, however, the undeviated ray is the ray passing

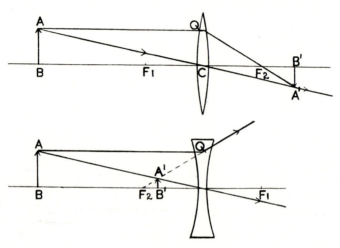

FIG. 282. Formation of the image of an extended object by a convex and a concave lens.

through the *centre of the lens* (the ray AC of Fig. 282); a ray AQ, parallel to the axis, passes through the second principal focus of a converging lens, and diverges from that of a diverging lens.

The linear magnification is given by the ratio:

$$\frac{Size\ of\ Image}{Size\ of\ Object} = \frac{i}{o} = \frac{v}{u} \qquad . \qquad . \qquad . \qquad . \ (12)$$

Relative Positions of Object and Image. The position and nature of the image, formed by a converging or diverging lens, for different positions of the object may be deduced quite simply from the lens formula. The results of a systematic calculation are given in Table 9.

Parallel Rays. The same arguments regarding parallel rays, brought forward earlier, may be applied to lenses; in view of the practical importance of the results we may briefly recapitulate the argument.

The second principal focus of a lens is the point to which rays from an infinitely distant point object, on the axis, converge (in the case of a converging lens) or from which they diverge (in the case of a diverging lens). Rays from an infinitely distant point are parallel with themselves and, if the point is on the principal axis, parallel with the latter. If the distant point object is not on the principal axis, the rays reaching the lens are parallel with themselves but are inclined to

TABLE 9

Nature of Lens	Nature and position of object	Nature and position of image
Converging.	Real. Outside $2f$.	Real. Inverted. Diminished. Between f and $2f$.
,,	Real. At $2f$.	Real. Inverted. Same size as object. At $2f$.
,,	Real. Between f and $2f$.	Real. Inverted, Magnified. Outside $2f$.
,,	Real. At f.	Virtual. Erect. Magnified. At infinity.
,,	Real. Inside f.	Virtual. Erect. Magnified. Farther from lens than object.
,,	Virtual. Any position.	Real. Erect. Diminished. Inside focus.
Diverging.	Real. Any position.	Virtual. Erect. Diminished. Inside focus.
,,	Virtual. Outside focus.	Virtual. Inverted. Outside focus.
,,	Virtual. Inside focus.	Real. Erect. Magnified. Further from lens than object.

the principal axis. They come to a focus, F'_2, on a subsidiary axis drawn through the centre of the lens and the distant object, and since the same formula applies to determining the relative positions of object and image on this subsidiary axis, F'_2 is in the same plane as F_2, so that the plane through F'_2 perpendicular to the principal axis is called the *focal plane* of the lens, and is the plane in which all rays from distant objects come to a focus (Fig. 283).

It will be seen that if the bundle of rays parallel to the principal axis are considered to emanate from the bottom point of a distant object, and the bundle

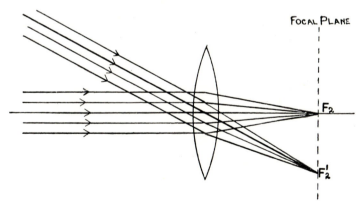

FIG. 283. The second focal plane.

of parallel rays, inclined to the axis, to emanate from the top of the same object, $F_2F'_2$ represents the image of the distant object; *e.g.* if the lens is directed at the sun so that the principal axis coincides with the bottom of the disc, F'_2 corresponds to the image of a point on the top of the disc.

Conversely, if we have an object at the first principal focus of a converging lens, the rays in any pencil, after refraction, all emerge parallel to one another. Thus if AB is the object, the image, as seen by the eye, is infinitely far away since the pencils from A and B are pencils of parallel rays (Fig. 284).

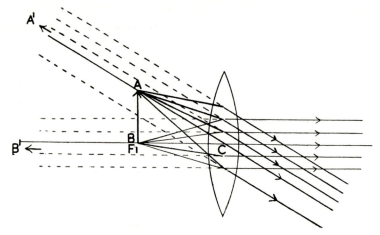

FIG. 284. The magnifying glass. The object AB is at the first principal focus of a convex lens. The image is at infinity.

The Magnifying Glass. Fig. 284 illustrates a special instance of the use of a convex lens as a magnifying glass—when the image is at infinity. If the object is within the first principal focus, as in Fig. 285, the virtual erect image, A'B', may be measured, and it is quite clear from the construction that it is magnified. This may be verified by calculation, since the magnification is given by:

$$\frac{\textit{Size of Image}}{\textit{Size of Object}} = \frac{v}{u}.$$

Here v is greater than u, so that the magnification is greater than unity. When the object is at the first principal focus (Fig. 284) the ratio v/u becomes

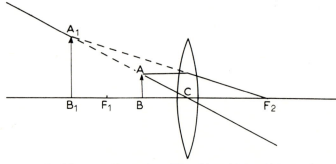

FIG. 285. The magnifying glass. The object AB is within the first principal focus.

∞/f, which is infinite, and it is clear that when dealing with parallel rays, the *linear magnification*, given by the ratio of the lengths of image and object, cannot be used to indicate the effective magnification. The apparent absurdity is due to the fact that the ratio indicating magnification only takes into account the lengths of object and image and not their distances from the eye; thus a very large object like the sun does not appear very large to the eye, because of its distance away. From the point of view of an image viewed by the eye, there-fore, we must choose a more satisfactory criterion of size, the *apparent size*, given by the ratio of its length by its distance away. Thus AB, A′B, A″B″ in Fig. 286 all have the same apparent size because the ratios: AB/BN, A′B′/B′N′, A″B″/B″N are equal (this amounts to the statement that AB, A′B′, etc. subtend the same angle at the eye).

This definition of apparent size permits the assignment of a definite magnitude to the size of an image at infinity. Thus the image of A (Fig. 284) lies on a subsidiary axis through A and the centre of the lens, infinitely far away to the left of the lens. The image thus subtends an angle ACB at the centre of the lens;

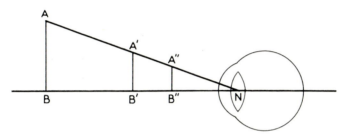

FIG. 286. Illustrating apparent size.

if the eye is very close to the lens, the image subtends approximately the same angle at it. It will be seen that the *object* subtends the same angle at the eye, namely, ACB. Thus the apparent sizes of object and image are the same and if the magnification were to be expressed as the ratio:

$$\frac{Apparent\ Size\ of\ Image}{Apparent\ Size\ of\ Object}$$

it would be unity. A convex lens is, nevertheless, a useful magnifying instrument when the image is at infinity, since it permits the perception of details indistin-guishable by the naked eye. The reason for this resides in the fact that the lens permits the eye to approach very close to an object and still obtain a distinct visual image. If the eye, without the lens, could see an object 1 cm away distinctly, placing a convex lens in front would not give any magnification. For comfortable observation an object is viewed at a distance of about 25 cm, consequently the *magnifying power* of the lens is defined by the ratio:

$$\frac{Apparent\ Size\ of\ Image}{Apparent\ Size\ of\ Object\ 25\ cm\ from\ Eye}$$

The apparent size of the object at 25 cm is given by the ratio: AB/25 cm and the apparent size of the image by the ratio: AB/BC (the image, even though infinitely far away, lies on the line AC, and by similar triangles the ratio of its height by its distance from the lens is always given by AB/BC).

The magnifying power of a convex lens depends on the position of the image; if this is 25 cm away, it is given by the expression: $1 + 25/f$, where f is the focal length in cm. If the image is at infinity it becomes: $25/f$.

Thus a convex lens, of focal length 5 cm, has a magnifying power of five when the object viewed is at the first principal focus.

Dioptric Power. The shorter the focal length of a lens the more strongly are rays made to converge or diverge after refraction; the reciprocal of the focal length is therefore the best measure of the refracting power of a lens. When the focal length is expressed in metres, the reciprocal of this value gives the *power* of the lens in *dioptres*. Thus a lens of $+ 5$ cm focal length has a power of $1/0 \cdot 05 = 100/5 = + 20$ *dioptres*.

When it is desired to express the power of a single spherical refracting surface in dioptres, we must remember that the first and second focal lengths are not equal. The dioptric power in these circumstances is given by: $P = n/f_2$ or $P = - 1/f_1$ where n refers to the index of refraction of the surface; when the object is in air, n becomes the refractive index of the medium separated from air by the curved surface.

When two thin lenses are placed in contact, their combined focal length, F, is given by:

$$1/F = 1/f_1 + 1/f_2 \quad . \qquad . \qquad . \qquad . \qquad . \quad (13)$$

or their combined power by : $\quad P = P_1 + P_2 \quad . \qquad . \qquad . \qquad . \quad (14)$

The Concept of Vergence. The concept of power, as a reciprocal of the focal distance, may be extended to other distances in optical systems. For example, the reciprocal of the radius of curvature, $1/r$, may be called the *curvature* of the surface, $1/r = C$ dioptres when the radius is expressed in metres. The

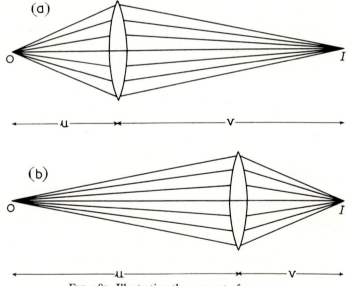

FIG. 287. Illustrating the concept of vergence.

distance of the object or image from the refracting surface is a measure of the degree of divergence or convergence of the rays in relation to this surface; thus in Fig. 287, *a*, where the object is close to the convex lens, the divergence of the rays from the object is high whilst the convergence of the rays to the image is small, by contrast with the opposite relationship in Fig. 287, *b*. The reciprocals of the object- and image-distances may be defined as the *vergence* of the rays belonging to the object and image respectively; thus $1/u = L$, the object vergence, and $1/v = L'$, the image vergence, once again expressed in dioptres when the distances are expressed in metres. The thin lens formula becomes:

$$L' - L = P \qquad . \qquad . \qquad . \qquad . \qquad (11a)$$

REDUCED VERGENCE

Where the refractive indices of the object- and image-spaces are different the concept of reduced vergence, introduced by Gullstrand, becomes useful. If n_1 is the refractive index of the object-space, the reduced vergence of the object is $n_1/u = L$, whilst the reduced vergence of the image is $n_2/v = L'$ when the refractive index of the image-space is n_2. The formula for the spherical refracting surface (Eqn. 9, p. 396) takes the form :—

$$L' - L = P' \qquad . \qquad . \qquad . \qquad . \qquad . \qquad (9a)$$

The Thick Lens

The formula relating the positions of object and image for a thin lens was obtained by considering the refraction at the first surface and treating the image so formed as the object for the next surface. The thickness of the lens was ignored. For most ophthalmic lenses the thin lens formula is quite adequate ;

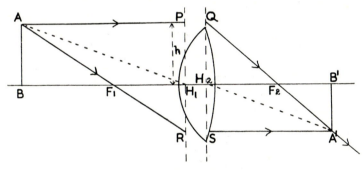

FIG. 288. Formation of the image by a thick lens. H_1 and H_2 are the principal points; F_1 and F_2 the principal foci.

however, in treating the eye as an optical instrument, where there are three main refracting surfaces, namely, the cornea and the anterior and posterior surfaces of the lens, the problem is very much simplified if we make use of concepts derived from the study of the thick lens.

The thick lens formula is:

$$1/V - 1/U = 1/F_2 \qquad . \qquad . \qquad . \qquad . \qquad (15)$$
$$= -1/F_1$$

where the distances U and V do not mean quite the same thing as before. V is the distance of the image from a certain point, the *second principal point*, whose exact position can be calculated from the curvatures of the surfaces, the thickness of the lens and the refractive index of its material. U is the distance of the object from another point, the *first principal point*, whose position can be similarly calculated. F_2 is the distance of the second principal focus from the

14—2

second principal point whilst F_1 is the distance of the first principal focus from the first principal point. The principal foci have the same meaning as for a thin lens, and the two focal lengths are equal but of opposite sign. The principal points and foci of a thick lens are shown in Fig. 288.

A plane at right-angles to the principal axis through H_1, the first principal point, is called the *first principal plane*; a similar plane through H_2 is called the *second principal plane*. These planes have the important property that any ray directed towards a point on the first, at a height h above the axis, leaves the second at the same height, h, above the axis. With this knowledge we can construct the image of an object formed by a thick lens, given the positions of the principal points and foci.

In Fig. 288, AB is the object. A ray parallel to the axis strikes the first principal plane at P and leaves the lens as if it had come from Q, on the second principal plane at the same height above the axis as P. It passes through F_2. A ray through F_1 strikes the first principal plane at R and leaves the lens as from S. The two rays intersect at A', which is the position of the image of A. A'B' is thus the image of AB.

Nodal Points. Listing introduced two other points, the *nodal points*, corresponding to the centre of a thin lens. Any ray directed towards the first point, N_1, leaves the system as though it had come from the second point, N_2, and parallel with its original direction. In the case so far treated, where the thick lens is surrounded by the same medium on both sides, the nodal points coincide with the principal points (thus in Fig. 288 AH_1 is parallel with H_2A'). When the media on opposite sides of the lens are different, the principal and nodal points do not coincide.

It will be noted that we are able to treat a thick lens, which consists of two refracting surfaces separated by a finite distance, as a single lens of focal length F only if distances are measured from certain calculated points. This really means that a single refracting surface cannot be found which will behave as a combination of two surfaces separated by a finite distance; instead we have to imagine that any ray is refracted at the first principal plane and then refracted again at a new surface, the second principal plane. It must be emphasized that these surfaces are entirely fictitious; refraction takes place at the surfaces of the lens, but the result of this refraction is the same as if it had taken place at these two surfaces with their special property described above.

REFRACTION BY THE EYE

The thick lens is only a special case of the more general Gaussian treatment of any number of spherical refracting surfaces with a common axis, separated from each other by finite distances. Each surface, separating two media of different refractive index, has its own principal plane, nodal point, and first and second principal foci; by a simple calculation these so-called *cardinal points* can be combined to give a single set, no matter how many surfaces there are; thus if we had six separate surfaces, their refracting properties could be described in terms of a pair of principal points, a pair of nodal points, and a pair of principal foci. It may be asked, what are the principal point and nodal point of a single spherical refracting surface, since we must know them in order to obtain the cardinal points of the combined surfaces. The nodal point is a point such that a ray, incident on the refracting system and directed towards this point, emerges after refraction parallel with its original direction; with a single spherical surface this point is equivalent to the centre of curvature; similarly, the principal point of a single surface is the pole and the principal plane corresponds to the surface itself.*

The Schematic Eye

Refraction by the eye may be approximately described as the effect of the bending of light at three spherical surfaces, refraction at the posterior surface of the cornea being ignored since the difference in refractive index of cornea and aqueous humour is not large. To obtain by the Gaussian treatment the cardinal points of the combined system of surfaces, we require to know their radii of curvature, indices of refraction, and distances apart. The experimental determination of these quantities, the *optical constants of the eye*, will be described later.

TABLE 10. *Cardinal points of the Eye* (Gullstrand)

Cardinal Point.						Distance from Ant. Surface of Cornea.
First principal point	.	.	.	.	.	1·35 mm
Second principal point	.	.	.	.	.	1·60 mm
First nodal point	.	.	.	.	.	7·08 mm
Second nodal point .	.	.	.	.	.	7·33 mm
First focal point	.	.	.	.	.	−15·7 mm
Second focal point .	.	.	.	.	.	24·4 mm

The positions of the cardinal points, calculated from Gullstrand's measurements of the optical constants,† are given in Table 10, where all positions are referred to the anterior surface of the cornea. As we should expect, the second principal focus, 24·4 mm behind the cornea, coincides with the retina of the normal eye.

The first focal length, F_1, is the distance of the first focus from the first principal point, *i.e.* ($-15\cdot7 - 1\cdot35$) or $-17\cdot05$ mm. The second focal length,

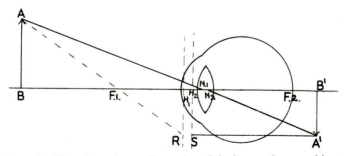

FIG. 289. The schematic eye. Formation of the image of a near object.

* It is, of course, a contradiction in terms to describe a spherical surface as a "plane"; the curvatures, however, are in practice sufficiently small to justify this idealization.
† For the purposes of this discussion it is sufficient to retain the classical figures of Gullstrand; the results of more recent and accurate determinations are described later.

F_2, is the distance of the second focus from the second principal point, *i.e.* $(24\cdot4 - 1\cdot6)$ or $+ 22\cdot8$ mm. The refractive power of the eye is given by:

$$P = -1/F_1 = n/F_2 = 58 \text{ dioptres}$$

The construction of the image of an object close to the eye is indicated in Fig. 289; a ray through the first focus strikes the first principal plane at R and leaves the second principal plane at the same height, parallel to the axis. A ray through the first nodal point emerges through the second, parallel with its original direction. The rays intersect behind the retina.

The formula relating positions of object and image is of the same type as for a single spherical refracting surface (Eqn. 6, p. 394), namely:

$$n/V - 1/U = n/F_2$$
$$= -1/F_1 \qquad . \qquad . \qquad . \qquad . \quad (16)$$

where distances are measured from the principal points.

The Reduced Eye

The first and second principal and nodal points of the schematic eye are quite close to each other; Listing simplified the treatment of the eye as a refracting system by choosing a single principal point, lying midway between the two actual points, and a single nodal point likewise situated between the real nodal points. This gives a principal point, H (Fig. 290), $1\cdot5$ mm behind the

Fig. 290. The reduced eye.

anterior surface of the cornea, and a nodal point, N, $7\cdot2$ mm behind the surface. The first and second focal lengths are now referred to a single principal point (as are also U and V) and have values of $-17\cdot2$ and $+22\cdot9$ mm respectively.

This simplification of the schematic eye corresponds, in effect, to the treatment of the eye as a *single spherical refracting surface*, the single nodal point representing the centre of curvature whilst the surface itself is a plane, passing through H, $1\cdot5$ mm behind the cornea. The radius of curvature of this surface is clearly $7\cdot2 - 1\cdot5 = 5\cdot7$ mm. Thus the reduced eye of Listing may be defined as a fictitious spherical surface, separating two media of refractive indices 1 and

1·336, situated 1·5 mm behind the cornea. Its radius of curvature is 5·7 mm and its anterior and posterior focal lengths are — 17·2 and 22·9 mm respectively.

The dioptric power of the eye is about + 58 D; the first focal length of the aphakic eye was found to be — 23·2 mm, corresponding to a dioptric power of + 43 D; consequently the lens contributes some 15 dioptres to the total power of the eye.*

Donders' Reduced Eye. Donders, in the interests of simplicity, treated the eye as a single surface 2 mm behind the cornea, with a radius of 5 mm and anterior and posterior focal lengths of 15 and 20 mm respectively. This is a gross simplification, but has the advantage that the appropriate figures can be remembered easily.

Image of Distant Object. Fig. 291 represents the normal reduced eye, refraction taking place at the plane H. The eye is looking at a distant object

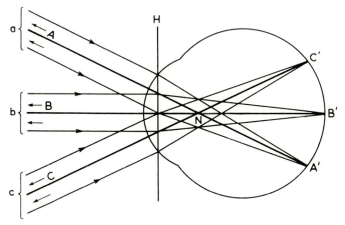

Fig. 291. Formation of the image of a distant object by the reduced eye.

such that the principal axis passes through its mid-point. A parallel bundle of rays, (*b*), from the centre of the object is refracted at H and comes to a point focus on the retina, R, which corresponds to the second focal plane. Another bundle, (*a*), from the top of the object is inclined to the principal axis and forms an image on the subsidiary axis through the top of the object and the nodal point, N. Since the rays are parallel they come to a focus at the intersection ot this subsidiary axis with the retina, at A'. In a similar way a bundle (*c*) from the bottom of the object comes to a focus at C'. The image is thus inverted.

Image of Near Object. The construction is identical with that described for a spherical refracting surface (p. 397); the image of AB (Fig. 292) falls behind the retina; for the image to fall on the retina the refracting power of the eye would have to be modified in the sense that the rays would have to be refracted more strongly; thus if the second principal focus,† F_p, were brought

---

* This does not mean that the *power of the lens* is + 15 D, since we cannot obtain the dioptric power of a refracting system by a mere summation of the powers of its constituents. Its power is given by Gullstrand as + 19·1 D (p. 459).
† In future the first and second principal foci of the eye will be referred to as the *anterior* (F_a) and *posterior* (F_p) foci respectively. This will save a great deal of confusion since the point in front of the eye we call the first principal focus may be regarded as the second

closer to the cornea (to F_p') the ray AP would be bent in more strongly and would intersect the ray through the nodal point* sooner, and thus produce a point image of A on the retina. This shortening of the focal length, or increase in the dioptric power, is called *accommodation*.

From Fig. 291 it will be clear that the size of the image, i, of a distant object of size o is given by substituting in the equation: $i/o = B'N/BN$, where B represents the position of the distant mid-point of the object. B'N is the distance of the retina

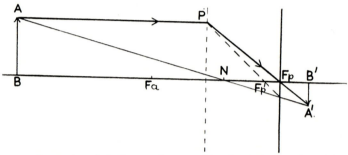

FIG. 292. Formation of the image of a near object by the reduced eye. Fp must come forward to F_p' if the image is to be formed on the retina.

from the nodal point, namely, $24\cdot4 - 7\cdot2 = 17\cdot2$ mm. Hence if d is the actual distance of the object from the nodal point, the size of the retinal image is given by: $i = \dfrac{17\cdot2 \times o}{d}$, remembering that d must be sufficiently large that rays from the object are, in effect, parallel.

AMETROPIA AND ACCOMMODATION

Ametropia

An unaccommodated eye, in which the image of a distant object falls on the retina, is called a normal or *emmetropic eye*. If the image of a distant object falls behind the retina, the eye is "long-sighted" or *hypermetropic*; if the image falls in front of the retina, the eye is "short-sighted" or *myopic*. The three conditions are indicated in Fig. 293 for the case of a point object infinitely far away on the axis.

We may thus regard the myopic eye, for example, as one that is too long for its refracting system, or alternatively as an eye of normal length but with an abnormally high dioptric power. Myopia can be due to either of these causes but it is thought that the more common condition is an abnormal length of the eye. Hypermetropia may be regarded as the condition in which the eye is too short or in which the dioptric power is inadequate.

Ametropia due to a defect in the axial length of the eye is referred to as *axial ametropia*, whereas ametropia due to a defective refractive power is called *refractive ametropia*.

principal focus if light is considered to be passing out of the eye. The same applies *mutatis mutandis* to the retina of the normal eye.
* A shortening of the focal length would be associated with a shift of the nodal point towards F_p.

The Far Point. In the myopic eye, parallel rays are brought to a focus in front of the retina. Our consideration of lenses has shown us that a real image of a real object is closest to the refracting surface when the incident rays are parallel, *i.e.* when the real object is at infinity. To produce an image farther away from the refracting surface we must bring the object closer, *i.e.* the eye must be presented with *divergent*, not parallel, rays. Hence if an object is brought from

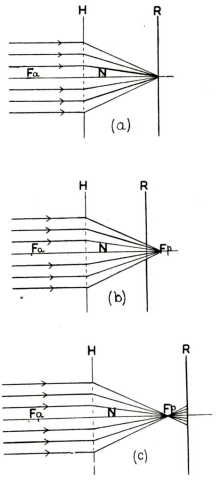

FIG. 293. (*a*) Emmetropic, (*b*) hypermetropic, and (*c*) myopic eyes.

a large distance closer and closer to a myopic eye, a point is reached—the *far point*, or *punctum remotum*—at which the object is seen distinctly.

The distance of the far point from the eye is generally symbolized by the small letter *r*; *r* is thus the distance of an object from the completely relaxed eye at which it can be seen distinctly.

For the emmetrope, the far point is at infinity; for the myope it is a finite distance in front of the eye (Fig. 294, *a*), and in accordance with the sign convention its distance from the principal plane has a *negative* value.

In the hypermetropic eye, parallel rays are brought to a focus behind the retina, *i.e.* the rays, after refraction, do not converge sufficiently to produce an image on the retina. To correct this, we must present the eye with *converging* rays. This cannot, of course, be achieved by moving a real object towards, or away from, the eye, since rays from any object are always divergent. A lens must therefore be used to impose the necessary convergence on the rays from an object if the latter is to be seen clearly by the completely relaxed hypermetropic eye. This is equivalent to presenting the eye with a *virtual object*, and the far point of a hypermetropic eye is, consistently with our definition, the position

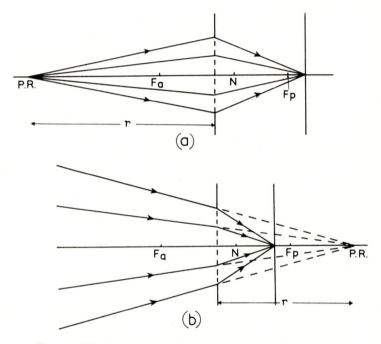

Fig. 294. The far point. (*a*) Myopic eye. (*b*) Hypermetropic eye.

of a virtual object such that its image falls on the retina in the absence of accommodation. The position of the far point is shown in Fig. 294, *b*; the rays falling on the eye are convergent and would, in the absence of the eye, meet at P.R. After refraction by the eye they come to a focus on the retina. The distance of the far point, P.R., from the principal point of the eye is indicated by *r* once again. This time it has a positive value.

The Ametropic Error. The conception of the far point provides an easy method of assessing the strength of lens required to correct an ametropic condition. Thus, if an individual has a far point of — 2 metres, our problem is to permit him to see infinitely distant objects as though they were 2 metres distant, since they would then produce clear images on the retina. We require, therefore, a lens which, when placed in front of the eye, will give an image of distant objects at 2 metres from the principal point, *i.e.* in the lens formula:

$$1/v - 1/u = 1/f$$

$u = \infty$
$v = -2$ m. Hence $-\frac{1}{2} = 1/f$
f = – 2 metres; P $= -\frac{1}{2}$ **Dioptres.**

A concave lens of focal length 2 metres, placed at the principal point of the eye, would produce an image of a distant object at the far point.

In general, if *r* is the distance of the far point in metres, *r* is the focal length of the lens which must be placed at the principal point of the eye to correct it for distant vision, and 1/*r* is the dioptric power of the lens.

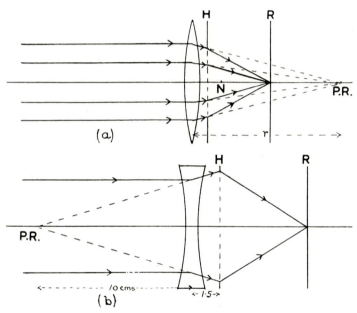

Fig. 295. (*a*) Correction of hypermetropia. (*b*) Correction of myopia.

With a hypermetrope, as we have seen, it is not possible to find a real position of the object to give a distinct image on the retina; the far point can therefore only be found by placing convex lenses in front of the relaxed eye until the necessary convergence has been imposed on the rays, emanating from a distant object, to permit them to come to a focus on the retina. The distance of the far point from the principal point of the eye, *r*, is thus given by the focal length of the necessary correcting lens (Fig. 295, *a*).

The reciprocal of *r*, expressed in metres, is symbolized by R; it is the inverse distance of the far point from the principal point of the eye, expressed in dioptres, or the *dioptric value of the far point distance*. R is thus the measure of the refractive error of the eye, and is referred to as the *static refraction* or the *ametropic error*.

Spectacle Point. In the treatment of ametropia the distances have been correctly referred to the principal point of the eye, and the refractive error has been assessed in terms of the correcting lens that must be placed at the principal point. Whereas this gives a true picture of the refractive error, it is inadequate as a measure of the necessary strength of spectacles, owing to the fact that spectacles are worn at a distance in front of the eye, at the so-called *spectacle point*, which is, on the average, 12–13 mm in front of the cornea.

Thus let us suppose that the far point of a subject is 10 cm in front of the principal point; we require the strength of lens, placed at the spectacle point (say, 1·5 cm in front of the principal point) which will make the rays from a distant object appear to diverge from the far point.

The state of affairs is illustrated in Fig. 295, *b*; the far point, P.R., is at the second principal focus of the concave lens whose focal length is clearly: — (10

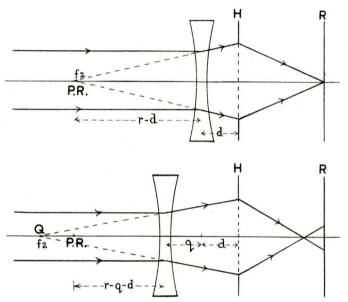

FIG. 296. Illustrating the change in effectivity of a concave lens on moving it away from the eye.

—1·5) = — 8·5 cm, or — 0·085 m. The dioptric power of the correcting lens is thus: — 1/0·085 = — 11·75 D. The ametropic error is given by $1/r$ in metres, *i.e.* — 1/0·1 = — 10 D. The strength of the correcting lens, worn at the spectacle point, is called the *spectacle correction*; in this case it is — 11·75 D.

Effectivity. The general effects of moving a lens farther away from, or closer to, the eye may now be deduced. In Fig. 296, we may consider a concave lens, *d* metres in front of the principal point of the eye. A parallel bundle of rays from an infinitely distant object is made to diverge from the far point of the myopic eye, P.R., and thus comes to a focus on the retina, R. The power of the lens is clearly $1/(r - d)$.* If the lens is now moved a distance q away from the eye, the rays after refraction by the lens diverge from a point Q, more distant than the far point, so that the eye fails to bring them to a focus on the retina.

* The distances r, d, and q are all negative; $(r - d)$ is therefore a negative quantity less than r.

The eye is "under-corrected" and it is said that the *effectivity* of the lens has been reduced by moving it away from the eye. A new lens of focal length equal to the distance $(r - d - q)$, is necessary. If the lens is brought a distance q *closer* to the eye, it will be seen, on the same reasoning, that the effectivity is increased.

The convex correcting lens is treated in Fig. 297; a parallel bundle of rays is caused to converge on the far point, P.R., by the convex correcting lens of focal length equal to $(r - d)$.* Moving the lens a distance q from the eye causes the rays to converge on a point Q, closer to the retina, R, than P.R.; as a result, the image formed by the eye falls too close to the cornea and the eye is over-corrected. A lens of focal length $(r - d - q)$ is now sufficient for correction, *i.e.* one of less power. The effectivity of a convex lens is therefore increased

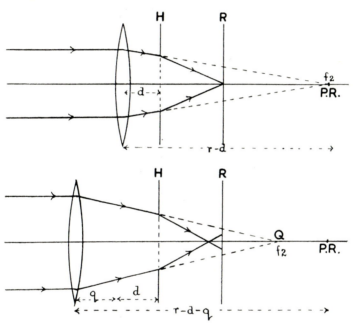

FIG. 297. Illustrating the change in effectivity of a convex lens on moving it away from the eye.

by moving it away from the eye, and conversely, it is decreased by bringing it closer in.

In general, if a lens of focal length f, at a given position in front of the eye, is required to correct it, a lens of focal length $(f - q)$ is required when the lens is moved a distance q either towards or away from the eye, the value of q being given a negative sign if the direction of movement is away from the eye.

Size of Retinal Image in Corrected Ametropia. We have so far considered the use of correcting lenses from the point of view of moving the image, formed by the eye, forwards or backwards; it is important to know whether the size of the image on the retina is affected by the use of a correcting lens; when the

* Here, r is positive whilst d and q are negative; $(r - d)$ is therefore a positive quantity greater than r.

refractive error is not the same in the two eyes (*anisometropia*) this consideration becomes important.

Fig. 298, *a* represents an axially hypermetropic eye; a parallel bundle of rays from the top of a distant object is brought to a focus at A'; a bundle from

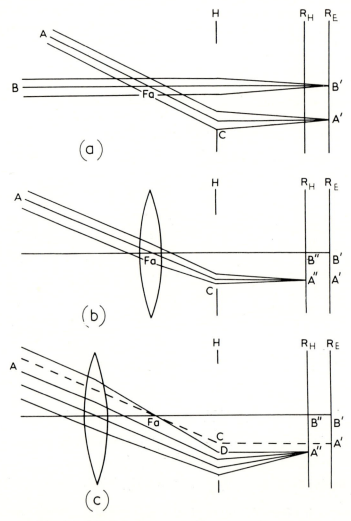

FIG. 298. The size of the image in corrected hypermetropia: (*a*) The image of a distant object is formed behind the hypermetropic retina. (*b*) A convex lens at F_a brings the image into the plane of the retina keeping the size the same. (*c*) A correcting lens beyond F_a produces a larger image.

the bottom of the object (on the axis) comes to a focus at B'. B'A' is the inverted image of the distant object; it falls behind the retina, R_H, in the plane R_E, *i.e.* where the emmetropic retina would be. The size of the image of A'B' is clearly determined by the ray through F_a (the anterior focus of the eye) which, after refraction, runs parallel with the axis.

A convex correcting lens is now placed at F_a; as a result, the image is brought forward into the plane of the hypermetropic retina, R_H. The size of the image is determined, once again, by the ray through F_a, and since this passes through the correcting lens undeviated, the size of the image formed on the hypermetropic retina is the same as that which would have been produced on the emmetropic retina. By a similar construction it can be shown that the image formed in corrected myopia is of the same size as that formed in the emmetropic eye, provided that the correcting lens is at the anterior focus of the eye.

In Fig. 298, *c* the correcting lens has been placed in front of F_a. In the absence of the lens the dotted ray through F_a would strike the principal plane of the eye at C and would determine the size of the image, B′A′, *i.e.* the size of the emmetropic image. In the presence of the lens, the ray through F_a converges more strongly on the axis, as a result of refraction, and consequently strikes the principal plane of the eye at D, lower down than C; it runs parallel to the axis of the eye and strikes the retinal plane, R_H, at A″. All other rays meet here, since the eye is corrected. B″A″ is therefore the size of the image when the correcting lens is in front of the anterior focus of the eye; it is larger than the image formed in the emmetropic eye. Moving the lens forwards therefore increases the size of the retinal image; moving the lens backwards decreases it. By a similar

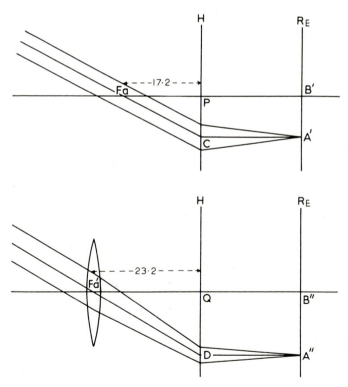

FIG. 299. The size of the image in corrected aphakia. *Above:* The image of a distant object formed by the normal emmetropic eye. *Below:* The image of the same object formed by the corrected aphakic eye, the lens being at $F_a′$, the anterior focus.

construction it can be shown that the reverse effects are obtained with a concave correcting lens.

Size of Image in Corrected Aphakia. Aphakia is a condition of refractive hypermetropia. In Fig. 299 we have, as before, the passage of a bundle of rays giving the image, A′B′, of a distant object on the emmetropic retina. The size is given by the length B′A′ or by PC. In the same figure the image of the object is formed by the aphakic eye, with an appropriate correcting lens at its anterior focus, F_a'. Because the anterior focal length of the aphakic eye is greater than that of the normal (− 23·2 mm compared with − 17·2 mm) the size of the image B″A″, which is equal to QD, is clearly larger than that in emmetropia, PC. A comparison shows that the sizes are proportional to the anterior focal lengths:

$$\frac{\textit{Size of Image in Corrected Aphakia}}{\textit{Size of Image in Emmetropia}} = \frac{23\cdot2}{17\cdot2} = 1\cdot35$$

i.e. the image in corrected aphakia is 1·35 times as big as that in the emmetropic eye.

Accommodation

Amplitude of Accommodation. We have seen (p. 412) that an increase in the dioptric power of the eye is necessary to bring near objects in focus; as an object is moved closer and closer to the eye, at a certain point—the *near*

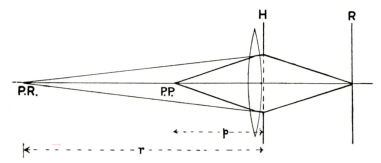

Fig. 300. The amplitude of accommodation.

point of accommodation—the eye can no longer increase its dioptric power and the object becomes indistinct. It will be remembered that the far point is the position of an object such that its image is formed on the retina of the completely relaxed eye. We may define the *amplitude of accommodation*, therefore, as the difference in refracting power of the eye in the two states of complete relaxation and maximal accommodation. Thus if Q is the refracting power of the eye in maximum accommodation, and S its power when completely relaxed, the amplitude, A, is given by:

$$A = Q - S \qquad . \qquad . \qquad . \qquad . \qquad . \ (17)$$

Since the amplitude is a *difference* in refracting power of the eye in two conditions, it is not necessary to know its actual power in either; the amplitude may be calculated from the near and far points quite simply, as follows.

In Fig. 300 the near and far points of a myopic eye are shown. It is required to find how much the power of the eye is increased when an object, formerly at the far point, is seen distinctly at the near point. To do this we can imagine that the eye, instead of accommodating, has remained in the relaxed condition and that the increased dioptric power to permit distinct vision of the object at the near point has been provided by a converging lens. The power of this lens would represent the increase in dioptric power of the eye in maximum accommodation. The completely relaxed eye sees distinctly an object at the far point; the lens must be chosen, therefore, of such a strength that it will form an image of an object, situated at the near point, at the far point. In the lens formula:

$$1/v - 1/u = 1/f$$

$v = r$, where r is the distance of the far point in metres,
$u = p$, where p is the distance of the near point in metres.

Thus $$1/r - 1/p = 1/f.$$

If we let $1/r$ in metres be R; $1/p$ be P; the power of the lens, A, is given by:

$$R - P = A \qquad . \qquad . \qquad . \qquad . \qquad . \quad (18)$$

R may be called the *dioptric value of the far point distance*; P the *dioptric value of the near point distance*, and A is the amplitude of accommodation, in dioptres.

This relationship between R, P, and A has been derived from the lens formula, consequently it will only hold if the usual sign convention is applied. Thus in the case of the myope R and P are both negative.

Near Point in Different Refractive Conditions. As examples of the application of this formula, we may choose three subjects with the same amplitude of accommodation, namely, 12 D; the first is an emmetrope, the second a hypermetrope of + 6 D and the third a myope of − 8 D.

Emmetrope. The far point is at infinity, whence R = o. From Equation (18) we have:

$$o - P = 12.$$

i.e. P = − 12 D; p = − 1/12 metres = − 8·33 cm.
The near point is **8·33 cm** in front of the eye.

Hypermetrope. The dioptric value of the far point distance is the ametropic error, hence R = + 6 D.
From Equation (18) we have: 6 − P = 12,
i.e. P = − 6 D; p = − 1/6 metres = 16·7 cm.
The near point is **16·7 cm** in front of the eye.

Myope. Here R = − 8 D.
From Equation (18) we have: − 8 − P = 12
i.e. P = − 20 D; p = − 1/20 metres = − 5 cm.
The near point is **5 cm** in front of the eye.

Thus the myope has the shortest near point distance; this is to be expected since no accommodative effort is required until the object has been brought in to his far point; the hypermetrope, on the other hand, in order to see distant objects clearly, must accommodate; for example, in the case considered, he uses 6 dioptres of his total amplitude in order to bring images of distant objects on his retina.

Hypermetropia and Accommodation. It will be evident that the hypermetrope can see distant objects by accommodating, provided that his amplitude of accommodation is adequate to overcome his refractive error. If the error is sufficiently great, or if the amplitude is sufficiently restricted, distant objects cannot be seen clearly without a positive correcting lens, but so long as he has some accommodative power, the hypermetrope can see distant objects clearly with a *weaker* lens than that necessary to correct his hypermetropia fully. It is therefore customary to divide the hypermetropia into several parts.

The weakest positive lens, required to give distinct vision of distant objects, is said to measure the *absolute hypermetropia (Ha)*; it is that part of the hypermetropia the subject is unable to correct by accommodation.

The strongest positive lens tolerated for distant vision measures the extent to which the hypermetrope can relax his accommodation, and therefore indicates his *total hypermetropia, (H)*. It is found in general, however, that the hypermetrope cannot relax his accommodation completely without the use of a cycloplegic, *i.e.* that there is a certain amount of *latent hypermetropia (Hl)*. The total hypermetropia is thus only given by the strongest positive lens tolerated when the accommodation is completely relaxed by a cycloplegic. The strongest positive lens tolerated in the absence of a cycloplegic is called the *manifest hypermetropia (Hm)*; the difference between the total and the manifest hypermetropia is the latent hypermetropia. Finally, the difference between the manifest and absolute hypermetropia is called the *facultative hypermetropia (Hf)*, it is the hypermetropia that can be voluntarily overcome.

Thus if the strongest positive lens tolerated by a hypermetrope with a cycloplegic is $+ 9$ D, his total hypermetropia is $+ 9$ D. If, without a cycloplegic, it is $+ 8$ D, the manifest hypermetropia is $+ 8$ D, and the latent hypermetropia is $9 - 8 = + 1$ D. If the weakest positive lens tolerated without a cycloplegic is $+ 2$ D, the absolute hypermetropia is $+ 2$ D, and the facultative hypermetropia is $8 - 2 = + 6$ D.

Range of Accommodation. The *range of accommodation* is defined as the difference between the near and far point distances:

$$p - r = a \qquad . \qquad . \qquad . \qquad . \qquad . \quad (19)$$

For the myope, considered above, p was found to be $- 5$ cm. R, the dioptric value of the far point distance, was $- 8$ D, whence $r = - 1/8$ metres, or $- 12 \cdot 5$ cm. The range is thus:

$$- 5 + 12 \cdot 5 = 7 \cdot 5 \text{ cm}$$

In the case of the emmetrope the far point is at infinity, so that the range is infinite; with the hypermetrope the far point is behind the eye, *i.e.* a certain "distance beyond infinity" and the range must likewise be considered to be infinite. The conception of the range of accommodation is thus not a very useful one, and the accommodative power should always be indicated by the *amplitude* of accommodation.

NON-SPHERICAL LENSES AND ASTIGMATISM

The Cylindrical Lens

Asymmetrical Refraction. The curved refracting surfaces, so far considered, have been portions of spheres so that refraction has been symmetrical about the principal axis. By this we mean that if we work out the refraction of a ray in any one plane, we know that the refraction of a similar ray in any other plane will be identical. Thus in all constructions we have confined attention to the rays in the plane of the paper; the rays from a point, striking a lens, actually form a cone in three dimensions, and it is only because we know that

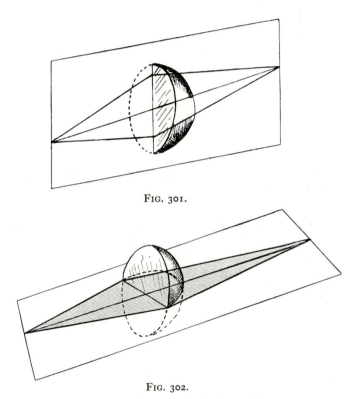

FIG. 301.

FIG. 302.

FIGS. 301 and 302. A vertical plane and a horizontal plane intersect a spherical lens in the arc of a circle.

the rays not in the plane of the paper will behave in the same way as similar rays in the plane that we can state that they will all meet in the image. The same thing is meant when we state that the curvature of a spherical lens is the same in all meridians; any plane through the optic axis intersects the lens in the arc of a circle of the same curvature; this is indicated in Figs. 301 and 302, where a vertical and horizontal plane intersect a spherical lens.

A cylindrical lens is one whose surfaces may be represented as portions of cylinders (Fig. 303). The axis of a cylinder is a line running through its centre, and the axis of a cylindrical lens may be taken as a line running through it, parallel to the axis of the cylinder of which it forms a part (Fig. 303). A principal optic axis of a cylindrical lens is a line, perpendicular to the axis, passing through the centre of curvature. Since a cylinder can be considered to be made up of a large number of circles, one on top of the other, we can have any number of principal optic axes.

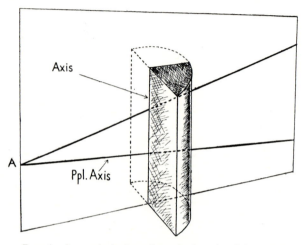

Fig. 303. Rays in the vertical plane through the axis of the cylindrical lens are undeviated.

A cylindrical lens is clearly not symmetrical about its optic axis; a plane through the axis of the cylinder, as in Fig. 303, intersects the surface in a straight line; rays in this plane, therefore, meet a linear, as opposed to a curved surface, and therefore pass through the lens finally undeviated. We may say that there is no curvature in the meridian parallel to the axis. A plane at right-angles to the axis of the cylinder intersects the latter in the arc of a circle (Fig. 304) so

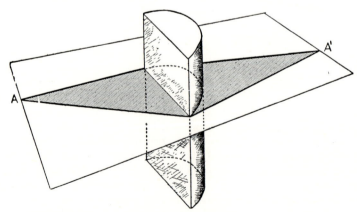

Fig. 304. Rays in the plane at right-angles to the axis are made to converge on the point A'.

that rays in this plane are deviated as by a spherical lens. We may say that the lens has curvature in the meridian at right-angles to its axis.

Image Formation. To understand the formation of the image of a luminous point by a cylindrical lens, we have only to consider the behaviour of rays in these two mutually perpendicular planes; rays in all other planes may be considered to be partly in one, and partly in the other of these two, and will therefore not modify the shape of the image formed by the rays in these mutually

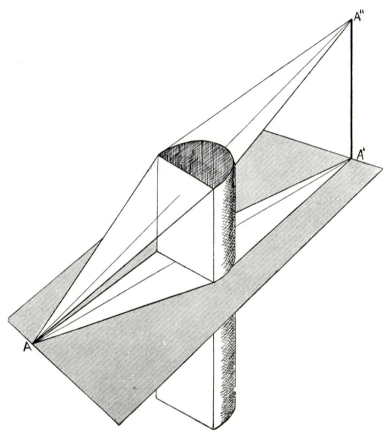

FIG. 305. Illustrating the formation of a line image of a point object by a cylindrical lens.

perpendicular planes. The rays in the vertical plane through the axis (Fig. 303), emanating from A, pass through undeviated; the rays in the horizontal plane (Fig. 304) are brought to a point focus at a distance determined by the curvature in this meridian, namely at A'. If Figs. 303 and 304 are combined mentally, it will be seen that the image of A at A' becomes a vertical straight line, *i.e.* a line parallel with the axis of the cylinder.

This is made clearer by Fig. 305; here the refraction in two planes is shown in perspective. The lower plane is horizontal through A, and the rays are brought to a point focus at A' on the principal axis through A; the upper plane is inclined upwards, and the rays in this plane are bent inwards, but not downwards as they would be by a spherical convex lens. They thus converge to the point A″ vertically above A′. A′A″ is therefore a part of the line image of A.

Cylindrical lenses may be plano-convex, convexo-convex, plano-concave, etc. The important feature of a cylindrical lens is that it modifies the degree of convergence or divergence (the "vergence") of rays striking it, *only in the plane at right-angles to its axis*. The vergence in the plane parallel with the axis remains unchanged.

The Toric Lens

The cylindrical lens is a special case of an *astigmatic lens*—a lens which fails to give a point image of a point object; any lens in which the curvatures in different planes are not equal will be astigmatic, but the only other case with which we need concern ourselves here is the lens of *toric surface*—a lens in which the curvatures in two meridians at right-angles are different. A toric surface is defined as the surface formed by the revolution of a circle about a line parallel with a diameter. For example, the surface of a tyre inner-tube could be formed by rotating a circle of diameter d, equal to the cross-sectional diameter of the tube, about a line distant R from the circle. If we hold the inner-tube horizontally, the curvature in the vertical meridian is given by the curvature of the small circle whereas the curvature in the horizontal meridian is given by that of the large circle of radius R.

We may deduce the refracting properties of a toric surfaced lens in the same way as for a cylinder; instead, however, of treating the components of rays in one plane as being undeviated, we must imagine that rays in all planes are deviated, but that their components in two mutually perpendicular planes converge on (or diverge from) two different points.

Image Formation. Let us consider a plano-toric convex lens with a radius of curvature in the horizontal plane, R_H, and a radius of curvature in the vertical plane R_V, and let us assume that R_H is greater than R_V, *i.e.* that the *curvature* or *dioptric power* in the horizontal meridian is less than that in the vertical (Fig. 306).

OC and OD are two rays in the vertical plane through the optic axis; they meet at I_V. A pair of rays in the horizontal plane, OA and OB, meet at I_H.

Since the dioptric power is greater in the vertical meridian, the rays OC and OD converge to the point I_V sooner than the rays OA and OB converge to I_H. The refraction of rays in intermediate planes may be treated by resolving

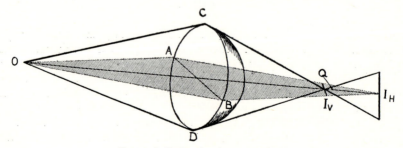

FIG. 306. Refraction by a toric lens.

them into the two planes we have just considered, and the result is that at I_V a horizontal line is formed, due to the fact that rays in the vertical plane have come to a focus whilst those in the horizontal plane have not. At I_H the rays in the horizontal plane have come to a focus whilst those in the vertical plane have diverged from I_V, so that at I_H a vertical line is formed.

At the point Q, on the axis of the lens, the degree to which the rays in the vertical plane have diverged from the axis is equal to the degree to which the rays in the horizontal plane have converged on it; the image of O on a screen placed at Q is therefore a circle, referred to as the *circle of least confusion*; it is the nearest approach to a point image of the point object O. If the screen is moved closer to, or farther from, the lens, the image becomes oval. It is not difficult to envisage the shape of the cross-section of the beam at any point; at I_V it is a line; beyond I_V in the direction of Q the rays in the horizontal plane converge, whilst those in the vertical plane diverge, so that the cross-section is an ellipse with its long axis horizontal; at Q the cross-section is a circle; beyond Q it is an ellipse with its long axis vertical; at I_H it is a vertical line. The shape of the emergent beam through a toric lens is called *Sturm's conoid*. It should be noted that the first line-image (I_V of Fig. 306) is parallel to the meridian of least curvature whilst the second line-image is at right-angles to this meridian.

A toric lens may be made up of two lenses in contact, where one is a cylinder and one a sphere, or alternatively of two cylinders of unequal power with their axes at right-angles. Thus if we take a convex cylinder of $+ 5$ D and a convex sphere of $+ 3$ D and place them in contact, with the axis of the cylinder vertical, the power of the combination in the horizontal meridian will clearly be $+ 8$ D; in the vertical meridian the cylinder has no refracting power (its axis is vertical) and the power of the combination is only $+ 3$ D. We thus have a toric, or astigmatic, combination with a curvature in the horizontal meridian greater than that in the vertical. An infinitely distant point object will produce a line-image at the first line-focus and this line will be vertical (parallel to the meridian of least curvature) at a distance of $100/8 = 12 \cdot 5$ cm. A second, horizontal, line-image will be formed at a distance of $100/3 = 33 \cdot 3$ cm.

Astigmatism

Astigmatism in the eye is a condition of *refractive ametropia*, consisting of a difference in the refracting power of the eye in two planes or meridians; the astigmatism is called *regular astigmatism* if the meridians of extreme curvature are at right-angles to each other—as in the toric surfaces considered—and we need only concern ourselves with this form of astigmatism here. If the meridian of least curvature is horizontal* the astigmatism is described as *direct* or "*with the rule*" whilst if the meridian of least curvature is vertical it is called *inverse* or "*against the rule*." An astigmatic individual does not see a point object distinctly, the best image obtainable on the retina being, theoretically, the circle of least confusion; extended objects are thus blurred. Under certain conditions,

* The meridians of differing curvature must be at right-angles in regular astigmatism; they need not, of course, be absolutely vertical or horizontal. So long as the meridian of least curvature makes an angle of less than 30 degrees with the horizontal plane the astigmatism is said to be "with the rule." If the meridian of least curvature is within 30 degrees of the vertical plane the astigmatism is "against the rule."

however, a clearly defined image of a line can be formed on the retina as the following will make clear.

Image of a Line. In Fig. 307 L is an astigmatic convex lens and O'OO'' is a distant vertical line-object. Let us assume that the astigmatism is such that refraction in the vertical meridian is greater than that in the horizontal, *i.e.* the astigmatism is regular and direct. A point O on the optic axis forms two line-images at the first and second line-foci, I_V and I_H respectively; since refraction is greater in the vertical meridian, rays in this plane come to a focus first and I_V is a horizontal line; I_H is vertical. Other points, O' and O'' form horizontal and vertical lines I'_V and I''_V, I'_H and I''_H. The appearance of the image of the vertical line O'OO'' formed on a screen placed at I_V therefore consists of a series of short parallel lines placed one above the other and gives the impression of a blurred vertical line (Fig. 307; *inset*). The image of O'OO'' formed at I_H, on the other hand, consists of a series of vertical lines superimposed one above

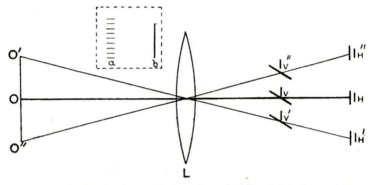

Fig. 307. Refraction by a toric lens. A vertical line O'O'' gives a clear line image at the focus of the horizontal meridian.

the other and the appearance on a screen is that of a well-defined vertical line (Fig. 307; *inset*).

With a vertical line-object, therefore, we have a clear line-image at I_H, the focus of the horizontal meridian, and we may state that the *meridian in focus is at right-angles to the clearly defined line.*

If we apply the same argument to the images of a horizontal line formed by the same toric surface, we find that the one formed at the first line-focus, I_V, consists of overlapping horizontal lines, *i.e.* it is a clearly defined horizontal line, whilst the image formed at the second line-focus, I_H, consists of a series of short parallel vertical lines, and has the appearance of a blurred horizontal line. Thus with a horizontal line-object, we have a clear line-image at the point I_V, the focus of the vertical meridian, and once again the *meridian in focus is at right-angles to the clearly defined line.*

Hence if the object consists of a cross with arms vertical and horizontal, a screen at the first line-focus receives a clearly defined horizontal line and a blurred vertical, the blurred line being parallel with the meridian in focus (vertical); a screen at the second line-focus receives a clearly defined vertical line and a blurred horizontal, the latter being parallel with the meridian in focus.

We may thus make the generalization: If a screen intercepts the image of two lines at right-angles formed by a toric surface, at such a point that the image of one of the lines is clear and the other blurred, *the screen is at the focus of the meridian parallel to the blurred line.*

Estimation of Astigmatic Correction. This principle—that, when a line is clearly defined whilst a line at right-angles is blurred, the retina is at the focus of the meridian parallel to the blurred line—provides the means for determining the degree of astigmatism of an eye and its meridians of greatest and least curvature. To the astigmatic eye no point is seen distinctly but a line may be, provided that this line is at right-angles to the meridian in focus at the retina. Thus a series of radiating lines are presented to the subject (an *astigmatism chart*); if all the lines are clearly defined there is no astigmatic error; if regular astigmatism is present one line is sharper than the rest, whilst the line at right-angles to this is most blurred. The retina is thus at the focus of the meridian parallel to the blurred line and the eye requires no correction in this meridian. The meridian at right-angles, on the other hand, is out of focus so that a correcting cylinder is necessary. It will be remembered that a cylinder modifies the vergence of rays in the meridian at right-angles to its axis, consequently, in order that the cylinder may modify the refraction in any meridian, its axis must be at right-angles to this meridian. We must therefore place the axis of the correcting cylinder parallel with the direction of the most blurred line or at right-angles to the direction of the sharply defined line.

Let us suppose that we are confronted with a subject who is unable to see clearly, and that this defect cannot be remedied with the aid of spherical lenses only. We may place the subject before the astigmatism chart and put up spherical lenses until one of the lines, say a vertical one, appears distinct whilst a horizontal line is blurred. Suppose that this is achieved with a + 6 D sphere. We now know that the subject is astigmatic and that with a correction of + 6 D the horizontal meridian is in focus on the retina. In this meridian, therefore, a correction of + 6 D *cyl.* is necessary and the axis must be vertical. More spheres are put up until the horizontal line is distinct and the vertical blurred; suppose a + 8 D sphere is required. The retina is now at the focus of the vertical meridian and a correction of + 8 D *cyl.*, axis horizontal, is required. The eye may thus be fully corrected by two cylinders: + 6 D, axis vertical, and + 8 D, axis horizontal; their combined effect is clearly the same as that of: + 6 D *spher.*, and + 2 D *cyl.*, axis horizontal.

NEUTRALIZATION AND DECENTRING

Neutralization of Lenses

Two lenses of the same power, but of opposite sign, when placed in contact have no dioptric power and behave as a piece of plate glass; the power of a lens may thus be estimated by determining the power and sign of the lens necessary to make its combination with the unknown lens behave as a piece of plate glass, *i.e.* by *neutralizing* it.

If a lens is moved in front of the eye, objects seen through it appear to move, whereas objects appear to remain stationary when viewed through a thin piece of plate glass under the same conditions. A lens is thus neutralized when moving the combination in front of the eye leads to no apparent movement of objects in the field of view.

In Fig. 308, *a*, a converging lens is placed in front of the eye so that the optic axes coincide. The lens would form an image of O at *i*; this image behaves as a virtual object for the eye, which produces an image I, on the common optic axis.

In Fig. 308, *b* the lens has been moved to the right; an image of O is formed by the lens at *i'* on the optic axis *of the lens*; *i'* serves as a virtual object for the eye and the position of the image of this object on the retina is given, as always, by drawing a line from *i'* through the nodal point; it cuts the retina at I'. The image of I on the retina is projected along I'O' so that moving a convex

Fig. 308. The effect of decentring a convex lens

lens in front of the eye causes an apparent displacement of objects *in the opposite direction.*

Fig. 309 demonstrates the effects of moving a concave lens, and it is clear that the apparent displacement of objects is *in the same direction* as that of the movement.

An inspection of Fig. 309, for example, shows that the greater the strength of the lens, the greater the apparent displacement; thus if the power of the lens were increased, *i'* would be closer to C, and the line *i'*N would be more strongly inclined to the eye's optic axis, thereby making the excursion II' larger.

There is an exception to the rule which states that the apparent movement of objects viewed through a converging lens is "against" the movement of the lens. When the image of the object viewed is formed in front of the eye's principal plane, the apparent movement is in the same direction as the movement of the lens (Fig. 310).

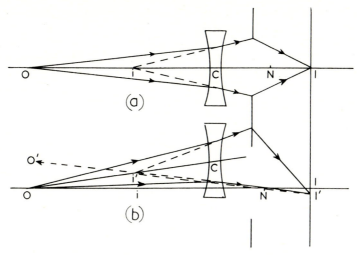

FIG. 309. The effect of decentring a concave lens.

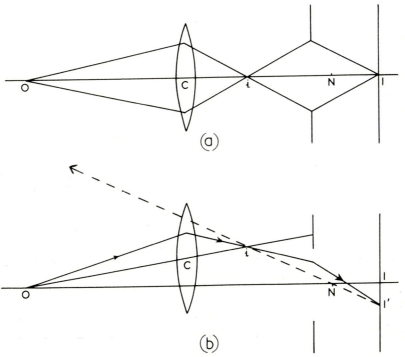

FIG. 310. The effect of decentring a convex lens when the image is formed in front of the eye. The image moves *with* the direction of decentration.

Decentring of Lenses

Spherical Lenses. A spectacle lens whose optic axis does not coincide with that of the eye is said to be decentred; it is clear from the foregoing discussion

that a decentred spherical lens has a prismatic effect in addition to its modification of the vergence of incident rays. Thus in Fig. 308, *b*, an object O appears
to be at O′; if the eye is imagined to be a right eye, it must be adducted if
it is to form an image on the fovea, I. A converging lens whose centre has
been moved outwards thus behaves as an adducting, or base-out, prism (p. 392).
From Fig. 309, *b*, it is seen that decentring a concave lens outwards causes
abduction.

In the spherical lenses so far considered, the optical centre corresponded with
the geometrical centre, so that decentration had to be achieved by moving the
lens bodily; the same prismatic effect can, however, be obtained by making
use of a lens whose geometrical and optical centres do not correspond. If a circular

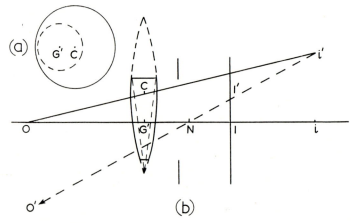

FIG. 311. Illustrating the cutting of a decentred lens from a larger lens. C is
the optical centre of the lens but it does not coincide with the geometrical
centre G′.

piece of the large lens in Fig. 311, *a* is cut out asymmetrically, the geometrical
centre of the piece is at G′, whereas the optic centre is at C. Such a lens, when
mounted so that its geometrical centre corresponds with the optic axis of the
eye, shows a prismatic effect (Fig. 311, *b*).

The prismatic effects are greater, the greater the degree of decentration and
the power of the lens; in general, a displacement of the image equal to one
prism dioptre is obtained for each centimetre of decentration of a 1 D lens;
thus half a centimetre of decentration of a 6 D lens corresponds to 3 prism
dioptres.

Cylindrical Lenses. A study of Fig. 303 (p. 424) will show us that, if a
cylindrical lens is decentred in the direction of its axis, there is no
prismatic effect, in fact it would be incorrect to speak of decentring in this
special case, since the optic axis of the eye would still coincide with a principal
axis of the cylinder. Moving the lens in a direction at right-angles to its axis
must, on the other hand, have a prismatic effect, since now the optic axis of
the eye is inclined to all the principal optic axes of the cylinder. The direction
of the axis of a cylinder may therefore be obtained by finding the direction
in which it must be moved across the eye to give no apparent displacement

of the image When this has been found, the cylinder may be neutralized by placing other cylinders in contact, with their axes parallel, until there is no apparent displacement on moving the lens at right-angles to the direction of the axis.

A cylinder modifies the vergence of light in one meridian but not in another at right-angles; the magnification in the two meridians is therefore different, with the result that a distorted image is seen; thus a convex cylinder with its axis vertical may magnify dimensions in the horizontal meridian and leave them unchanged in the vertical; if a cross is regarded through a cylinder, one arm corresponding in direction with the axis, this distortion is not evident since

Fig. 312. The scissors effect.

one line is only made a little longer; on rotating the cylinder about the optic axis of the eye, however, a characteristic "scissors effect" is obtained (Fig. 312) since the greatest magnification is obtained, now, along a line between the two arms of the cross.

Diagnosis of a Lens

A spectacle lens of unknown characteristics may be completely diagnosed by the following procedure. A cross is viewed through the lens, care being taken to make the geometrical centre coincide with the optic axis of the eye. Any prismatic effect is revealed by a bodily shift of the centre of the cross (Fig. 313, *a*); when this has been neutralized by a prism, the combination

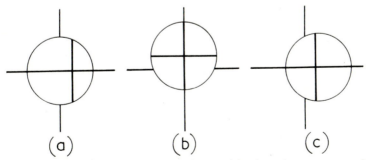

Fig. 313. (*a*) The effect of a prism (or decentred lens) on the appearance of a cross. (*b*) The effect of curvature in the vertical meridian on the appearance of the cross on moving the lens upwards. (*c*) The effect of curvature in the horizontal meridian on the appearance of the cross on moving the lens sideways.

may be rotated until any "scissors" distortion disappears; the axis of the cylindrical component now coincides with one of the arms of the cross. The combination is now moved up and down; dioptric power in the vertical meridian will cause the centre of the cross to move vertically up or down, and this is revealed by an apparent movement of the horizontal line (Fig. 313, *b*). This movement may be neutralized by a cylinder or sphere; thus when the horizontal line remains stationary on moving the combination vertically, the vertical meridian is neutralized. The combination is now moved horizontally and new spheres or cylinders are added until apparent movement of the vertical line (Fig. 313, *c*) ceases. In this way the prism strength, and the dioptric powers in the vertical and horizontal meridians, are found.

CONTACT LENSES

The contact lens consists of a glass shell which fits in close apposition to the cornea and sclera, and accompanies the eye in its movements. We need only concern ourselves here with the *corneal segment, i.e.* the portion fitting over the cornea, the function of which is to correct optical defects. This is achieved by eliminating the cornea as a refracting surface and, in effect, replacing it by a perfectly spherical one.

Fig. 314. Refraction of a ray by an afocal contact glass.

The general principle of the use of a contact lens is indicated in Fig. 314. The corneal segment is separated from the cornea by a thin film of saline. Refraction of light takes place as indicated, *i.e.* the ray is deviated by the anterior surface of the contact glass and also by the posterior surface; since saline has approximately the same refractive index as that of the cornea, no further refraction takes place until the lens is reached. Thus the cornea has been replaced as a refracting surface, and if it contains irregularities (astigmatism, etc.) they are unable to influence the refraction of light since the layer of saline fills in these irregularities and gives a surface corresponding exactly in shape with that of the posterior surface of the contact glass. If the eye is emmetropic apart from these corneal defects, the contact glass need only be designed so that it contributes nothing to the focal power of the system, modification of the vergence of incident rays being, in effect, carried out by the spherical surface of saline. This is achieved by making the curvatures of the two surfaces of the contact glass equal to that of the cornea; in this event the glass is *afocal*—it is equivalent to a parallel-sided thin plate glass; any influence one surface of the glass may have on the dioptric power of the system is cancelled out exactly by the effect of the other surface.

If a spherical refractive error is present, it can be corrected by modifying the curvature of the anterior surface of the contact glass. If this curvature is made greater, the contact glass behaves as a convex meniscus lens and corrects hypermetropia.

The Glass and Liquid Lens Systems. When the spherical correction in a contact lens is achieved by modifying the curvature of the anterior surface, as in Fig. 315, *a*, the system is referred to as a *"glass lens,"* the increased dioptric power being provided by the extra curvature of the anterior surface of the glass.

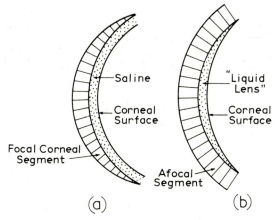

FIG. 315. The "glass lens" (*a*) and the "liquid lens" (*b*).

If, on the other hand, the glass is kept afocal by making its surfaces concentric, corrections can still be made by modifying the effective curvature of the cornea, *i.e.* a so-called *"liquid lens"* is formed (as in Fig. 315, *b*) where the two glass surfaces are concentric but the curvature of the glass is different from that of the cornea; a meniscus-lens shaped space is thus left between glass and cornea; this is filled with saline and the curvature of the cornea has, in effect, been modified.

The term "liquid lens," as opposed to a glass lens, is somewhat of a misnomer; the liquid between the cornea and the glass is lens-shaped, but since the refractive index of the liquid is taken as being equal to that of the cornea, the liquid behaves optically, not as a lens, but as a *single* spherical refracting surface—a modified cornea.

Advantages of the Contact Lens

We have seen that a decentred lens behaves as a prism; when the eyes look obliquely through spectacles the lenses are, in effect, decentred and the consequent prismatic effect can be annoying, especially when the corrections applied to the two eyes are of opposite sign. The contact lens, by moving with the eye, does not suffer from this defect.

The retinal image in corrected ametropia is equal in size to that obtained in the emmetropic eye if the correcting lens is placed at the anterior focus (p. 417). In anisometropia, therefore, the images in both eyes may be made equal with correcting lenses at the anterior foci. When the correcting lens is brought closer to the eye, the image becomes larger, if the correction is for myopia, and smaller for hypermetropia. In anisometropia, therefore, there may be a considerable disparity in the sizes of the corrected images when contact lenses are worn. Contact lenses, from this point of view, are a positive disadvantage. However, it has been found that the discomfort associated with the prismatic effect of spectacles is greater than that due to the *"aniseikonia"* of contact glasses in corrected anisometropia; the contact glass is therefore often chosen as the lesser evil.

In corrected unilateral aphakia, however, the condition is different; here the image in the corrected aphakic eye is some 33 per cent larger than that in the emmetropic eye. By moving the correcting lens closer to the eye, the size of the image is diminished. In the case of a $+15$ D correction, the size is reduced by 20 per cent by using a contact glass, so that the disparity is diminished sufficiently to permit fusion of images in binocular vision.

OPHTHALMOSCOPY

Ophthalmoscopy is concerned with the observation of the interior of the eye, principally the fundus; this is viewed by an observer as an image formed by the dioptric system of the eye. We shall be concerned here with the optical principles governing the appearance of the image under different refractive conditions; since the light normally falling on the fundus is entirely inadequate for the purposes of observation, we shall also be concerned with the optical principles involved in the illumination of the eye.

The Direct Method

In Fig. 316 R and H represent the retina and principal plane of an emmetropic eye; N is the nodal point. A point O, on the optic axis, emits a pencil of rays whose size is determined by the pupil; the rays emanate from the posterior focus and consequently run parallel to the axis after refraction at H. A point

Fig. 316. The direct method of ophthalmoscopy. Showing that the field of view depends on the distance between observer and subject and the sizes of their pupils.

O', on the retina but a little way off the axis, gives rise to another parallel bundle of rays, inclined to the first. In order that the two points may be visible to an observer in front of the eye, at least some of the rays from each point, O and O', must enter the observer's eye. If the eye is close to the subject's principal plane this occurs, but when it is far away the beam from O', owing to its deflexion downwards, misses the observer's pupil entirely; in this event O' is *outside the field of view*, the limit being given by a point closer to O. Thus the *field of view* of an observer, looking directly into the eye, decreases with his distance away; it will be clear from Fig. 316 that the field increases with the size of the subject's and observer's pupil (sight-hole). In this, the *direct method of ophthalmoscopy*, the observer's eye must be as close as feasible to the subject's if a reasonable field of view is to be obtained.

We may now consider the passage of light from the subject's fundus to the retina of the observer. In Fig. 317 R_s is the retinal plane, H_s the principal plane, N_s the nodal point, and F_a the anterior focus of the subject's eye; corresponding

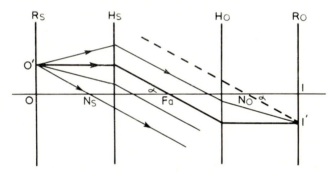

FIG. 317. The direct method. Passage of rays from emmetropic fundus to observer's retina.

positions for the observer are R_o, H_o, and N_o.* The subject is emmetropic, so that O corresponds to the posterior focus. A ray from a point O' on the subject's retina passes through the nodal point undeviated. A ray from O' parallel with the optic axis passes through F_a; since the eye is emmetropic all rays from O' leave the eye as a parallel bundle. To determine the passage of this bundle through the observer's eye we proceed as follows: A ray through the observer's nodal point, N_o, parallel to the bundle, would strike the observer's retinal plane at I'. If the observer is emmetropic, parallel rays meet in the retinal plane, consequently the bundle from O' comes to a focus at I'.

Rays from O emerge parallel to the axis and come to a focus at I, so that II' is the image, on the observer's retina, of the portion OO' of the subject's fundus. It is an inverted image on the retina, and the fundus is therefore seen *erect*.

The apparent size of OO' is determined by the size of II', and this may be represented by the angle II' subtends with the nodal point, N_o, *i.e.* the angle a.

* In this, and subsequent diagrams, the observer's anterior focus is not assigned any particular position; the constructions are thus independent of the position of the observer's eye provided, of course, that light from the fundus may enter it. The student may work out for himself the special case where the two anterior foci coincide.

The formation of the image of a hypermetropic fundus may be tackled in the same way, but here the emergent beam is not parallel and to trace it we must know the degree of hypermetropia and thus the position of the far point.

The construction is shown in Fig. 318; the far point is the position of an object such that its image falls on the retina of the unaccommodated eye; the far point and retina are thus conjugate foci, and the image of OO′, formed by the dioptric system of the eye, is therefore at the far point, *i.e.* behind the eye of a hypermetrope. Let us construct this image. A ray parallel to the axis passes through the anterior focus, F_a. A ray through the nodal point passes on un-

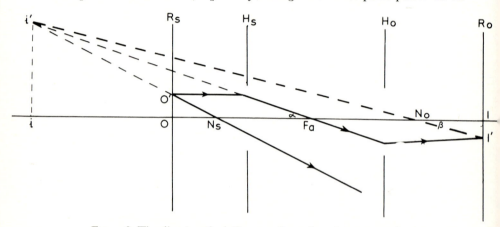

FIG. 318. The direct method. Passage of rays from hypermetropic eye.

deviated. These two rays diverge and, when produced backwards, meet at *i′*, the image of O′. *ii′* is the image of OO′, and all rays emanating from O′, for example, appear, after refraction by the subject's eye, to diverge from *i′*.

The diverging rays from O′ are brought to a focus on the observer's retina, to give an image I′; the position of this point is given by considering the ray through the nodal point, N_o; this ray appears to diverge from *i′*; all other rays converge on I′, the point of intersection of this ray with the observer's retina.

With the myope, the far point is in front of the eye, *e.g.* at *i* (Fig. 319). The

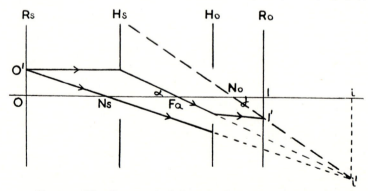

FIG. 319. The direct method. Passage of rays from myopic eye.

image of OO′ is thus *ii′* and may be derived by the appropriate construction. Rays from O′ therefore converge, after refraction, on *i′* and thus provide a virtual object for the observer's eye. The image of *i′*, formed by the dioptric system of the observer's eye, is given, once again, by the ray through the nodal point, N_o.

Magnification. If the images II′ are compared in Figs. 317–319, it will be seen that their apparent sizes are determined by the angle α for the emmetrope, the angle β for the hypermetrope, and the angle γ for the myope. Since β is less than, whilst γ is greater than α, the apparent size of the subject's fundus is greatest in myopia and least in hypermetropia. The magnification can be calculated quite simply; in the emmetropic eye it is 15.

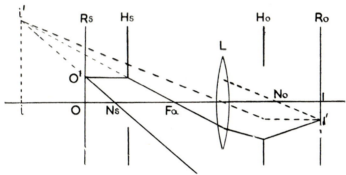

FIG. 320. The direct method. Passage of rays from hypermetropic eye; the observer is using a correcting lens.

Correcting Lens. When the subject is hypermetropic, the emergent rays from the fundus diverge and the observer must either accommodate or put up a correcting lens; the construction of the image in the presence of a correcting lens is shown in Fig. 320; the emergent beam may be constructed as before; after striking the correcting lens the rays emerge parallel, with their direction determined by the ray from *i′* through the centre. Parallel rays now strike the observer's principal plane and converge on I′ whose position is determined by the ray in this parallel bundle passing through N_o.

Field of View. In Fig. 321 R_s and H_s have the same meaning as before; CD is the subject's pupillary aperture and AB that of the observer or, to be

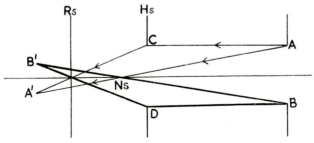

FIG. 321. A′B′ is the image of the sight-hole, AB, formed by the refracting system of the subject's eye.

more accurate, the sight-hole. Let us construct the image of AB formed by the dioptric system of the subject's eye, assuming that this remains unaccommodated. A ray through the nodal point, N_s, passes on undeviated; a ray parallel to the axis passes through the posterior focus. The image of the top of the aperture, A, is thus formed at A′, behind the retina; the image of B is formed at B′.

Having established the position of this image, we may now consider the paths of the complete pencils of light from A and B, as in Fig. 322; it will be seen that the pencils cut the subject's fundus in two blur-circles, *cb* and *ca*. We may now show that *ab* represents the total field of view available to an observer looking through the aperture AB. This is best done by imagining that the rays from the image of the sight-hole are reversed; thus the ray *b*C, on emerging from the eye, strikes the bottom of the sight-hole. All other rays from *b* will, after emerging from the eye, run parallel with this ray and will therefore fail to get through the sight-hole. The point *b* thus represents a point on the fundus, the top of whose emergent pencil just grazes the sight-hole; it is consequently the farthest point above the optic axis consistent with permitting any light from it to enter the sight-hole and is thus the upper limit to the field of view.

Fig. 322. The projected image of AB on the retina, *acb*, represents the field of view.

The same argument may be applied to the ray *a*D from *a*; it strikes the top of the sight-hole and other rays emerge parallel with it and fail to get through.

ab is thus the field of view of the subject's fundus; it is, in fact, the *projected image of the sight-hole on the fundus*. We have thus far considered that the subject was emmetropic; the statement that the field of view is the projected image of the sight-hole on the fundus can be shown to be quite general and independent of the refractive condition; we can therefore derive an estimate of the qualitative effects of ametropia on the field of view by simply imagining that the fundus is nearer to, or farther away from, the principal plane. Thus in Fig. 322 it is evident that the field of view is greatest in hypermetropia and least in myopia.

Method of Illumination. The classical method of illumination of the fundus by means of a concave mirror is indicated in Fig. 323 (not drawn to scale). The mirror is tilted so that the image of the source S_1S_2 lies symmetrically about the optic axis of the eye. In the absence of the eye an inverted, diminished, real image of S_1S_2 would be formed by the mirror at $S_1′S_2′$; this behaves as a virtual object for the dioptric system of the eye which produces an image $S_1″S_2″$ in front of the retina. The retina is thus illuminated by blur-circles formed by the diverging rays from $S_1″S_2″$ and from intermediate points on the image. It

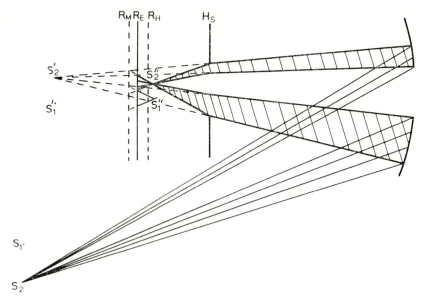

FIG. 323. Illumination with a concave mirror in the direct method.

is clear that the field of illumination is greatest in myopia and least in hypermetropia. If a plane or convex mirror is used, the image of the source, formed by the eye, is behind the retina, since the rays entering the eye are divergent. The fundus is illuminated by blur-circles formed by rays converging on points behind the fundus and the order of field size is reversed, the greatest field being in hypermetropia.

SELF-LUMINOUS INSTRUMENT

In modern practice, of course, the separate source and mirror have been substituted by a compact instrument, the *self-luminous ophthalmoscope*. Fig. 324 illustrates the essential principles; the light from a lamp, L, is brought to a point-focus on the edge of the mirror, so that the effective source is very close to the subject's eye. The rays are so strongly divergent, therefore, that the fundus is illuminated with a large out-of-focus patch. In order to reduce the nuisance caused by the reflexion off the cornea, the *corneal reflex*, the axis of the sight-hole, C, is above that of the illuminating beam.

The Indirect Method

With the direct method of ophthalmoscopy, the effective field of view in emmetropia is about 6·5°, *i.e.* little more than the optic disc; it is considerably more restricted in myopia. A glance at Fig. 316 shows us that the restriction in the field is determined, other things being equal, by the deflexion of the pencils of light as they leave the eye; if these pencils could be deflected again towards the observer's eye, the field could be increased. In the *indirect method* this is brought about by interposing a convex lens of about 13 D between the subject's and observer's eyes.

FIG. 324. Modern self-luminous ophthalmoscope of
the Fincham type.
(Emsley *Visual Optics*.)

The passage of light from an illuminated point O′ on the fundus, under these conditions, is illustrated in Fig. 325. The total separation between the eyes of subject and observer is now large, say 60 cm. The condensing lens is placed at a point, C, such that the sight-hole and the subject's pupil are conjugate foci, *i.e.* the sight-hole is imaged in the subject's pupillary plane; for a 13 D lens the necessary position is about 9 cm from the subject's eye. f_1 and f_2 are respectively the first and second principal foci of the condensing lens.

A ray O′X, parallel to the axis, passes through F_a and strikes the lens in Y. If the eye is emmetropic, all other rays from O′ emerge parallel with this ray

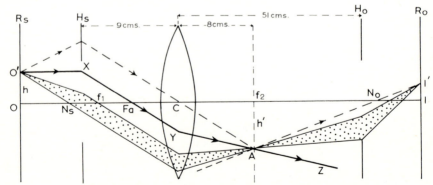

FIG. 325. The indirect method of ophthalmoscopy. The passage of rays from the fundus of an emmetropic eye to the observer's retina.

and after refraction by the condensing lens they converge on to its second focal plane through f_2. The actual point to which they converge may be found by drawing in the ray through the centre of the lens; it is parallel with XY and strikes the focal plane in A. All rays leaving the eye therefore meet in A, which is the image of O′ formed by the refracting system of the subject's eye and the condensing lens. It is this *real* image that the observer sees; the image of A on the observer's retina is given in the usual way by drawing a ray through the nodal point, N_o. If the observer accommodates, all the rays from A, entering his eye, meet at I′. The actual pencil of light entering the observer's eye is thin compared with that obtained in the direct method; this follows from the fact that the sight-hole and the pupillary plane are conjugate foci; only light from the image of the sight-hole in the pupil can pass through the sight-hole itself; the size of the image of a 4 mm sight-hole is about 0·7 mm.

It will be noted that the image of the fundus, as seen in the indirect method, is inverted. The magnification for the particular set-up shown in Fig. 325 amounts to about 2·7, being much less than in the direct method.

Field of View. It will be evident from Fig. 325 that, so long as an emergent pencil of rays strikes the condensing lens, it will be bent back towards the optic axis to converge on the focal plane of the condensing lens, producing an image

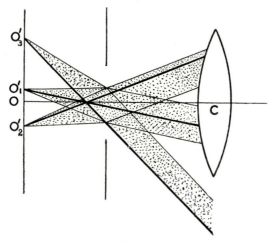

Fig. 326. The indirect method. The field of view is determined by the size of the condensing lens.

which the observer can see. Thus the two points $O_1′$ and $O_2′$ (Fig. 326) on the subject's fundus are both visible because pencils from them strike the condensing lens; the point $O_3′$ is not seen. The size of the condensing lens therefore determines the field of view in the indirect method. For manipulative purposes a large condensing lens is used, but owing to aberrations, the effective useful aperture is about 4 cm. The field of view is easily calculated and amounts to about 25°, *i.e.* it is about four times larger than the effective field in the direct method.

In myopia it may be shown that the angular field of view is greater than in emmetropia, whilst the reverse relationship is found with hypermetropia.

Path of Rays in Ametropia. Exactly the same principles of ray tracing may be applied to determining the image of the fundus of hypermetropic and myopic eyes in the indirect method. Thus, as with the direct method, the position of the image of the fundus at the far point is first determined (Figs. 327 and 328). The emergent pencil from O', in the case of hypermetropia, diverges from its image i'; the course of the rays after striking the condensing lens is determined by considering the ray through its centre. It appears to come from i' and passes

FIG. 327. The indirect method. Hypermetropic eye.

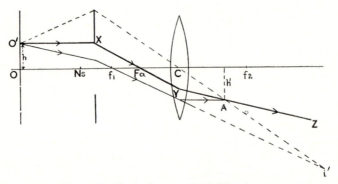

FIG. 328. The indirect method. Myopic eye.

through undeviated. Another ray from i', through the first principal focus of the condensing lens, runs parallel to the axis after refraction. These two rays intersect at A, the image of O' seen by the observer. The further passage of the rays to the observer's retina may be drawn in as before.

The constructions show quite clearly that the size of the image of the fundus, seen by the observer, is greatest in hypermetropia, intermediate in emmetropia, and least in myopia.

Estimation of the Refractive Condition. We may analyse the effects of moving the condensing lens nearer to, or farther away from the subject by deriving the essential features of the three preceding constructions (Figs. 325, 327 and 328). There is a ray common to all three conditions, namely, the ray O'X, parallel to the optic axis of the eye. This passes through the anterior focus of the subject's eye, F_a, in each case and, since it strikes the lens at the same point, Y, and at the same angle, it is refracted in the same direction (along YZ). We may thus draw a general diagram to embrace the three refractive conditions, as in Fig. 329, the ray O'XYZ being considered to have emanated from a point *h* mm above the pole of the fundus in each condition.

The position of the image of O', formed by the eye's refractive system and the condensing lens, is, of course, different in the three conditions. In emmetropia it is determined by a ray through f_1 (the first focus of the lens) which, belonging to a parallel pencil, meets the ray O'XYZ in the second focal plane of the condensing lens. In hypermetropia, this second ray through f_1 diverges from XY and therefore meets the ray XYZ beyond f_2 and, because YZ slopes away from the axis, the size of the image, h', is greater than in emmetropia. In myopia,

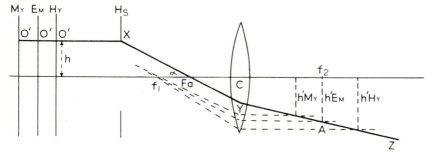

FIG. 329. The indirect method. First focus of the condensing lens is within the anterior focus of the eye. The ray O'XYZ diverges from the axis and the image, h', is greatest in hypermetropia.

the second ray, through f_1, converges towards XY and therefore meets this ray at a point within the second principal focus, f_2, and the size of the image, h', is smaller.

The relative sizes of the images in different refractive conditions are thus determined by the fact that the ray YZ slopes away from the axis.

If the condensing lens is brought farther from the subject, so that f_1 coincides with F_a, the determining ray, O'XYZ, after refraction at the condensing lens, now runs parallel to the optic axis, since it has passed through the first principal focus of this lens (Fig. 330). The image of O' is given as before by the intersection with any other ray from O', but clearly the size is now independent of the position of the point of intersection, so that we may conclude that, in this special case, the size is the same in all three refractive conditions. A comparison of Figs. 329 and 330 shows, moreover, that the size of the image is the same as for an emmetrope when the condensing lens was closer to the subject.

If, now, the condensing lens is moved so that its first focus, f_1, is farther from the eye than F_a (Fig. 331), the determining ray O'XYZ converges on to the optic axis; it is converging because it comes from a point on the axis, F_a, outside the first focus of the lens; the point to which it converges is found by considering a ray, parallel to it, passing through f_1; the two rays must meet in the second

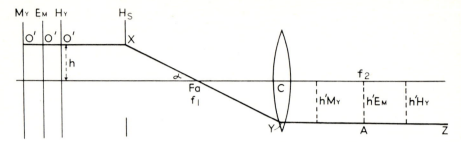

FIG. 330. The indirect method. First focus of the condensing lens coincides with the anterior focus of the eye. The ray O'XYZ runs parallel with the axis and the images are of the same size in all refractive conditions.

focal plane of the condensing lens, at A. The point A corresponds to the position of the image of O' in the emmetropic eye, since it is the point to which parallel rays converge; the height h' is the same as before and consequently the size of the image of the emmetropic fundus is still unchanged. With the hypermetrope, as before, the image is formed farther away along the ray O'XYZ, and since this converges on the optic axis, it will now be smaller than in emmetropia. In myopia the image, being formed closer to the lens, will be larger than in emmetropia.

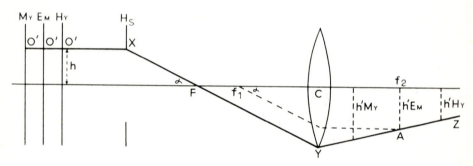

FIG. 331. The indirect method. First focus of the condensing lens is outside the anterior focus of the eye. The ray O'XYZ converges on the axis and the image, h', is greatest in myopia.

To take a numerical example, suppose that with the condensing lens close to the subject (Fig. 329) the sizes in the refractive conditions are:

Hypermetropia	*Emmetropia*	*Myopia*
3	2	1

When the lens is brought out so that the first principal focus corresponds with the anterior focus of the subject's eye (Fig. 330) the sizes are:

Hypermetropia	*Emmetropia*	*Myopia*
2	2	2

being equal and of the same size as that in emmetropia under the first conditions. When the first focus of the lens is outside the anterior focus of the eye we have:

Hypermetropia	*Emmetropia*	*Myopia*
I	2	3

Thus on moving the condensing lens from a point close to the subject to a point far away, if the size of the image remains constant the eye is emmetropic; if the size diminishes, the eye is hypermetropic; whilst if it increases, the eye is myopic.

Illumination

The illumination in the indirect method is complicated by the presence of the condensing lens but otherwise the optical principles are the same as those involved in the direct method. The source of light, $S_1 \ldots S_2$ (Fig. 332) is imaged by the mirror at $S_2' \ldots S_1'$ in front of the subject's eye. The condensing

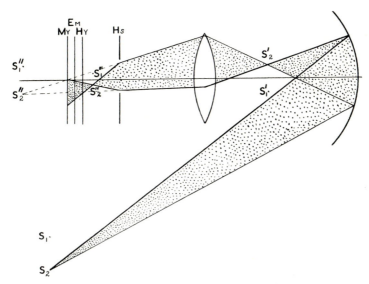

Fig. 332. The indirect method. Illumination of the eye.

lens forms an image $S_1'' \ldots S_2''$ behind the subject's eye; this behaves as a virtual object for the refracting system of the eye which produces a real image, $S_1''' \ldots S_2'''$ in front of the fundus. A pencil of rays from S_2, for example, after reflexion at the mirror converges on to S_2' and after passing through this point diverges until it strikes the lens; it then converges towards S_2'' until it meets the principal plane of the eye, when it converges on to S_2'''. A blurred image of $S_1''' \ldots S_2'''$ is formed on the fundus and it is evident from Fig. 332 that the field of illumination is greatest in myopia and least in hypermetropia.

RETINOSCOPY

By the aid of ophthalmoscopy, particularly with the indirect method, an estimate of the subject's refractive condition can be made, but by no means accurately. *Retinoscopy*, or *skiascopy*, is the name given to a more accurate objective method of determining refractive errors. By means of a mirror, as in ophthalmoscopy, the fundus is illuminated; the study of the movements of the image of the fundus, when the mirror is tilted, permits an accurate estimate of the subject's refractive condition.

In Fig. 333, *a* the point O on the optic axis and fundus is illuminated; the pencil of light from O fills the pupil; since it emerges symmetrically disposed about the optic axis, it enters the pupil (or sight-hole) of an observer's eye placed so that its optic axis coincides with that of the subject. The point O is illuminated,

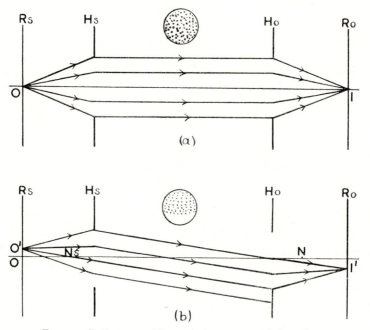

Fig. 333. Retinoscopy. Illustrating movement of the reflex.

as in ophthalmoscopy, with a mirror, and the reflected light from the fundus is called the *reflex*. The observer views this reflex in relation to the subject's pupil, *i.e.* he "projects" it on to the pupil. It will be seen that light from all points on the subject's pupil enters the sight-hole, with the result that the reflex fills the pupil. If, now, the illumination of the fundus is altered so that the point O' is illuminated, the light leaving the eye no longer travels symmetrically about the axis but is deviated downwards; rays from the lower part of the pupil thus fail to enter the sight-hole and this part of the pupil appears dark. To the observer, then, the reflex now occupies only the upper part of the pupil, and it is said to move upwards (Fig. 333, *b*; *inset*).

The change in the illumination of the fundus from O to O' is achieved by moving the mirror; if the latter is plane, it must be tilted upwards; the movement of the reflex is thus "with" the movement of the mirror (Fig. 334).

We may now consider how the movement of the reflex varies with the refractive condition of the subject's eye.

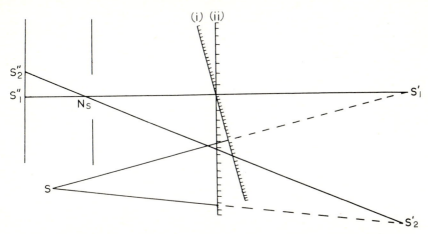

FIG. 334. Effect of rotation of a plane mirror. An upward movement of the mirror causes the illuminated point to move from S_1'' to S_2''; the reflex therefore moves upwards, *i.e.*, it moves "with" the mirror.

Emmetropia. In Fig. 335 R_s and R_o are the retinal planes of subject and observer, H_s and H_o their principal (pupillary) planes. The image of O is formed at I on the common optic axis. If the mirror is moved so that O′ is illuminated, the image of O′ on the observer's retina is at I′, the point of intersection of the ray, in the parallel emergent beam, through the nodal point, N_o, with the observer's retina. I′ is below I and the movement of the reflex is interpreted, therefore, as an upward movement through an angle a, the angle subtended by II′ at the observer's nodal point.

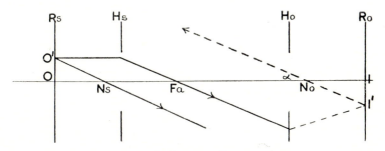

FIG. 335. Retinoscopy. Emmetropia.

Hypermetropia of Low Degree. Fig. 336 represents the condition in hypermetropia. The image of O falls, as before, at I. The image of O′ is at I′, this position being obtained, as in the construction in the direct method of ophthalmoscopy, by considering the image of OO′ formed by the subject's eye at its far point, namely, ii'. The image on the observer's retina is obtained by drawing a ray from i' through the nodal point, N_o. I′ is below I, and the movement of the reflex is therefore upwards, through the angle β, which is less than a; consequently the movement appears less rapid.

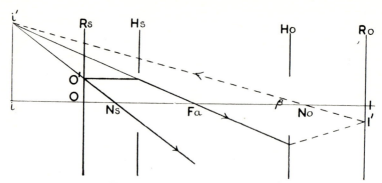

FIG. 336. Retinoscopy. Hypermetropia.

Hypermetropia of High Degree. Here the image of OO′ at the far point is smaller, so that the angle γ, formed at the observer's nodal point, is smaller than either α or β; the movement of the reflex is in the same direction as before, but slower (Fig. 337).

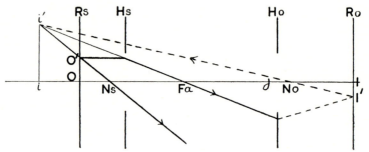

FIG. 337. Retinoscopy. Hypermetropia of high degree.

Myopia of Low Degree. In myopia the far point is in front of the eye; if it is beyond the nodal point of the observer's eye, as in Fig. 338, the image of O′ formed on the observer's retina is still such that I′ is below I. Thus the image of OO′ formed by the subject's dioptric system is at *ii*′; this acts as a virtual object for the observer's eye, and the image is constructed by drawing a ray from *i*′ through the nodal point, N_o; this strikes the retina below the optic

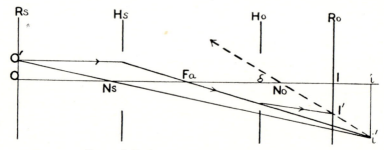

FIG. 338. Retinoscopy. Myopia of low degree.

axis. The movement of the reflex is thus, once again, upwards or "with," and the angle δ measures the speed of movement. δ is clearly greater than α.

Myopia of High Degree. If the far point falls between the subject and observer, as in Fig. 339, the image of O' falls at I', *above* the optic axis, *i.e.* the reflex appears to move downwards or "against" the movement of the plane mirror. The angle ϵ measures the rate of movement and this will clearly decrease, the greater the degree of myopia.

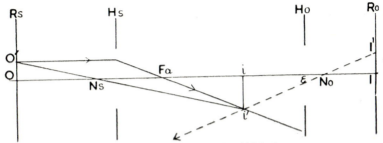

FIG. 339. Retinoscopy. Myopia of high degree.

Point of Reversal. Neutral Point. Between the condition of myopia, with the far point behind the observer's nodal point, and that in which it is in front, the movement of the reflex changes sign; the actual point at which this change takes place is called the *point of reversal* or *neutral point*; it is the point at which the observer's nodal point coincides with the subject's far point. Thus in Fig. 340 the far point, i, coincides with N_o. The image of OO' formed by the dioptric system of the subject's eye is thus ii' in the plane of the nodal point, N_o. If O is illuminated, it forms an image at N_o and the reflex is seen by the observer. O', however, forms an image, i, vertically below N_o, and to construct the image

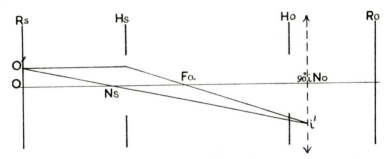

FIG. 340. Retinoscopy. Point of reversal.

of i' formed by the observer's dioptric system we would have to draw a line through i' and N_o, *i.e.* a line vertically up and down. Under these conditions, therefore, there is no image of O' formed by the dioptric system of the observer's eye. Moreover, as soon as we pass from the point O, on the axis, to any other point very close, the image is vertically above or below N_o and consequently the smallest movement of the mirror makes the reflex invisible. We may therefore say that at this, the point of reversal, the movement of the reflex is infinitely rapid and is measured by the angle $90°$.

A review of Figs. 335-340 shows us that as we pass from extreme hypermetropia, through emmetropia, to myopia of low degree the movement of the reflex is "with" the movement of a plane mirror, and increases progressively in speed. At the point of reversal the speed is infinite. When the myopia is greater than this, the movement is reversed and decreases in speed with increasing degree of myopia.

The refractive condition of a subject may be determined quantitatively by observing the direction and speed of movement of the reflex, obtained by directing light on to the fundus with a mirror. If the subject is myopic, the far point lies at a finite distance in front of the eye; the observer may find its position by moving the mirror and his eye backwards and forwards until reversal is obtained. In other refractive conditions, the subject may be made artificially myopic by putting up positive lenses, and the point of reversal then determined. Thus if the point of reversal is found to be 20 cm in front of the spectacle point when a + 5 D lens is put up, the subject is emmetropic because a + 5 D lens in front of an emmetropic eye gives a far point of 20 cm. If the point of reversal is 20 cm in front of the eye with a + 7 D lens, the refractive error is now hypermetropia of + 2 D, 5 D of the lens strength being necessary to bring the far point from infinity to 20 cm and the remaining 2 D to correct the actual hypermetropia. In general, if R' is the dioptric value of the distance of the point of reversal from the spectacle point, when a lens of D dioptres is placed at this point, the spectacle refraction is given by D + R', attention being paid to the signs; R' is in front of the eye and is given a negative value in accordance with the sign convention.

Illumination. In general, a plane mirror is used and the principles involved are similar to those in the direct method of ophthalmoscopy.

OPTICAL CONSTANTS OF THE EYE

In order to elucidate the refracting properties of a spherical optical system, we must know:

(*a*) The index of refraction of the various surfaces, *i.e.* the refractive indices of the different phases.

(*b*) The radii of curvature of the surfaces.

(*c*) The relative positions of the surfaces.

Refractive Index

The best known instrument for the measurement of the refractive index of a liquid is the *Abbé refractometer*. If ABC (Fig. 341) is the section of a prism, the liquid whose refractive index is required is spread over the surface AC. The surface AB, which is ground, is illuminated; some of the rays, emanating from a point S, are both refracted at the surface AC and reflected; the ray SP strikes the surface at the critical angle of incidence (p. 389) and thus just grazes the surface, whilst a ray ST, making a greater angle of incidence, is totally internally reflected. A ray SX, on the other hand, is partly reflected and partly refracted. To an observer looking towards the face BC through a telescope, the field of view is sharply divided into a bright area, corresponding to rays of light that have not suffered refraction, and a darker area corresponding to rays that have suffered both refraction and reflexion. By measuring the position at which this division of the field occurs, the critical angle can be calculated and hence the refractive index of the liquid.

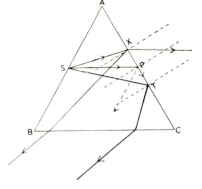

FIG. 341. Principle of the Abbé refractometer.

The figures given by Gullstrand for the refractive indices of the transparent tissues of the eye are:

Cornea	1·376
Aqueous	1·336
Vitreous	1·336
Lens	1·386 (Cortex)
Lens	1·406 (Core)

Radii of Curvature

A refracting surface does not transmit all the incident light, but a certain proportion is regularly reflected, the greater the index of refraction the greater the proportion reflected. A spherical surface may thus be treated as a mirror and its radius of curvature may be deduced from the magnification of the image. The magnification is given by:

$$i/o = - v/u$$

If u, the distance of the object, is made large, v, the distance of the image, is approximately equal to the focal length, f, which is half the radius of curvature.

Hence
$$i/o = - R/2u$$
And
$$R = - 2i.u/o$$

The quantities i, u, and o can all be measured, and R can be calculated.

Purkinje-Sanson Images. The images (catoptric) formed by reflexion at the eye surfaces are called *Purkinje-Sanson images*; the principal ones are four in number, formed respectively by the anterior and posterior surfaces of the cornea and lens; their mode of formation is indicated in Fig. 342 from Emsley.

It should be noted that images II, III and IV are formed by reflexion followed by refraction; thus image III is formed by reflexion at the anterior surface of the lens followed by refraction at the posterior and anterior surfaces of the cornea; allowance must be made for these refractions when calculating the radius or curvature of the reflecting surface from the size of image III.

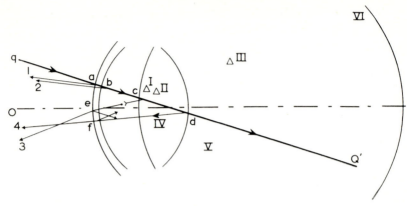

FIG. 342. Formation of the Purkinje-Sanson images. (Emsley, *Visual Optics*.)

The Ophthalmometer. The main problem in estimating the radius of curvature of a refracting surface thus resolves into measuring the size of the catoptric image; the difficulty in the way results from the movements of the eye and to overcome this Helmholtz made use of the principle of "*doubling.*" If we know by how much the centres of two identical objects must be separated so that their edges just touch, we know the size of the objects; *e.g.* in Fig. 343 the centres of two identical circles of radius *r* are separated so that their circumferences just touch; the diameter of the circles is given by the separation of their centres.

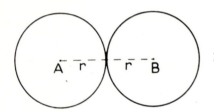

FIG. 343. Illustrating the principle of doubling.

In the *Helmholtz ophthalmometer*, the image, I, of an object in front of the corneal surface, is observed through the optical system indicated by Fig. 344; two inclined glass plates cause the rays from I to diverge from I′ and I″, and thus the image I is doubled. The two lenses behave as a telescope for the observation of I′ and I″, real images X and Y being formed by L_1; these are viewed through the eye-piece lens, L_2. The separation of I′ and I″ is determined by the inclination of the glass plates to the vertical, so that the two images can be made just to touch by varying this inclination. The separation of the images, under these conditions, may be calculated and thence the size of the image I. Small involuntary movements of the eye during the measurement do not disturb the observer since both images move together. Helmholtz found a value of 7·83 mm for the radius of curvature of the anterior surface of the cornea.

In the Javal-Schiøtz instrument, the inclined plates are replaced by a Wollaston prism, consisting of two rectangular quartz prisms cemented together, with

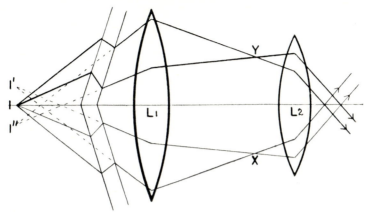

FIG. 344. The Helmholtz ophthalmometer.

their optic axes at right-angles, to form a plate. Such a prism is doubly refracting (p. 475) and gives two images of a single object. With this system, the separation of the images is fixed, and the size of the object in front of the cornea is varied until its doubled images I′ and I″ just touch. To facilitate the variation in object-size, so-called "*mires*" are used mounted on a circular frame. The mires are pieces of opal glass illuminated by electric lamps (Fig. 345) and are treated as the two ends of the object; by sliding them closer together or farther apart, the size of the object is decreased or increased.

FIG. 345. The Javal-Schiøtz ophthalmometer.

The mires, A and B, are shaped as in Fig. 346 (*inset*), and the object is considered to extend from the point *a* to the point *b*, *i.e.* it may be treated as the line *ab*. Two images of AB, XY and X′Y′, are formed by the doubly refracting system, and the appearance seen through the telescope will depend on the distance apart of A and B. Let us suppose that the appearance is that shown in Fig. 346, *a*, A giving the two images X and X′ and B the images Y and Y′. The object was considered to be the line *ab*, and its images are *xy* and *x′y′*; it is clear that these images are *too small* to permit the lower edge of the one (*y*) to coincide with the upper edge of the other (*x′*).

In Fig. 346, *b* the distance *ab* has been increased, so that *xy* and *x'y'* are greater, but still not large enough to give exact abutment. In Fig. 346, *c* the distance *ab* has been adjusted to give exact abutment, so that *y* coincides with *x'*. In Fig. 346, *d* the condition in which the object is *too large* is shown.

The ophthalmometer may be used for measuring the curvature of the cornea in different meridians; thus the circular frame may be placed vertically in front of the eye and the mires A and B adjusted to give exact abutment. The frame is then turned through 90° and if the curvature is different in the horizontal meridian, coincidence of the points *x'* and *y* will no longer be obtained and the appearance will be as in Fig. 346, *b* or *d*. If the latter, it can be said that the image size, *xy*, is too large and since the object size, *ab*, has been kept constant, it can be deduced that the curvature is less in the horizontal meridian than in

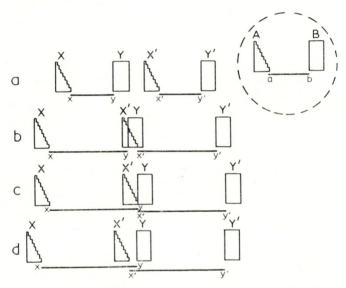

FIG. 346. Appearances of the images of the mires when the object-size is too small (*a* and *b*), correct (*c*), and too large (*d*) for abutment.

the vertical, *i.e.* that the astigmatism is with the rule. The mire A is designed so that an overlap of one step corresponds to a difference in refracting power of 1 D.

The Keratoscopic Disc. It should be noted that the ophthalmometer utilizes only a small portion of the cornea (1 to 2 mm) and the figures obtained for the radius of curvature apply to the central area only; more extensive studies with the keratoscopic disc have shown that it is only a central zone of about 4 mm diameter that can be treated as a spherical surface; peripherally the cornea is considerably flattened.

The *keratoscopic disc* (Fig. 347) is a card on which concentric circles are drawn; it may be used as an object in the ophthalmometer with the doubly refracting prism removed. The images of the circles would be perfect circles if the cornea were a perfectly spherical surface (apart from aberrations, p. 462); if the curvature were variable, the circles would be deformed, becoming elon-

FIG. 347. The keratoscopic disc.

(a)

Regular astigmatism of 5.5 D
with the rule.

(b)

Regular astigmatism against the
rule.

(c)

(d)

Irregular astigmatism. Eczematous keratitis; course of affection within
fourteen days.

(e)

Conical cornea-base of cone.

(f)

Conical cornea—apex of cone.

FIG. 348. Appearances of photo-keratoscopic images. (Emsley,
Visual Optics.)

gated along the meridian of least curvature. Some typical appearances are shown in Fig. 348. Even in the optical zone of the normal cornea a certain amount of astigmatism is generally present ("physiological astigmatism"). On the average, the difference in refracting power in two meridians at right-angles amounts to 0·5–0·74 D in 89·4 per cent of individuals, the meridian of least curvature being horizontal (with the rule). The keratoscopic disc has revealed a considerable peripheral flattening of the normal cornea.

For routine measurements of the curvatures of both corneal and lens surfaces Sorsby, Benjamin & Sheridan photographed the Purkinje images and with the aid of nomograms, computed by Bennett, the necessary parameters were quickly calculated from the measured sizes of these images.

The results of Gullstrand's measurements of the curvatures of the central regions of the refracting surfaces of the eye may be summarized as follows:

Anterior surface of cornea . . .	7·7 mm
Posterior surface of cornea . . .	6·7 mm
Anterior surface of lens	10·0 mm
Posterior surface of lens	6·0 mm

Positions of the Surfaces

The apparent positions of the refracting surfaces of the eye can be measured with the slit-lamp microscope; the instrument is arranged so that the microscope is directed constantly towards the focus of the illuminating system. By moving the system towards the eye the anterior surface of the cornea can be brought into focus. The instrument is then racked forward until the surface in question is in focus, and the focusing scale on the slit-lamp is read. In routine examinations it is more convenient to photograph the optical section of the anterior segment of eye and to measure the required distances afterwards, applying the necessary corrections for angle of view, apparent position, etc. (Bennett, 1961). The positions of the refracting surfaces are shown in Table 11.

TABLE 11. *Positions of the Refracting Surfaces of the Eye, referred to the Anterior Surface of the Cornea* (Gullstrand).

Cornea. Ant. surface	0 mm
Cornea. Post. surface	0·5 ,,
Lens. Ant. surface	3·6 ,,
Lens. Post. surface	7·2 ,,

The Lens

If the lens consisted of a homogeneous medium, its optical properties could be easily determined from its refractive index and curvatures; in fact, of course, the refractive index varies from cortex inwards. Gullstrand treated the lens schematically as a "core" of refractive index 1·406 surrounded by material of refractive index 1·386 (Fig. 349), the so-called "*equivalent core lens.*" In order that this schematic lens may have the dioptric power actually found, the core must have entirely fictitious curvatures (anterior and posterior radii of 7·91 and 5·76 mm respectively). It should be noted that the refracting power of such a system is greater than that of a homogeneous lens of the same dimensions, even if the refractive index throughout were as high as that of the core. As the lens ages the cortex hardens and the whole lens tends towards homogeneity; this may lead to a diminished dioptric power in spite of the over-all increase in refractive index. For this reason the myope in old age may tend to become emmetropic.

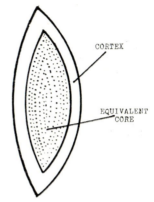

Fig. 349. The equivalent core lens.

CORTEX

EQUIVALENT CORE

Length of Eye

Up till recently the figures accepted for the dimensions of the eye have been obtained by measurements on the excised organ. With the aid of X-rays, however, an accurate estimate of the length of the eye in the living subject can be made (Rushton). A beam of X-rays at right-angles to the optic axis strikes the dark-adapted eye; as a result, a circle of light is seen by the subject, corresponding to an optical section of the globe. If the slit through which the X-rays pass is moved posteriorly by an apparatus orientated in relation to the cornea, the circle decreases in size and ultimately disappears. At this position of the slit, the beam of X-rays just grazes the pole of the retina. By measuring the distance of the slit from the cornea, the length of the optic axis could be determined to within 0·1 mm. The average length of the emmetropic globe was found by Goldmann and Hagen to be 23·4 mm, comparing with Gullstrand's value of 24·4 mm. In myopic eyes the lengths were greater.

Dioptric Power

The X-ray technique has been applied to determining the size of the image of an external object formed on the retina; the X-ray tube, just below the line of sight, projected two beams through the eye; X-rays are not significantly refracted by the media of the eye so that the two beams appeared to the subject as two lines separated by a definite distance. This distance was determined by causing the subject to gaze at a wall on which lines of known distance apart were projected with a lantern. The image on the retina was projected on to this wall and the pair of lines whose separation corresponded with that of the projected image was found. The X-ray beams struck the retina 5 mm apart; consequently the pair of lines on the screen formed an image on the retina this distance apart. The magnification of the eye was thus determined and the refractive power could be calculated. The figure obtained by Goldmann and Hagen was 59·2 D, comparing with Gullstrand's value of 58·6 D. The corneal refraction was measured in the usual way, whence the dioptric power of the lens was determined; it came out at 19·2 D comparing with Gullstrand's value of 19·1 D.

Emmetropia and Ametropia

Stenström published the results of a study of the optic elements of the eyes of 315 human subjects chosen without reference to their refractive condition, the X-ray technique being used for determining the axial length. His results may be summarized as follows:

Corneal radius	7·86 ± 0·008 mm
Depth of anterior chamber . . .	3·68 ± 0·009 mm
Power of cornea	42·84 ± 0·044 D
Power of lens	17·35 ± 0·044 D
Total power of eye	58·13 ± 0·056 D
Length of optic axis	24·00 ± 0·035 mm

The extreme limits of variation in the length of the eye were 20 and 29·5 mm. Although there was a strong correlation between axial length and refractive error—myopes having longer axial lengths usually than emmetropes—Stenström's results showed that it would be quite wrong to speak of a fixed "normal" axial length to give the condition of emmetropia; both the axial length and refractive power of the emmetropic eye varied over quite a large range, the larger emmetropic eye having the weaker power, and *vice versa*. Emmetropia is therefore achieved rather by a balance of refractive power and axial length. This is in some measure understandable since the larger the eye the smaller will be the curvature of the cornea, other things being equal.

A later study by Sorsby *et al.* (1957) reemphasized that emmetropia was essentially the result of a correct balance between the optic elements of the eye, especially between axial length and corneal curvature. Thus, in the emmetropes, the axial length varied between 22 and 26 mm, the condition of emmetropia resulting from a correlation between corneal power and axial length, a strongly curved cornea being accompanied by a short axial length and *vice versa*. Moreover, with hypermetropia and myopia up to 4 D, the axial lengths varied over the same range, so that the ametropia within this range must be regarded as the result of a faulty correlation of axial length with corneal power, rather than as a result of an "abnormal" axial length. With refractive errors above 4 D the correlation between axial length and refractive error was strong.

Changes During Growth. Sorsby, Benjamin & Sheridan studied some 1432 children aged between 3 and 15 years in which the refractive error, corneal and lens curvatures, and depth of the anterior chamber were measured by photographic techniques. As Fig. 350 shows, children at the age of 3 years have an average hypermetropia of 2 D and an axial length of 23 mm. With increasing age the ametropia decreases whilst the axial length increases to reach a probable limiting length for boys of 24·1 mm and 23·7 mm for girls (Sorsby *et al.* 1957). The increase in axial length from the age of 3 to 14, whilst it is continuous, is remarkably small, only about 1 mm, or some 4–5 per cent, compared with an increase in body-length of some 60 per cent. After adolescence little further change occurs. The changes in corneal power with age are slight, so that the decrease in power of the optic elements necessary to compensate

FIG. 350. *Upper.* Variation of ocular refraction with age. *Lower.* Variation of axial length with age. (Sorsby, Benjamin & Sheridan. *M.R.C. Sp. Rep.* By permission of Her Majesty's Stationery Office.)

for the increase in axial length is due mainly to a fall in lens-power from 21·8 to 19·8 D. The depth of the anterior chamber increased by about 0·1 to 0·2 mm. By following up some 386 children over a period of 2–6 years, some of the changes with age, already manifest by the initial cross-sectional study just described, could be seen more definitely, and it became clear that the increase in axial length that usually takes place during normal growth is largely compensated by a reduced dioptric power. For example, although 32 per cent of cases showed an increase of length during the period of study that would have led to a myopia of 2 D if uncompensated, only 5 per cent actually showed this amount of increase in refractive error. During growth, therefore, the axial elongation, with its tendency to myopia, is compensated by a decreased power of cornea and lens, in particular of the lens.

Studies on children younger than 3 years are not easy, so that the changes taking place between birth and this age have not been so accurately ascertained. Sorsby & Sheridan give a mean axial length of 17·9 for full term male infants, so that by the age of 3 years the axial length of the eye has increased by 5 mm, comparing with only 1 mm for the remainder of its growth. According to Cook & Glasscock, who refracted the eyes of 1000 newborn babies under atropine, there is a wide scatter of refractive errors at birth, ranging between 7 D hypermetropia to 7 D of myopia, whilst the mean refraction was one of 1·5 D of hypermetropia. Thus the classical view that all newborn babies are strongly hypermetropic is not born out, some 25 per cent of the total examined being myopic. The actual refractive error that an adolescent or adult has may usually be regarded as a failure of coordination of axial length with the powers of the optic elements; it seems likely that the large errors, however, are due to defective growth in the 0–3 years-old period, so that the child begins the "definitive stage" of development with too high an error to permit adequate compensation.

DEFECTS IN THE IMAGE

The laws relating to the formation of images by mirrors and refracting surfaces were derived on the assumption that the rays concerned made small angles with the axis (so-called *paraxial rays*), in which event it could be shown that all rays from a point on the object would meet at a point in the image. If this condition is not fulfilled, the light from any point on the object occupies a definite area in the image, with the result that overlapping of the images of adjacent points on the object gives rise to blurring of the over-all image. In practice it is often difficult, or disadvantageous, to limit the light to paraxial beams and we must now determine the consequences of permitting non-paraxial or *marginal* rays to enter into image formation.

Points on the Axis

Spherical Aberration. It may be shown that marginal rays are brought to a focus closer to the refracting or reflecting system than paraxial rays; the consequence of this variation in focal length is called *spherical aberration*. In

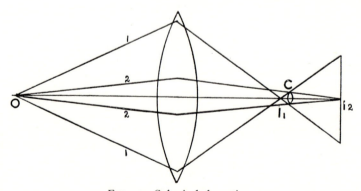

Fɪɢ. 351. Spherical aberration.

Fig. 351 the rays from O marked (1), are brought to a focus at a point I_1, whilst the paraxial rays, marked (2), are brought to a focus at I_2, the so-called *paraxial image of* O. Rays intermediate between these extremes come to foci between I_1 and I_2. The distance I_1I_2 is the *axial spherical aberration*; a screen placed at I_2 receives a circle of light instead of a point image; as the screen is moved towards I_1 the circle diminishes in size and passes through a minimum at c, the *circle of least confusion*. The diameter of this circle is called the *lateral spherical aberration*.

If a series of rays are drawn as in Fig. 352, it will be will be seen that in

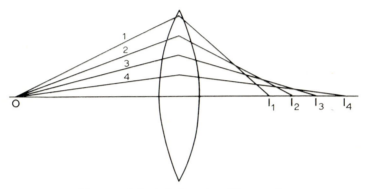

FIG. 352. Spherical aberration. The caustic.

approaching their respective foci they cross; the envelope of these rays is called a *caustic*, and constitutes a bright line because of the concentration of rays.

Spherical aberration can be partially remedied by placing a stop in front of the lens so as to permit only paraxial rays to enter, but this is disadvantageous in that it restricts the field of view and reduces the brightness of the image. It can be shown that the spherical aberration of a lens is considerably reduced if the bending of rays by each surface is the same; spherical aberration thus depends on the shape of a lens and on which surface faces the incident light; in Fig. 353 different types of converging lens are shown; the spherical aberra-

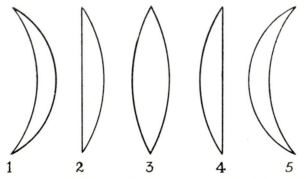

1   2   3   4   5

FIG. 353. Spherical aberration in different types of lens. The aberration is at a minimum with a type intermediate between (3) and (4).

tion decreases on passing from left to right to reach a minimum between types 3 and 4, if the incident light comes from the left of the lens.

The influence of shape on the deviations at the two surfaces is made clearer by considering the plano-convex lens in Fig. 354; rays parallel to the axis, incident on the plane surface, pass through undeviated, since they are normal; at the second surface they are refracted away from the normal, *i.e.* bent towards the axis. All the bending is thus done at the second surface. If the convex surface faces the incident light, the rays are bent towards the normal at the first surface and away from it at the second; both refractions cause a bending of the ray towards the axis, and if spherical aberration is reduced by dividing up the deviations between the two surfaces, clearly it will be less when the convex surface faces the incident light.

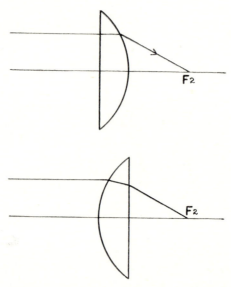

Fɪɢ. 354. Illustrating the importance of lens shape. *Above:* All the bending occurs at the second face. *Below:* The bending is divided between the two faces.

For a certain special position of object and image a single spherical refracting surface may produce no spherical aberration; under these conditions the surface is said to be *aplanatic,* and the positions of object and image are *aplanatic points.*

Points off the Axis

Spherical aberration represents a failure of all rays from a point object to meet at the same point in the image, due to the variation of the focal length of the lens according as the rays are marginal or paraxial. If we wish to consider the possible aberrations in the image of a finite object we must study the images of points off the axis, and we must consider, moreover, the *spatial relationships* between the points on the object and the points on the image. Failure to bring all rays from a point on the object to a point on the image leads to a loss of definition, whereas a disturbance in the spatial relationships of the points in the image leads to distortion of some sort, *e.g.* curvature.

The image of a point object, not on the principal axis, suffers spherical aberration as might be expected, but in addition two other aberrations enter, due to the asymmetrical position of the object in relation to the lens; these are *coma* and *astigmatism*.

The spherical aberration for the point off the axis is shown in Fig. 355; this error can be reduced, as before, by a stop to cut out marginal rays, or by the design of the lens shape.

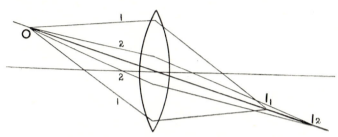

FIG. 355. Spherical aberration with a point off the axis.

Coma. In Fig. 356, the lens is assumed to have been corrected for spherical aberration, so that the focal length is the same for all rays. However, the paraxial rays meet at the paraxial image, I_2, on the central ray through the lens, whereas the marginal rays meet at a point I_1, at the same distance from the lens as I_2, but closer to the axis. Rays intermediate between (1) and (2) meet at points between I_1 and I_2, and thus the image of O is far from being a point, its shape being similar to the tail of a comet, from which the aberration takes its name.

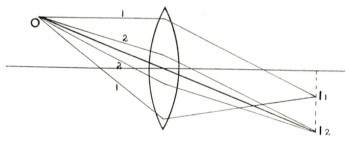

FIG. 356. Coma.

Spherical aberration and coma are related defects, which can be abolished by a suitable design of the lens surfaces and choice of the position of the object.

Astigmatism. Because of its asymmetrical position in respect to the lens, the curvatures in two planes at right angles through the point object are not the same. If the point is vertically above the optic axis in the plane of the paper, the *meridional plane* of the system, defined as the plane containing the object and the axis, is the plane of the paper (Fig. 357); the curvature of the lens in the meridional plane is greater than that in the plane at right-angles, the so-called *sagittal plane*. Rays in the meridional plane from O (rays marked 1) thus come to a focus before those in the sagittal plane, and form a *tangential*

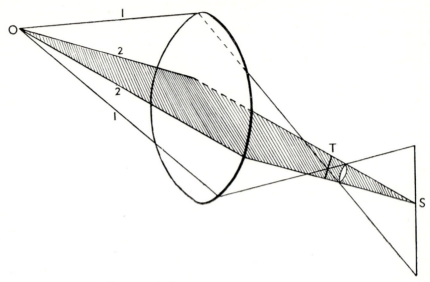

FIG. 357. Astigmatism due to oblique pencils.

line focus, T; the rays in the sagittal plane, coming to a focus later, form a vertical *sagittal line focus*, S. Consequently, in a lens in which both spherical aberration and coma are corrected, the best image of a point object, off the axis, is a circle of least confusion; hence the image of an extended object will have poor definition unless this error, too, is corrected. This is generally done by combining a converging and diverging lens, with focal lengths and refractive indices conforming to the relationship:

$$n_1 f_1 + n_2 f_2 = 0 \qquad . \qquad . \qquad . \qquad . \qquad (20)$$

This is known as the *Petzval condition*.

Curvature and Distortion. Spherical aberration, coma, and astigmatism are defects in a lens that prevent a point object from producing a point image. Even when these three aberrations are remedied, a perfect image of an extended object is not formed, owing to the defects of *curvature* and *distortion*.

Let us imagine that spherical aberration, coma, and astigmatism have been corrected in a lens, as in Fig. 358. Curvature is due, principally, to the fact that

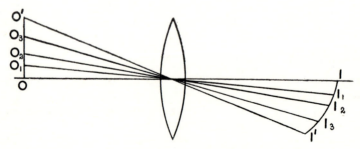

FIG. 358. Curvature of field.

the focal lengths along the subsidiary axes are shorter, the more the pencils are inclined to the lens; thus although all rays from any point on the object come to a point focus in the image, the image of O is at I, whilst the images of O_1, O_2, O_3, etc. are at I_1, I_2, I_3, etc. progressively closer to the lens; the image of OO' is thus a curved line, II', concave to the object. With a concave lens the curvature is in the opposite sense.

Curvature and astigmatism are related defects, and both are abolished on applying the Petzval condition, the curvature due to the convex lens of the combination being cancelled by that due to the concave lens.

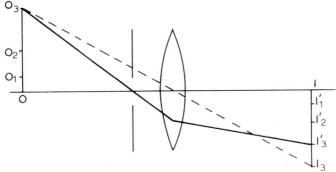

FIG. 359. Barrel distortion.

When all the preceding aberrations are cancelled out, one final defect can be present if a stop is placed on the optic axis of the lens, so as to prevent the principal ray from any point (*i.e.* the central ray of a pencil) from passing through the centre of the lens.

In the absence of the stop, the image of the point O_3 (Fig. 359) on the object would be at I_3 on the ray that would pass through the centre of the lens; however, in the presence of a stop a finite distance from the lens, the central ray

FIG. 360. Image of a gauze showing barrel distortion. (Barton, *Text-book on Light*. Photo by Mitchell.)

FIG. 361. Image of a gauze showing pin-cushion distortion. (Barton, *Text-book on Light*. Photo by Mitchell.)

from O_3 does not pass through the centre of the lens, but is refracted as shown, and all rays from O_3 come to a focus on this ray and produce an image at I'_3. The image of OO_3 is thus II'_3, smaller than if the stop were absent. Similarly, the image of O_2 falls at I'_2 and II'_2 is smaller than if the stop were absent, but not so much smaller in proportion; O_1, close to the axis, produces an image, I'_1, such that II'_1 is of approximately the theoretical size. Thus the magnification of different parts of the image varies, being least on the parts farthest from the principal axis. The appearance of the image of a gauze is consequently that indicated in Fig. 360, the distortion being called *barrel distortion*. When the stop is on the other side of the lens, the magnification is greatest for points farthest off the axis, and a gauze gives an image of the shape shown in Fig. 361, the distortion being called *pin-cushion distortion*.

Chromatic Aberration

The aberrations considered above are called *monochromatic aberrations*, since they occur when light of a single wavelength is used; chromatic aberration results from the use of mixed wavelengths, *e.g.* white light, and is due to the dependence of the refractive index on the wavelength of light; with a long wavelength like red, a material exhibits a smaller refractive index than with a

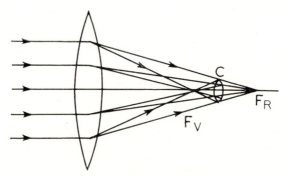

FIG. 362. Chromatic aberration.

short wavelength like violet. In a convex lens, uncorrected for chromatic aberration, the red rays, being refracted least strongly, come to a focus F_r (Fig. 362) farther away from the lens than the violet rays with a focus at F_v. The best image of a point is thus a circle of least confusion. Chromatic aberration is far more serious a defect than spherical aberration. The variation of the refractive index with wavelength of light for any given material is indicated by its *dispersive power*; this characteristic does not run strictly parallel with the refractive index when different materials are compared, so that it is possible to make a combination of a convex and concave lens such that the chromatic aberration of the one is cancelled by that of the other, their dioptric powers being only partially cancelled. Such a combination is called an "*achromatic pair*". Since the diameter of the circle of least confusion in chromatic aberration depends on the diameter of the lens, the defect can be reduced by the presence of a stop.

Chromatic Aberration and the Magnifying Glass. It is worth noting that when a convex lens is used as a magnifying glass, chromatic aberration is not apparent, owing to the fact that the different coloured images subtend the same angle at the eye. Thus in Fig. 363, F_v and F_r are the second principal foci for violet and red light respectively. The virtual images of OO' lie on the ray through the centre of the lens and, although they are at different distances from the lens, they have the same apparent size to an eye close to the lens; their images on the retina thus overlap exactly.

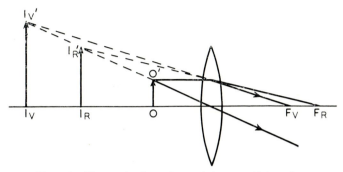

FIG. 363. Chromatic aberration and the magnifying glass.

Aberrations in the Eye

The eye is not a perfect optical instrument and exhibits the aberrations described above to a greater or less extent. Chromatic aberration can be demonstrated by looking at a distant luminous point through a cobalt glass which transmits the red and violet ends of the spectrum and cuts out the intermediate band. The appearance varies with the refractive condition of the eye; to

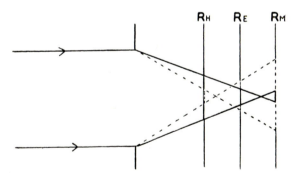

FIG. 364. Chromatic aberration in the eye. Red rays in full lines; violet rays broken.

the myope it is that of a red spot surrounded by blue; to the hypermetrope it is that of a blue spot surrounded by red, and to the normal eye the spot appears purple with perhaps a blue border due to the partial overlapping of the blue and red blur-circles (Fig. 364).

Hartridge has calculated that the difference in the focal lengths of the eye for red and violet lights amounts to 0·47 mm. As a result, a point source of white light on the optic axis of the eye forms an image consisting of concentric fringes of colour. Generally the eye focuses for yellow light, in which event the fringes have the following diameters (calculated by Hartridge):

> Red (6,500 Å) 0·0216 mm (6·4 cones).
> Yellow (6,000 Å) 0·0078 mm (2·3 cones).
> Green (5,500 Å) 0·0090 mm (2·7 cones).
> Blue-green (5,000 Å) 0·03 mm (9 cones).
> Blue (4,500 Å) 0·0588 mm (17·5 cones).

the number of foveal cones covered by the fringes being indicated in brackets. A bright point, viewed on a dark background, should thus appear as a central yellow spot merging, through yellowish white, greenish white, bluish white and purple, with blue. In actual fact a white point source appears white; moreover Hartridge has shown that even when the chromatic aberration of the normal eye is doubled by the use of appropriate lenses, it is not normally detected; only when the aberration is quadrupled are the blue and yellow fringes distinctly visible. Hartridge has suggested that there is a suppressor mechanism in the retina or brain which depresses the sensitivity to both blue and yellow. In evidence he adduces the fact that a small point source of yellow light appears white, whilst a similar blue source appears black. The chromatic fringes on the retina are small; the suppressor mechanism operates to convert the yellow to white and the blue to black, that is, to make the image resemble the object. When the images of coloured objects formed on the retina are large, the suppressor mechanism does not operate and the colours are correctly appreciated.

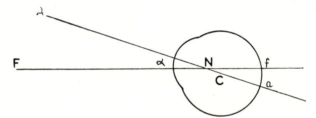

FIG. 365. The angle alpha.

It should be noted that the chromatic aberration so far considered has been a defect observable with a point object on the optic axis; with a point off the axis, the asymmetry introduced causes a chromatic difference of magnification; *i.e.* the lens is effectively decentred and has a prism effect causing a spectrum to be formed as the image of a point.

Spherical aberration is present in the eye and may be demonstrated subjectively. Aberrations due to obliquity of points from the optic axis must enter, even with foveal fixation, because the optic axis does not coincide normally with the visual axis. Thus in Fig. 365 the point F is fixated so that its image falls on the fovea, *f*. FN*f* represents the *visual axis*. The optic axis, AN*a*, diverges from the visual axis, the angle between the two being called the *angle alpha*; it amounts on the average to 5°; when the visual axes are parallel, *e.g.* when viewing an infinitely distant object, the optic axes of the two eyes thus diverge by 10°.

The angle alpha may be approximately determined on the perimeter. The subject looks at a light at the centre of the arc so that F*f* (Fig. 366) represents the visual axis. The point B, on the perimeter, is determined at which the reflex image of the light on the cornea appears to an observer to occupy the centre of the pupil. Since ∠FDA = ∠BDA, the angle read off on the perimeter represents twice the angle FDA; this is approximately equal to ∠FNA, the angle between the visual axis and the optic axis. (Actually the line ADN, through the centre of the pupil, does not coincide exactly with the optic axis— it is called the *central pupillary line* and the angle ADF is called the *angle kappa*.) The fixation axis, it will be remembered, is the line joining the fixation point with the centre of rotation of the eye; the angle made by the fixation axis and the optic axis is called the *angle gamma*.

Thus a centrally fixated point is actually viewed obliquely, so far as the optic axis of the eye is concerned, and we must expect coma and astigmatism to be present. Coma and spherical aberration are reduced by the pupil and also by

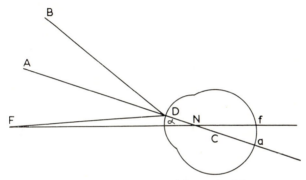

Fig. 366. Measurement of the angle alpha.

the peripheral flattening of the lens and cornea. Curvature of the field is not a defect, owing to the curvature of the retina. The pupil does not coincide with the nodal point of the optical system so that some barrel distortion should be present.

The image of a point, formed by the eye, is thus very far from being a point, as the geometrical constructions might lead us to believe, the most serious defect being chromatic aberration, but, as we have seen, this appears to be compensated by a physiological mechanism; in a similar way it seems likely that, even with monochromatic errors, inductive processes, which accentuate the response of the most strongly stimulated cone and reduce those of nearby elements, generally sharpen the image. It will be appreciated that, as a result of spherical and chromatic aberrations, there is no single focal length of the eye; this permits a certain tolerance in the focusing of the dioptric system, so that small variations in the axial length of the eye need not necessarily be associated with a significant degree of ametropia; moreover, small changes in the vergence of the light entering the eye need not necessarily be followed by a change in accommodation. The aberrations thus give the eye a certain depth of focus, or tolerance to a change in vergence, which would be absent were the formation of the image to follow strictly the "paraxial laws." It seems probable that the tolerance of ± 0·25 D, observed by Fincham (p. 294), is due to these causes. The retinoscopy test for ametropia is said to be accurate to within $\frac{1}{8}$ D, but it seems doubtful whether such precision is necessary, when the aberrations are taken into account.

INTERFERENCE AND OTHER PHENOMENA

Wave-Motion

The passage of light through a medium may be regarded as a series of waves or "ripples"; these waves are made up of the movements of "particles" in the medium in a direction at right-angles to that of propagation. When a wave-motion is established in any medium, the position of any given particle goes through a cyclical change, as in Fig. 367, *a* where the displacement of the particle from its position of rest is plotted against time. The time required for a complete cycle is called the *period*, T, of the vibration. The *amplitude* of the vibration, which measures its energy,* is the height of a crest.

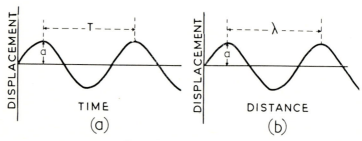

FIG. 367. Wave-motion.

Fig. 367, *a* represents the displacement of a single particle at different times; since wave-motion is due to the propagation of a disturbance by one particle to another, points adjacent to the one just considered likewise pass through the cyclical change depicted in Fig. 367, *a*, but they are "out of phase" in the sense that they reach their crests at different times. Instead of plotting the displacement of one particle against time, we can plot the displacements of all the particles in a plane at a given moment against the distance from a given point, as in Fig. 367, *b*. The curve has the same shape as the first, and as before the height of the crest is the amplitude; the distance between two crests, however, represents an interval of space, and is called the *wavelength*, λ.

The time taken by any particle to go through a complete cycle, T, also represents the time taken for a disturbance to be propagated through a distance λ, the wavelength. Hence the velocity of light is equal to λ/T. If 1/T is called the *frequency*, n, we have:

$$V = n.\lambda \qquad . \qquad . \qquad . \qquad . \qquad . (21)$$

Interference

If a continuous series of waves is propagated through a medium from a point, the motion of any particle is that represented by Fig. 367; if now a new set

* The energy of the vibration varies as the square of the amplitude. If, as a result of interference, the amplitude at a point is doubled the brightness at this point will be quadrupled.

of waves is propagated from another point, the motions of the particle are modified; this modification is called *interference*, and its nature depends on the
difference in phase of the disturbances due to the two wave-motions. Thus
in Fig. 368 the displacements of a given particle due to the first wave-motion
are represented by the curve A; those due to the second motion by the curve
B. The waves are out of phase and tend to cancel each other in some parts and
to accentuate each other elsewhere; for example at t_1 the particle would have
been at its maximum height due to the first wave; the second wave, acting
alone, would have raised it, but not so much, and the resultant position is given
by the algebraic sum of the two displacements. It is easy to see that if the second
wave is half a wavelength out of phase with the first the result will be complete
suppression of particle movement; if the two waves are completely in phase,
the amplitude of the motion will be doubled.

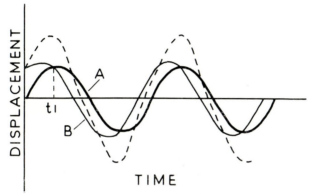

Fig. 368. Illustrating interference.

If light is to be regarded as a wave-motion we must expect interference,
resulting in light and dark patches of illumination, when two sources of light
illuminate the same screen. That this phenomenon is not normally observed
is due to a number of factors. In the first place the sources must be "*coherent*,"
i.e. they must retain the same phase difference continuously, otherwise the points
in space at which interference takes place will vary, and a point of darkness at
one moment will become a point of maximum brightness at another. Sources
of light commonly used vary in phase continuously, so that we cannot expect
interference to be observed with two lamps, for example. Secondly, the sizes
of the dark and bright patches, the so-called *fringe-widths*, decrease with increasing distance apart of the sources; unless the sources are very close together,
the interference pattern consists of innumerable very thin lines of black and
white which are unresolvable by the eye. Thirdly, the fringe widths decrease
with decreasing wavelength.

   Young's Slits. Interference may be demonstrated quite simply by the experimental set-up depicted in Fig. 369, known as *Young's slits*. Light is focused on
to a slit S; it diverges from S and meets two other slits S_1 and S_2 which behave
as two separate sources of light; they are coherent because they both arise
from S, any variation in phase in this source being reflected in similar changes
in both S_1 and S_2. Where the two beams from S_1 and S_2 overlap, interference

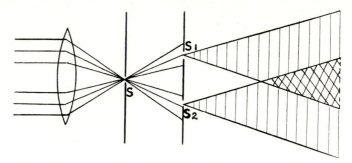

Fig. 369. Young's slits.

occurs and a series of black and white lines are seen on a screen placed in this region. The wavelength of the light can be calculated quite simply from the fringe width.

Diffraction

If vibrations are set up at a point in a homogeneous medium they spread in all directions; the locus of all points suffering the same displacement at any given moment is the surface of a sphere; it is called the *wave-front*. (The ripples in water are wave-fronts; here the disturbance is propagated in two dimensions and the front appears as a circle.) In Fig. 370, *a* each of the circles represents

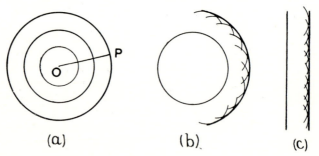

(a)   (b)   (c)

Fig. 370. (*a*) Successive wave-fronts. OP is a ray. (*b*) Huygens' construction for circular wave-front. (*c*) Huygens' construction for plane wave-front.

a wave-front due to successive disturbances propagated from the same point O. The direction, OP, in which any very small portion of a wave-front travels, is normal to the wave-front and is called a *ray*. As the wave gets farther from its point of origin, the surface of its front gets flatter and flatter so that when the disturbance arises at a point infinitely far away the wave-front becomes a plane, and the rays are parallel.

According to Huygens' Principle, the position of a wave-front, *t* sec after its present position, is found by regarding each point of the front as the source of secondary wavelets, travelling at the speed of light in the same manner as the original wave. Hence the new position of the wave-front is given by drawing spheres of radius $c \times t$ (where *c* is the velocity of light) round each point on the front; the envelope of these spheres is the new position (Fig. 370, *b* and *c*). A plane wave-front clearly propagates as a plane.

This mode of viewing the propagation of light raises the problem as to why reasonably clear-cut shadows of objects are seen; thus in Fig. 371 the plane wave-front AB strikes an object PQ which casts a shadow P'Q' on the screen; this shadow, according to the laws of geometrical optics, should be of the same size as PQ since the rays are parallel. However, if the propagation of the wave-front at P can be considered to be due to the setting up of wavelets, the point P, on the edge of the object, must give rise to disturbances reaching all parts of P'Q', *i.e.* light must travel round corners and P'Q' must be illuminated in spite of the obstruction PQ. Such a deviation from the rectilinear propagation of

Fig. 371. The plane wave-front, AB, meets an obstacle PQ. The geometrical shadow is P'Q'.

light would be called *diffraction*, and it is easy to show that this does occur. We may reasonably ask, however, why PQ casts a shadow at all, and, moreover, why the size of the shadow is such as to make us think that light *does* travel in straight lines. In general terms the explanation lies in the fact that although the wavelets from P and Q do strike P'Q', as a result of interference their effects are largely cancelled out and P'Q' is a well-defined shadow. The edges of the shadow are, however, not perfectly defined since the cancellation of wavelets is not complete and it is possible to show, with a narrow obstacle such as a pin, that the shadow consists of a central bright line and, on its edges, a series of black and white lines.

As a result of diffraction, light passing through a small circular aperture, *e.g.* the pupil of the eye, is not a perfect circle of white; in general it consists of a central bright spot with concentric rings of dark and light. Consequently the image of a luminous point formed by the dioptric system of the eye is not a point but a series of rings of finite magnitude. Thus although decreasing the aperture of the eye reduces the aberrations discussed earlier, it tends to blur the image as a result of diffraction effects. It is found that, with pupil sizes above 3 mm, visual acuity is independent of pupil size, a decrease in diffraction being counter-balanced by an increase in aberrations.

Polarization and Double-Refraction

A doubly-refracting material produces two images of a point object because a part of the light is refracted in accordance with Snell's Law, giving rise to the "*ordinary ray*," whilst the remainder gives a value of the ratio: Sin *i*/Sin *r*, varying with the angle of incidence; it is thus generally refracted to a different extent and gives rise to the *"extraordinary ray."*

It is easy to show that the light emerging from a doubly refracting crystal, such as tourmaline or calcite, is modified during its passage; thus on passing light through two flat tourmaline crystals (which absorb the ordinary ray and only transmit the extraordinary ray) the amount of light passing through the second crystal depends on the position of its axis in relation to that of the first; if the axes are parallel, all the light emerging from the first is transmitted by the second, whilst at intermediate angles smaller amounts pass through and, when the axes are at right-angles, no light at all is transmitted. The light emerging from a doubly refracting crystal is therefore said to be *polarized*; non-polarized light consists of transverse vibrations in all planes at right-angles to the direction of propagation of the light, whereas in polarized light the transverse vibrations are confined to a single plane; the light is said to be *plane polarized*.

The process of polarization of light may be likened to passing the vibrations through a slot; if the slot is vertical, only vibrations in a vertical plane parallel with the direction of propagation can pass through, so that the slot acts as a sorter or polarizer. If it is desired to determine in what plane the vibrations are polarized, another slot is used, the direction in which the slot must be placed, to permit the light to pass through, giving the plane of polarization. Thus if a beam of polarized light is viewed through a tourmaline crystal, it may appear quite bright at one position of the axis, but in another position at right-angles to this, no light at all may be transmitted.

Various devices are used for obtaining and analysing polarized light. In the Nicol prism the ordinary ray is got rid of by causing it to be totally internally reflected at a Canada-balsam surface. "Polaroid" is made up of a large number of very small crystals of a substance, herapathite, which behave effectively as a single crystal. The substance is similar to tourmaline in that it absorbs the ordinary ray. The crystals are embedded in nitrocellulose sheets.

GENERAL REFERENCES

BARTON, A. W. (1944). A Textbook on Light. London: Longmans Green.

BENNETT, A. G., & FRANCIS, J. L. (1962). Visual optics. In *The Eye*. Ed. Davson. Vol. IV. Pt. 1. London & New York: Academic Press.

DUKE-ELDER, W. S. (1954). The Practice of Refraction. London: Churchill.

EMSLEY, H. H. (1944). Visual Optics. London: Hatton Press.

TREISSMAN, H. & PLAICE, E. A. (1946). Principles of the Contact Lens. London: Kimpton.

SPECIAL REFERENCES

BENNETT, A. G. (1961). The computation of optical dimensions. Appendix D in Sorsby, Benjamin & Sheridan (1961).

COOK, R. C. & GLASSCOCK, R. E. (1951). Refractive and ocular findings in the newborn. *Amer. J. Ophthal.*, **34**, 1407–1413.

GOLDMANN, H. & HAGEN, R. (1942). Zur direkten Messung der Totalbrechkraft des lebenden menschlichen Auges. *Ophthalmologica, Basel,* **104,** 15–22.

HARTRIDGE, H. (1947). The visual perception of fine detail. *Phil. Trans.*, **232**, 516–671.

RUSHTON, R. H. (1938). Clinical measurement of the axial length of the living eye. *Trans. Opthal. Soc. U.K.*, **58**, 136–142.

SLATEPER, F. J. (1950). Age norms of refraction and vision. *Arch. Ophthal.*, **43**, 466–481.

SORSBY, A., BENJAMIN, B., DAVEY, J. B., SHERIDAN, M. & TANNER, J. M. (1957). Emmetropia and its aberrations. *Med. Res. Counc. Sp. Rep. Ser.* No. 293.

SORSBY, A., BENJAMIN B. & SHERIDAN, M. (1961). Refraction and its components during the growth of the eye from the age of three. *Med. Res. Counc. Sp. Rep. Ser.* No. 301.

SORSBY, A. & SHERIDAN, M. (1960). The eye at birth: measurement of the principal diameters in 48 cadavers. *J. Anat. Lond.*, **94**, 193–197.

STENSTRÖM, S. (1946). Untersuchungen uber die Variationen und Kovariationen der Elemente des menschlichen Auges. *Acta. ophthal. Kbh. Suppl.*, **26.**

INDEX

PRINTED IN GREAT BRITAIN BY THE WHITEFRIARS PRESS LTD.
LONDON AND TONBRIDGE